B. I. BALINSKY, Dr.Biol.Sc.

Professor of Zoology
University of the Witwatersrand
Johannesburg, South Africa

SECOND EDITION

AN
INTRODUCTION
TO
EMBRYOLOGY

W. B. SAUNDERS COMPANY
Philadelphia and London   1965

An Introduction to Embryology

Preface to the
Second Edition

In the short time since the publication of the first edition of this book, embryology has made significant progress requiring a revision of many parts of the text in respect to both factual statements and interpretations. This progress is the result mainly of investigations of a biochemical nature and the wide application of electron microscopy to embryological problems. The organization of the eggs and sperm in particular has emerged in a new light because of electron microscopic investigations of the last few years. On the biochemical side, the discovery of the way in which protein synthesis is controlled by nucleic acids has made such a profound change in biological concepts that development of the egg cannot be dealt with at present without consideration of the DNA-RNA codes and the mechanism of protein synthesis.

In preparing the second edition of *An Introduction to Embryology* I have made an attempt to reflect these advanced trends and to incorporate them into the text as well as to fill the gaps which have been pointed out by reviewers and critics.

The chapter on the organization of the egg has been greatly expanded, and much more attention has been given to the spermatozoon. The mechanism of gene action in development has been presented in the light of decoding of information encoded in the nuclear DNA. New data on the mechanism of embryonic induction and on cell growth and differentiation have been included. The list of references has been increased by over 200 titles, drawn mainly from the literature that has appeared during the last three years. The current research literature has been systematically studied and utilized.

To meet the wishes of users of the book who found that the text of the first edition contained insufficient information on the morphological aspects of development, I have considerably expanded the descriptive parts of the book and have given more emphasis to mammalian development. The illustrations have been augmented by the addition of 153 new figures, some of them composite. Some of the new figures have been grouped together to illustrate a few of the developmental stages of the frog and the chick, in the section on "Stages of Development." It is hoped that this section will help the student to grasp the development of the embryo as a whole, and that it will present a background against which the development of the various organ systems can be studied in greater detail.

Some of the views and statements contained in the first edition have been challenged by critics and reviewers, and in many cases I have accepted the criticisms and made corresponding changes in the text. Occasionally these changes concern terminology. In a few cases, however, I do not agree with the proposed corrections, and here perhaps is the right place to state my reasons, in order to avoid misunderstandings.

The controversial terms which I prefer to retain without change are "blastoderm" and "blastodisc." The term "blastoderm" is used here to denote the layer of cells surrounding the blastocoel of a blastula, in whatever form the blastula is encountered—whether as a hollow sphere formed after complete cleavage, as a disc after discoidal cleavage or as a layer of cells surrounding the yolk in centrolecithal eggs. This layer of cells should have a specific name, and the term blastoderm is a very appropriate one, as it matches the terms "blastula" and "blastocoele." Also etymologically it is constructed similarly to the terms ectoderm, mesoderm and endoderm, and thus helps the student to see the continuity of structural units in the embryo. The term "blastoderm" in the sense just defined has been used before by both older and contemporary embryologists. It was used in this sense by Haeckel (*The Evolution of Man*, Vol. 1, 1874, English translation by McCabe; Watts and Co., 1923, p. 62), by Korschelt and Heider (*Text-book of the Embryology of Invertebrates*, Part 1, 1893, English translation 1895; Swan Sonnenschein and Co., p. 4), and in our times by Nelsen (*Comparative Embryology of Vertebrates*, 1953) and by Witschi (*Development of Vertebrates*, 1956). Also in the same sense the term blastoderm is used in Figure 5–1 of Patten's *Foundation of Embryology* (1958), although not in the text of that book.

If the term blastoderm is to be applied to the cellular lining of any type of blastula, and not only to blastulae of animals having discoidal cleavage as some would like to have it, then the cap of cells on the animal pole of a discoblastula should obviously be called a "blastodisc." In the past the term "blastodisc" has been used either to denote the concentration of cytoplasm on the animal pole of the uncleaved hen's egg or to denote the mass of cells into which this cytoplasm becomes subdivided during cleavage, or for both. In recent literature, usage of the term blastodisc has been extended to include the chick embryo in the primitive streak stage or even in later stages. Thus while some looseness in the application of the term seems to be in practice, I should like to confine the term to those stages in which the developing embryo does have the shape of a disc, that is, mainly to the stages of meroblastic discoidal cleavage.

In the task of preparing the second edition I have been greatly assisted by numerous teachers and research workers who have given me the benefit of their opinions. To all those I should like to express my sincere gratitude, but most especially to the following colleagues whose advice and constructive criticisms have been most helpful: Professor Joseph T. Bagnara of the University of Arizona, Professor James T. Duncan of the San Francisco State College, Professor Royal F. Ruth of the University of Alberta, Professor Nelson T. Spratt of the University of Minnesota, Professor Malcolm S. Steinberg of the Johns Hopkins University and Professor Roland Walker of the Rensselaer Polytechnic Institute.

I should like also to record my special thanks to a number of embryologists who have kindly supplied me with original drawings and photographs, which have been invaluable in improving the illustrations. The names of these colleagues appear in the legends of the corresponding figures.

In conclusion I should like again to thank my assistants in the Zoology Department of the University of the Witwatersrand, Mr. M. J. de Kock for helping me with the preparation of new figures appearing in the second edition, and Mrs. E. J. Pienaar, who has been most helpful in searching for literature when it was not at hand and in typing the new sections of the text.

B. I. BALINSKY

Preface to the
First Edition

The teaching of embryology has long been an established
feature at universities throughout the world, both for students in
biology and students in medical sciences. Although overshadowed
during a large part of the twentieth century by the rapid development of genetics and cytology, embryology has also made rapid
advances, especially as an experimental science — as experimental
or physiological embryology. It is realized now that embryology
is a branch of biology which has a most immediate bearing on the
problem of life. Life cannot be fully accounted for without an
understanding of its dynamic nature, which expresses itself in the
incessant production of new organisms in the process of ontogenetic development.

In the midst of the rapid changes of outlook that the experimental method has brought with it, it has been difficult to coordinate the older data of purely descriptive embryology with the new
discoveries. This has hampered the teaching of embryology and
is to this day reflected in the subdivision of most textbooks of embryology into two groups. Books of the first type deal with the
classic "descriptive" embryology and are written mainly for the
use of medical students. Short chapters on experimental embryology are appended to them, but these chapters are extremely
brief and not organically connected with the description of the
morphology of the developing embryos. The second type of book
deals with experimental embryology or "physiological" embryology. These books are written for advanced students and the basic
facts of development are more or less taken for granted, so that a
student cannot profitably proceed to the study of such a book without previously making himself familiar with "descriptive" embryology from one of the books of the first type.

In the course of many years' teaching of embryology to university students I have endeavored to present embryology as a single science in which the descriptive morphological approach and the experimental physiological approach are integrated and both contribute to the understanding of the ontogenetic development of organisms. This integrated approach to development is now incorporated in the present book. Data of a more purely physiological and biochemical nature are adduced inasmuch as it is practicable to treat them in a book that does not presuppose an advanced knowledge of biochemistry in the student.

The subject of embryology is interpreted in my book in a broad sense, as the science dealing with ontogenetic development of animals, and includes therefore such topics as postembryonic development, regeneration, metamorphosis and asexual reproduction, which are seldom handled in students' textbooks at any length. Lastly I believe that embryology cannot be presented adequately without establishing some connection with genetics, inasmuch as processes of development are under the control of genes. The connection between inheritance and development is therefore also indicated in the text.

With such a wide scope, my book can only be "an introduction to embryology." The whole field could not be covered in the same detail as is customarily given in textbooks dealing with only one aspect of the science of embryology. The student having studied this book, however, will be prepared to understand and appreciate special information in any section of the science which would be of interest to him in his further studies.

The first draft of this book was written in 1952, and duplicated copies of the manuscript were used by my students during subsequent years. This gave me an opportunity to convince myself of the usefulness of the book and also to eliminate some defects in the original text. For the present printed edition the book has been completely revised and brought up to date. An extensive study of special literature up to the end of 1958 has been carried out for this purpose (as can be seen from the list of references). Later publications could not be included in the text.

In illustrating the book I have drawn on my own experience in embryological work wherever practicable, but of course most of the illustrations have been reproduced from other sources.

In preparing the book for print I have been assisted by a number of persons to whom I should like to express my gratitude on this occasion. In the first place I wish to thank all the authors and publishers who have kindly agreed to the reproduction of figures used to illustrate this book, as well as colleagues in many countries who by sending me reprints of their publications have facilitated the arduous task of keeping track of current embryological literature.

Of my immediate collaborators and friends I am most profoundly indebted to Dr. Margaret Kalk of the University of the

Witwatersrand for reading the whole text of the book and for many valuable suggestions and helpful criticism. I am indebted to Dr. H. B. S. Cooke of the same University for his expert advice on the preparation of illustrations for the book. I am very grateful for the invaluable assistance of Mrs. E. J. Pienaar, who has typed the manuscript, has assisted me in preparing the index, and has been of great help on diverse occasions during the work on the manuscript and on the proofs. I should like to thank Miss R. J. Devis, Mrs. E. du Plessis and Mr. M. J. de Kock for their help in preparing the illustrations for the book.

Last but not least I should like to express my gratitude to the staff of the W. B. Saunders Company, whose friendly encouragement has done much to bring this book to its present form.

Johannesburg   B. I. BALINSKY

Contents

PART IV. GASTRULATION AND THE FORMATION OF THE PRIMARY ORGAN RUDIMENTS

Chapter 8.

MORPHOLOGICAL ASPECTS OF GASTRULATION AND PRIMARY
ORGAN FORMATION 175

Chapter 9.

PHYSIOLOGY OF GASTRULATION 213

Chapter 10.

DETERMINATION OF THE PRIMARY ORGAN RUDIMENTS 230

Chapter 19.

REGENERATION 587

Chapter 20.

ASEXUAL REPRODUCTION 617

PART I

THE SCIENCE OF
EMBRYOLOGY

The Scope of Embryology and Its Development as a Science

1 — 1   ONTOGENETIC DEVELOPMENT AS THE SUBJECT MATTER OF EMBRYOLOGY

The aim of this book is to make the student familiar with the basic facts and problems of the science of **embryology**. The name "embryology" is somewhat misleading. Literally it means: the study of **embryos**. The term "embryo" denotes the juvenile stage of an animal while it is contained in the egg (within the egg membranes) or in the maternal body. A young animal, once it has hatched from the egg or has been born, ceases to be an embryo and would escape from the sphere pertaining to the science of embryology if we were to keep strictly to the exact meaning of the word. Although birth or hatching from the egg is a very important occasion in the life of the animal, it must be admitted that the processes going on in the animal's body may not be profoundly different before and after the hatching from an egg, especially in some lower animals. It would be artificial to limit the studies of the juvenile forms of animal life to the period before the animal is hatched from the egg or born. It is customary, therefore, to study the life history of an animal as a whole, and accordingly to interpret the contents of the science of embryology as **the study of the development of animals.**

Now the word "development" has to be qualified in turn. In the sphere of biology with which we are concerned here, the term "development" is used with two different meanings. It is used to denote the processes that are involved in the transformation of the fertilized egg, or some other rudiment derived from a parent organism, into a new adult individual. The term development may, however, also be applied legitimately to the gradual historical transformation of the forms of life, starting with simple forms which might have been the first to appear and leading to the contemporary diversity of organic life on our planet. Development of the first type may be distinguished as individual development or **ontogenetic development**. Development of the second type is the historical development of species or **phylogenetic development**. Phylogenetic development is often referred to as evolutionary development or simply **evolution**. Accordingly we will define embryology as **the study of the ontogenetic development of organisms**. In this book we will be dealing only with the ontogenetic development of multicellular animals, the **Metazoa**.

In multicellular animals, the typical and most widespread form of ontogenetic development is the type occurring in sexual reproduction. In sexual reproduction new individuals are produced by special **generative cells** or **gametes**. These cells differ essentially from other cells of the animal, in that they go through the process of maturation or **meiosis**, as a result of which they lose half of their chromosomes and become **haploid**, whereas all other cells of the parent individual, the **somatic cells**, are, as a rule, **diploid**. Once a cell has gone through the process of meiosis, it can no longer function as an integral part of the parent body but is sooner or later extruded to serve for the formation of a new individual. In multicellular animals there exist two types of sex cells: the female cells or **ova**, and the male cells or **spermatozoa**. As a rule the two cells of the opposite sexes must unite in the process of fertilization before development can start. When the two gametes (the ovum and the spermatozoon) unite, they fuse into a single cell, the **zygote**, which again has a diploid number of chromosomes. The zygote, or fertilized ovum, then proceeds to develop into a new adult animal.

Side by side with sexual reproduction there exists in many species of animals a different mode of producing new generations — asexual reproduction. In asexual reproduction the offspring are not derived from generative cells (gametes) but from parts of the parent's body consisting of somatic cells. The size of the part which is set aside as the rudiment of the new individual may be large or small, but in the Metazoa it always consists of more than one cell. The development of an animal by way of asexual reproduction obviously belongs in the same category as the development from an egg and should be treated as a special form of ontogenetic development. It will be dealt with in Chapter 20. To distinguish between the two forms of ontogenetic development, the term **embryogenesis** may be used to denote the development from the egg, and the term **blastogenesis** may be used for the development of new individuals by means of asexual reproduction.

1—2 THE PHASES OF ONTOGENETIC DEVELOPMENT

From what has already been said it is clear that the processes leading to the development of a new individual really start before the fertilization of the egg, because the ripening of the egg and the formation of the spermatozoon, which constitute the phase of **gametogenesis**, create the conditions from which the subsequent embryogenesis takes its start. In both oogenesis and spermatogenesis, meiosis, by discarding half of the chromosomes, singles out the set of genes which are to operate in the development of a particular individual. In both sexes the initial cells giving rise to the gametes are very similar and, as a rule, not essentially different from other cells of the body except that these cells are not involved in any of the differentiations serving to support the life of the parent individual. In both sexes the first step in the production of gametes is a more or less rapid proliferation of cells by ordinary mitosis. The proliferating cells in the testes are known as the **spermatogonia**; the proliferating cells in the ovaries are called **oogonia**. Once proliferation ceases, the cells are called **spermatocytes** in the male and **oocytes** in the female. They now enter into a stage of growth and later into a stage of maturation.

Although the stage of proliferation is not essentially different in the male and female, the processes of growth and maturation in the two sexes differ to a very great extent. The cytoplasmic differentiations of the spermatozoon enable it to reach the egg by active movement and to fertilize it. On the other hand, the egg cell accumulates in its cytoplasm substances which are used up during development—either directly, by becoming transformed into the various structures of which the embryo consists, or indirectly, as sources of energy for development. The elaboration in the egg cell of cytoplasmic substances to be used by the embryo, and their placing in correct positions, are essential parts of what occurs during the first phase of development.

The second phase of development is **fertilization**. Fertilization involves a number of rather independent biological and physiological processes. First of all, the spermatozoa must be brought into proximity with the eggs if fertilization is to occur. This involves adaptations on the part of the parents, ensuring that they meet during the breeding season, discharge their sex cells simultaneously in cases of external fertilization, or copulate in cases of internal fertilization. Next, the spermatozoa must find the egg and penetrate into the egg cytoplasm. This entails a very finely adjusted mechanism of morphological and physicochemical reactions. Next the egg is **activated** by a spermatozoon and starts developing. A further rearrangement of the organ-forming substances in the egg is among the first changes that take place in the egg after fertilization (see section 6–6).

The third phase of development is the period of **cleavage**. The fertilized egg is still a single cell, since the nucleus and cytoplasm of the spermatozoon fuse with the nucleus and cytoplasm of the egg. If a complex and multicellular organism is to develop from a single cell, the egg, the latter must give rise to a large number of cells. This is achieved by a number of mitotic cell divisions following each other in quick succession. During this period the size of the embryo does not change, the **cleavage cells** or **blastomeres** becoming smaller and smaller with each division. No far-reaching changes can be discovered in the substance of the developing embryo during the period of cleavage, as if the preoccupation with the increase of cell numbers excludes the possibility of any other activity. The whole process of cleavage is dominated by the cytoplasmic organoids of the cells: the centrosomes and achromatic figures. The nuclei multiply but do not interfere with the processes going on in the cytoplasm. The result of cleavage is sometimes a compact heap of cells, but usually the cells are arranged in a hollow spherical body, a **blastula**, with a layer of cells, the **blastoderm**, surrounding a cavity, the **blastocoele**.

There follows the fourth phase of development, that of **gastrulation**. During this phase the single layer of cells, the blastoderm, gives rise to two or more layers of cells known as the **germinal layers**. The germinal layers are complex rudiments from which are derived the various organs of the animal's body. In the higher animals the body consists of several layers of tissues and organs, such as the skin, the subcutaneous connective tissue, the layer of muscles, the wall of the gut, and so on. All these tissues and organs may be traced back to three layers of cells—the aforementioned germinal layers. Of these the external one, the **ectoderm**, always gives rise to the skin epidermis and the nervous system. The layer next to the first, the **mesoderm**, is the source of the muscles, of the blood vascular system, of the lining of the secondary body cavity (the **coelom**, in animals in which such a cavity is present), and of the sex organs. In many animals, in particular in the vertebrates, the excretory system and most of the internal skeleton are also derived from the mesoderm. The third and innermost germinal layer, the **endoderm**, forms the alimentary canal and the digestive glands.

The germinal layers are produced by the disappearance of a part of the blastoderm from the surface and its enclosure by the remainder of the blastoderm. The part that remains on the surface becomes ectoderm; the part disappearing into the interior becomes endoderm and mesoderm. The disappearance of endoderm and mesoderm from the surface sometimes takes the form of a folding-in of part of the blastoderm, so that the simple spherical body becomes converted into a double-walled cup, as if one side of the wall of an elastic hollow ball had been pushed in by an external force. This infolding or inpushing of endoderm and mesoderm is known as **invagination**, and the resulting embryo is known as a **gastrula**—whence the term **gastrulation**. The way in which the endoderm and mesoderm become separated from each other in the interior of the gastrula varies a great deal in different animals, and cannot be described in this general review. (See Chapter 8.) If the gastrula is formed by invagination, the cavity of the double-walled cup is called the **archenteron**, and the opening leading from this cavity to the exterior is called the **blastopore**. In animals in which the gastrula is formed in a different way—not by invagination—the cavity (archenteron) and the opening of the cavity to the exterior (blastopore) may still appear later on.

The archenteron, or part of it, eventually gives rise to the cavity of the alimentary system. The fate of the blastopore differs in the three main groups of Metazoa. In **Coelenterata** it becomes the oral opening. In **Protostomia** (including Annelida, Mollusca, Arthropoda and allied groups) it becomes subdivided into two openings, one of which becomes the mouth and the other the anus. In **Deuterostomia** (including Echinodermata and Chordata) only the anal opening is connected in its development with the blastopore, the mouth being formed later on as an independent perforation of the body wall. The whole of the lining of the alimentary canal does not always consist of endoderm: in all groups of animals the ectoderm may be invaginated secondarily at the oral or at both oral and anal openings to become a part of the alimentary canal. The parts of the alimentary canal lined by ectoderm are known as the stomodeum (adjoining the mouth) and proctodeum (adjoining the anus).

With the formation of the three germinal layers, the process of subdivision of the embryo into parts with specific destinies commences. This subdivision is continued in the next (fifth) phase of development, the phase of **organogenesis** (organ formation). The continuous masses of cells of the three germinal layers become split up into smaller groups of cells, each of which is destined to produce a certain organ or part of the animal. Every organ begins its development as a group of cells segregated from the other cells of the embryo. This group of cells we will call the **rudiment** of the respective organ. The rudiments into which the germinal layers become subdivided are called **primary organ rudiments**. Some of these are very complex, containing cells destined to produce a whole system of organs, such as the whole of the nervous system, or the alimentary canal. These complex primary organ rudiments later become subdivided into **secondary organ rudiments**—the rudiments of the subordinated and simpler organs and parts. The formation of the primary organ rudiments follows so closely on the processes of gastrulation that the two processes can hardly be considered apart. Dynamically they are linked into one whole, and will be described in conjunction in the following pages. The chapters on organogenesis will then be concerned with the later development of the primary organ rudiments and with the formation of the secondary organ rudiments. With the appearance of primary and secondary organ rudiments the embryo begins to show some similarity to the adult animal, or to the larva if the development includes a larval stage.

The sixth phase of development is the period of **growth** and **histological differentiation**. After the organ rudiments are formed they begin to grow and greatly increase their volume. In this way the animal gradually achieves the size of its parents. Sooner or later the cells in each rudiment become histologically differentiated, i.e., they acquire the structure and physicochemical properties which enable them to perform their physiological functions. When the cells in all the organs, or at least in the vitally important organs, have become capable of performing their physiological functions, the young animal can embark upon an independent existence—an existence in which it has to procure food from the surrounding environment.

In rather rare cases (in the nematodes, for instance) the young animal emerging from the egg is a miniature copy of the adult animal and differs from the latter only in size and in the degree of differentiation of the sex organs. In this case the subsequent development consists only of growth and the maturation of the gonads. It is more usual, however, for the animals emerging from the egg to differ from the adult to a greater extent: not only the gonads but other organs may not be fully differentiated, or they may even be absent altogether and have to develop later. Sometimes the animal emerging from the egg possesses special organs which are absent in the adult but which are necessary for the special mode of existence of the young animal. In this case the young animal is called a **larva**. The larva may lead a different mode of life from the adult, and therein lies one of the advantages of having a larval stage in development. The larva undergoes a process of **metamorphosis** when it is transformed into an animal similar to the adult. The metamorphosis involves more or less drastic changes in the organization of the larva, depending on the degree of difference between the larva and the adult. During metamorphosis new organs may develop, so that morphogenetic processes become active again after a more or less prolonged period of larval life.

A secondary activation of morphogenetic processes may be produced in a different way. Many animals possess a considerable plasticity and may be able to repair injuries sustained from the environment or caused experimentally. Lost parts may be **regenerated**, and this means that the developmental processes may sometimes be repeated in an adult or adolescent organism.

The asexual reproduction of animals involves the development of new parts and organs in animals that had already achieved the adult stage.

All morphogenetic processes occurring in the later life of the animal, after the larval stage, or even when the adult stage has been achieved, will be dealt with as constituting a seventh and last phase of development.

1 – 3 HISTORICAL REVIEW OF THE MAIN TRENDS OF THOUGHT IN EMBRYOLOGY*

Descriptive and Comparative Embryology. Although the correct understanding of ontogenetic development could be achieved only after the establishment of the cell theory, fragmentary information on the development of animals has been obtained since very ancient times. Aristotle had described the development of the chick in the egg as early as 340 B.C. Many observations on development of various animals, especially of insects and vertebrates, were made in the seventeenth and eighteenth centuries. However, the data of embryology were first presented in a coherent form by Karl Ernst von Baer (1828). In his book "Ueber Entwicklungsgeschichte der Tiere, Beobachtung und Reflexion," Baer not only summed up the existing data and supplemented them by his original investigations but also made some important generalizations. The most important of these is known as **Baer's law.** The law can be formulated thus: "More general features that are common to all the members of a group of animals are, in the embryo, developed earlier than the more special features which distinguish the various members of the group." Thus the features that characterize all vertebrate animals (brain and spinal cord, axial skeleton in the form of a notochord, segmented muscles, aortic arches) are developed earlier than the features distinguishing the various classes of vertebrates (limbs in quadrupeds, hair in mammals, feathers in birds, etc.). The characters distinguishing the families, genera and species come last in the development of the individual. The early embryo thus has a structure common to all members of a large group of the animal kingdom and may be said to represent the basic plan of organization of that particular group. The groups having a common basic plan of organization are the **phyla** of the animal kingdom.

Baer's law was formulated at a time when the theory of evolution was not recognized by the majority of biologists. It has been found, however, that the law can be reinterpreted in the light of the evolutionary theory. In its new form the law is known as the **biogenetic law** of Müller-Haeckel. Müller propounded the law in its new form and supported it by extensive observations on the development of crustaceans (1864). Haeckel (in 1868)

---

*Further references: Nordenskiöld, 1929; J. Needham, Part II, 1931; C. Singer, 1931; Hall, 1951; Gabriel and Fogel, 1955; Needham, 1959.

gave it the name of biogenetic law and contributed most to its wide application in biology.

According to Baer's law, the common features of large groups of animals develop earliest during ontogeny. In the light of the evolutionary theory, however, these features are the ones that are inherited from the common ancestor of the animal group in question; therefore, they have an ancient origin. The features that distinguish the various animals from one another are those that the animals have acquired later in the course of their evolution. Baer's law states that these features in ontogeny develop at later stages. Briefly, the features of ancient origin develop early in ontogeny; features of newer origin develop late. Hence the ontogenetic development presents the various features of the animal's organization in the same sequence as they evolved during the phylogenetic development. **Ontogeny** is a recapitulation of **phylogeny**.* The repetition is obviously not a complete one, and the biogenetic law states that "Ontogeny is a shortened and modified recapitulation of phylogeny." The shortening of the process is evident not only from the fact that what had once taken thousands of millions of years (phylogeny) is now performed in a matter of days and weeks (ontogeny), but also from the fact that many stages passed through in the original phylogenetic development may be omitted in ontogeny. The modifications arise mainly because the embryo at any given time is a living system which has to be in harmony with its surroundings if it is to stay alive. The embryo must be adapted to its surroundings, and these adaptations often necessitate the modification of inherited features of organization. A good example of such adaptation is the placenta in mammals. The placenta is a structure developed by the embryo to establish a connection with the uterine wall of the mother and thus provide for the nutrition of the embryo. This structure, though developed rather early in the life of the embryo, could not have existed in the adult mammalian ancestors. It is obviously an adaptation to the special conditions in which a mammalian embryo develops.

Even if the repetition of features of their ancestors in the ontogenetic development of contemporary animals is not complete, still even the fragmentary repetition of certain ancestral characters may be very useful in elucidating the relationships of animals. As an example of this we may consider the formation of gill pouches in the ontogenetic development of all vertebrates. In the aquatic vertebrates, such as Cyclostomata and fishes, the gill clefts serve as respiratory organs. In the adult state of terrestial vertebrates, the gill pouches have disappeared completely or have been modified out of all recognition, and the function of respiration has been taken over by other organs—the lungs. Nevertheless, the gill pouches appear in the embryo (Fig. 213). In amphibians whose larvae are aquatic, the gill pouches at least temporarily serve for respiration. In reptiles, birds and mammals, the gill pouches of the embryo do not serve for respiration at all. Their formation can only be explained as an indication that the terrestrial vertebrates have been derived from aquatic forms with functional gills. The paleontological evidence fully confirms this conclusion.

The systematic position of some animals cannot be recognized from adult

---

*For a modern explanation of the facts on which the biogenetic law is based see p. 537.

structure, owing to profound modification acquired as a result of adaptation to very special conditions. Here the knowledge of the development sometimes throws unexpected light on true relationships. The adult ascidian is a sessile animal with no organs of locomotion and a nervous system of a very primitive nature. The adult animal had been classed as a near relative of molluscs until Kowalevsky (1866) discovered the larvae of the ascidians. The larvae of ascidians possess a well-developed dorsal brain and spinal cord, a definite notochord, and lateral bands of muscles (in short, organs that are typical for the vertebrates). The ascidians are therefore considered as belonging to the same phylum as the vertebrates, the phylum Chordata (Fig. 1).

In the adult parasitic animal *Sacculina,* the organization of the animal is very much simplified in connection with the easy life that the parasite enjoys; it is reduced practically to a shapeless sack producing eggs and a system of branched rhizoids, by means of which the parasite is attached to its host, the crab, and absorbs the host's body fluids on which it feeds. It would be impossible to place *Sacculina* in any group of the animal kingdom if its development were not known (Fig. 2). However, the larva of *Sacculina* is a typical arthropod, bearing a close similarity to the larvae of the lower crustaceans, the Entomostraca (Delage, 1884).

A rather similar larva is also found in the barnacles (*Cirripedia*) which, though possessing jointed legs like other arthropods, have lost the segmentation of the body in the adult state.

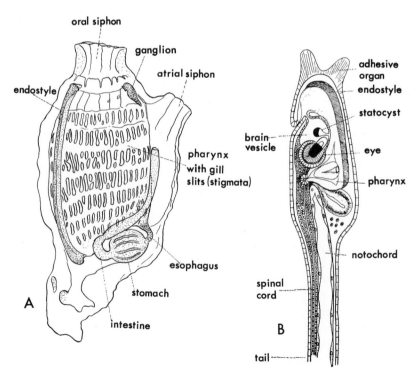

Figure 1. A, Adult ascidian, *Ciona intestinalis. B,* Larva of ascidian, lateral view. (After Kowalevsky, from Korschelt, 1936.)

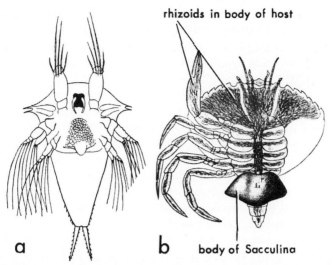

Figure 2. Parasitic cirripede, *Sacculina*. Nauplius larva (*a*) and adult (*b*) attached to a crab. (After Delage, from Parker and Haswell. Text-book of Zoology, Macmillan, London, and from Korschelt, 1936.)

The attachment of the starfish larva, the brachiolaria, to the substrate while it is metamorphosing into the definitive form is an indication that the free-living echinoderms have been derived from sessile forms. This conclusion is again borne out by the evidence of paleontology.

Following the principles of Baer's law and the biogenetic law, embryologists have systematically investigated the development of animals belonging to all the major groups of the animal kingdom. As a result of very extensive and painstaking investigations, a magnificent edifice of **comparative embryology** has been built up.

Explaining Development: Theories of Preformation and Epigenesis.   Neither the description of morphological transformations occurring in the embryo nor the comparison of embryos and larvae among themselves and with the adult animals exhausts all the problems presented by the ontogenetic development of animals. The fundamental problem presented by the existence of cyclical ontogenetic changes is the question: Why does ontogeny occur at all? What are the forces which produce the changes? How is it that, starting from a simple spherical cell, the process always ends in producing a highly complex and specific structure which, though varying in detail, reproduces with astonishing perseverance the same or almost the same adult form?

Attempts at solving this basic problem have been made ever since the human mind recognized the existence of development. For a long time the explanations proposed were purely speculative.

Aristotle attempted to give a solution to the problem of ontogeny along the general lines of his philosophical teaching, distinguishing between the **substance** and the **form** of things. The form appears in this concept as the creative principle. Aristotle further supposed that the substance for the development of a child is given by the mother (in the form of nutrition) but that the creative principle is supplied by the father. He thus accounted also for the necessity of fertilization. Although this treatment of the phenomena of development is completely contradictory to what we now know of the material basis of development (the parts played by the ovum and the spermatozoon), still the concept of a creative principle has turned up repeatedly in the teachings of embryologists up to the twentieth century.

In the seventeenth and eighteenth centuries, when all biological sciences developed rapidly, together with the physicochemical sciences, there existed a widespread theory explaining the ontogenetic development of animals. This was the **theory of preformation**. The theory of preformation claimed that if we see that something develops from the egg, then this something must actually have been there all the time but in an invisible form. It is common knowledge that in a bud of a tree the leaves, and sometimes also the flowers with all their parts, can be discovered long before the bud starts growing and spreading and thus exposing to view all that before was hidden inside, covered by the superficial scales of the bud. Furthermore, it was known that in a chrysalis of a butterfly the parts of the butterfly's body—the legs, the wings, etc.—can be discovered if the cuticular coat of the chrysalis is carefully removed a few days before the butterfly emerges from the chrysalis. Something of this sort was supposed to exist in the egg. All the parts of the future embryo were imagined to be already in the egg, but they were transparent, folded together and very small, so that they could not be seen. When the embryo began to develop, these parts started to grow, unfold and stretch themselves, become denser and therefore more readily visible. The embryo, and therefore indirectly also the future animal, was **preformed** in the egg. Hence the theory is called the theory of preformation.

When spermatozoa were discovered in the seminal fluid, the relative significance of the ova and spermatozoa had to be accounted for. It is obvious that a preformed embryo cannot be present in both the egg and the spermatozoon. The preformationists were split therefore into two rival schools; the ovists and the animalculists. (The latter name comes from the word **animalcule**, as the spermatozoa were then called.) The ovists asserted that the embryo was preformed in the egg. The spermatozoa then seemed superfluous, and in fact they were declared parasites living in the spermatic fluid. On the other hand the animalculists declared that the embryo was preformed in the spermatozoon and that the egg served only to supply nutrition for the developing embryo. A lively discussion arose, which ended in favor of the ovists. The victory of the ovists was due to the discovery of the parthenogenetic development in some insects, e.g., the aphids (Bonnet, 1745). If the egg could develop without fertilization it was clear that the embryo could not be preformed in the spermatozoon.

The theory of preformation, although very popular in its time, did not satisfy all biologists, and opposing views, denying the existence of a preformed embryo in the egg, were proposed. The most important contribution in this field was the **theory of epigenesis**, proposed by Caspar Friedrich Wolff (1759). In favor of his theory Wolff adduced his own observations on the formation of the chick embryo. In the earliest stages of the development of the chick he could not find any parts of the future embryo. What is more, he found that the egg was by no means devoid of any visible structure; there was a structure present, but it was different from that of the later embryo. Wolff found that the substance of which the embryo is built up is granular. Presumably the granules must have been the cells or their nuclei. These granules were later arranged into the layers which we now call the **germinal layers**. Wolff saw that by the formation of local thickenings in some parts of these layers, by thinning out in others, by the formation of folds and pockets, the layers are transformed into the body of the embryo. He concluded, therefore, that in the early egg there does not exist a preformed embryo but only the material of which the embryo is built. This material did not represent an embryo any more than a heap of bricks represents the house that will be built of these bricks. In both cases there had to be an architect who would use the material for a purpose that he had in mind. In the case of the developing embryo the architect was represented by a vital force, perhaps not essentially different from the "creative principle" postulated by Aristotle.

Experimental Embryology. Wolff's observations, however, could not be considered as final in deciding between the alternative theories of preformation and epigenesis. In spite of what he actually observed it was still conceivable that organs and parts of the body of the future embryo were represented in the egg by discrete particles, qualitatively different among themselves. The granules which he saw might have been different in their properties. Even if the transformation of such qualitatively different parts into the organs of the embryo should have been more complicated than was envisaged by the crude preformistic theory, the principle of preformation might well have held true in spite of the apparent homogeneity of the material of which the embryo was supposedly made. Observation alone could not go any further toward the solution of this problem, and further progress could be achieved only with the aid of experiment.

One of the experiments which is relevant to the above problem is the separation of the two cells into which the egg is divided at the beginning of development. If the theory of preformation is correct, we should expect that one of the two first blastomeres, containing one half of the egg material, should develop into an embryo lacking one half of its organs and parts. If on the other hand the substances contained in the egg are but the building material used for the construction of the embryo, then it is conceivable that a half of the material might be sufficient for making a complete embryo even if it may have to be on a diminished scale, just as the bricks prepared for the construction of a big house may be used for building two houses of a smaller size.

The first embryologist to see this way of solving the problem was Wilhelm Roux (1850-1924). Accordingly he proceeded to test one of the first two cleavage cells in the common frog for its ability to develop. To achieve his end Roux destroyed one of the two cleavage cells with a red-hot needle (1888). The embryo that was derived from the surviving cleavage cell was found to develop, at least at first, as if it were still forming a half of a complete embryo. In other words, the developing embryo was defective, as it should have been according to the theory of preformation (Fig. 3). It was found later, however, that the technique used by Roux was too crude. The damaged cleavage cell was not removed, and it was the presence of this damaged cleavage cell, as was later found out, that caused the defects in the surviving embryo. If the two cleavage cells of the egg were separated completely, two whole and, ex-

Figure 3. Half embryo produced by W. Roux by killing one blastomere of a frog's egg with a hot needle. (After Roux, from Morgan, 1927.)

cept for their size, normal embryos could develop, one from each of the two cleavage cells. This result was first found by H. Driesch (1891), working on sea urchin eggs (Fig. 4), and later by Endres (1895) and Spemann (1901, 1903), working with eggs of newts. Eventually the experiment was repeated by Schmidt (1933) on the frog, the same animal that served for the experiments of Roux. Schmidt found that if the two cleavage cells were completely separated, each could develop into a whole embryo (Fig. 5).

The first experiments on the developing embryo were followed by many others, and soon a new science was born: **experimental embryology** (Roux, 1905).

Experimental embryology, in contrast to comparative embryology or descriptive embryology, uses experiment as a method of investigation. However, the use of the experimental method in itself does not create a science or a branch of science. New branches of science are created by novel viewpoints and novel problems set before science. It was the problem of what ontogenetic development actually is, what the driving forces behind it are, that necessitated the application of experiment after the methods of speculation and of pure observation were found to be impotent in solving the problem.

Naturally, experiment can be used for purposes other than those of discovering the nature of the driving forces in ontogenetic development. Even in the case of embryonic development there may be many ways in which experiment can be applied. The embryo in every stage of its development is a living organism and, as such, performs all the basic functions of living matter. It is, for instance, subject to the processes of metabolism, and these processes may be studied by experimental methods without the investigator's being concerned with answering the question of why a simple egg is converted into a complex new individual. The supply of nutrition to the embryo,

Figure 4. Separation of the first two blastomeres in the sea urchin, resulting in the development of two whole embryos. (After Driesch, from Gabriel and Fogel, 1955.)

Figure 5. Separation of the first two blastomeres in the frog, resulting in the development of two whole embryos. (From Schmidt, 1933.)

whether through the medium of the egg or directly from the maternal organism, as in mammalian development, is another problem that may be, and is, studied by physiological methods. Some of these researches may be concerned with the problem of ontogenetic development. Others may be purely physiological in the ordinary sense of the word, the fact that the embryo is a developing system being irrelevant to the ends aimed at in the investigation. Recently, the more physiological ways of approach to the developing embryo have been treated as a special branch of embryology: **chemical embryology** (J. Needham, 1931; J. Brachet, 1950) or **physiological embryology** (Lehmann, 1945).

In this "introduction to embryology" all three branches of embryology, i.e., the descriptive and comparative embryology, the experimental embryology, and the physiological embryology, will be dealt with together as far as possible.

PART II

GAMETOGENESIS

Storage and Transmission
of Genetic Information
by the Generative Cells

Gametogenesis is the first phase in the sexual reproduction of animals. The essential process during this phase is the transformation of certain cells in the parents into specialized cells: the eggs, or ova, in the female and the spermatozoa in the male (or in the female and male organs in hermaphrodite animals).

The egg and the spermatozoon jointly constitute the material system, or contain jointly all the essential factors, which, given a suitable environment, will produce in the course of time a new individual with, in the main, the same characters as the two parent organisms. The various properties of both the paternal and maternal progenitor must thus be contained, in some form, in either the egg or the spermatozoon or both. It is obvious, however, that the characters of adult organisms are not there to be seen or directly detected in either the eggs or spermatozoa, the latter being single cells of a highly peculiar structure. It follows that the characteristics of the adult organisms are contained in the egg and sperm in a different and not immediately recognizable form. It is said, therefore, that these characteristics are encoded in the structure of the egg and sperm, just as a transmitted message may be concealed by the use of a code which makes the message unintelligible except for a person in possession of the code. It is also said that the egg and spermatozoon possess the "information" that is needed to build a new organism, meaning by this that all the specifications for the future organism are contained in the egg and sperm. As the information is contained in the egg and spermatozoon in a form which does not bear an obvious relationship to the

19

characters of the adult organism, we may say that it is contained in an encoded form. During the development of the egg the encoded information is decoded; that is, translated or transformed from a concealed to an overt form; characters inherent in the egg and sperm serve to determine the properties of the adult organism. The decoding or "reading" of the information contained in the gametes is then equivalent to the process of ontogenetic development, as defined on Page 3.

The encoded information which is possessed by the egg and the spermatozoon may be contained in the structure (including the chemical composition) of either the nuclei or the cytoplasm of the gametes. Generally speaking, both the nucleus and the cytoplasm are indispensable for development to occur, as animal cells are only fully viable when both these parts (the nucleus and the cytoplasm) act together and in harmonious cooperation with each other. However, the way the structure of the nucleus is maintained is very different from the mode of maintenance of cytoplasm, and it is therefore useful to consider separately the nuclear factors and the cytoplasmic factors controlling development.

2−1   NUCLEAR DNA AS DEPOSITORY OF GENETIC INFORMATION

The essential factors contained in the nuclei of the gametes are the **genes** or the structural carriers of hereditary properties of all organisms. As shown at the beginning of this century by investigations carried out mainly by T. H. Morgan and his school (Morgan, 1919) the genes are arranged in linear order in the chromosomes of the cells, and in fact constitute the essential part of the chromosomes. Recent investigations have shown that the chemical substance of which the genes consist is **deoxyribonucleic acid**, a complex chemical compound built up of three main kinds of molecules:

1. The **deoxyribose sugar** having the structural formula

2. The **phosphoric acid** with the structural formula

$$
\begin{array}{c}
\text{O} \\
\parallel \\
\text{H}-\text{O}-\text{P}-\text{O}-\text{H} \\
\mid \\
\text{O} \\
\mid \\
\text{H}
\end{array}
$$

3. The **nitrogen bases**

The last are somewhat more complex nitrogen-containing organic radicals which include rings of atoms: either purine rings or pyrimidine rings. Four different nitrogen bases are found in the material of the genes: namely, the purines adenine and guanine and the pyrimidines cytosine and thymine. The structural formulae of these compounds follow.

Adenine

Guanine

Thymine

Cytosine

In deoxyribonucleic acid, one molecule of a nitrogen base is joined to a molecule of deoxyribose and the latter to a molecule of phosphoric acid to form a unit called a **mononucleotide**. Depending on the nature of the nitrogen base, the following mononucleotides may be formed: adenylic acid (with adenine as base), guanylic acid (with guanine as base), cytidylic acid (with cytosine as base), and thymidylic acid (with thymidine as base). In the chromosomes, the mononucleotides are joined together in very long molecules of polynucleotides. In a molecule of a polynucleotide, the deoxyribose radical of one mononucleotide is linked to the phosphoric acid radical of the next mononucleotide, forming a long chain as shown in the following diagram:

In an epoch-making paper published in 1953, Watson and Crick have suggested that the deoxyribonucleic acid, as found in the cells of animals and plants, consists of pairs of polynucleotide molecules which are twisted spirally around each other (Fig. 6). In the double spiral, the constituent mononucleotides are arranged in such a way that the alternating radicals of deoxyribose and phosphoric acid are on the outside of the spirals, forming the backbone of each spiral, while the nitrogen bases are on the inside, those of the two spiraling polynucleotide molecules facing each other (Fig. 7). The "Watson and Crick model" of DNA is now generally accepted as an accurate representation of the structure of hereditary material.

It will be recalled that the nitrogen bases of deoxyribonucleic acid are of two types: the ones with a purine ring (adenine and guanine) and the ones with a pyrimidine ring (cytosine and thymine); the molecules of the former two are therefore larger and take up more space than the latter two. In the double spirally twisted molecule of deoxyribonucleic acid a larger molecule, containing a purine ring, can only fit in together with a smaller molecule, containing a pyrimidine ring. Details of configuration of the nitrogen bases restrict even further the possibilities of their pairing so that only two kinds of pairs can actually fit into the space inside a double deoxyribonucleic acid spiral—namely, adenine with thymine or guanine with cytosine. The pairs of

Figure 6   **Figure 7**

Figure 6. Diagrammatic representation of a double DNA molecule. The two ribbons sym-
bolize the two phosphate-sugar chains, and the horizontal rods the pairs of bases holding the
chains together. The vertical line marks the fiber axis. (From Watson and Crick, 1953.)

Figure 7. Structure of the double helix of DNA. The phosphate units are shown as dark gray:
the deoxyribose units are shown as light gray; black denotes the thymine and cytosine; white,
adenine and guanine. (After Wilkins, from Sinsheimer, 1962.)

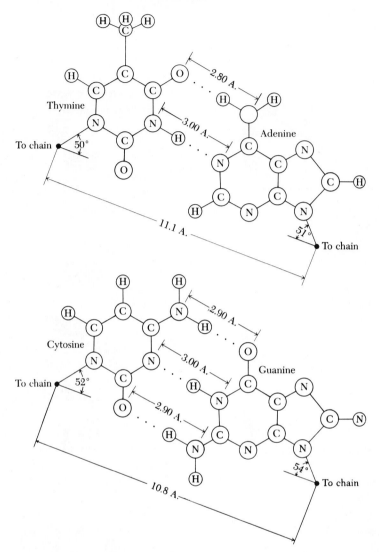

Figure 8.   Pairing of bases: thymine with adenine and cytosine with guanine. (From Giese: Cell Physiology, Ed. 2. Saunders Co., 1962.)

nitrogen bases are held together by hydrogen bonds as shown in Figure 8, and it is this hydrogen-bonding between corresponding pairs of nitrogen bases that holds the two molecules of deoxyribonucleic acid together.

Considering that the carriers of heredity, the genes, are responsible for the immense variety of organisms, those existing now as well as those which existed in the past, the chemical substance of which the genes consist appears to have a fairly simple structure. Its constituent elements — the phosphoric acid, the pentose sugar (deoxyribose), and the nitrogen bases — are quite simple molecules. Furthermore, the "backbones" of the spiralized pairs of molecules, consisting of deoxyribose and phosphoric acid molecules, are exactly the same in all animals and plants. The only difference is found to be in the relative quantities and arrangement of the nitrogen bases. All the hereditary peculiarities, all the "information" contained in the genes of any animal or plant, depends on the sequence of the nitrogen bases in the molecules of deoxyribonucleic acid. As there are only four different bases, we may compare the information laid down in the genes of an animal or plant to a message written with an alphabet of only four signs (letters). That quite a complex message may be conveyed using even a smaller number of signs is shown by the Morse code, where only three signs (dots, dashes and intervals) are used to spell the same message as can be expressed with the aid of the 26 letters of the Latin alphabet.

There appears to be no set limit to the length of a double DNA molecule, and there is thus no reason why the whole of the genetic material in a cell could not be contained in one such double molecule. In multicellular animals, however, the hereditary material is subdivided into several separate units, each consisting of at least one double DNA thread; these units are the **chromosomes** of classic cytology. In a chromosome, the DNA is associated with protein of the histone type and may also be linked with certain quantities of ribose nucleic acid—RNA (see further p. 33).

It is by no means clear that a chromosome must always be equivalent to one double strand of DNA. As a matter of fact there is every reason to believe that, at least in some cells (as in cells of the salivary glands of fly larvae), the chromosomes contain more than one double strand of DNA. In this case, however, it is accepted that the multiple strands are produced by repeated replication of one original double strand, and that the corresponding sections of the molecules remain joined together at the same levels of the complex chromosome. The giant salivary gland chromosomes, however, are a special case, and the cells containing them are incapable of further reproduction by mitosis.

The usefulness of the Watson and Crick model of the DNA molecule for understanding hereditary transmission and development depends on our ability to answer two important questions:

1. How can the details of structure of the molecule (as expressed in the arrangement of the nitrogen bases along its length) be transmitted without change from cell generation to cell generation?

2. How can the more tangible and overt properties of cells (such as their chemical composition, structure and functional peculiarities) be determined by the arrangement of bases along the length of the DNA molecule?

2—2   TRANSMISSION OF GENETIC INFORMATION DURING CHROMOSOME REPLICATION

The answer to the first question is comparatively simple and may be derived directly from a knowledge of the structure of the double DNA molecule. As the nitrogen bases can only be paired in certain combinations (adenine with thymine and guanine with cytosine), the arrangement of nitrogen bases in the two chains of the molecule are complementary to one another. It is assumed that from time to time the two component chains of a double DNA molecule separate, and that each then serves as a template for the construction of a new polynucleotide chain. The new polynucleotide chains would be built from a pool of free mononucleotides available in the

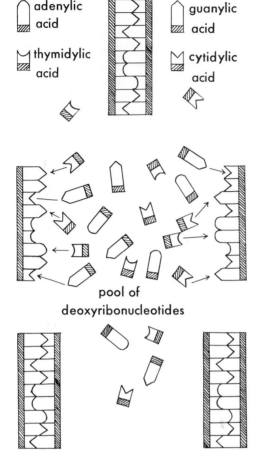

⌂ adenylic
acid

⌂ guanylic
acid

thymidylic
acid

cytidylic
acid

pool of
deoxyribonucleotides

Figure 9. Diagram showing the mode of duplication in a section of a DNA molecule. The two strands of the molecule separate, and each picks up a set of complementary mononucleotides from a deoxyribonucleotide pool. The cross-hatched stripes represent the phosphate-dexoyribose "backbones" of the molecules; the differently shaped figures represent the bases—adenine, thymine, guanine and cytosine. (System of representation of DNA molecule components based on the paper of M. B. Hoagland, 1959.)

cell in such a way that each of the mononucleotides in the old chain would pick out a complementary mononucleotide from the pool. Where an adenylic acid mononucleotide was present in the old chain, a thymidylic acid mononucleotide would become attached to it. A thymidylic acid mononucleotide in the old chain would attract an adenylic acid mononucleotide, and the guanylic acid and cytidylic acid nucleotides of the old chain would become associated respectively with cytidylic acid and guanylic acid mononucleotides from the pool. It is obvious that in this way each half of the original DNA molecule would supplement itself with a new half which would in every respect be identical to the alternate half of the original molecule (Fig. 9).

The result would be the formation of two double-intertwined DNA molecules, each similar to the original one. It should be assumed that at least one replication of this kind occurs between each two mitotic divisions of a cell, with the result that at the beginning of a mitotic division each chromosome is composed of two chromatids, each chromatid consisting of a double-stranded molecule of DNA. In anaphase the two chromatids separate, and each becomes a daughter chromosome which is then drawn into one or the other daughter cell. In this way every peculiarity of each DNA molecule available in the mother cell becomes transmitted to both daughter

cells. There is experimental evidence to show that replication of DNA molecules does in fact proceed as described above.

In one experiment cells derived originally from hamster embryos were
grown as a tissue culture *in vitro* (see Prescott and Bender, 1963). A nucleic
acid precursor, thymidine, labeled with tritium (radioactive hydrogen) was
added to the culture. The radioactive thymidine was taken up by the cells
and was used in the replication of the chromosomal DNA. After 30 minutes,
the cultures were washed with fresh medium containing only unlabeled
thymidine. They were then left in the "cold" medium for further growth.

The fate of the radioactive thymidine could be traced when the treated
cells entered the metaphase stage after varying lengths of time. If the treated
cells are placed in contact with photographic film, the emulsion of the film
shows black dots where the film is hit by electrons shooting out from the
radioactive tritium atoms in the chromosomes. The dots in the emulsion
appeared along the whole length of the treated chromosomes if the test
was done within the period of one cell generation after the original treatment
of the cells with labeled DNA precursor (Fig. 10).

If, however, the cells, after being transferred into a "cold" medium were
allowed to remain there for over one cell generation, the results of a test for
incorporated tritium were essentially different. Now black dots in the emul-

Figure 10. Results of experiment showing the mode of duplication of chromosomes; autoradiographs of chromosome sets freed from cytoplasm. *a,* A complete set of chromosomes at the
first metaphase following DNA labeling. All chromatids are labeled equally except one arm of
the X chromosome (arrow) which synthesizes DNA out of step with the other chromosomes. *b,*
Metaphase chromosomes of second division after labeling; in each pair only one of the chromatids is labeled. At the arrow the two chromatids of a long chromosome are twisted across one
another. *c,* Metaphase chromosomes of third division after labeling. Roughly half of the chromosomes are completely free of labeling; the other half have one chromosome labeled and one
unlabeled. (Courtesy of Dr. D. M. Prescott, from Prescott and Bender, 1963.)

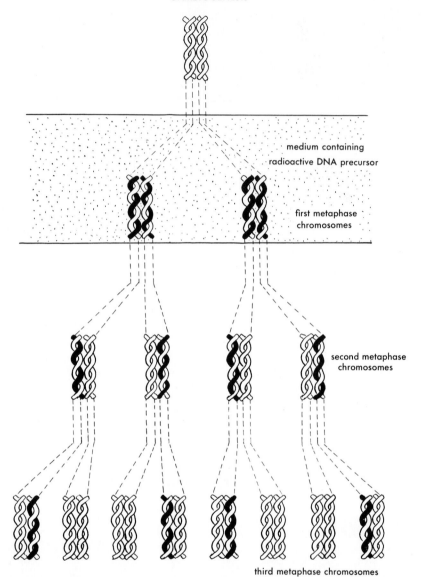

Figure 11. Diagram showing mode of duplication of chromosome DNA strands as revealed by experiments incorporating radioactive precursors into DNA. Chromosomes shown as consisting of two chromatids, each constituted of a double-stranded DNA helix. The stippled zone represents the sojourn of the cells in a medium containing a radioactive DNA precursor. As the chromosomes duplicate in this medium, the newly synthesized strands become labeled (black). During the subsequent two replications the labeled strands are transmitted intact to some of the chromatids. A chromatid in which at least one strand is labeled registers as radioactive in an autoradiograph.

sion appeared only over one chromatid in each chromosome, while the other chromatid did not cause the appearance of dots in the emulsion, thus showing that it did not contain any radioactive hydrogen. After a further cell generation (at the third mitosis), about half of the chromosomes were clear of radioactive material while the other half of the chromosomes had one chromatid labeled and the other unlabeled.

These results can be easily understood. In the first replication, the new halves of the DNA double molecules were built at the expense of a pool of mononucleotides containing radioactive thymidine; the old half in each case (the one serving as template) did not include any radioactive material, but this could not be seen as it was closely intertwined with the new half (Fig. 11).

Both chromatids of each chromosome showed the same labeling. In the next generation of cells the two halves of each double molecule separated again, and each served as a template for the formation of a further polynucleotide chain. As the pool of nucleotides by this time did not contain labeled molecules, the new chains would be free of radioactive materials. In this way the original unlabeled DNA chain, supplemented by a new nonradioactive complementary chain, would show no radioactivity. On the other hand, the chain built at the time when the mononucleotide pool contained radioactively labeled precursors still showed radioactivity, although its complementary partner, built at a later stage, did not contain radioactive hydrogen.

In the next generation the nonradioactive chromatid became a separate chromosome, consisting in its turn of two chromatids, which were both free of radioactivity. The chromatid containing a radioactive strand in its DNA passed it on to one of the daughter chromatids. Similar results were obtained with a culture of human leucocytes (Prescott and Bender, 1963) and also with plant cells (Taylor, Woods and Hughes, 1957).

2 – 3   CONTROL OF PROTEIN SYNTHESIS BY THE NUCLEIC ACIDS, THE GENETIC CODE AND THE MESSENGER RNA

The second question set out on page 25 must now be considered: it must be shown how the genetic material contained in the chromosomes controls the structural and functional properties of cells. In other words, how the information contained in the chromosomal DNA is "read" and put into action. The answer to this question can only be presented here in a rather categorical form, omitting the experimental support for the various claims and statements.

It is believed that the immediate function of the genetic material is to determine the kinds of proteins which may be manufactured by the cells. Probably the majority of the proteins determined in this way are enzymes; a smaller number are structural proteins, which are devoid of enzymic action but which are used for building certain parts of the cell as well as extracellular cuticles, fibers, etc. Presumably, under normal conditions no protein is manufactured by a cell unless it is specified by the structure of the chromosomal DNA. All chemical substances of a nonprotein nature which are produced in the cells, such as organic acids, carbohydrates and lipids, do not have a direct representation in the chromosomal DNA but are manufactured through the action of the (protein) enzyme systems.

In its function of determining specific proteins, the genetic material acts as a series of discrete units which are sections of the DNA double strand molecule and which correspond to the mendelian genes. Each unit (gene) is responsible for the formation of one particular protein molecule or, when in some cases a complex protein molecule consists of two or more subunits, the formation of each subunit is due to a separate chromosomal gene. Protein molecules, as is well known, are essentially chains of amino acids joined together by a peptide bond; that is, the acidic carboxyl $C\!\!\!\diagup^{\displaystyle O}_{\diagdown OH}$ group of one

molecule is joined to the basic amino $^{H\diagdown}_{H\diagup}N$ group of the next molecule with the

release of a molecule of water according to the reaction:

The specificity of a protein molecule depends primarily on the kind of amino acids included in the molecule and on the sequence in which the amino acids are joined together. The functional properties of protein molecules, especially when acting as enzymes, depend also on the shape of the molecule, the manner in which it is twisted or coiled; but there is reason to believe that the actual configuration of a protein molecule is not determined independently but is a direct result of its amino acid composition.

The following 20 amino acids are common constituents of protein molecules in practically all organisms: animals, plants and microbes:

alanine	glutamic acid	leucine	serine
arginine	glutamine	lysine	threonine
asparagine	glycine	methionine	tryptophane
aspartic acid	histidine	phenylalanine	tyrosine
cysteine	isoleucine	proline	valine

There is a very convincing body of evidence to suggest that the sequence of amino acids in every protein is unequivocally determined by the sequence of bases in the chromosomal DNA. As there are only four different bases in the DNA and there are 20 different amino acids in the proteins, it follows that an amino acid must be determined by some sort of combination of bases rather than by a single base. The evidence available at present suggests that the group of bases responsible for each amino acid is a group of three, or a triplet. In this way a molecule consisting of, say, 200 amino acid molecules must be determined by $3 \times 200 = 600$ bases.

A simple calculation shows that by joining four different bases in groups of three one can obtain 64 different combinations, more than adequate to account for the 20 amino acids in proteins. One could imagine that of the 64 combinations only 20 are actually in use, the rest having no meaning ("nonsense" combinations). However, it has been found that this is not the case and actually most of the combinations, perhaps even all, have a definite meaning; this is possible because some of the amino acids are determined by more than one specific base triplet, as will be shown below.

Great efforts are being made to decipher the "genetic code"; that is, to find which base triplets determine each of the 20 amino acids (see Crick, 1962, Nirenberg, 1963). So far a direct approach to this problem has not been possible. Although the amino acid sequence is already known for a few proteins, present techniques do not allow the sequence of bases in a DNA molecule to be determined directly; neither is it possible as yet to synthesize a DNA molecule in which the four bases—adenine, thymine, guanine and cytosine—are in a desired sequence*.

However, by painstaking experiments, the details of which cannot be stated here, considerable progress has been achieved. Table 1 gives a summary of the results as they were available in 1963 (see Nirenberg, 1963, and Abelson, 1963).

The following code is given not in terms of deoxyribonucleic acid triplets but as "translated" into terms of triplets of ribonucleic acid (RNA), a substance chemically closely related to deoxyribonucleic acid (see p. 00). This is done because in actual experiments the incorporation of amino acids into protein chains has been observed when ribonucleic acid was used as a template for protein synthesis.

TABLE 1.   THE GENETIC CODE (AFTER NIRENBERG, 1963, AND ABELSON, 1963)

Amino Acid	RNA Code Triplets*			
Alanine	CCG	UCG	CAG	
Arginine	CGC	AGA	UCG	
Asparagine	ACA	AUA	CAU	
Aspartic acid	GUA	GCA		
Cysteine	UUG	UGG		
Glutamic acid	GAA	AGU		
Glutamine	ACA	AGG		
Glycine	UGG	AGG	CGG	
Histidine	ACC	AUC		
Isoleucine	UAU	UAA		
Leucine	UUG	UUC	UUA	UUU
Lysine	AAA	AAG	AAU	AAC
Methionine	UGA			
Phenylalanine	UUU	UUC		
Proline	CCC	CCU	CCA	CCG
Serine	UCU	UCC	UCG	ACG
Threonine	CAC	CAA	AUC	CGC
Tryptophane	GGU			
Tyrosine	AUU			
Valine	UGU			

* A = adenine
  C = cytosine
  G = guanine
  U = uracil, which in ribonucleic acid takes the place of thymine

The "genetic code" shown in Table 1 is still of a preliminary nature. For one thing, it has not yet been possible to determine in what sequence the bases are arranged in each triplet. Much of the ambiguity of the "code," as it is shown, might be eliminated if the sequence were known. In the table, for instance, the combination of bases, AUU (one adenine and two uracils), stands for both isoleucine and tyrosine. As the actual sequence is not known, it is very likely that one sequence—say, AUU—determines only one of the amino acids—for instance, tyrosine—while the other amino acid, isoleucine, is determined by a different sequence of the same three bases—perhaps UAU.

*Attempts are being made nevertheless along both lines: to determine with the aid of the electron microscope and suitable staining the actual sequence of the bases in a DNA molecule (see M. Beer, "Electron microscopy," Science *144*:431-432, 1964) and to synthesize DNA polynucleotides with a known sequence of bases (see Scientific Amer. *210*(6):56, 1964).

Some of the data included in Table 1 are uncertain, and there can be no doubt that in the course of the next few years much more reliable information on the subject will become available.

What has been said does not yet explain how the sequence of bases (or base triplets) in the chromosomal DNA can affect the process of protein synthesis. The DNA carrying genetic information never leaves the chromosomes, but protein synthesis occurs mainly in the cytoplasm of the cells (see Zalokar, 1960), although a certain amount of intranuclear protein synthesis is known to take place.

In the control of protein synthesis, the chromosomal DNA is believed not to take part directly but only through a second type of nucleic acid, **ribonucleic acid** or RNA.

Ribonucleic acid is a chemical substance closely resembling DNA in its make-up, but with certain minor differences. The sugar molecule taking part in the construction of the mononucleotides is **ribose** instead of deoxyribose which is present in DNA. The structural formulas of these sugars differ only slightly, as shown in the following:

Deoxyribose   Ribose

Ribonucleic acid contains four nitrogenous bases, of which three — adenine, guanine and cytosine — are exactly the same as in deoxyribonucleic acid. The fourth base is, however, not thymine but uracil. Like thymine, uracil is also a pyrimidine and differs from thymine only slightly in the absence of one carbon atom in a side chain:

Thymine   Uracil

Uracil pairs with adenine, just as thymine does.

The ribonucleic acids are known to form long chains similar to those of deoxyribonucleic acid, but the molecules do not join to form regular double spirals or they join only incompletely.

In cells, three different kinds of RNA exist (see Watson, 1963), namely ribosomal RNA, messenger RNA, and transfer RNA.

The first kind of RNA is found in the cytoplasm in the form of small granules, the **ribosomes**, which are usually between 150 and 250 Å* in diameter. The granules are composed of ribonucleic acid and protein in roughly equal amounts. In differentiated cells the ribosomes are mostly attached to the outer surfaces of the membranous structures of the cytoplasm, the endoplasmic reticulum, but in embryonic and quickly growing cells the ribosomes are found to be free and constitute the ground substance of the cytoplasm. The ribosomal RNA has been found to be present in the sedimented fraction of ultracentrifuged cells and is therefore sometimes referred to as "insoluble RNA."

If radioactively tagged amino acid molecules are supplied to growing cells, they become deposited in the first place on the ribosomes; it is therefore believed that the ribosomes are the actual site of protein synthesis. The ribosomal RNA apparently does not supply any information in the synthesis of protein molecules and the same ribosomes are supposed to be able to participate in the formation of different proteins. It is generally believed that the ribosomal RNA is synthesized in the nucleoli of the cells and at some stage it is passed out of the nucleus into the cytoplasm (see p. 86). Some data have been presented, however, that a certain amount of ribosomal RNA may be produced *in situ* in the cytoplasm (Harris and La Cour, 1963). The role of the ribosomes in protein synthesis will be explained in another section.

The messenger RNA has received its name from the belief that molecules of this kind of RNA take up the genetic information from the chromosomal DNA and carry it to the cytoplasm to be used in protein synthesis. The molecules of messenger RNA are believed to be molded on the DNA strands much in the same way as the DNA replicates itself. The two strands of DNA become separated from each other and then, instead of picking up deoxyribonucleic acid mononucleotides, the two single DNA strands, or possibly only one of them (see Roth, 1964), serve as templates for the fixation of ribonucleic acid mononucleotides. The assembly of these mononucleotides into a continous chain molecule is assisted by an enzyme, RNA polymerase. In the synthesis of the ribonucleic acid molecule the complementarity of the bases is made use of, just as in the replication of DNA, except that uracil and not thymine pairs with adenine. In this way the molecule of RNA, being complementary to the DNA molecule, comes to contain the complete genetic information of the latter (Fig. 12).

The RNA molecule now splits off from the DNA molecule and travels from the nucleus into the cytoplasm (probably making use of the pores in the nuclear membrane!), and in the cytoplasm it becomes associated with a

---

*1Å (read Ångström) = $\dfrac{1}{10{,}000{,}000}$ of a millimeter.

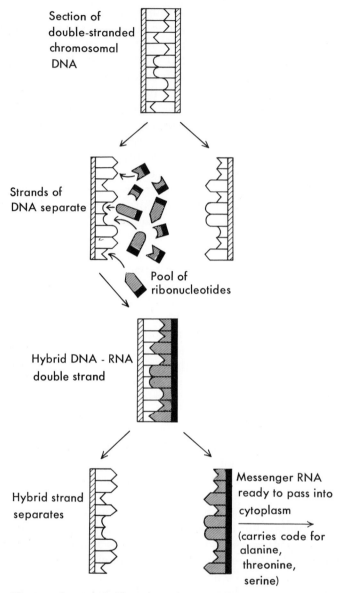

Section of
double-stranded
chromosomal
DNA

Strands of
DNA separate

Pool of
ribonucleotides

Hybrid DNA - RNA
double strand

Hybrid strand
separates

Messenger RNA
ready to pass into
cytoplasm

(carries code for
alanine,
threonine,
serine)

Figure 12. Diagram showing the formation of messenger RNA on a section of a DNA molecule. The two strands of the DNA molecule separate, and then complementary RNA mononucleotides are picked up from the RNA mononucleotide pool and assembled on a single stranded DNA molecule. After the assembly is complete, the RNA strand separates from the DNA strand. The RNA components have been darkened.

ribosome or rather with a group of ribosomes. The messenger RNA molecule is then ready to direct the arrangement of amino acids into a particular protein molecule. The base triplets of the messenger RNA correspond in arrangement to the base triplets of the chromosomal DNA; if the corresponding amino acids were placed opposite the messenger RNA base triplets, and all amino acids were joined together, the task of building a specific kind of protein would be completed.

2—4   THE ROLE OF THE TRANSFER RNA AND OF THE RIBOSOMES

To help the amino acid molecules in the recognition of the coding triplets of the messenger RNA is the task of the third kind of RNA—the transfer RNA. As this kind of RNA is found in the supernatant fraction of ultracentrifuged cells it is also known as "soluble RNA."

The placing of amino acids against the corresponding triplets of messenger RNA is performed in a series of stages (see Fig. 13). First of all, the

Figure 13.   The process of activation of amino acids and their coupling to the transfer RNA. A molecule of an amino acid (cube with handle) and a molecule of adenosine triphosphate containing two high energy bonds (represented by springs) become attached to corresponding active sites of an activating enzyme (hatched structure). The adenosine triphosphate sheds two phosphate radicals and becomes connected by one remaining high energy bond to the amino acid molecule (in B). Next a molecule of transfer RNA (a molecule bent on itself and with its two arms twisted around each other) becomes attached to the same activating enzyme, with its "recognition triplet" at the apex establishing connection with the third active site on the enzyme (C, D). An adenosine monophosphate molecule is given off and the transfer RNA molecule becomes connected by the high energy bond to the molecule of amino acid (D). Lastly, the molecule of the transfer RNA with the amino acid molecule attached is released from the enzyme (E). (Modified after Hoagland, 1959.)

free amino acids contained in the cell cytoplasm become activated with the aid of special activating enzymes. For every kind of amino acid there is a special enzyme, so that there are 20 different activating enzymes. The activation consists in the joining of the amino acid to a molecule of adenosine triphosphate (ATP). In the process, two of the three phosphoric acid groups of the adenosine triphosphate are released and the remaining adenosine monophosphate is attached to the acidic group of the amino acid. The energy-rich bond by which the outer phosphate groups of the ATP molecule are bound to the adenosine monophosphate becomes transferred to the complex, amino acid + adenosine monophosphate. Next, the complex of activator enzyme + amino acid becomes coupled with a molecule of transfer RNA.

Transfer RNA appears to be a comparatively short strand of RNA mononucleotides (70 to 80 nucleotides; Perutz, 1961). The molecule is bent on itself and the two arms of the molecule are twisted around each other and probably bonded together much like the two strands of DNA molecule. The base composition of transfer RNA is not known completely,* but it is known that at one free end it has an adenylic acid group and, next to it, two cytidylic acid groups — in other words, it ends with the triplet ACC. It is this end of the molecule which serves for the attachment of the amino acid.

In the process of this attachment, the molecule of adenosine monophosphate is discarded and the energy-rich bond which connected the adenosine monophosphate to the amino acid is now used to bind the amino acid to the adenylic acid group at the end of the transfer RNA molecule. As is the case with the activating enzyme, each amino acid is served by its own specific kinds of transfer RNA molecules. Indeed, some of the amino acids are served by more than one kind of molecule of transfer RNA, corresponding to more than one kind of base triplet that may code for a particular amino acid. Apart from having the end group, ACC, and the twisted section in which the bases may be bonded to each other pairwise, the molecule of transfer RNA must have somewhere an unbonded triplet which serves for the "recognition" of the code triplet on the messenger RNA. For lack of more exact information, we may imagine that the "recognition triplet" is placed on the bent tip of the molecule.

When the amino acid molecule becomes linked to the transfer RNA molecule, attached to the adenylic acid of the latter by an energy-rich bond, the task of the activating enzyme is completed and it falls away. The complex of amino acid + transfer RNA is then ready to become attached to a molecule of messenger RNA. This is done through the aid of the "recognition triplet" of the transfer RNA which finds its complementary counterpart, a base triplet on the messenger RNA, with which the "recognition triplet" becomes bonded. When a number of transfer RNA molecules have found their correct positions on the messenger RNA, the amino acid molecules are also thus arranged in the required order. What remains to be done is the linking of the amino acids into one continous chain to form a protein molecule. The amino acid molecules become detached from the transfer RNA molecules, and the energy-rich bonds which they had previously received from the ATP molecules are utilized to establish peptide bonds between them. The synthesis of a specific protein molecule is then complete.

---

*The complete composition and base sequence of alanine transfer RNA has been worked out by R. W. Holley et. al., 1965, Science *147*, 1462–1465.

It is believed that the alignment of the amino acids on the messenger RNA molecule proceeds in a definite sequence along the length of the molecule, similar to the closing of a zipper, and that, while more and more amino acids are added at one end, the amino acids which were attached earlier and have already been joined together start separating from the nucleic acid components. The synthesis of protein on a messenger RNA template progresses at the rate of about one amino acid per half second; a hemoglobin molecule of $\pm$ 150 amino acids is completed in 1.5 minutes.

In the meantime, the transfer RNA molecules become detached from the messenger RNA molecule and may be used again for further protein synthesis. The messenger RNA molecule also may act as a template repeatedly, according to some data, serving for the synthesis of up to 20 protein molecules in succession. Eventually, however, the messenger RNA molecule becomes degraded and further synthesis of protein requires new messenger RNA to be produced by the nucleus.

The interaction between the messenger RNA and the molecules of transfer RNA, which carry with them activated molecules of amino acids, takes place in the cytoplasm of cells in connection with ribosomes. The role of the ribosomes in this process is not yet quite clear, but according to a theory which seems to have much support for it (see Warner, Rich and Hall, 1962), the ribosomes are by no means a passive element in this transaction. At the time when protein synthesis is taking place, ribosomes apparently actively attach themselves to molecules of messenger RNA. The average diameter of a ribosome is about 200 Å; the length of a messenger RNA molecule carrying the code for a protein unit can be calculated from the fact that for each amino acid unit in the protein molecule there must be three mononucleotides in the messenger RNA molecule. The spacing of the mononucleotides is equal to 3.4 Å; therefore a moderately large protein molecule having, say, 150 amino acids must be encoded by a messenger RNA molecule having a length of at least 1500 Å (3.4 × 3 × 150 Å). Thus the extended length of the messenger RNA molecule by far exceeds the diameter of a single ribosome. It is possible that several ribosomes may attach themselves simultaneously to the same messenger RNA molecule. As a matter of fact, groups of ribosomes ("polyribosomes") have been observed with the electron microscope joined together by a thin thread which has been assumed to be a messenger RNA molecule (Fig. 14).

It seems highly improbable that a single protein molecule should be built piecemeal on or in connection with several ribosomes. Rather one would expect that the whole process of building of any single protein molecule should be started and completed through the action of one ribosome. Since at any one time a ribosome can be attached to only a part of the messenger RNA molecule (see Fig. 14), the assumption has to be made that, in order to utilize the whole of the information encoded in the messenger RNA, the ribosome concerned with the formation of a protein molecule must travel along the length of the messenger RNA molecule, picking up successive transfer RNA molecules (with their attached amino acids) as it goes, in conformity with the sequence of the base triplets on the messenger RNA, and linking them together to form the protein chain. There is evidence that the synthesis of a protein molecule always begins at the same end (the end bearing the free

Figure 14. Polyribosomes from rabbit reticulocytes (electronmicrograph). Individual ribosomes are joined together by a thread which is presumably a molecule of messenger RNA. (Courtesy of Dr. H. S. Slayter, from Slayter, Warner, Rich and Hall, 1963.)

amino group) and proceeds, adding one amino acid after another, until the whole molecule is complete. This would then have its counterpart in the movement of a single ribosome over the messenger RNA molecule; the ribosome may attach itself at the end bearing the code triplet for the first amino acid, may glide along the length of the molecule and, after reaching the other end, detach itself again; the protein molecule by this time would be complete (Fig. 15).

The ribosome may thus be compared to the lock in a zipper: by traveling along its length, the lock brings together the two sides of the zipper. In the case of protein synthesis, one side of the zipper is represented by the messenger RNA molecule; the other side of the zipper is represented by the "recognition" triplets on the transfer RNA molecules (Fig. 16). The analogy is of course a very crude and incomplete one, the main difference being that in the case of protein synthesis the two sides of the zipper become disconnected again after the passage of the lock (the ribosome). The result of the temporary union of the messenger RNA molecule and the transfer RNA molecules is, however, the linking together of the amino acids in a chain as a protein molecule, in which the order of the amino acids corresponds to the code embodied in the sequence of bases in the messenger RNA molecule.

The mode of encoding genetic information in the chromosomal DNA, and the way it is implemented in the synthesis of proteins as it has been outlined above, seems to be cogent enough and will be accepted as correct in the interpretation of developmental processes described in the following chapters of this book. It must be stressed, however, that much of the story presented here is still hypothetical, and the experimental work in the next

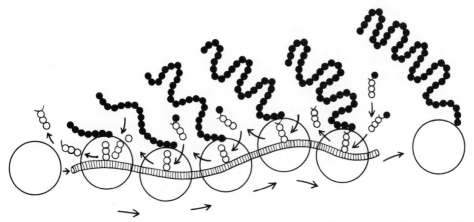

Figure 15. Diagram showing the supposed relation between the messenger RNA molecule and the ribosomes in the process of protein synthesis. Ribosomes become attached to one end of the messenger RNA molecule. As they travel along the length of the messenger RNA molecule, molecules of transfer RNA with the attached amino acids are picked up and the amino acids are joined together in a polypeptide chain. By the time the ribosome reaches the end of the messenger RNA molecule, the polypeptide chain is completed and is released from the ribosome. (Modified after Rich, 1963.)

few years may modify some aspects of the story quite substantially, though it is hardly likely that the essence of the interpretation presented here will be found to be entirely wrong.

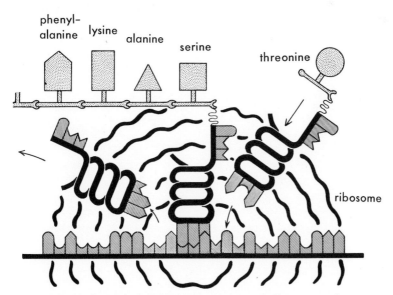

Figure 16. Diagram representing the attachment of the transfer RNA to the messenger RNA molecule and the subsequent joining of the amino acid molecule to the polypeptide chain, whereupon the transfer RNA molecule is released (left). The process is represented as occurring inside a ribosome (represented by wavy lines). The diagram is highly hypothetical (as well as the others in this series). In particular, the shape of the transfer RNA molecule and the position on it of the "recognition triplet" are not known, and the relation of the messenger RNA molecule and the ribosome is only a matter of conjecture.

Some conclusions may now be drawn about the conditions for the transmission of hereditary characters from parents to offspring and about the nature of developmental processes which lead to the reappearance of the parents' characters in their children after they had been present only in a cryptic form in the gametes.

The transmission of hereditary characters from parents to offspring is essentially a matter of passing on the DNA double-stranded molecules contained in the nucleus of the cells and of their unimpeded and correct reproduction in the course of mitotic divisions of cells. The reappearance of the hereditary characters in the offspring in an overt form rests on the activity of the RNA of different types during the development of the embryo.

It would be pertinent to ask whether the mechanism of DNA replication and of RNA activity in protein synthesis is the same in different organisms. While there are certainly some distinctions—for instance, some viruses do not possess DNA and the repository of their hereditary information is only RNA—the uniformity of the basic mechanisms in most organisms is really remarkable. The DNA in the overwhelming majority of all organisms, where it does exist, consists of the same four mononucleotides. Proteins of all organisms are built of the same 20 amino acids. The genetic code so far as has been investigated is the same in bacteria and in higher animals. Messenger RNA from one organism combined with cytoplasm of other organisms may initiate the synthesis of proteins, thus showing that in this respect living things have a common language (see Vogel, Bryson and Lampen, 1962; Protass, Speyer and Lengyel, 1964).

Against this uniformity of basic biological processes, it is the task of embryology to explain the development of diversity—diversity of organisms in general and, more specifically, the diversity of parts in any one organism.

CHAPTER

3

Spermatogenesis

3—1 CELLS IN SEMINIFEROUS TUBULES

The development of the spermatozoa takes place in the male gonads, the **testes**. In the vertebrates and insects, the testes are composite organs consisting of numerous **seminiferous tubules** converging toward common ducts leading the mature sperm to the exterior.

Spermatogenesis is a continuous process, and various stages of development of the sperm may be observed in the seminiferous tubules at the same time. In the tubule there is, however, an orderly arrangement of cells undergoing different phases of development. In insects, the proximal ends of the tubules contain the spermatogonia—the cells undergoing proliferation by mitosis. Further down the tubule, the cells in the growth and maturation stages (the spermatocytes) are to be found. The ripe spermatozoa fill the most distal parts of the tubules. In vertebrates, the arrangement of the cells in the seminiferous tubules is somewhat different: all stages, from spermatogonia to mature spermatozoa, may be found at the same level of the tubule, but while the early stages (the spermatogonia) are located at the outer surface of the tubule in an epithelium-like arrangement next to the basement membrane, the later stages of differentiation, including ripe spermatozoa, lie nearer to the lumen of the tubule (Fig. 17).

A special feature in the testes of vertebrates is the presence in the seminiferous tubules of somatic cells, which assist the developing spermatozoa by anchoring the differentiating cells and possibly nourishing them during the latter part of sperm development. These cells, known as **Sertoli cells**, are tall columnar cells attached proximally to the basement membrane and reaching distally to the lumen of the tubule. The Sertoli cells have large pale nuclei with conspicuous nucleoli, thus differing from the rather dense chromatin-rich nuclei of spermatogonia and spermatocytes. The cells differentiating into spermatozoa become partially embedded in the cytoplasm of the Sertoli cells (see Burgos and Fawcett, 1955), the future heads of the

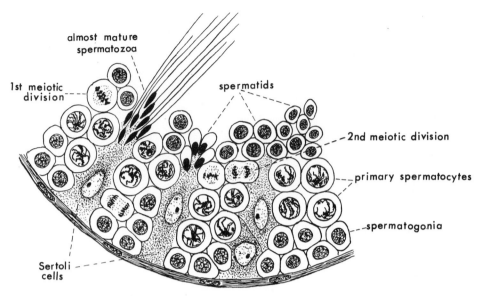

Figure 17. Diagram of part of a seminiferous tubule in a mammal. (Redrawn from Balinsky: "Vorlesungen über Histologie," München, 1947.)

spermatozoa pointing toward the base of the Sertoli cells and the tails growing out toward the lumen of the seminiferous tubule. There are no Sertoli cells in the seminiferous tubules of insects, but similar cells are found in the testes of molluscs (Yasuzumi, Tanaka and Tesuka, 1960).

The spermatogonia, as has been already stated, are found in vertebrates next to the basal membranes of the seminiferous tubules, and in microscopic preparations many of these may be seen to be in mitosis. While part of the spermatogonia remain in this condition and form a source of new sex cells throughout the reproductive life of the animal, some of the cells produced move toward the lumen of the tubule and enter the next phase of spermatogenesis: the phase of growth. The cells in this stage are called **primary spermatocytes**. The growth of the spermatocytes is actually very limited, though as a result they become perceptibly larger in volume than the spermatogonia (roughly by a factor of 2). However, the main feature in these cells is that they enter into the prophase of meiotic divisions which are of the greatest importance in the reproductive cycle of all organisms, but which can be dealt with only in their essentials here.

3 – 2 MEIOSIS

The somatic (body) cells in multicellular animals have, as a rule, a **diploid** or double number of chromosomes; that is, apart from some exceptions due to the presence of sex chromosomes, every kind of chromosome in the set is represented by a pair of chromosomes of which one is derived from the male parent and one from the female parent. The total number is then an even one (Fig. 18). The two chromosomes of each pair are called **homologous** chromosomes. The **haploid** number is found in the gametes of animals and is half

1   2   3   4   5   6

7   8   9   10   11   12   13

Figure 18. Set of chromosomes from a bone marrow cell of a frog. Each chromosome consists of two chromatids connected at the centromere. Homologous chromosomes are grouped together. (Redrawn after Di Berardino, King and McKinnell, 1963.)

the number in the somatic cells. The diploid and haploid numbers of chromosomes in a few representatives of the animal kingdom are:

	Diploid Number	Haploid Number
Man	46	23
Mouse	40	20
Frog	26	13
Fruit fly *Drosophila melanogaster*	8	4

The process of meiosis consists of two divisions of the nucleus, as the result of which the diploid number of chromosomes present immediately before is reduced to the haploid number.

The reduction of the chromosome numbers from the diploid to the haploid state can be considered as a means of preventing a continuous increase of chromosome numbers which become doubled at each fertilization through the addition of the chromosomes of the egg and the spermatozoon with a subsequent perpetuation of the increased number by mitotic divisions. This reduction can also be considered to be the last stage in the follow-up of the preceding sexual process which had caused a doubling of chromosome numbers in the zygote, after which the chromosome numbers again revert to the original haploid state. In many unicellular organisms the reduction of chromosome numbers immediately follows the fusion of the gametes, the very first division after the fusion being a meiotic division. The cells not involved in the sexual process are then all haploid. In multicellular animals, however, the reduction of chromosome numbers is delayed and the somatic or body cells are diploid. Reduction occurs only during the next reproductive cycle.

The mechanism by which a reduction of chromosome numbers is achieved is a sequence of two divisions during which, however, the chromosomes divide only once. In ordinary mitosis, each chromosome splits during the prophase to form two chromatids; these separate in anaphase to become the daughter chromosomes. In this way each of the two daughter cells receives as many chromosomes as there were in the original cell. The chromosome numbers remain the same from cell generation to cell generation. In meiosis the chromosomes also split into two chromatids during the prophase, but instead of one division, producing two cells, two divisions occur in more or less quick succession, so that the available chromatids are distributed among four cells, each of which then receives only half the chromosomes present originally. The distribution of the chromosomes among the four cells is not haphazard but is the result of a peculiar feature of meiotic prophase which must now be considered.

When the chromosomes first become visible as thin chromatin threads in the early meiotic prophase (the **leptonema** stage) (Fig. 19, *a*) the number of chromosomes is a diploid one: there are as many threadlike chromosomes as could be seen during mitosis of somatic cells. It can often be noticed that the chromosomes at this stage take up a specific orientation inside the nucleus: the ends of the chromosomes converge toward one side of the nucleus, that side where the centrosome lies (the **bouquet stage**). Next the chromosomes become sorted out in pairs: the two homologous chromosomes of each pair apply themselves to one another at first only at certain points, especially at the end where they are nearest to the centrosome, but later the two homologous chromosomes are joined along their whole length (the **zygonema stage**) (Fig. 19,*b,c*). The joining together of the homologous chromosomes is known as the process of **synapsis** and is the most important part of the meiotic prophase. The pair of chromosomes become twisted spirally around each other and cannot be distinguished separately; they appear to form a single thick thread (**pachynema stage**) (Fig. 19,*d*). The number of these thick threads corresponds to the number of pairs of chromosomes in the somatic set and is half the number of thin threads appearing in the preceding stage. Some time during the pachynema stage each of the two conjoined chromosomes splits lengthwise to form two chromatids.

Actually, the doubling of the DNA molecule strands which is necessary for the subsequent duplication of chromosomes occurs earlier, before the beginning of meiotic prophase, as can be shown by measuring the amount of DNA in the nucleus. (The mechanism of this doubling is presumably the one described on p. 26.) Through the earlier part of the meiotic prophase, however, the DNA molecules in each chromosome remain closely joined together, and each chromosome behaves as a single body. In the pachynema stage this is now changed: the two chromatids of each chromosome, containing half of the DNA present in the chromosome at the start, become partially independent of one another, although they still continue to be linked together by their common centromere. Nevertheless, it is important to know that a pachynema chromatin thread consists really of four chromatids closely joined together in one complex unit called a **bivalent**, because it actually contains a pair of chromosomes.

While the chromatids are in close proximity, breakages occur along the length of the chromatids and subsequently parts of the chromatids join up in new combinations, so that sections belonging originally to different partners of the pair of chromosomes become now joined in one and the same chromatid. This is the phenomenon of **crossing over**, which enables an exchange of parts of the chromosomes to take place. The importance of crossing over

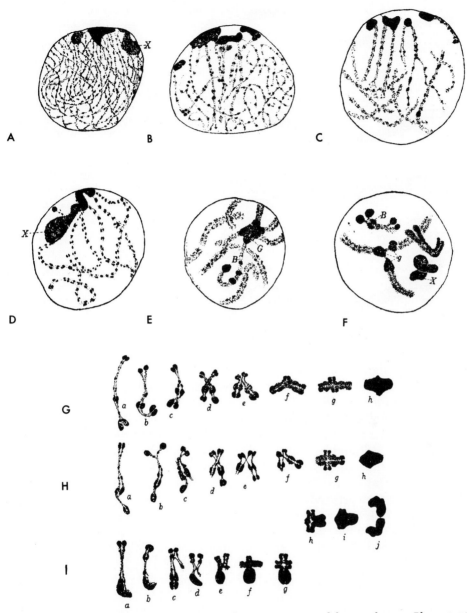

Figure 19. Stages of meiotic prophase in the spermatocytes of the grasshopper *Phrynotettix magnus*. A, Leptonema stage; B and C, zygonema stage; D, pachynema stage; E, diplonema stage; F, transition to diakinesis; G, H, I, chromosome bivalents condensing in diakinesis stage and showing chiasmata. (From Wenrich, 1916.)

stems from the fact that the hereditary material of the two parents, embodied in the two homologous chromosomes, is now reshuffled and redistributed to the four chromatids joined in synapsis. At any point breaks and crossing over occur between only one of the two chromatids of each of the chromosomes; the other chromatid in each of the chromosomes remains intact (Fig. 20). Barring some irregularities which occasionally happen, the two chromosomes exchange corresponding parts; that is, sections of the chromosomes

Figure 20. The crossing over of two chromosomes during synapsis *(b, c)* and the subsequent opening up of the bivalent in diakinesis *(d)*. (From Morgan, 1919.)

consisting of the same genes. As a rule, therefore, each chromatid emerges with a full complement of genes.

After the pachynema stage, the chromatids united in each bivalent start separating from each other, as if the forces of attraction which had led to the joining of homologous chromosomes in synapsis have now been replaced by forces of repulsion. A distinct split appears between the two chromosomes in each bivalent (**diplonema stage**) (Fig. 19,*e*) and also the two chromatids belonging to the same chromosome become distinguishable. The complex, however, continues to be held together, because at every place where a crossing over has occurred the chromosomes are connected by a **chiasma**. The chiasma is a link between chromatids belonging to different chromosomes of a pair, owing to the fact that a part of a chromatid of one chromosome has been joined by crossing over to a complementary part of a chromatid of the other chromosome. As the crossing over is a reciprocal process, the chiasmata appear as X-wise links between the chromosomes (Fig. 20). Depending on how many times crossing over has occurred in any bivalent, there may be one or more chiasmata present.

Toward the end of the meiotic prophase, the chromatids joined in the bivalent contract and thicken in a very marked degree, leading to the **diakinesis** stage (Fig. 19,*f,g,h,i*). In diakinesis the chromatids of every bivalent are typically short stout rods, still united by the chiasmata. With the attainment of this stage the chromosomes are ready to enter into the meiotic divisions.

The two meiotic divisions which follow, in the case of spermatogenesis, are very similar to ordinary mitosis insofar as the mechanism of cell division is concerned. An achromatic figure is formed, and in the first meiotic division the bivalents are placed in the equatorial plate of the achromatic figure. At the start of anaphase, the two chromosomes forming a bivalent separate from one another and are drawn to the opposite poles and thus to the two daughter cells, which are known as the **secondary spermatocytes**. In each chromosome the two chromatids are still joined by the common centromere. There follows a short interphase which, however, may be very much reduced so that the chromosomes do not change substantially from their condition during the first meiotic metaphase. Even if a resting nucleus is formed, there is no duplication of chromatids and no synthesis of genic material at this stage.

In the second meiotic division, each chromosome on the equatorial plate consists of only two chromatids linked together by the centromere. The centromere now breaks and the chromatids pass to the opposite poles. As a result of the two divisions, four cells are formed from each primary spermatocyte. These are called **spermatids**. Each spermatid gets one chromatid (now becoming an independent chromosome) from a bivalent. As the bivalents are pairs of homologous chromosomes, it follows that the spermatids possess one

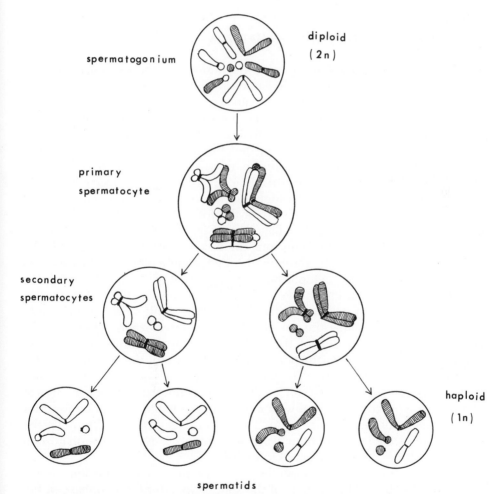

spermatogonium   diploid (2n)

primary spermatocyte

secondary spermatocytes

haploid (1n)

spermatids

Figure 21. Distribution of chromosomes during meiotic divisions in spermatogenesis. The animal is presumed to have in its somatic cells, including the spermatogonia, four pairs of chromosomes of different shapes. The homologous chromosomes join to form four bivalents, each consisting of four chromatids, and these are subsequently distributed to the spermatids, each receiving the haploid number of chromosomes.

chromosome for each pair of chromosomes present in somatic cells; that is, they now have a **haploid set of chromosomes** (see Fig. 21).

The two homologous chromosomes joined in the bivalent are normally derived from different parents: from the father through the spermatozoon and from the mother through the egg. Thus the usual condition is that half the chromosomes in somatic cells are maternal and half are paternal. In the bivalents, one of the component chromosomes is paternal and the other maternal. There is ample genetic evidence that during the first meiotic division the distribution of the paternal and maternal chromosomes is at random, each chromosome having equal chances of being delivered into the one or the other secondary spermatocyte. It follows that a secondary spermatocyte and consequently also every spermatid may have any combination of paternal and maternal chromosomes, provided that it can have only one chromosome from each pair. This, together with crossing over, provides for an almost infinite variety of combinations of paternal and maternal genes in any gamete.

3–3   DIFFERENTIATION OF THE SPERMATOZOA

The spermatids, though having a haploid set of chromosomes, are still not capable of functioning as male gametes. They have to undergo a process of differentiation to become the spermatozoa.

The function of the spermatozoon, for which its whole organization is adapted, is to reach the egg and, by fusing with the egg, to cause the egg to start developing and to transmit to the developing embryo the paternal genes.

In most cases this means that the spermatozoon must have a high degree of mobility, and in fact the organization of typical spermatozoa is largely determined by the presence of a highly developed locomotory mechanism.

A typical spermatozoon consists of the following main parts: the head, the middle piece and the tail or flagellum (Fig. 22). The anterior tip of the head is differentiated as the **acrosome**, the function of which is to enable the spermatozoon to penetrate through the egg membranes and to establish connection with the egg cytoplasm. The major part of the head is occupied by the nucleus containing the genes and is thus responsible for the transmission of hereditary characters from the male parent. The posterior part of the head also contains the centriole of the spermatozoon, which will be necessary for the initiation of the cell division in the fertilized egg. The middle piece of the spermatozoon contains the base of the flagellum and— around it—the mitochondria. The latter, being carriers of oxidative enzymes and the enzymes responsible for oxidative phosphorylation, are the "power plant" supplying the flagellum with energy in a suitable form to be used for the propulsion of the spermatozoon. The tail or flagellum, usually by far the longest part of the spermatozoon, by its movements causes the spermatozoon to swim with the head (acrosome) foremost.

The changes which transform the spermatid into a spermatozoon are of a most radical nature. The nucleus of the spermatid, after the telophase of the second meiotic division, assumes the typical structure of an interphase nucleus with finely dispersed chromatin and a nuclear membrane. During transformation of the spermatid into a spermatozoon, the nucleus shrinks by losing water from the nuclear sap, and the chromosomes become closely

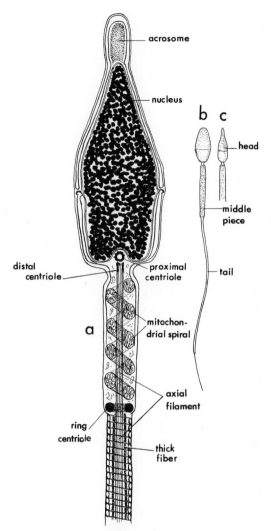

Figure 22. A mammalian spermatozoon. *a*, Semidiagrammatic drawing (redrawn after an electron micrograph by
Burgos and Fawcett: J. Biophys. & Biochem. Cytol., 1955). *b*, *c*, The same, as
seen in the light microscope; the head is
seen from the flattened side in *b* and from
the narrow side in *c*.

packed into a small volume. This is necessary to reduce the dead weight to
be carried by the locomotory apparatus of the spermatozoon and to enhance its
motility. It appears that everything superfluous is removed from the nucleus,
everything not directly concerned with transmission of hereditary characters,
leaving only the actual material of the genes. All ribonucleic acid, which is
abundant in the functioning nucleus, especially in the nucleolus, is eliminated, leaving only the deoxyribonucleoproteins present—the material of the
genes. The shape of the nucleus changes also: instead of the usual spherical
form the nucleus becomes elongated and narrow—an obvious adaptation for
propulsion in water. In different animals the shape of the head of the spermatozoon (largely dependent on the shape of the nucleus) varies considerably.
It may be ovoid and flattened from the sides (in man and bull), the head may
be drawn out into a scimitar shape with a pointed tip (in rodents and amphibia), or the head may be spirally twisted like a corkscrew (in birds and
some molluscs); occasionally it may be almost round (bivalve molluscs).
Some of these shapes may be also interpreted as an adaptation for propulsion
in water.

The acrosome of the spermatozoon is derived from the **Golgi bodies**. The Golgi body in an early spermatid consists of a series of membranes arranged concentrically around an aggregation of small vacuoles (Fig. 23). In the next stage one or more of the vacuoles start enlarging and inside the vacuole there appears a small dense body, the **proacrosomal granule**. If more than one vacuole and granule are found, as sometimes happens, these fuse together so that eventually one big vacuole remains, containing a single large dense granule. The contents of the vacuole and the granule give a positive staining reaction for mucopolysaccharides—the so-called "periodic acid-Schiff" reaction (see Clermont and Leblond, 1955). The vacuole with its granule become now closely applied to the tip of the elongating nucleus. The granule increases further and becomes the **acrosomal granule** which forms the core of the acrosome. The vacuole now loses its liquid content and its walls become spread out over the acrosomal granule and the front half of the nucleus, covering them with a double sheath known as the **cap** of the spermatozoon (Fig. 24). The remainder of the Golgi body undergoes a gradual regression and eventually is discarded as the "Golgi rest," together with some of the spermatid's cytoplasm (Fig. 25).

The foregoing description of the acrosome development is derived from a study of spermatogenesis in the cat (Burgos and Fawcett, 1955). In other animals the development may be complicated by the formation of a second main component which appears between the acrosomal granule and the nu-

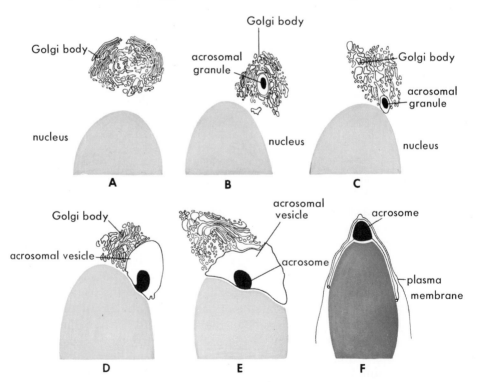

Figure 23. Sequence of stages in the formation of the acrosome and head cap from the Golgi complex during spermatogenesis in the cat. In drawings *A, B, C, D,* and *E* only the nucleus and the Golgi body with the developing acrosome are shown; *F* represents the anterior part of the sperm head, including the plasma membrane. (Redrawn from Burgos and Fawcett, 1955.)

Figure 24. Electronmicrograph of late spermatid of cat. (After Burgos and Fawcett, from Bloom and Fawcett: A Textbook of Histology, Ed. 8. Saunders, 1962.)

cleus, protruding itself from behind into the acrosomal granule in the direction of the main axis of the spermatozoon. This **axial body** (Galtsoff and Philpott, 1960) or **acrosomal cone** (Kaye, 1962) may perhaps be the rudiment of the **acrosomal filament** developing in the spermatozoon during its approach to the egg (see p. 107). As to the acrosomal granule, there is evidence that the acrosomal granule contains a supply of enzymes which are used to dissolve the egg membranes during fertilization (L. H. Colwin and A. L. Colwin, 1961).

The centrosome of a spermatid after the second meiotic division consists of two centrioles, which can be shown with the aid of an electron microscope to have the structure of two cylindrical bodies, lying at right angles to each other. At an early stage in the differentiation of the spermatozoon, the two centrioles move to a position just behind the nucleus. A depression is formed in the posterior surface of the nucleus and one of the two centrioles becomes placed in this depression with its axis approximately at right angles to the main axis of the spermatozoon. This is the **proximal centriole** of the spermatozoon; the other centriole, the **distal centriole**, takes up a position behind the proximal centriole with its axis coinciding with the longitudinal axis of the spermatozoon. This distal centriole now gives rise to the axial filament of the flagellum of the spermatozoon for which it serves as a starting point or as basal granule (Figs. 24, 26, 27). The axial filament of the spermatozoon has the same organization as the axial filaments of the flagella and kinocilia present in other animal (and plant) cells; that is, it has a pair of longitudinal fibers along its middle and a ring of nine pairs of longitudinal fibers sur-

Figure 25. Transformation of the young spermatid (upper left-hand corner) into a free sperma-tozoon (lower left-hand corner) in the ram, as seen in preparations with periodic acid–Schiff staining. The acrosome granules and acrosomes are shown in black; the head cap and Golgi body (including Golgi body rest) are stippled. The mass of mitochondria in middle piece of sperma-tozoon is indicated by very close stippling. The nuclei, which are not stained by the periodic-acid-Schiff method, are shown only in contour. The heads of ram spermatozoa are flattened; therefore in later stages the drawings show the spermatozoa as viewed from the broad side and from the narrow side. (Redrawn from Clermont and Leblond, 1955.)

rounding it (see Fawcett and Porter, 1954; and Afzelius, 1959). These fibers are anchored in the distal centriole in the same way as the fibers of a cilium or flagellum are connected to their basal granules (see Figs. 26 and 27).

The distal centriole and the proximal part of the axial filament lie in the middle piece of the spermatozoon. They are surrounded by the mitochondria, which become concentrated in this region from other parts of the cell. In the middle piece, the mitochondria lose their individuality to a certain degree by

Figure 26. Electronmicrograph of posterior part of the head and middle piece of a spermatozoon of the annelid *Hydroides hexagonus*. Ax, Axial filament of tail; Cp, proximal centriole, cut transversely; Cd, distal centriole, cut longitudinally; M, mitochondrial body; N, nucleus; T, beginning of tail. (Courtesy of Dr. A. L. Colwin and Dr. L. H. Colwin, 1961.)

fusing together to a greater or lesser extent. In many animals (in mammals in particular) the mitochondria join in one continuous body which becomes twisted spirally around the axial filament and the proximal centrosome. However, in other animals the spiral arrangement of the mitochondria is lacking, and the mitochondria are joined in one or more massive clumps (mitochondrial bodies) forming the bulk of the middle piece of the spermatozoon (Figs. 66 and 69). Around the periphery of the middle piece the cytoplasm forms a condensed layer known as the **manchette**; the manchette surrounds

Figure 27. Electronmicrographs of the posterior head and middle piece region of late spermatids of the domestic fowl. The photographs show the two centrioles: the proximal centriole (C) in cross section in *A* and in longitudinal section in *B* and the distal centriole (C') in longitudinal section in both photographs. D, Dense material which forms the so-called "ring centriole"; M, "manchette" surrounding the posterior part of the nucleus (N) and the middle piece of the spermatozoon; T, axial filament of the tail. (Courtesy of Dr. T. Nagano, 1962.)

also the posterior part of the head of the spermatozoon, where it is not covered by the cap (Figs. 24, 27).

A dark ring is sometimes seen at the posterior end of the middle piece forming the boundary between the middle piece and the tail (Figs. 22 and 24). The structure has been known as the "ring centriole" but it has been shown by electron microscopy that it does not in any way resemble a centriole in its structure and that therefore it must have a completely different origin. The function of the ring is not known.

The axial filament is the main part of the tail or flagellum of the spermatozoon. The structure of the axial filament of the spermatozoon is essentially similar to that found in cilia and flagella of other cells. The presence and arrangement of ten pairs of longitudinal fibers has been mentioned above. The axial filament is surrounded in the simpler cases by a very thin layer of cytoplasm and by the plasmalemma. Some further structures may also be present.

In mammals the nine pairs of longitudinal fibers are accompanied on the outside by nine much thicker fibers which are wedge-shaped in cross section. These fibers start in the middle piece of the spermatozoon but do not quite reach the tip of the flagellum (Yasuzumi, 1956; Telkka, Fawcett and Christensen, 1961). Another set of threads—or, actually, flattened bands—surround the longitudinal fibers of the spermatozoon tail in mammals. For a long time the threads were supposed to be coiled spirally around the central core of the tail, but careful electron microscopic studies have shown that the fiber does not form a continuous spiral but is composed of semicircular ribs articulating with each other on the opposite sides of the sperm tail (Telkka, Fawcett and Christensen, 1961). The tip of the mammalian sperm tail (the "end piece") lacks the additional elements and consists only of the axial filament covered with cytoplasm and plasmalemma—a structure similar to the structure of the whole tail of less elaborately differentiated invertebrate spermatozoa.

A different kind of complication is present in some fishes and amphibians: in spermatozoa of these animals there is an undulating membrane which stretches along most of the length of the tail and presumably takes an active part in the locomotory activity of the sperm (Burgos and Fawcett, 1956).

Much of the cytoplasm of the spermatid becomes redundant in the spermatozoon, and it is simply discarded. As the acrosome is being formed at the anterior end of the spermatid nucleus, the cytoplasm flows away from it in the opposite direction, leaving only an extremely thin layer with the plasmalemma covering the acrosome and the nucleus. The bulk of the cytoplasm is then attached to what will be the middle piece of the spermatozoon, while the tail is growing out at the posterior end (Fig. 25). After the mitochondria have arranged themselves around the base of the axial filament of the flagellum, the remainder of the cytoplasm (containing also the "Golgi rest") is simply pinched off from the spermatozoon, leaving only a fairly narrow sleeve of cytoplasm surrounding the mitochondria in the middle piece. The detached part of the cytoplasm disintegrates.

In a few groups of animals, such as in the nematodes and the decapod crustaceans, the spermatozoa do not have flagella and are therefore incapable of swimming. These spermatozoa are also in other respects profoundly different from those in other animals. When the spermatozoa of a decapod were examined with the electron microscope, it was found that these do not possess centrioles and are completely devoid of mitochondria—which makes sense, as they do not require large amounts of energy for movement (Moses, 1961). The mechanism of the penetration of the nonflagellate spermatozoa into the egg must be very different from that in the flagellate spermatozoa, and in Chapter 6 on fertilization only the latter will be dealt with.

CHAPTER

4

Oogenesis

4–1 GROWTH OF THE OOCYTE

In the female sex the first stage of the development of gametes is similar to that found in spermatogenesis: the **oogonia**—the cells eventually giving rise to the eggs—undergo proliferation by mitotic divisions. They then become **oocytes** and enter a period of growth. Owing to the fact that the egg contributes the greater part of the substances used in development, growth plays a much greater role in oogenesis than in spermatogenesis. Also the differentiation of the egg occurs simultaneously with growth, rather than after maturation.

The period of growth in the female gametes is a very prolonged one, and the increase in size is very considerable. In frogs a young oocyte may be about 50 μ in diameter, and the fully developed egg in many species is between 1000 μ and 2000 μ in diameter. If *Rana pipiens,* in which the diameter of the mature egg is about 1500 μ, is taken as an example, the increase in size of the oocyte is by a factor of 27,000. This growth takes place over a period of three years. The young oocytes start growing after the tadpoles metamorphose into young froglets. One-year-old and two-year-old frogs do not yet have mature eggs, but by the third year the eggs are ready and the frogs may spawn for the first time. Every year a new batch of oocytes is produced as the result of oogonial divisions, but these do not mature until three years later, so that oocytes of three generations may be contained in the ovary at the same time. The growth of the oocytes is fairly slow during the first two seasons but becomes much more rapid in the summer of the third year of the frog's life, so that by the autumn the eggs reach their maximum dimensions (Fig. 28) (Grant, 1953).

In other animals the growth of oocytes may proceed at a much higher rate and take a shorter time for completion. In the hen the last rapid growth of oocyte occurs in the 6 to 14 days preceding ovulation, and during this time the volume of the oocyte increases 200 fold. In mammals the proliferation of the

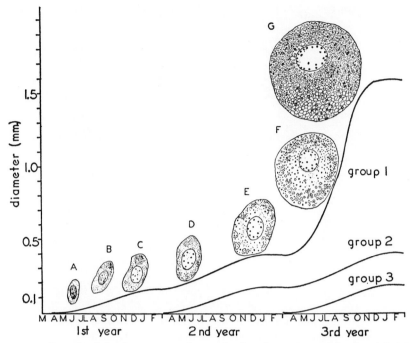

Figure 28. Growth of the frog oocytes during the first three years of the female's life. The curves show the increase in diameter of three generations of oocytes; the drawings represent the changes in size and structure of oocytes of the first generation. (Modified from Grant, 1953.)

oogonia is restricted to the intra-uterine period of life, and all the eggs produced by a mammalian female throughout her reproductive life are derived from oocytes already present at birth. The oocytes reach their full size in 16-day-old mice. The eggs of mammals are, of course, much smaller than those of amphibians. The oocyte of a mouse grows from a size of about 20 μ in diameter into the ripe ovum of about 70 μ in diameter, an increase by a factor of only 43 as against an increase of 27,000 in the frog.

The fully grown egg is a relatively large cell, always larger than the average somatic cell in the animal. When large quantities of foodstuffs are stored in the egg cell, it may attain giant proportions. The yolk of a hen's egg, which represents the egg cell in this case, has an average weight of 55 gm. and is, of course, by no means the largest of its kind. Very large eggs are also found in reptiles and in some sharks. However, the quantity of active cytoplasm in such large eggs is comparatively rather small, and the nucleus, although larger than in the somatic cells, never increases in proportion to the bulk of the whole egg.

In many groups of animals, notably in the chordates, the oocytes are surrounded during the whole time of their growth and maturation by special cells of the ovary, the **follicle cells**. In mammals the follicle cells are derived from the germinal epithelium of the ovaries, and initially the young oocyte is surrounded by one layer of follicle cells, forming a simple cuboidal epithelium around the oocyte. Later, the number of follicle cells increases greatly, the cells becoming arranged in several rows. As the egg approaches maturity, an eccentric cavity appears in the mass of the follicle cells. This cavity is filled with fluid secreted presumably by the cells of the follicle. The

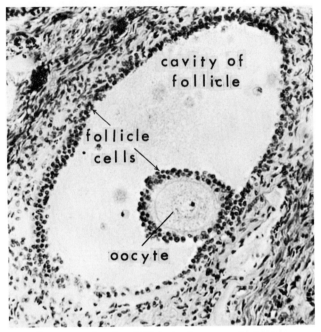

Figure 29.   Graafian follicle in the ovary of a bitch.

follicle at this stage is known as a **Graafian follicle** (Fig. 29). The oocyte is surrounded by follicle cells not only in mammals but in other vertebrates as well, though due to the larger size of the egg the follicle cells are not so conspicuous. It is believed that the follicle cells actively assist the growth of the oocyte by secreting substances which are taken up by the oocyte.

The structural relationships between the follicle cells and the oocytes, revealed by electron microscopic studies in recent years, are very peculiar. Originally there is a simple apposition of the follicle cells and the oocyte, similar to the one existing between ordinary epithelial cells: the cytoplasmic membranes of the adjoining cells are separated only by a narrow gap of about 80Å (Fig. 30). At certain points the two cytoplasmic membranes show a close connection in the form of **desmosomes**: here the plasma membranes of the adjoining cells are thickened and the space in between appears to be filled by a denser substance which presumably holds the two cell membranes together (Anderson and Beams, 1960; Franchi, 1960; Wartenberg, 1962). At a later stage a wider space appears between the follicle cells and the oocyte. The follicle cells, however, retain contact with the oocytes at the points where the desmosomes could be noticed in the previous stage. The cytoplasm of the follicle cell becomes drawn out into elongated processes or **microvilli** reaching across the space separating the follicle cell and the oocyte. At the same time the surface of the oocyte is drawn out into numerous fingerlike **microvilli** projecting into the space between the oocyte and follicle cells (Fig. 31). The microvilli of the oocyte interdigitate with those of the follicle cells (Kemp, 1956; Sotelo and Porter, 1959) (Fig. 32). With the light microscope, individual microvilli cannot be seen, and the zone of microvilli appears as a radially striated layer, which has long been known, in mammals, as the **zona radiata**. The presence of the microvilli greatly increases the surface area of

Figure 30. Young oocyte of guinea pig (electronmicrograph), showing Golgi material ("yolk nucleus"). Inset: oocyte in a similar stage, with "yolk nucleus," as shown by ordinary microscopy. N, Nucleus; Ncl, nucleolus; Nm, nuclear membrane; G, Golgi material; M, mitochondria; D, desmosomes at junction of oocyte and follicle cells; Fn, nuclei of follicle cells; E, endoplasmic reticulum in follicle cells. (Courtesy of Prof. E. Anderson.)

the oocyte. In the frog oocyte such an increase in surface area has been estimated to be by a factor of about 35. It would appear that the increase in area facilitates metabolic turnover between the oocyte and its environment.

Small inpocketings of the oocyte cytoplasm may often be observed at the base of the microvilli, and these are interpreted as an indication that the oocyte is taking in fluids and dissolved substances from the space between itself and the follicle cells by means of **pinocytosis** or "cell drinking" (Press, 1959; Anderson and Beams, 1960).

Toward the time when the oocyte reaches its full size a denser material, often of fibrillar structure, appears in between the interdigitating processes of the oocyte and the follicle cells. The material becomes consolidated and eventually fills most of the space between the follicle cells and the oocyte, becoming the egg membrane (see further on page 90).

In the last stages of oocyte maturation the cytoplasmic processes of the oocyte and of the follicle cells may be withdrawn, and the space between the two is then taken up by the egg membrane. This is the case in all vertebrates studied so far and in mammals in particular (Odor, 1960). In bivalve molluscs, however, the microvilli of the oocyte are not withdrawn, and at the time when the egg is released from the ovary, its vitelline membrane is still perforated by long processes of the egg cytoplasm; these persist even at the

Figure 31. Advanced oocyte of guinea pig (electronmicrograph), showing zona radiata and microvilli. CO, Cytoplasm of oocyte; Mv, microvilli produced by the oocyte; Fm, cytoplasmic projections from the follicle cells; F, follicle cell; ZR, zona radiata; D, desmosome at point of contact of follicle cell projection and surface of oocyte; M, mitochondria; Fn, nucleus of follicle cell; G, Golgi body. (Courtesy of Prof. E. Anderson.)

beginning of the cleavage (Reverberi and Mancuso, 1961; Humphreys, 1962; Rebhun, 1962; Pasteels and Harven, 1962). In fishes the perforations in the egg membrane left after the cytoplasmic processes are withdrawn become canals ("micropiles") through which the spermatozoa can reach the egg (Sadov, 1956).

The development on the surface of the oocyte of a system of microvilli which interdigitate with cytoplasmic processes of the follicle cells is a general rule, but there are some exceptions, the most important of which are in the eggs of sea urchins. The follicle cells in these animals are closely apposed to the surface of the oocyte, and no interdigitating microvilli are present. Nevertheless when the mature egg leaves the ovary it is surrounded by a thin layer of jelly, which must have been formed during the growth of the oocyte in the space between the oocyte and the surrounding follicle cells.

In some insects, molluscs and annelids the relationship between the oocyte and the rest of the ovary is further complicated by the presence of special nurse cells which, together with the follicle cells, take part in providing the nutrition for growing oocytes. The nurse cells are closely related in

Figure 32. Young oocyte of a mammal surrounded by follicle cells. D, Desmosomes; ER, endoplasmic reticulum; FE, follicle cells; FGC, Golgi complex in follicle cells; GC, Golgi complex in oocyte; IB, inclusion body; M, mitochondria; MV, microvilli; MVB, multivesicular body; N, nucleus; NCL, nucleolus; PFE, processes of follicle cells; PO, oocyte (primary oocyte); V, vacuoles formed during pinocytosis; ZP, zona pellucida. (From Anderson and Beams, 1960.)

their origin to the egg cell, and may be considered to be abortive oocytes. In *Drosophila* an oogonial cell gives rise, by four successive mitotic divisions, to 16 cells of which one becomes an oocyte and the other 15 become nurse cells. The nurse cells are thus siblings of the oocyte. The whole complex is surrounded by follicle cells (Fig. 33). The mode of transfer of materials from nurse cells to the oocyte is radically different from the way matter is given off to the oocyte by the follicle cells. No microvilli or cytoplasmic processes are developed at the interface between the oocyte and nurse cells. Instead gaps may appear through the cell membranes of the oocyte and the nurse cell, and through such gaps the cytoplasm of the nurse cell pours into the oocyte (King and Devine, 1958). In any case the nurse cells become used up during the growth of the oocyte (some insects and annelids; see Fig. 34), or they may be completely engulfed in the cytoplasm of the oocyte (in the snail *Helix*).

The materials used in the growth of the oocytes are to a large extent produced outside, in other parts of the body of the female, and brought to the

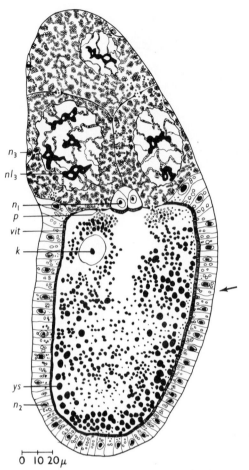

n_3

nl_3

n_1
p
vit

k

ys

n_2

0 10 20μ

Figure 33. Diagram of an ovarian follicle of *Drosophila melanogaster.* n_1, n_2, n_3, Nuclei of various types of follicle cells; nl_3, a portion of the compound nucleolus of the nurse cell; p, pore (intercellular bridge) connecting a nurse cell to the oocyte; k, karyosome in the nucleus of oocyte; vit, vitelline membrane; ys, yolk sphere. (Courtesy of Dr. R. C. King and Dr. E. A. Koch, 1963.)

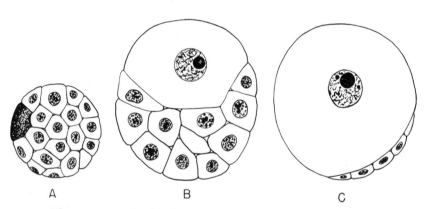

A   B   C

Figure 34. Three stages in the development of the oocyte of the leech *Piscicola,* which uses up the follicle (nurse) cells as it grows. (From Jörgensen, in Willier, Weiss and Hamburger, 1955.)

gonads by way of the bloodstream. In vertebrates the site of synthesis of egg proteins and phospholipids appears to be the liver. This may be proved by using precursors marked by a radioactive isotope atom such as P^{32} in disodium hydrogen phosphate. When such a precursor was injected into the blood of a laying hen and the amount of radioactivity was measured in different tissues, it was found that after six hours the radioactivity was highest in the liver (164.0 units / γ phosphate); the radioactivity was weaker in the blood (38.3 units / γ phosphate), and very small indeed in the growing oocytes (0.62 units / γ phosphate). This shows that the injected phosphate was mainly taken up by the liver. Twelve hours later the radioactivity in the liver was down to 101.0 units / γ phosphate but increased slightly in the blood (to 45.4 units / γ phosphate). There was a very strong increase of radioactivity in the oocytes to 4.1 units / γ phosphate. This indicates that the substances synthesized in the liver with inclusion of the injected phosphate found their way via the blood into the growing oocytes (Flickinger and Rounds, 1956). By direct chemical analysis it can be shown that a chemical constituent of the egg yolk (phosvitin — see further p. 65) is present in the blood plasma of a laying hen (Mok, Martin and Common, 1961). By use of serological methods (see p. 228) it was found that, in the frog, substances (antigens) identical to the ones found in the growing oocytes are present in the liver and in the blood serum (Flickinger and Rounds, 1956). A similar investigation has been performed with females of the cecropia silk moth (*Platysamia cecropia*). It was proved by using serological methods that a specific protein contained in the blood plasma of female pupae passes into the developing eggs and becomes a major part of the yolk of the egg (Telfer, 1954). As only larger molecules can be detected by serological methods, the last-mentioned investigations serve to indicate that not only building materials such as amino acids are brought to the oocytes from without but that macromolecules (proteins, phosphoproteins and phospholipids) can be supplied to the oocytes in the same way.

That the building materials are supplied to the oocytes through the mediation of the follicle cells and the nurse cells (where such exist) could also be demonstrated by using radioactively marked precursors. Females of the common fly, *Musca domestica,* were injected with tritiated (containing radioactive hydrogen, H^3) cytidine, a nucleic acid precursor, or tritiated (H^3 containing) histidine, a protein precursor. After varying intervals the animals were fixed, the gonad sectioned and the sections were treated by methods of autoradiography (see p. 27) (Bier, 1963). Figure 35 shows the results of these experiments. Thirty minutes after the injection, the radioactively labeled amino-acid molecules are lodged predominantly in the follicle cells (Fig. 35a), but after three hours, radioactivity in the follicle cells disappears and intense radioactivity is present in oocyte cytoplasm, mainly in the surface layer (Fig. 35b), thus showing that the labeled material has been passed from the follicle cells to the oocyte. The nucleic acid precursors, on the other hand, appear to be taken primarily into the nuclei of the nurse cells, which are intensely radioactive one hour after the injection (Fig. 35c). The newly synthesized radioactively labeled ribonucleic acid soon passes out of the nuclei into the cytoplasm of the nurse cells, so that in five hours the nuclei are practically free of radioactivity (Fig. 35d). From the cytoplasm of the nurse cells the labeled RNA then passes into the cytoplasm of the oocyte through the gaps connecting the nurse cells to the oocyte (see p. 61).

A comparison of work done on the growth of avian, amphibian and insect oocytes shows that the mechanism of food supply to the oocyte is rather similar in all these animals.

The young oocyte just emerged from the oogonial mitotic divisions does

Figure 35. Passage of radioactive nucleic acid precursors and protein precursors into the growing oocyte of the common fly, *Musca domestica*. The figure shows autoradiographs of sections. *A*, Follicle 30 minutes after injection of H³-T-histidine. *B*, Follicles 3 hours after injection of radioactive histidine. *C*, Follicle 1 hour after injection of H³-cytidine. *D*, Follicle 5 hours after injection of radioactive cytidine. Arrows in *C* and *D* indicate the intercellular bridges through which the radioactively labeled RNA streams from the nurse cells into the oocyte. Compare with diagram of egg follicle, Figure 33. (Courtesy of Dr. K. Bier, 1963.)

not possess special cytoplasmic zones any more than does any undifferentiated cell of the animal's body. Neither is it able to develop into a new individual. The special organization of the egg cell which makes it capable of developing into a new individual is elaborated gradually and usually over a considerable period of time. The changes that the future cell undergoes during this period can in part be directly observed in microscopic preparations, but some of the changes are still completely unknown to us.

4–2 ACCUMULATION OF FOOD RESERVES IN THE CYTOPLASM OF THE OOCYTE

During the growth of the oocyte not only does the amount of cytoplasm increase in quantity, but it changes in quality by the elaboration and regular distribution of various cell inclusions and specially modified parts of the cytoplasm which, as we will see, are essential for the development of the embryo. Of these the food supplies stored in the cytoplasm of the egg should be mentioned first.

The most usual form of food storage in the egg consists of granules of **yolk.** Yolk is not a definite chemical substance, but rather a morphological term; the chemical substance may not be the same in all cases.

The main chemical components of yolk are proteins, phospholipids and, to a lesser extent, neutral fats. Depending on which components predominate, we can distinguish "protein yolk," which may contain variable amounts of lipids as well as protein, and "fatty yolk," which in addition to phospholipid and fat may contain some admixture of protein. Protein yolk and fatty yolk are present side by side in the eggs of many animals.

Protein yolk is the main form of food reserve in many invertebrates (for instance, in echinoderms) and in lower chordates (*Amphioxus*, tunicates) (Fig. 36). The amount of yolk in these animals is relatively small; in the sea urchin *Arbacia* the yolk granules take up about 27 per cent of the total volume of the egg (Harvey, 1956). The yolk granules are fine and fairly evenly distributed in the cytoplasm of the egg. Eggs with a small amount of yolk are called **oligolecithal**.

In amphibian eggs the protein yolk is found in the form of rather large granules, usually described as the **yolk platelets**. The yolk platelets have an oval shape and are flattened in one plane. The cytoplasm is densely packed with them (Fig. 37). The amphibian egg is much larger, so that not only the relative but also the absolute amount of yolk is far in excess of that found in the eggs of *Amphioxus* or the echinoderms. The distribution of yolk in the amphibian egg is distinctly unequal: the yolk platelets are densest in the lower part of the egg, and there is relatively more cytoplasm in the upper part of the egg. Eggs of this type are known as **telolecithal**.

The yolk platelets of amphibians contain two main proteinaceous substances: phosvitin and lipovitellin. Phosvitin is a highly phosphorylated protein (phosphorous content: 8.4 per cent), with a molecular weight of 35,000. Lipovitellin is a protein with a very much larger molecule (molecular weight 400,000) and containing a very considerable amount of bound lipid (17.5 per cent). In the yolk platelets two molecules of phosvitin are associated with each molecule of lipovitellin in a structural unit, the units being arranged in the platelet in a crystalline lattice with regular hexagonal packing (Fig. 38) (Wallace, 1963). This can be clearly seen in electron micrographs of amphibian yolk (Fig. 39).

In addition to the yolk platelets the amphibian egg contains stored supplies in the form of lipoid and glycogen. Lipoid is distributed throughout the cytoplasm of the egg in the form of organized inclusions, the **lipochondria** (Holtfreter, 1946), which consist of an internal core of lipoid surrounded by

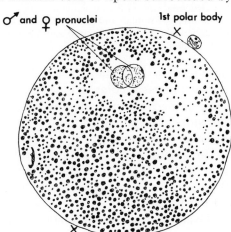

Figure 36. Oligolecithal egg of *Amphioxus* shortly after fertilization. The animal and vegetal poles are indicated by crosses. (After Kerr, 1919.)

Figure 37. Electronmicrograph of cytoplasmic inclusions in an unfertilized egg of a frog *Xenopus laevis*. *y*, Yolk; *lp*, lipochondria; *m*, mitochondria; *v*, vacuoles. Inset, A group of mitochondria under higher magnification.

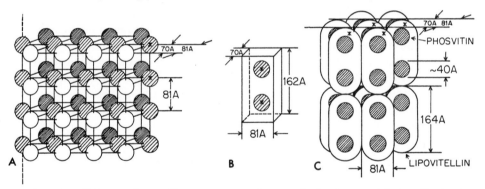

Figure 38. Diagram of crystalline structure in the main body of an amphibian yolk platelet. *A*, Arrangement of phosvitin molecules (seen as dark dots in electronmicrographs) in the lattice. *B*, A structural unit of the crystal consisting of two molecules of phosvitin and one molecule of lipovitellin. *C*, Arrangement of phosvitin and lipovitellin molecules in a simple hexagonal lattice (when viewed end on). The figures show actual dimensions in *A*. (Courtesy of Dr. R. Wallace and Dr. S. Karasaki.)

a thin protein coat. The lipochondria are much smaller than the yolk platelets and have a less regular shape (Fig. 37). Glycogen is present in the egg cytoplasm in the form of small granules. Fat may also be stored in the egg for the nourishment of the developing embryo, but its quantity is relatively small in the lower vertebrates.

In a mature amphibian egg, protein yolk constitutes roughly 45 per cent of the dry weight, lipoids 25 per cent, and glycogen 8.1 per cent. Only about 20 per cent of the dry weight of the mature egg is active cytoplasm (Barth and Barth, 1954).

Cyclostomes, elasmobranchs, ganoids and the lungfishes have eggs with

Figure 39. Electronmicrograph of a yolk platelet from an amphibian embryo, showing the crystalline structure of the main body of the platelet. R, Ribosomes in the cytoplasm; S, superficial layer of yolk platelet; V, cytoplasmic vesicle. Arrows indicate fibrillar structures in the superficial layer. (Courtesy of Dr. S. Karasaki, 1963.)

a distribution of food reserves much the same as in amphibians, though the amount of yolk may be greater, especially in some selachians. In the higher teleosts, on the other hand, the yolk is completely segregated from the cytoplasm. The yolk constitutes the greater part of the egg, and the cytoplasm is restricted to a thin surface layer covering the yolk and thickened on the uppermost side of the egg in the shape of a cytoplasmic cap. The nucleus of the egg in this case lies inside this cytoplasmic cap.

In the bony fishes the fat may be present in the form of large fat droplets inside the mass of yolk. The number and size of the fat droplets is typical for different families of fishes. Sometimes only one large droplet is present; at other times there is a large number of smaller droplets.

The yolk of a bird's or a reptile's egg, as in the case of the bony fishes, lies in a compact mass in the interior of the egg, and the cytoplasm is restricted to a thin layer on the surface, with a thickened cap of cytoplasm on the upper side. As in bony fishes this cytoplasmic cap also contains the nucleus of the egg cell. Most of the yolk is liquid, but about 23 per cent is in the form of solid "yolk spheres." The yolk as a whole contains 48.7 per cent of water, 16.6 per cent proteins, 32.6 per cent phospholipids and fats and 1 per cent carbohydrates (Romanoff and Romanoff, 1949). The proteins of the avian yolk are chemically closely related to those of the amphibian yolk: phosvitin and lipovitellin are the main components. Part of the lipovitellin is bound to phosvitin; this part of the yolk protein is insoluble in water. The remainder of the lipovitellin (referred to by some authors as "Livetin" — Flickinger, 1961) is water soluble. The fatty portion of avian yolk is predominantly neutral fat (50 per cent of the yolk dry weight), the rest being phosphatides and cholesterol.

Some of the invertebrates have also developed eggs in which the relative amount of yolk is high and more or less segregated from the cytoplasm. In cephalopods and some gastropods among the molluscs the eggs are telolecithal, much as in the lower vertebrates (Fig. 40). Arthropods, especially insects, have developed a different type of egg: the yolk is concentrated in the interior of the egg and the cytoplasm is distributed as a thin coat on the external surface; however, there is also an island of cytoplasm in the center of the egg. This island, surrounded on all sides by yolk, contains the nucleus of the egg cell (Fig. 41). Eggs of this type are called **centrolecithal**.

The arrangement of various substances and cellular constituents in the advanced oocyte, and, later, in the egg shows a polarity; that is, an unequal distribution in respect to what may be called the two opposite poles of the egg and in respect to the main axis of the egg — the line connecting the two poles. The nucleus of the egg is approximated to one pole of the egg, which is termed the **animal pole**. The opposite pole is termed the **vegetal pole**, because the accumulation of yolk at that pole serves for the nutrition of the

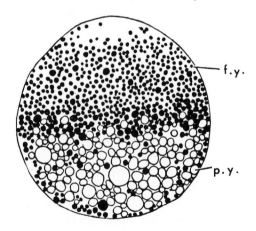

f.y.

p.y.

Figure 40. Telolecithal egg of the mollusc *Aplysia limacina*. *f.y.*, Fatty yolk. *p.y.*, Protein yolk. (After Ries and Gersch, from Raven, 1958.)

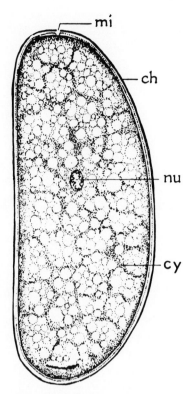

Figure 41. Insect egg, diagrammatic. *nu*, Nucleus; *cy*, cytoplasm; *ch*, chorion; *mi*, micropyle. (From Johannsen and Butt, 1941.)

developing embryo. When the cell undergoes meiosis, the nucleus of the egg cell approaches the animal pole of the egg, and the polar bodies are always discharged at the animal pole. This process serves to distinguish the animal pole in oligolecithal eggs if the concentration of the yolk at the vegetal pole is not very distinct, as is often the case, and also in centrolecithal eggs.

In eggs in which the yolk is completely segregated from the cytoplasm, as in the bony fishes, reptiles and birds, the thickened cytoplasmic cap containing the nucleus denotes the animal pole of the egg.

In most animals which have been investigated with modern methods, young oocytes show a very similar and fairly simple organization. The cytoplasm in young oocytes is rather poor in complex inclusions and possesses practically none of the specialized structures found in the adult oocyte and mature egg (Fig. 42). Large amounts of nucleic acids, mainly in the form of ribonucleic acid but possibly with some amount of deoxyribonucleic acid as well (Sze, 1953), are present in the cytoplasm of young oocytes. As seen with the electron microscope the cytoplasm is finely granular. The granules are almost certainly ribonucleoprotein in nature, as the cytoplasm is strongly and uniformly stained by pyronin or azure B (see Brachet, 1941), stains used to reveal ribonucleic acid. Mitochondria are fairly scarce in young oocytes but may increase in numbers very considerably during the growth of oocytes and may, in some animals (amphibia, birds), be aggregated in the form of large "mitochondrial clouds" (Romanoff, 1960; Wartenberg, 1962; Balinsky and Devis, 1963) (Fig. 43). As mitochondria are carriers of oxidative enzymes, the overall oxygen consumption increases during the growth of the oocyte. It has been found that the young frog oocytes, before the beginning of yolk forma-

Figure 42. Surface of young frog oocyte with adjoining follicle cell (electronmicrograph). OC, Cytoplasm of oocyte; G, Golgi body; M, mitochondrion; Pl, plasmalemma of oocyte; FC, follicle cell; Fn, nucleus of follicle cell; MF, mitochondrion in follicle cell; E, endoplasmic reticulum (vesicular form).

tion, absorb 0.69 cu. mm. of oxygen per cubic millimeter of oocyte. At the stage when the yolk platelets begin to form, the oxygen consumption rises to 1.5 cu. mm. per cubic millimeter. In older oocytes nearing maturity, the oxygen consumption per cubic millimeter falls to 1.2 cu. mm. This is still a high value, considering that a large part of the volume of the oocyte is filled with inert yolk; thus the remaining active cytoplasm continues to respire at a high rate (Mestcherskaia, 1935, cited after Brachet, 1950).

Golgi bodies are found in younger oocytes around the centrosome.

In oocytes of some mammals (guinea pig, Anderson and Beams, 1960; rat, Odor, 1960) Golgi-type membranes form a large spherical mass (see Fig. 30, p. 59) which later disperses. In oocytes which have advanced in growth, small Golgi bodies become scattered throughout the whole cytoplasm, or they may be located in the subcortical cytoplasm, sometimes distributed there at fairly regular intervals (frog, Balinsky and Devis, 1963; chick, Bellairs, 1963) (Fig. 42). In mature oocytes Golgi bodies sometimes disappear completely (Odor, 1960) possibly indicating that these organoids have been used up or transformed into some other structures.

Typical endoplasmic reticulum, in the form of double lamellae with ribosomes attached to their outer surfaces, is very rarely found in young oocytes.

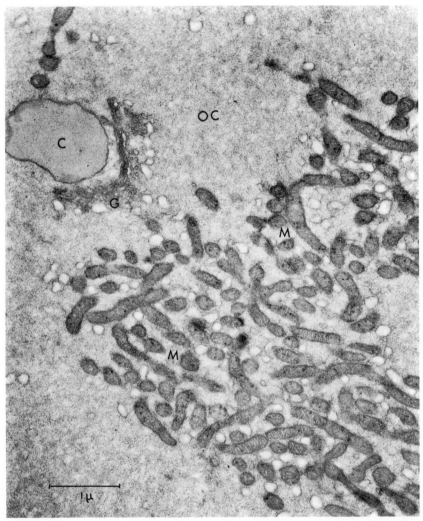

Figure 43. Edge of the "mitochondrial cloud" in the cytoplasm of a young frog oocyte (electronmicrograph). M, Mitochondria; G, Golgi body; C, cortical granule; OC, finely granular ground substance of cytoplasm.

The cytoplasm instead contains fairly numerous vesicles surrounded by a simple membrane. These vesicles are generally believed to be equivalent to or to be a modification of the endoplasmic reticulum. Ribosomes are often found to be attached to the surface of the vesicles. A different kind of membranous structure is, however, often found in oocytes: this takes the form of stacks of double membranes, sometimes in parallel, and sometimes in spiral arrangement (Fig. 44). The membranes usually do not have ribosomes attached to them but instead are perforated by pores, which closely resemble the pores of the nuclear membrane (Merriam, 1959; Wischnitzer, 1960; and Rebhun, 1961). For this reason the membranes are regarded by some authors as being derived from the nuclear membrane (see Kessel, 1963).

For a long time it has been believed that the production of yolk in the oocyte is the result of the activity of a special body, found in the oocytes

Figure 44. System of membranes in the cytoplasm of a frog oocyte. Mb, Membranes; Y, yolk; L, lipochondria. (d, Dirt on section.)

of many animals, which accordingly was called the "yolk nucleus" or "yolk nucleus of Balbiani" (see Raven, 1961). This body was first discovered in the oocytes of spiders, but later it was shown to be present in avian oocytes and in the oocytes of some mammals and amphibians. In the early stages this body lies next to the nucleus (Fig. 45), but in later stages it breaks up and its fragments are distributed to the periphery of the oocyte.

As it is at the periphery of the oocyte that the yolk platelets appear first, the conclusion has been drawn that vitellogenesis (production of yolk) is initiated by the components of the "yolk nucleus." At present it is not possible to support this conclusion, at least not in a general form. Electron microscopic investigations have shown that "yolk nuclei" in different animals are not always of a similar nature. In spiders the yolk nuclei consist of numerous stacked membranes with mitochondria and vesicular structures surrounded by the membranes or interspersed between them (Sotelo and Trujillo-Cenóz, 1957; André and Rouiller, 1957). There is no indication that

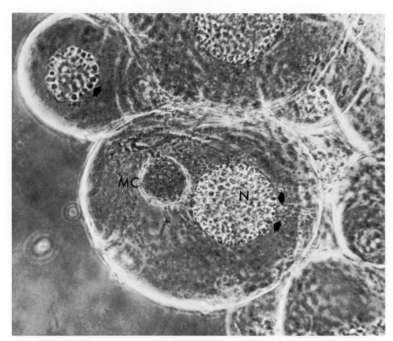

Figure 45. Phase contrast photograph of living young oocytes from the ovary of a juvenile frog. N, Nucleus; MC, mitochondrial cloud ("yolk nucleus"). Nucleoli indicated by arrows.

these bodies have anything to do with the formation of yolk. In amphibians the name "yolk nucleus" has been applied to the mitochondrial cloud mentioned earlier (p. 69), and the same appears to be true of the avian oocyte (Romanoff, 1960), although an electron microscopic verification of the nature of the body in the bird is still outstanding. In amphibians (*Xenopus*), it was found that although parts of the mitochondrial cloud reach the periphery of the oocyte, they do so too late to participate in yolk platelet formation, which starts before the breakup of the mitochondrial cloud (Balinsky and Devis, 1963). In mammals a spherical body lying in the cytoplasm next to the nucleus and having, in the living state, the same appearance as the mitochondrial cloud of the amphibian oocyte, consists of a mass of Golgi-type membranes, and is now referred to as the Golgi material (see Fig. 30, p. 59 – Anderson and Beams, 1960). The Golgi material in mammals cannot be involved in yolk formation for the simple reason that, in the oocytes of higher mammals (see p. 273), yolk, at least in the form of yolk platelets, is completely lacking.

Apart from the "yolk nucleus," several cellular organoids have been considered responsible for yolk formation in different animals by different authors. The organoids most often mentioned in this connection are the Golgi bodies and the mitochondria. The evidence is rather contradictory, in part probably because the methods of light microscopy do not always allow the nature of small cellular inclusions to be distinguished with certainty. Electron microscopic investigations do not have this drawback and it is therefore to electron microscopy that we owe the most reliable data on yolk formation. The clearest results have so far been obtained in studies of amphibian oocytes.

There is conclusive proof that in amphibians the yolk platelets are formed inside modified mitochondria (Lanzaveccia, 1960; Ward, 1962; Balinsky and Devis, 1963). In this process the inner mitochondrial membranes become dislodged and eventually become arranged in concentric layers while the interior of the mitochondrion is taken up by the main body of the yolk platelet. Occasionally a yolk crystal may be seen lying inside a swelling of a mitochondrion, which in other parts still shows a typical structure with systems of transverse cristae (Fig. 46).

A somewhat similar origin of protein yolk has been described in gastropod molluscs (Carasso and Favard, 1960). The protein yolk platelets, which in gastropods also show crystalline structure, are formed either actually inside mitochondria or in between clumps of mitochondria.

As the yolk platelets increase in size and more yolk platelets are produced, they fill the cytoplasm from outside inward. In the last stages of the growth of the oocyte the yolk platelets are formed around the nucleus, so that the cytoplasm becomes filled up with yolk. The yolk platelets are not

Figure 46. Formation of a yolk crystal inside a mitochondrion in a frog oocyte. PY, Yolk platelet (crystal); MC, mitochondrial cortex; C, membrane of mitochondrial crista. (Courtesy of Dr. R. T. Ward.)

all of the same size. At the animal pole of the oocyte, where the polar bodies are to be given off later, the yolk platelets remain relatively small and are not packed quite so densely. At the vegetal pole they reach a larger size (about 1.5 μ in length) and they come to lie very close to each other, leaving little cytoplasm in between. The interior of the oocytes, the area surrounding the nucleus, is fairly closely packed with yolk platelets which are not quite so large as at the vegetal pole (see Wittek, 1952).

It has already been mentioned that young oocytes contain, in their cytoplasm, large amounts of ribonucleic acid. As the yolk platelets begin to accumulate at the periphery of the oocyte, the area of cytoplasm rich in ribonucleic acid becomes restricted to the deeper parts of the cytoplasm, and still later to the area around the nucleus (Fig. 47). Eventually the ribonucleic acid in the cytoplasm is reduced to very small quantities. In eggs having smaller amounts of yolk, such as the echinoderm or mammalian eggs, however, quite a considerable amount of ribonucleic acid remains even in fully mature eggs.

It has been indicated previously that the yolk is probably not synthesized in the oocytes at all but is produced elsewhere in the body (in the liver, in the case of vertebrates), and that it is then transported in a soluble form via the bloodstream and the follicle cells to the oocyte where it is finally deposited in the form of yolk platelets or yolk granules.

In this connection, some properties of the yolk proteins are of particular interest. The yolk protein phosvitin (p. 65) is insoluble in water when it is fully phosphorylated. If, however, part of the phosphate is removed by the action of a phosphatase, the remaining phosvitin becomes water soluble. The reverse would then also hold true: namely, if soluble partially phosphorylated phosvitin were more fully phosphorylated in the oocyte, it would become insoluble. An enzyme, protein kinase, has actually been found in the frog ovary which is capable of promoting the incorporation of phosphate into partially phosphorylated phosvitin (Wallace, 1964). The phosphate is taken from ATP. The reaction is fully reversible and takes place according to the following equation:

$$\begin{array}{c} \text{partially} \\ \text{phosphorylated} + \text{ATP} \\ \text{protein} \end{array} \underset{\text{Mg}^{++}}{\overset{\text{protein kinase}}{\rightleftharpoons}} \begin{array}{c} \text{fully} \\ \text{phosphorylated} + \text{ADP} \\ \text{protein} \end{array}$$

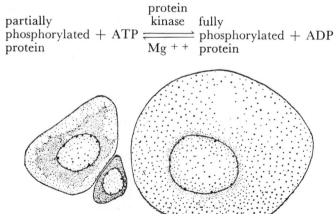

Figure 47. Distribution of ribonucleic acid (shown by stippling) in three stages of development of amphibian oocytes. (From Brachet: Chemical Embryology. New York, Interscience Publishers, Inc., 1950.)

The action of protein kinase is restricted to only one component of the amphibian yolk (phosvitin). However in the yolk crystal the lipovitellin is bound to phosvitin, and therefore the rendering of phosvitin insoluble fixes the lipovitellin in position as well. Now it is very important that protein kinase is a mitochondrial enzyme, and this explains why the yolk platelets are formed inside or in connection with mitochondria: it is there that the yolk proteins are converted from the soluble into the insoluble form. There remains obviously much to be done to explain the deposition of yolk in such animals as birds, in which no clear relation between mitochondria and yolk deposition has been shown (see Bellairs, 1964), and also to clarify the origin of fatty yolk.

4–3 ORGANIZATION OF THE EGG CYTOPLASM

Yolk and the other substances obviously destined to serve as food for the developing embryo are not the only ones that are laid down in the oocyte during its growth. A characteristic feature of the mature eggs in many animals is the presence of granules of pigment, which are elaborated during the growth of the oocyte.

In the oocytes of the ascidian *Cynthia partita*, besides the yolk, which accumulates at the vegetal pole, there appears in the later stages a yellow pigment in the form of granules distributed all over the surface of the oocyte in a thin cortical layer of cytoplasm. In the sea urchin *Paracentrotus lividus* a similar distribution of pigment granules is observed; only the pigment is red. We will see later that the yellow pigment of *Cynthia partita* and the red pigment of *Paracentrotus lividus,* although uniformly distributed over the surface of the maturing egg, will later be concentrated and come to lie in specific parts of the embryo—in the muscles and mesenchyme of the former, and in the walls of the gut of the latter. Although it does not necessarily follow that the pigment is in any way a precursor of muscular or intestinal differentiation, it may well be that the pigment is an indicator of some specialization in the cytoplasm of the oocyte which eventually leads to specific types of differentiation of parts of the embryo.

In the eggs of most amphibians there is present a greater or lesser amount of dark brown or black pigment. Depending on the amount of pigment, the egg may appear to be light fawn, through various shades of brown, to pitch black. However, the young oocytes have no pigment. Pigment granules start being formed somewhat later than the yolk platelets, in oocytes which have grown to about one half of the final diameter. The greatest number of pigment granules becomes located in the cortical layer of cytoplasm of the mature oocyte, but quite considerable amounts of pigment are distributed in the interior.

A remarkable feature in the distribution of pigment in the amphibian egg is that it is not uniform. There is much more pigment in the animal hemisphere of the oocyte than in the vegetal hemisphere. The difference may be very marked, so that while the animal hemisphere may be dark brown or black, the vegetal hemisphere appears clear white, although in reality a small number of pigment granules is practically always present in the vegetal hemisphere as well. The transition from the dark to the light areas is fairly

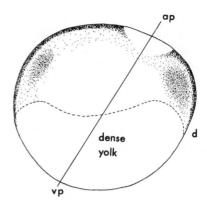

Figure 48. Distribution of yolk and pigment in the ripe egg of a frog. Median section. *ap*, Animal pole; *vp*, vegetal pole; *d*, dorsal side of the egg. (After Lehmann, 1945, and Wittek, 1952.)

sharp, but there is always a zone of intermediate, gradually fading, pigmentation, which can be referred to conveniently as the **marginal zone**.

In cross section of a ripe amphibian egg (Fig. 48) it may be seen that the vegetal half of the egg is filled by a densely packed mass of yolk containing very little pigment. This mass of yolk is slightly concave on the top. The center of the egg is taken up by a roughly lens-shaped mass of cytoplasm with middle-sized yolk platelets and a moderate amount of pigment. This zone also contains the nucleus in the immature oocyte. On the outer edges of this interior mass of protoplasm lies a ring-shaped area containing large amounts of pigment. The ring is thicker on one side of the egg, where it also reaches nearer to the surface. This side of the egg corresponds, as we will see later, to the future dorsal side of the embryo and thus, in conjunction with the differences along the main axis of the egg, indicates a plane of bilateral symmetry. Lastly, on top of the interior mass of protoplasm lies, like an inverted saucer, a layer of cytoplasm of the animal hemisphere (the "animal cap"), which is rich in pigment, especially in the cortical layer, and relatively poor in yolk.

The pigment granules in themselves may perhaps not be very important for the development of the embryo; in fact, there are some species of amphibians which do not have any pigment in their eggs (the large European crested newt *Triturus cristatus* and some frogs making foam nests, like the African *Chiromantis xerampelina*) and yet develop in the same way as related species having pigmented eggs. However, the uneven distribution of the pigment may be considered as an indicator of qualitatively different areas in the cytoplasm of the egg. This can be corroborated by some further observations. We have seen that the cytoplasm of young frog oocytes contains large amounts of ribonucleic acid. It has been observed that in oocytes 400 to 500 μ in the diameter the ribonucleic acid is especially concentrated in the surface layer of the animal hemisphere of the oocyte. With the development of yolk platelets in the subcortical layer of cytoplasm, the ribonucleic acid concentration disappears, but it seems very probable that the localization of pigment in the animal hemisphere reflects some peculiarities in the cytoplasm—peculiarities which are related to the distribution of the ribonucleic acid in the preceding stage (Wittek, 1952; Kemp, 1953, p. 493).

In the elephant tusk mollusc *Dentalium*, very distinct cytoplasmic areas can be seen in the egg even before it leaves the ovary. The fully grown oocyte contains a pigment varying in different individuals from olive green to brick red. However, the pigment does not encroach on two areas at the opposite sides of the egg, which are therefore colorless. One of the two colorless areas lies on the side with which the egg is attached to the wall of the ovary. While the oocyte is in the ovary, this part is somewhat drawn out, so that the oocyte is more or less pear-shaped. The second pigment-free area is on the free surface of the oocyte, and it is in the center of this area that the polar bodies are given off, thus marking this side as the animal pole.

The egg is released from the ovary with the germinal vesicle still intact, and it proceeds to the meiotic divisions only afterwards. After release from the ovary, the egg partially rounds up but remains slightly flattened from animal to vegetal pole. In a vertical section through the egg (Fig. 49) the light area at the vegetal pole (the pole that was attached to the wall of the ovary) is seen to be made up of clear protoplasm which contains no yolk granules. This protoplasm reaches inward to the nucleus and surrounds it, and at the outer edges it is continuous with a very thin cortical layer covering the whole of the egg surface. There is also a small patch of clear cytoplasm at the opposite pole; this is the place where the polar bodies will be given off. The rest of the cytoplasm is filled by rather densely packed yolk granules. The yolk-free and unpigmented cytoplasm at the vegetal pole may be termed the **vegetal polar plasm**. The pigment-free **animal polar plasm** is only partly free from yolk. The significance of the two polar plasms for the development of the embryo will be considered in a later section (7–6).

It has been stated already that the oocytes of higher mammals do not increase to a very great extent during the period of growth. This is because the embryo receives its nutrition from the maternal body, and there is in consequence no need to accumulate large amounts of food supplies in the egg. There are some other features in mammalian oocytes, however, which bear a relation to the differentiation of parts of the embryo from the egg. Already in very early mammalian oocytes there exists a polar organization: the nucleus of the oocyte lies nearer to one pole of the egg, the animal pole. A "yolk nucleus" is present in the younger oocytes as an area of basophilic cytoplasm containing ribonucleic acid and a concentration of mitochondria. This basophilic area lies next to the nucleus, nearer to the vegetal pole but somewhat to one side of the main axis. In middle-sized oocytes the basophilic area next to the nucleus becomes less conspicuous, and the mitochondria are now found distributed next to the cortex of the egg. They become

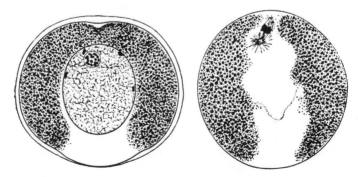

Figure 49. Oocytes of *Dentalium* just before the beginning of meiotic divisions (left) and in the stage of first meiotic division (right). (From Wilson, 1904.)

especially numerous on one side of the egg—opposite from where the yolk nucleus was to be seen. The mitochondria are accompanied by large amounts of basophilic granules containing ribonucleic acid, and the ground substance of the cytoplasm is here very dense and rich in proteins. The zone in question covers about half the surface of the egg, on one side of the main axis, reaching from the animal to the vegetal pole. The opposite side of the egg surface appears to be richer in water and contains numerous vacuoles, the latter being especially distinct in some animals such as the mole.

This distribution of cytoplasmic constituents shows that the mammalian oocyte not only has a polarity but actually possesses a bilateral organization (Fig. 50). The side of the egg rich in ribonucleic acid corresponds to the dorsal side of the embryo, and the side with vacuolated cytoplasm corresponds to the ventral side (Jones-Seaton, 1950; Dalcq, 1954). The position of the animal pole is reaffirmed at the time of the meiotic divisions, as shown in Fig. 50 b.

Of all the developments in the cytoplasm of the oocytes, perhaps the most important are those which concern the surface layer of the oocytes. The superficial layer of cytoplasm in oocytes differs in its physical properties from the rest of the cytoplasm. Most of the oocyte cytoplasm is in the physical state of a suspension, with a continuous liquid phase (containing in solution various large and small particles, ranging in size from simple inorganic ions to protein molecules), and with larger inclusions such as mitochondria and ribosomes dispersed more or less at random in the continuous phase. These inclusions are freely movable, in natural conditions owing to cytoplasmic streaming, or in experiments in which the cells are exposed to a centrifugal force. The superficial layer is, on the other hand, in a gelated state or at least in a very much more viscous state so that its components are not readily displaced during cytoplasmic streaming or in moderately strong centrifugation. This superficial layer of the cytoplasm is known as the **cortex**, and it plays the role of a fixture in the cell, remaining in the same position for continuous periods of growth and development. The thickness of the cortex has been measured by various means and the results are somewhat contradictory. It has been claimed on the grounds of centrifugation experiments that the

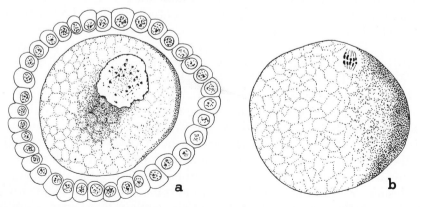

Figure 50. Oocytes of the rat before the first meiotic division (a) and during the first meiotic division (b). Ribonucleic acid is shown by the close stippling. (From Jones-Seaton, 1950.)

only immovable parts of the egg are the cell membrane and the particles immediately attached to the cell membrane, which would then represent the cortex of the egg (Mercer and Wolpert, 1962). It is more generally recognized, however, that in addition to the cell membrane a layer of cytoplasm, about 2 to 3 μ in thickness, is in a gelated state and thus constitutes the cortex of the egg (Hiramoto, 1957; Mitchison, 1956). The larger cytoplasmic inclusions are either embedded in or attached to the cortex and so remain in fixed position. In addition to fixing the position of parts of the oocyte cytoplasm, the cortex is the bearer of some differentiations which are highly characteristic of the late oocyte and mature egg.

The development of the microvilli on the surface of oocytes as well as the formation of the pinocytotic vesicles have been dealt with earlier. Both seem to be concerned with the transport of substances from the follicle cells into the oocyte. An entirely different aspect of cortical differentiation is seen in the formation of special structures known as the **cortical granules**. These are spherical bodies, varying in diameter from 0.8 μ (in sea urchins) to 2 μ (in frogs), surrounded by a simple membrane and containing acid mucopolysaccharides (Fig. 51). In mature oocytes the cortical granules are arranged in a layer close to the plasmalemma. Cortical granules have been found in oocytes of many animals, but not in all. They are present in sea urchins (Afzelius, 1956), frogs (Kemp, 1956), fishes (Yamamoto, 1954), bivalve molluscs (Reverberi and Mancuso, 1961; Rebhun, 1962; Pasteels and Harven, 1962; Humphreys, 1962), some annelids (Lillie, 1911), and some mammals, such as the hamster and the rabbit (Hadek, 1963a), but they are absent in other mammals, such as man (Wartenberg and Stegner, 1960), the rat (Sotelo and Porter, 1959; Odor, 1960), and the guinea pig (Anderson and Beams, 1960). They are also absent in gastropod molluscs (Recourt, 1961), urodele amphibians (Wartenberg and Schmidt, 1961), insects (Okada and Waddington, 1959) and birds (Bellairs, 1964).

In most cases the mucopolysaccharide content of the cortical granules is fairly homogeneous, finely granular or floccular, but in sea urchins the cortical granules show a complicated internal structure consisting of a system of concentric or possibly spirally arranged denser lamellae, separated by less dense material (Fig. 52). The cortical granules are known to be formed in the interior of the oocyte, possibly in connection with Golgi bodies (Balinsky and Devis, 1963), and later to move to the periphery to the cortical layer of cytoplasm. The cortical granules appear to play an important role at the time of fertilization, when the granules burst and their contents contribute to the accumulation of fluid around the fertilized egg (see pp. 109, 112).

In the last stage of maturation, the nuclear membrane of the oocyte breaks down and the chromosomes move to the surface at the animal pole to take part in the maturation divisions. At the same time the nuclear sap merges with the cytoplasm of the oocyte. It has been observed in some animals that the nuclear sap does not mix completely with the cytoplasm, but that it forms a more or less separate mass, thus increasing the diversity of the cytoplasmic areas of the eggs. In amphibians the nuclear sap differs from the cytoplasm of the oocyte in that its proteins contain large amounts of SH— groups (owing to the presence of the amino acid, cysteine). The reaction with ammonium or sodium nitroprusside, which causes a red color to appear in

Figure 51. Advanced oocyte of frog showing interdigitating microvilli in the zona radiata and a layer of cortical granules. *A,* Electronmicrograph; *B,* contours of cell organoids corresponding to electronmicrograph.

the presence of SH— groups, is restricted in the mature oocyte to the germinal vesicle. Once the nuclear membrane breaks down, the red straining with nitroprusside reagent is observed in the cytoplasm at the animal pole, obviously due to the admixture of the nuclear sap released from the germinal

Figure 52. Surface of a ripe, unfertilized sea urchin egg showing layer of cortical granules (electronmicrograph). C, Cortical granule; Y, yolk granule; M, mitochondria; Pl, plasmalemma; J, jelly coat.

vesicle. After fertilization the cytoplasm containing the SH– spreads out along one side of the egg which will become the dorsal side, thus accentuating the bilateral symmetry of the egg (Fig. 53) (Brachet, 1950).

As a general rule mature eggs are spherical in shape, though elongated eggs are not infrequently found, especially among insects. Among vertebrates, oval-shaped eggs are found in the hagfish *Myxine* and in the ganoid fishes. The elongated shape of the bird's egg, on the other hand, is not due to an elongated shape of the egg cell itself. The egg cell, which is the yellow of the egg, is in this case spherical.

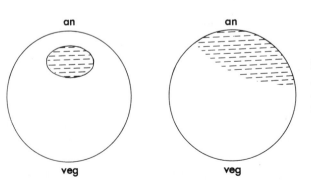

Figure 53. Distribution of sulfhydryl groups in the frog egg before rupture of the germinal vesicle (left) and after maturation (right). (After Brachet, from Kühn, 1955.)

Before concluding this chapter on the organization of the egg and the processes which provide for the arrangement of the various cytoplasmic substances in the egg, we must return once more to the polarity of the egg and consider its origin. The polarity of the egg is discernible from the position of parts in the egg cell: the nucleus, yolk and other cytoplasmic substances.

Many efforts have been made to elucidate what factors are responsible for the unequal distribution of these parts. It has been claimed that the polarity of the egg may be imposed on it by the direction of flow of the nutrient substances during the growth of the oocyte. It has been mentioned that in the molluscs and echinoderms the vegetal pole of the egg develops from that end of the oocyte by which it is attached to the wall of the ovary. The nutrient substances, at the expense of which the oocyte grows, presumably enter the ovary from outside, from the body cavity. It would stand to reason, then, that greater amounts of yolk might be deposited in the part of the cell nearest to the proximal surface of the ovary, thus causing this part to become the vegetal pole. This explanation would not hold, however, for oocytes which are surrounded by follicle cells from all sides, as are the oocytes of amphibians or mammals. It has been suggested that the course of the nearest blood vessel supplying parts of the ovary with nourishment might cause the parts of the oocyte nearest to the vessel to develop into the vegetal pole. But according to the views of Child (1941), the animal pole, as the more active one, should develop from that part of the oocyte which has a better oxygen supply, and on this principle the part of the oocyte nearest to a blood vessel should become the animal pole.

Actually, there does not seem to be a very clear connection between the position of the animal and vegetal pole of the egg and the course of the blood vessels. In view of the differences in the structure of ovaries in different animals, it would seem rather hopeless to try to find a common factor in the environment of the growing oocyte which could be held responsible for the origin of polarity of the egg.

Polarity is, however, a phenomenon which is found not only in egg cells but in other cells as well. In epithelial cells there is a distinct difference between the proximal end of the cell (the end resting on the underlying basement membrane) and the distal end (which forms the free surface of the epithelium). In nerve cells the polarity of the cell takes the form of the opposite differentiations of axon and dendrites. In mesenchyme cells the polarity shows itself in the direction of movement of the cells, in their possessing an anterior and a posterior end when in movement (Holtfreter, 1947a, b).

In the interior of any cell, the position of the centrosome in respect to the nucleus establishes a general form of polarity, the main axis of which is the line drawn through the centrosome and the nucleus. This polarity affects not only the distribution of cytoplasmic inclusions (the Golgi bodies are often found grouped around the centrosome) but may involve the intimate structure of the nucleus itself. When the oocytes are in the early leptonema stage of the meiotic prophase the chromosomes become arranged in a definite way, converging to that side of the nucleus which is nearest to the centrosome. This stage is known as the "bouquet stage" (Fig. 55, p. 85). Early oocytes thus already possess a polarity, and this intrinsic polarity may well serve as a basis for the distribution of cellular constituents during the growth and maturation of the oocyte.

What has been said so far refers to the polarity along the main axis of the egg (along the axis going from the animal to the vegetal pole). A similar sort of polarity may be responsible for the difference between the side which is to develop into the dorsal side of the embryo and that which is to develop into the ventral side of the embryo. However, even less is known about the origin of this polarity than about the origin of polarity along the main axis.

4—4 CHANGES IN THE NUCLEUS OF THE OOCYTE

Simultaneously with the growth of the oocyte its nucleus enters into the prophase of the meiotic divisions; the homologous chromosomes pair together similarly to what occurs in the primary spermatocytes. But the subsequent stages of meiosis are postponed until the end of the period of growth. Instead, the nucleus of the oocyte increases in size, though not nearly to the same extent as the cytoplasm. The increase in size is due mainly to the production of very large amounts of nuclear sap, so that the nuclei of advanced oocytes appear to be bloated with fluid and are often referred to as **germinal vesicles**. The chromosomes at the same time may increase in length, but the amount of deoxyribonucleic acid in the chromosomes does not increase in proportion to the enlargement of the nucleus. In oocytes of animals having large eggs, the chromosomes acquire a very characteristic appearance: thin threads or loops are thrown out transverse to the main axis of the chromosomes, making the chromosomes look like lamp brushes: **lamp brush chromosomes** (Fig. 54).

It is believed that the loops represent actual sections of the chromosome which has become completely despiralized, and that this is a favorable condition for the main activity of the genes, namely to synthesize the messenger RNA, which is subsequently to control the synthesis of proteins in the cell. By using a radioactively labeled RNA precursor (uridine), it has actually been proved that RNA synthesis occurs on the loops of the lamp brush chromosomes. With the aid of very fine microchemical methods, it has been found that the chromosomal RNA in oocytes has a different base composition (that is, a different ratio of adenine and uracil to guanine and cytosine) from the base ratio of ribosomal RNA, but it fairly closely resembles the base ratio of the chromosomal DNA (with thymidine replacing uracil). (See Gall, 1963.) These observations are in keeping with the assumption that the RNA synthesized on the loops of the lamp brush chromosomes is, base for base, a copy of the chromosomal DNA; in other words, that it becomes a carrier of genetic information contained in the chromosomes. This genetic information is then presumably passed into the oocyte cytoplasm, where proteins are being synthesized in the course of the growth of the oocyte. Apparently, in addition to the passage of proteins from the follicle cells into the oocyte, there is some protein synthesis going on in the oocyte itself.

The nucleoli in the germinal vesicle seem to be very actively involved in the metabolism of the growing and maturing oocyte. The nucleolus of the oocyte increases greatly in size and becomes very conspicuous against the

Figure 54. Lamp brush chromosomes from an oocyte of the newt, *Triturus carnifex*. (Courtesy of Prof. H. G. Callan.)

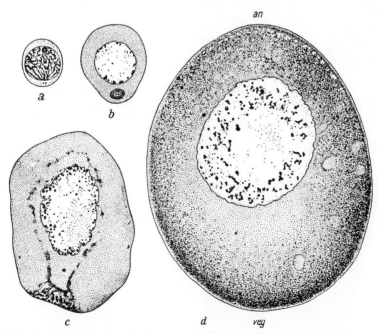

Figure 55. Four stages in the development of the amphibian oocyte. *a, Ambystoma,* young oocyte with chromosomes in the "bouquet stage." *b, c, d, Rana,* beginning of deposition of yolk. (After Witschi, from Kühn, 1955.)

background of the vesicular nucleus. In many animals, in amphibians in particular, instead of one large nucleolus, numerous smaller nucleoli are formed in the germinal vesicle. Most of these become localized on the periphery of the nucleus, immediately underneath the nuclear membrane (Fig. 55; see also Fig. 45, p. 73). There are many reports, both in the older and more recent literature (see, for instance, Bretschneider and Raven, 1951; Logachev, 1956), that nucleolar material may penetrate through gaps in the nuclear membrane and enter the cytoplasm (Fig. 56). As the nucleoli consist mainly of ribonucleic acid, the penetration of nucleolar material into the cytoplasm may account, at least in part, for the increase in cytoplasmic ribonucleic acid in oocytes. (See section 4–2.)

The nucleolar RNA has been compared with the RNA in the cytoplasm of the oocytes in several different animals, and it was found that the base composition (the relative amounts of adenine, uracil, guanine and cytosine) in the two kinds of RNA is strikingly similar. As the bulk of the RNA in the cytoplasm is ribosome RNA, it follows that it is this kind of RNA that is supplied by the nucleolus to the cytoplasm (see Gall, 1963).

As the oocyte nucleus grows, a remarkable change occurs in its ability to be stained by agents currently used for the demonstration of the presence

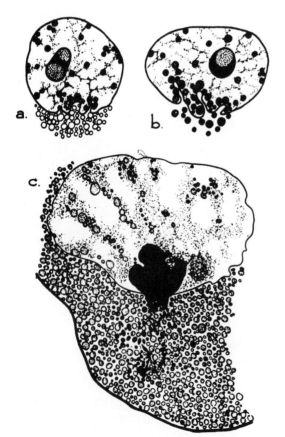

Figure 56. Extrusion of nuclear substances into the cytoplasm during oogenesis of *Limnaea stagnalis*. (From Bretschneider and Raven, 1951.)

of deoxyribonucleic acid. The chromosomes of the young oocyte can be clearly stained with methyl green or the Feulgen reagent, but at later stages the staining becomes paler and paler until it may be lacking altogether. When the oocyte reaches maturity and approaches the reduction divisions, the chromosomes reappear in a very much contracted form and may again be stained by the Feulgen reagent or by methyl green. There is, however, sufficient evidence that deoxyribonucleic acid is present in the nucleus at all stages, and that the failure of the Feulgen reagent to demonstrate its presence is due to the extreme dispersal of the chromosomal material in the oocyte nucleus.

After the oocyte completes its growth, it is ready for the reduction divisions. The chromosomes of the oocyte have reached, by this time, the stage of diakinesis. The meiotic division in the female gametes cannot, however, proceed in the same way as in the male gametes, that is, by dividing the original cell into four cells of equal size. Such a division would largely defeat the purpose of the accumulation of food reserves during the period of growth: each of the four cells would have received only one quarter of the stockpile of food supplies. What actually occurs is that during the meiotic divisions the cytoplasm is partitioned very unequally, the bulk of the cytoplasm with the yolk remaining intact at each division.

When the oocyte is ready to undergo reduction divisions, the nuclear membrane breaks up and the chromosomes, which have become greatly contracted and concentrated toward the center of the germinal vesicle, are carried to the periphery of the oocyte. Here an achromatic figure is formed, which takes up a position perpendicular to the surface of the oocyte. The bivalents are placed on the equatorial plate and in due course separate into the two component chromosomes (Fig. 57). A bulge now appears at the surface of the oocyte, and the outer pole of the spindle with half of the chromosomes during anaphase enters into this cytoplasmic bulge. The part of the cytoplasm with the chromosomes, which is bulging out, is then pinched off from the rest of the oocyte. The resulting small cell is called the first polar body. The set of chromosomes contained in the first polar body is equivalent to the set of chromosomes remaining in the oocyte (which can now be distinguished as the **secondary oocyte**) just as the two sets of chromosomes in secondary spermatocytes are equivalent to one another. The first polar body, however, receives only a very small quantity of cytoplasm, while all the rest goes to the secondary oocyte. The second meiotic division is carried out in the same way; that is, an achromatic figure is again formed at the surface and, when division takes place, half of the chromatids are given off, together with a small quantity of cytoplasm, as the second polar body. The large cell, which inherits the bulk of the cytoplasm together with one half of the chromatids, is now the fully mature egg. The chromosome set of the egg, as the result of two meiotic divisions, is a haploid one.

In the meantime the first polar body may sometimes divide, so that eventually four cells are produced from one oocyte: one cell is the mature egg, the second and third cells are produced by the division of the first polar body, and the fourth cell is the second polar body. These four cells can be compared to the four spermatids which are produced from a primary spermatocyte after two mitotic divisions, the difference being that each of the four

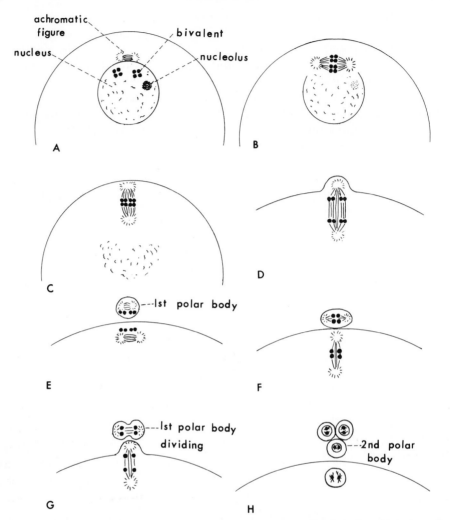

Figure 57. Reduction divisions in an oocyte. A, Oocyte immediately before the meiotic divisions; B, C, D, first meiotic division; E, first polar body separated, preparation for second meiotic division; F, G, second meiotic division and, simultaneously, division of first polar body; H, meiosis completed. (Redrawn with modifications after Wilson, 1925.)

spermatids later becomes a functional spermatozoon, while of the four cells produced by meiotic division in the female only one cell, the egg, is a functional gamete, and the other three cells (or two cells, if the first polar body does not divide further) later die off. Having so little cytoplasm, with no food reserves, they are not able to start developing.

The similarities (and differences) between oogenesis and spermatogenesis are illustrated in Figure 58.

It should be pointed out at this stage again that, after maturation (= reduction divisions), the spermatids must still go through the process of differentiation before they become spermatozoa, that is, functional male gametes. On the other hand the egg, after reduction divisions, does not undergo any further changes — it is quite ready to start developing.

A further distinction between the male and the female gametes is that

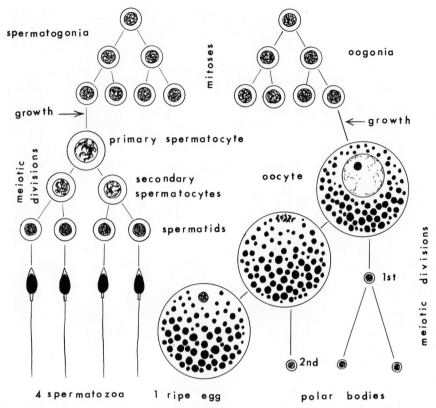

Figure 58. Comparison of gametogenesis in the male (left) and in the female (right). In both sexes the meiotic divisions produce four cells, but although in the male all four cells become functional gametes (spermatozoa), in the female only one cell is functional as the egg; the others are abortive.

the male gametes, the spermatozoa, become capable of fertilizing the egg some time after they have completed the reduction divisions and subsequently become differentiated. The eggs become capable of being fertilized sometimes *before* they have completed reduction divisions and before they have given off the polar bodies (p. 123).

4—5 THE EGG MEMBRANES

All eggs, like any other cells, are of course covered by the cell membrane or **plasmalemma.** Under the electron microscope the plasmalemma sometimes can be seen to be double, with two layers of electron-dense material about 50 Å thick separated by a less dense interval of about 60 Å. In addition to the plasmalemma, eggs of all animals, with the exception of sponges and some coelenterates, are surrounded by special egg membranes. Depending on their origin these may be subdivided in two groups: the primary membranes and the secondary membranes (Balfour, 1880). The primary egg membranes are the membranes which develop in the ovary between the oocytes and the follicle cells in the space occupied by the interdigitating microvilli. In the initial stages of its formation the membrane shows positive reactions for muco-

Figure 59. Low power electronmicrograph of the surface of an advanced amphibian oocyte with adjacent follicle cells. ZR, Zona radiata with interdigitating microvilli of oocyte and follicle cells; FL, fibrous layer—the precursor of the vitelline membrane; FC, follicle cell; Fn, nucleus of follicle cell; OC, cytoplasm of oocyte; C, cortical granules, not yet in position at surface; Y, yolk platelets; Pg, pigment granules; M, clusters of mitochondria.

polysaccharides, but in later stages it is fortified by addition of further substances and may consist of fibrous proteins (Fig. 59) or, in insects, it may be sclerotized and become highly impermeable. The membrane thus formed bears different names in different animals: it is known as the **vitelline membrane** in insects, molluscs, amphibians and birds; in tunicates and fishes it is usually called the **chorion**. In mammals the membrane of an exactly similar nature is called the **zona pellucida** (see Odor, 1960). The zona pellucida thus takes the place of the zona radiata mentioned earlier (p. 58). The jelly coat surrounding the eggs of sea urchin eggs belongs in the same group.

The origin of the materials forming these membranes is not quite obvious; usually it is believed that the membrane is secreted by the follicle cells (see Trujillo-Cenóz and Sotelo, 1959; King and Koch, 1963), but the oocyte may perhaps contribute to the formation of the membrane in some cases (Wartenberg, 1962; Okada and Waddington, 1959).

In insects a second, thicker membrane is secreted by the follicle cells on top of the vitelline membrane. This second membrane is called the **chorion**. In many insects its surface shows a complicated sculpture, different in different species. The primary egg membranes usually closely adhere to the surface of the oocyte, but at a later stage a space filled with fluid may appear between the cytoplasm and the membrane; this space is called the **perivitelline space**.

Figure 60. Mammalian egg after ovulation, surrounded by the zona pellucida (*z.p.*) and the corona radiata (*c.r.*). (After Hamilton, J. Anat., Lond. 78, 1944.)

In mammals an egg escaping from the ovary carries with it on the surface of the zona pellucida a layer of follicle cells known as the **corona radiata** (Fig. 60). The cells of the corona radiata are peeled off later, as the egg descends the oviduct.

The second group of egg membranes are those which are secreted by oviducts and other accessory parts of the genital organs while the egg is passing from the ovary to the exterior.

The eggs of amphibians are surrounded by a layer of jelly (Fig. 61), which protects the egg and sometimes serves to make the eggs adhere to one another and to submerged objects such as water plants. This jelly is secreted as the eggs pass through the oviducts. When the amphibian egg is deposited in water, the jelly absorbs water and swells. In the oviparous

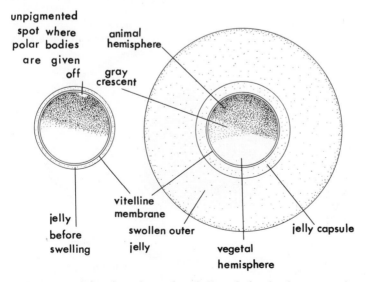

Figure 61. Frog egg as taken from the oviduct (left), and after fertilization, with swollen jelly membrane (right).

sharks and rays the egg is surrounded in the oviducts (in the special parts called the **shell glands**) by a hard shell of a complicated shape. The shell is drawn out into long twisted horns which serve to entangle the eggs among seaweed.

However, the most complicated egg membranes are found in the eggs of birds, where no less than five membranes can be distinguished (Fig. 62). The innermost egg membrane is the vitelline membrane—a very thin membrane covering the surface of the yellow of the egg (which is the true egg cell). This membrane is actually of double origin. An inner layer of the membrane is produced in the ovary, in the space between the oocyte and the follicle cells, as described above. This layer is composed of very rough fibers. An outer, more finely fibrous, layer is then formed on top of the first when the egg enters the upper portion of the fallopian tube (Bellairs, 1963). The next membrane is the white of the egg. Eighty-five per cent of the egg white is water; the rest is a mixture of several proteins, mostly albumens, which make up 94 per cent of the dry weight. A denser part of the egg white forms strands, known as the chalazae, which help to keep the egg cell in the center of the egg white. Next to the egg white come two layers of **shell membranes**. These consist of fibers of keratin matted together. Over most of the surface of the egg the shell membranes are in contact with each other, but at the blunt end of the egg they are separated: the inner membrane adheres to the egg white, and the outer membrane adheres to the shell. In between there is a space filled with air. The outermost membrane is the **shell**. This consists chiefly of calcium carbonate ($CaCO_3$), about 5 gm. in a hen's egg. The shell is pierced by a great number of fine pores which are filled by an organic (protein) substance related to collagen. In an average hen's egg the pores have a diameter of 0.04 to 0.05 mm., and the total number is estimated at about 7000. The membranes of a bird's egg are secreted one after another as the egg proceeds down the oviduct. The whole process takes slightly longer than 24 hours. After the egg has been released from the ovary, it quickly passes into

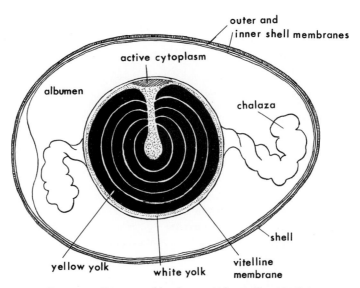

Figure 62.   Diagram of hen's egg. (After Lillie, 1919b.)

the oviduct and descends through the oviduct for about three hours, during which most of the egg white is secreted and envelops the egg cell. The lowest portion of the oviduct is widened and is termed the uterus. Here the egg remains for 20 to 24 hours, while the remainder of the egg white is secreted and eventually the shell membranes and the shell itself.

The membranes of a bird's egg serve not only for the protection of the egg cell; the egg white serves also as an additional source of nourishment and is gradually used up in the course of the development of the embryo.

5

The Developing Egg and the Environment

In every stage of its development the embryo is a living organism, and like every living organism it requires foodstuffs for its vital processes. It assimilates its food and metabolizes organic substances to gain energy for its maintenance and for performing the processes together constituting its development. Furthermore, the new individual has to increase in size to a variable, but usually very considerable, degree until it approximates the structure of its parents. The growth process again involves the consumption and processing and partial combusion of a vast quantity of foodstuffs. Since the egg is a single cell and does not have any of the organs which an adult uses to procure and utilize its food supply, the supply and utilization of food for the developing embryo have to be organized along lines that are quite special and specific for the process of embryonic development.

The primary source of nutrition in the eggs of most animals is the reserve material stored in the egg cell during its development in the ovary (see section 4–2). This material is metabolized; it is partly broken down as a source of energy and partly transformed into the substances of which the various organs of the new individual are built up in the course of development. In addition to materials contained in the egg, various substances may be taken up from the environment. The nature and the amount of extraneous materials used by the embryo depend very largely on the environment in which the embryo develops. A vast number of animals rather early attain a stage in which the young individual can start feeding and thus becomes self-supporting. This is often greatly facilitated by the egg's developing in the first instance into a **larva**, instead of directly into an adult.

The sea urchin egg may be taken as an example of a small egg with relatively little yolk. It develops in sea water and after a very short time (35 to 40 hours) produces a larva, called a **pluteus**, which has an alimentary canal of three parts: a foregut, opening to the exterior by a mouth, a dilated stomach and a hindgut with anus. The pluteus swims freely in the water with the aid of a ciliary band drawn out into loops along the edges of arms supported by a complicated calcareous skeleton. It feeds on minute planktonic organisms, mainly algae, which are injected into the gut by ciliary action of the stomodeum (Fig. 63). Table 2 gives an idea of the turnover of substances during the first 40 hours of development—up to the formation of the pluteus.

TABLE 2. CHEMICAL COMPOSITION OF SEA URCHIN EMBRYO (IN PER CENT OF WET WEIGHT) (AFTER EPHRUSSI AND RAPKINE, FROM LEHMANN, 1945)

Substance	Unfertilized Egg	Blastula, 12 Hours	Pluteus
Water	77.3	77.3	78.8
Dry substances	22.7	22.7	21.2
Protein nitrogen	10.7	10.2	9.7
Total carbohydrates	5.43	5.46	3.4
Glycogen	5.13	4.8	traces
Fat	4.82	4.43	3.69
Ash	0.34	2.07	3.56

Some points may be made from this table: The developing embryo takes up some water from the environment and also quite a considerable quantity of mineral substances which are mainly utilized in building up the calcareous skeleton. The embryo loses a large part of its carbohydrates (including almost all of the glycogen) and some fat. There is only a very slight decrease of nitrogen; according to some more recent investigations (Gustafson and Hjelte, 1951), the total nitrogen of the sea urchin egg does not change during the period up to the pluteus stage.

Water is absorbed as a general rule by embryos developing in an aquatic medium (see Table 4, p. 98). The amount absorbed may be quite consider-

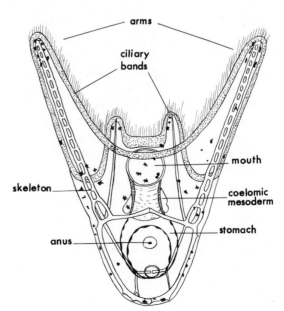

Figure 63. Pluteus—larva of a sea urchin (*Tripneustes gratilla*).

able, as can be seen in the case of an egg-laying dogfish *Scyllium canicula*. Additional ash (salts) is also taken up from surrounding sea water by marine invertebrates (coelenterates, molluscs, crustaceans and echinoderms). Among fishes the developing embryos of the elasmobranchs absorb salts, but the embryos of some fresh-water fishes, such as the Salmonidae, do not absorb salts from the surrounding medium although they take in water. The same is true of the developing embryos of the Amphibia. The animals whose eggs develop in fresh water cannot depend on the surrounding medium for the intake of salts because fresh water does not contain the necessary salts (especially Na and K ions) in sufficient quantity.

The turnover of substances in the developing egg of a frog will serve as an example of an animal developing in fresh water (see Table 3).

TABLE 3. CHEMICAL COMPOSITION OF THE EGG AND EMBRYO OF A FROG; WEIGHTS IN MICROGRAMS (AFTER GREGG, AND GREGG AND BALLENTINE, FROM BARTH AND BARTH, 1954)

Substance	Egg	Tadpole soon after Hatching (Stage 20)
Total nitrogen	162	159
Extractable nitrogen (= nitrogen of active protoplasm)	40	42.8
Nonprotein nitrogen (in nucleic acids ?)	4	5.0
Total carbohydrates	104	58
Glycogen	73.2	31

Table 3 shows that there is very little increase in the amount of active cytoplasm during the early development of the embryo, somewhat more in the amount of nucleic acid nitrogen (about 25 per cent), and that simultaneously there is a very considerable decrease of the total carbohydrates, due almost exclusively to the loss of glycogen, which is thus the main source of energy for the maintenance and the development of the embryo. The increase of water is considerable. It is not included in Table 3, but according to some available data it accounts for a 75 per cent increase of the total weight of the embryo during the corresponding stages. There is also some uptake of salts, particularly calcium, from the environment.

An entirely new situation is faced by animals that have abandoned the aquatic medium and become completely terrestrial. Some of these have attempted a compromise by returning to the water for egg laying. This is true of most of the amphibians. Other amphibians (many terrestrial frogs, some salamanders, and the Gymnophiona) lay their eggs on land but in damp places — in burrows underground, etc. — where the eggs can absorb the minimal quantities of water that are necessary for their development. Even among the reptiles there are some whose eggs take up water from the environment. This is the case in turtles. For instance, the egg of the turtle *Malaclemys centrata*, that weighs 10.58 gm., absorbs 3.07 gm. of water during its development. This is made possible because the eggs are laid in damp sand.

In the eggs of other reptiles and of birds there is no longer a possibility for the absorption of water from the exterior. The egg membranes have become watertight. On the other hand, the loss of water from the egg by evaporation is reduced to a minimum. The only substance that is taken from without is the oxygen necessary for the oxidative processes in the egg. Otherwise, the egg has become a closed system, developing at the expense of the substances stored inside the egg itself. Such an egg, which has become self-sufficient (except for oxygen intake and CO_2 outflow) is called a **cleidoic** egg (Needham, J., 1931). Cleidoic means boxlike.

Independently of the vertebrates, the terrestrial arthropods have also evolved cleidoic eggs. Some of the stages of this evolution can still be traced among contemporary insects. For instance, in the eggs of grasshoppers (*Melanoplus* and *Locusta*) there is an intake of water during development. In *Melanoplus* the water content increases from 2.5 mg. to 4.7 mg. In the eggs of other insects, however, no water can be taken in, and throughout the development of the eggs there is only a certain amount of water loss by evaporation. Such eggs are therefore as much cleidoic as the egg of a bird.

There is a fairly obvious advantage in the young individual's being more advanced in development and growth when it emerges from the egg. This advancement may be achieved by the amassing of greater and greater supplies of foodstuffs in the egg. Increase of food supplies in the egg may be correlated with the elimination of a larval stage—as in cephalopods, among the molluscs, and in elasmobranchs, reptiles and birds, in the vertebrate phylum.

The eggs of birds present an example of a very abundant supply of the egg with food material for the nourishment of the embryo. The chicken that hatches from the egg is already essentially a bird. The principal difference, besides the small size, lies in the development of the feathers. The body of a newly hatched chicken is covered with down, which is a simplified form of a feather. As soon as the down is replaced by typical feathers, the chicken acquires all the typical features of a bird.

A very special though widespread method of increasing the chances of survival of the offspring consists in retaining the eggs in the mother's body and letting them develop there to a greater or lesser degree. The eggs are usually retained in the oviducts (which are then usually referred to as **uteri**), but in some cyprinodont fishes (*Poecilia* and *Girardinus*) the eggs begin their development while still in the ovaries (see Needham, J., 1942). Sometimes, as in some salamanders, the young hatch from the eggs inside the mother's body. Occasionally, as in the adders, the eggs are laid intact, but the young begin to hatch as soon as the eggs are laid. The bearing of young developed from eggs which have been retained in the body of the mother, but without the maternal organism providing additional nourishment for the embryo, is known as **ovoviviparity**. **Oviparity** is, of course, the form of reproduction in which all or most of the development of the embryo in the egg occurs after the egg has been laid.

In typical cases of ovoviviparity the embryo is nourished by the food stored in the egg. A next step in evolution may be made when the embryo absorbs some substances present in the fluids filling the oviducts. The degree to which such oviducal fluids are used for the nourishment of the embryo is very variable. In different species of the sharks and rays, all possible gradations may be found between such forms in which the embryo depends chiefly

on the food supplied in the egg, and such forms in which the embryo depends chiefly on the food supplied by the mother. The proportions of these
two sources of nourishment may be best estimated by comparing the weight
of organic substances in the egg and in the newly born offspring. Table 4
presents a comparison of the turnover of materials in the eggs of an oviparous
and an ovoviviparous fish (as well as a viviparous species).

TABLE 4. CHEMICAL COMPOSITION OF THE EGGS AND OF LATER STAGES
OF DEVELOPMENT IN THREE SPECIES OF DOGFISH (AFTER RANZI FROM
J. NEEDHAM, 1942)

Species		Composition of Egg, and of Young at Hatching or Birth (Weight in Grams)	
		Egg	Young
Scyllium canicula	Total weight	1.3	2.7
(oviparous)	Organic substances	0.61	0.48
	Water	0.68	2.15
Mustelus vulgaris	Total weight	3.9	60.6
(ovoviviparous)	Organic substances	1.9	8.9
	Water	1.9	49.8
Mustelus laevis	Total weight	5.5	189.0
(viviparous)	Organic substances	2.8	32.0
	Water	2.6	152.0

It will be seen that in the development of an egg-laying fish the turnover
of substances is very similar to that in the embryo of the sea urchin or frog:
there is a decrease in organic substances, due to their combustion, and an
increase of water content which makes the young at hatching exceed the
weight of the egg. In the ovoviviparous fish, however, the uptake of organic
substances from the maternal body not only compensates for their loss
through combustion but brings about a total increase of the amount of organic
material during development. There is also a very considerable intake of
water, so that the over-all increase in weight of the embryo is many times
that observed in a species in which the embryo depends on the egg reserves
as the sole source of its organic materials. Ovoviviparity in several groups of
animals seems to have been a transitional phase in the development of true
viviparity.

True viviparity is shown when the embryo establishes a direct connection
with the maternal body, so that the nutrition can pass from the mother to
the embryo without the intermediate state of being dissolved in the uterine
fluid. The connection is established through a special organ, the **placenta**,
which is an outgrowth of the embryo joined to parts of the maternal body
especially modified for this purpose. Viviparity and placentae have been
developed in several groups of the animal kingdom independently of each
other. Placentae are found in the protracheates (*Peripatus*), in the tunicates
(*Salpa*), in several elasmobranchs and in the placental mammals. The mode
of origin and the structure of the placenta is different in each case mentioned.
The placenta of the mammals will be described later, in section 11–3.

The supply of nutrition to the embryo through a placenta appears to be a
very much more efficient method than the absorption of nourishment from the
uterine fluids. This fact may be illustrated by the third example in Table 4,
that of the dogfish *Mustelus laevis*, in which a placenta is developed when

the yolk sac of the embryo becomes connected to the walls of the uterus (see Chapter 11). In this particular case the increase in organic materials during intra-uterine life is more than tenfold as compared with the roughly fourfold increase of organic substances in *Mustelus vulgaris*, taken as an example of the ovoviviparous fish.

In mammals, which have developed the placenta to a degree of perfection not found in other animals, the increase in weight of the embryo is very much greater, especially as the eggs of mammals are very small as compared with the eggs of viviparous fishes.

PART III

FERTILIZATION AND THE BEGINNING OF EMBRYOGENESIS

6

Fertilization*

Fertilization is the fusion of two **gametes** (sex cells), a male and a female one, followed by the joining together of the nuclei of the two gametes. The fusion of the gametes in the Metazoa activates the egg so that it starts to develop, and the joining together of the nuclei of the egg and the spermatozoon results in the endowment of all the cells of the developing new organism with carriers of hereditary properties derived from the maternal and paternal organisms.

It should be pointed out here that the place of fertilization in the life cycle of various organisms is not always the same: although in the Metazoa and Metaphyta the fertilization starts the egg on its way of development into an embryo, in many protozoans the zygote enters into a dormant state, which may be interrupted later, usually by changes in the environmental conditions. Similarly, the fusion of the nuclei of the two gametes is deferred in some organisms (especially fungi), and occurs many cell generations later. There are thus two essentially independent aspects to fertilization: one is the **activation** of the egg, the other is the intermingling of the paternal and maternal hereditary characters in the offspring. The latter aspect of fertilization is also known as **amphimixis** and really falls within the sphere of the science of genetics.

We shall now consider the consecutive steps which lead to the fertilization of the egg and the changes in the egg occurring during and after fertilization, laying the main stress on those aspects of fertilization which contribute to the transformation of the egg into a new organism.

6−1 APPROACH OF THE SPERMATOZOON TO THE EGG

After both the eggs and the spermatozoa are discharged into the sur-

---

*Further references: Loeb, 1913; Lillie, 1919a; Rothschild, 1951 and 1956; Tyler and others, 1957.

rounding (aquatic) medium, or after the spermatozoa have been introduced into the genital ducts of the female, in the case of internal fertilization, the first step is the encounter of the spermatozoon and the egg. This encounter is brought about by the swimming movements of the spermatozoa. It would have been tempting to suggest that the spermatozoa are attracted by the eggs, or that their movement in space is somehow directed toward the eggs. In spite of numerous investigations, no such attraction or directing of the path of the spermatozoa of animals has been proved. The movements of the spermatozoa are entirely at random, and the spermatozoa collide with the eggs as a matter of pure chance. That this chance encounter occurs regularly in nature is partly a result of the enormous number of spermatozoa produced by the male gonads, and partly the result of the egg's being a relatively very large target, so that it can be hit fairly easily.

A very fine chemical mechanism now comes into play. In the presence of ripe eggs, or even in the water in which ripe eggs of the same species have been lying for some time ("egg water"), the spermatozoa become "sticky" and adhere to the surface of the egg and even to each other. The mutual adhesion of the spermatozoa results in their clumping or **agglutination**. The agglutination is more easily observed with sperm of some animals (especially sea urchins) than with sperm of others (for instance starfish), and it also depends to a large extent on environmental conditions. But the sticking of sperm to eggs of the same species is found in most animals, and possibly it is always present.

The substance causing agglutination of spermatozoa was studied in detail by F. R. Lillie (1919a), who called it **fertilizin**. He believed that fertilizin is continuously emitted from mature eggs and that it is directly involved in the reaction between the egg and spermatozoon. It was found later that the main source of fertilizin, after the maturation of the egg, is not the egg itself but the layer of jelly surrounding the egg (in echinoderms). This jelly consists wholly of fertilizin which gradually dissolves in the sea water after the eggs are laid. It is not definitely known whether the jelly surrounding sea urchin eggs is primarily produced by the oocyte or by the follicle cells, the latter being the more likely explanation.

Chemically, fertilizin is a glycoprotein or mucopolysaccharide. As a protein it contains a number of amino acids, and as a polysaccharide it includes molecules of one or more monosaccharides. The monosaccharides (glucose, fucose, fructose or galactose) are esterified by sulfuric acid, as shown in the formula (Runnström, 1952):

$$\text{—O}_3\text{SO} \qquad CH_2OH \qquad OH$$

Both the amino acids and the monosaccharides vary from one species to another, so that it is more correct to speak of **fertilizins** rather than of one

group of agglutinated
spermatozoa

Figure 64. Diagram showing binding of sea urchin spermatozoa by particles of fertilizin.
(Modified after Rothschild, 1951.)

fertilizin found in different animals. The molecules of the fertilizins are
quite large—the molecular weight is about 300,000—and each molecule may
have more than one "active group," so that one fertilizin particle may become attached to two or more spermatozoa, thus binding them together
(Fig. 64) (see Metz, 1957, and Rothschild, 1956).

The surface layer of the cytoplasm of the spermatozoon contains another
substance (or substances) known as the **antifertilizin** (or antifertilizins).
The antifertilizins can be extracted from the spermatozoa by heating, freezing and thawing, or acidifying the water. Their properties show that they are
acid proteins with a fairly small molecule—molecular weight about 10,000.

The remarkable peculiarity of the fertilizins and antifertilizins is that
they combine in a specific way; that is, the egg fertilizin of any species
reacts best with the sperm antifertilizin of the same species. Reactions with
other species, although possible, are very much weaker, and even so they
occur only when two species are fairly nearly related to one another. The
reaction between fertilizin and antifertilizin is thus very similar to reactions
which take place between the substances in the serum of immunized animals
(antibodies) and the foreign substances which caused the immunization
(antigens) (Tyler, 1948). In both cases, the bond between the two complementary substances is supposed to depend on the spatial arrangement of the
atoms on certain parts of the molecules in such a way that the shape of the
surface of one molecule fits closely onto the surface of the other. The two
bodies correspond to one another as a template to the model. Another often-

used analogy is the correspondence of the key to the lock. When the latter analogy is used, it may be pertinent to remember that sometimes a lock may be opened by a wrong key if it is sufficiently similar to the right one. This finds its counterpart in the cross reactions of fertilizins and antifertilizins of sufficiently nearly related species.

The adhesion of the spermatozoon to the surface of the egg has been interpreted as the result of the presence of fertilizin molecules in the surface layer of the egg cytoplasm. The linking of the fertilizin molecules with the antifertilizin molecules present on the surface of the spermatozoon would account for the establishment of an initial bond which would later lead to the penetration of the spermatozoon into the egg. Unfortunately the evidence as to whether any fertilizin is present in the egg or at its surface is very contradictory (see Metz, 1957). No fertilizin can be extracted from sea urchin eggs. In view of this it has been suggested that the main function of the fertilizin-antifertilizin reaction is to thin out the number of spermatozoa around the egg, so that the chances of two or more spermatozoa penetrating into the egg at the same time are diminished (Runnström and others, 1959).

We have seen (section 4–5) that the surface of the ripe egg is very seldom naked (as in coelenterates), but usually surrounded by membranes or follicle cells or both (as in mammals). The spermatozoon has to penetrate through these before it can reach the egg.

The mechanism of penetration is chemical. The spermatozoon produces substances of an enzymatic nature, known under the general name of **sperm lysins**, which dissolve the egg membranes locally and make the path clear for the spermatozoon to reach the surface of the egg (see Tyler, 1948). The sperm lysins are produced presumably by the acrosome of the spermatozoon (Colwin and Colwin, 1961). This is in accord with the origin of the acrosome; we have seen that the acrosome is developed from the Golgi bodies of the spermatid. There is clear evidence that in a normal animal cell at least some of the secretory activity is performed by the Golgi bodies. The production of sperm lysins is thus one of the aspects of the secretory activity of these bodies.

The sperm lysins certainly differ from one animal group to another. In some cases the dissolution of the egg membranes may be brought about by simpler means. Thus it is believed that the jelly coat of echinoderm eggs may be dissolved as a result of the acidification of sea water by the carbon dioxide developed by the spermatozoa in the course of their respiration.

In the case of eggs with very thick and resistant membranes, such as the egg membranes of fishes or insects, the sperm cannot reach the egg at all points out must penetrate through a special canal (the micropyle), or canals, left in the egg membrane (see section 4–1).

In mammals, as we have seen (p. 91), the situation is complicated by the presence around the egg membrane, the zona pellucida, of a layer of follicle cells, the corona radiata, which the egg carries with it when it leaves the ovary. The spermatozoon has to pass through this layer on its way to the egg. It has been found that mammalian spermatozoa produce an enzyme, **hyaluronidase**, which dissolves the mucopolysaccharide, hyaluronic acid, the substance cementing the follicle cells together. The enzyme thus enables the spermatozoon to make a way for itself through the corona radiata. Under experimental conditions, extracts containing large amounts of hyaluronidase may remove all the follicle cells from the surface of the egg, but this does not occur during normal fertilization; the corona persists for some time after the penetration of the spermatozoon into the egg. It later disperses before the implantation of the egg, but this is not the result of the action of the spermatozoa.

The agglutination of the spermatozoa is not the only change caused in them by the egg water or the proximity of ripe eggs. Under the influence of substances diffusing from the eggs (whether the substance in question is fertilizin, or some other compound, has not yet been determined) the structure of the spermatozoon becomes changed, as can best be seen by using the electron microscope. The main change concerns the acrosome, the peripheral part of which collapses and becomes extruded and partially dissolved in water (possibly releasing the lysins which were referred to earlier) (Figs. 65, 66). The central part of the acrosome, which appears rather transparent in electron micrographs, elongates and becomes transformed into a long (1 to 75 μ) thin filament, or possibly a tube, which has considerable rigidity and protrudes forward from the head of the spermatozoon (Figs. 65, 67, 68). This structure has been called the **acrosomal filament** (Dan and Wada, 1955). In a case which has recently been studied by electron microscopy, that of the annelid *Hydroides hexagonus*, several short acrosomal filaments take the place of a single long one (Fig. 69) (Colwin and Colwin, 1961). The spermatozoa which have developed acrosomal filaments are considered to have been activated and are then ready to penetrate into the egg. As the spermatozoon approaches the egg, the acrosomal filament is pushed through the jelly (where present) and through the vitelline membrane, the pathway for it being cleared by the action of the lysins, as explained above (Fig. 69). Eventually, the tip of the acrosomal filament touches the surface membrane of the egg cytoplasm and triggers off the next phase of the process of fertilization.

Figure 65. Change in the structure of a mollusc (*Mytilus edulis*) spermatozoon caused by "egg water." Left, untreated spermatozoon; right, "activated" spermatozoon with acrosomal filament. (After Dan and Wada from Colwin and Colwin, 1957.)

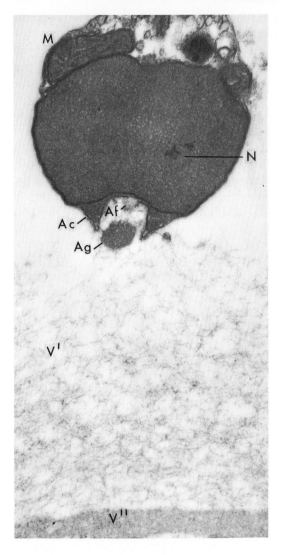

Figure 66. Spermatozoon of the enteropneust *Saccoglossus kowalevskii* approaching the vitelline membrane of the egg and releasing the acrosomal granule (Ag) through opening at apex of the acrosome (Ac) (electronmicrograph). Af, Beginning of formation of acrosomal fiament; M, mitochondrial body; N, nucleus of spermatozoon; V', outer layer of vitelline membrane of the egg; V", inner layer of vitelline membrane. (Courtesy of Dr. A. L. Colwin and Dr. L. H. Colwin, 1963.)

6–2 THE REACTION OF THE EGG

Immediately after the acrosomal filament of the spermatozoon touches the surface of the egg, the cytoplasm of the egg bulges forward at the point of contact, producing a process of hyaline cytoplasm, the **fertilization cone**. The fertilization cone may be in the form of a more or less simple conical protrusion (Fig. 70), or it may consist of several irregular pseudopodialike processes, or in some cases it may take the form of a cytoplasmic cylinder stretching forward along the acrosomal filament (Colwin and Colwin, 1957). Whatever its shape, the fertilization cone gradually engulfs the spermatozoon and then begins to retract, carrying the spermatozoon inward, surrounded by the hyaline cytoplasm of the fertilization cone (Figs. 71, 72).

Even before the spermatozoon thus penetrates into the interior of the egg, the egg shows signs that it has become profoundly changed, that it has been **activated**. By this statement we mean that the egg is now capable of

Figure 67. Changes in the spermatozoon during fertilization in the enteropneust *Saccoglossus kowalevskii*. A, Acrosome of unactivated spermatozoon; B, extrusion of acrosomal granule; C, formation of acrosomal filament (tubule); D, acrosomal filament reaches egg membrane; E, acrosomal filament reaches surface of cytoplasm. (From A. L. Colwin and L. H. Colwin, 1963.)

starting on its way to develop into an embryo. The first observable changes in the egg, however, bear only an indirect relation to the formation of the embryo. They are changes in the surface of the egg cytoplasm which are known under the general name of the **cortical reaction** (Pasteels, 1961). The cortical reaction may differ quite considerably from one group of animals to another, and it will be useful to describe first how it occurs in fertilized eggs of sea urchins, in which it has been studied most extensively, and then to review the corresponding phenomena in other animals.

If sea urchin eggs are observed under the microscope with dark-field illumination at the time of fertilization, it can be seen that the color of the egg surface changes from yellow to white. The change starts from the point of attachment of the spermatozoon and gradually spreads over the whole surface of the egg (Runnström, 1952) (Fig. 73), taking 20 seconds to be completed. The structural equivalent of this color change is not quite clear, but immediately following the color change a series of transformations takes place, profoundly affecting the organization of the egg cortex and involving, in particular, the cortical granules mentioned in section 4–3. These start swelling rapidly and then "explode." The mucopolysaccharides contained in the granules become liquefied with absorption of water and the resulting fluid is released on to the surface of the egg. At the same time a new membrane starts being formed around the egg which becomes the **fertilization membrane** when completed (compare Fig. 52, p. 82, and Fig. 74). The membrane at first closely adheres to the surface of the egg and may indeed be the external layer of the plasmalemma (in spite of numerous statements to the contrary there is no "vitelline membrane" in unfertilized sea urchin eggs apart from the plasmalemma—see Mitchison, 1956, and Balinsky, 1961a). The membrane is

Figure 68. Tip of spermatozoon of the enteropneust *Saccoglossus kowalevskii* penetrating through the vitelline membrane of the egg (electronmicrograph). Af, Acrosomal filament; N, nucleus of spermatozoon. (Courtesy of Dr. L. H. Colwin and Dr. A. L. Colwin, 1963.)

originally very thin but it is soon reinforced by the denser lamellar substance contained in the sea urchin's cortical granules, which does not dissolve when the granules explode but becomes attached to the membrane (Endo, 1952; Afzelius, 1956; Wolpert and Mercer, 1961). The fertilization membrane thus becomes much thicker (up to 900 Å) and stronger. The liquefied component of the cortical granules fills the space (the perivitelline space) between the surface of the egg and the fertilization membrane, and by further imbibition of water it assists in lifting the membrane still further, so that the lifted membrane becomes visible even with low powers of the microscope.

In addition to strengthening the fertilization membrane and producing, or helping to produce, the fluid filling the perivitelline space, the cortical granules also give rise to a viscous **hyaline layer** which adheres closely to the surface of the egg and during cleavage helps to keep the blastomeres together.

Figure 69. Spermatozoon of the annelid *Hydroides hexagonus* penetrating through the vitelline membrane of the egg. The electronmicrograph shows the formation of multiple acrosomal filaments and the resorption of the vitelline membrane by secretions from the acrosome of the spermatozoon. Ac, Aerosome, Af, aerosomal filaments; d, area where substance of vitelline membrane has been dissolved away; Ec, egg cytoplasm; M, mitochondrial body; N, nucleus of spermatozoon; Pe, plasma membrane of egg, V', external layer of vitelline membrane; V'', internal layer of vitelline membrane. (Courtesy of Dr. L. H. Colwin and Dr. A. L. Colwin, 1961.)

The jelly layer which surrounds the unfertilized egg persists for some minutes after fertilization but eventually dissolves without a trace (Fig. 74).

Since much of the experimental work on fertilization was done on sea urchin eggs (see Rothschild, 1951), it has often been tacitly assumed that the way fertilization occurs in sea urchins is typical of animals in general and, in particular, that the formation of a fertilization membrane is an essential part of the process of fertilization. It has now become obvious, however, that

Figure 70.   Sperm entry into the egg of the sea cucumber *Holothuria atra*, with formation of fertilization cone by the cytoplasm of the egg. (From Colwin and Colwin, 1957.)

the reactions of the sea urchin egg present a very special case, differing in several important aspects from what can be observed in most other animals. The special way in which the fertilization membrane is formed in the sea urchin egg has apparently not been found in any other animal (see Pasteels, 1961).

The greatest similarity to sea urchin fertilization may be seen in those animals which have cortical granules, such as bony fishes and frogs. In the eggs of these animals the cortical granules are broken down after sperm attachment, their contents becoming liquefied and extruded on to the surface of the egg (Figs 75, 76). In contrast with those of sea urchins, eggs of bony fishes and frogs are surrounded by distinct membranes which are produced while the eggs are in the ovary (see section 4–5: the vitelline membrane in the frog and the chorion in the bony fish). The perivitelline space—the space between the egg cytoplasm and the membrane—may be narrow in unfertilized eggs, especially in frogs, but after the breakdown of the cortical granules and the release of their contents into the perivitelline space the amount of fluid increases rapidly, and the membrane is lifted from the surface of the egg. In the fish the membrane is said to be hardened or "tanned" after fertilization, but no new membrane is developed which could be compared to the fertilization membrane of the sea urchin.

As we have seen (p. 80), the eggs of mammals do not all possess cortical granules. When cortical granules are present (in the hamster and in the rab-

Figure 71. Spermatozoon of the enteropneust *Saccoglossus kowalevskii* penetrating into the egg cytoplasm. *A*, Acrosomal filament fuses with egg cytoplasm; *B*, fertilization cone protrudes from egg and engulfs acrosomal filament; *C*, nucleus of spermatozoon is drawn out toward fertilization cone; *D*, elongated nucleus of spermatozoon reaches fertilization cone; *E*, nucleus enters fertilization cone, acrosome dissolving; *F*, head and middle piece of spermatozoon engulfed in egg cytoplasm. (From L. H. Colwin and A. L. Colwin, 1963.)

bit) these are released into the perivitelline space (the space between the egg and the membrane, the zona pellucida) and disappear, probably becoming dissolved (Hadek, 1963a, b). No new membrane is formed around the egg at the time of fertilization. The perivitelline space may increase slightly, not owing so much to the lifting of the membrane as to a shrinkage of the egg itself, which loses a certain amount of water to the perivitelline fluid.

Very peculiar conditions prevail in lamellibranch molluscs. These animals possess cortical granules containing acid mucopolysaccharides (see p. 80), but the cortical granules do not change at the time of fertilization, and there is also no change in the membranes or the perivitelline space surrounding the eggs. A gradual breakdown of the cortical granules may be observed but this occurs both before and after fertilization and does not seem to

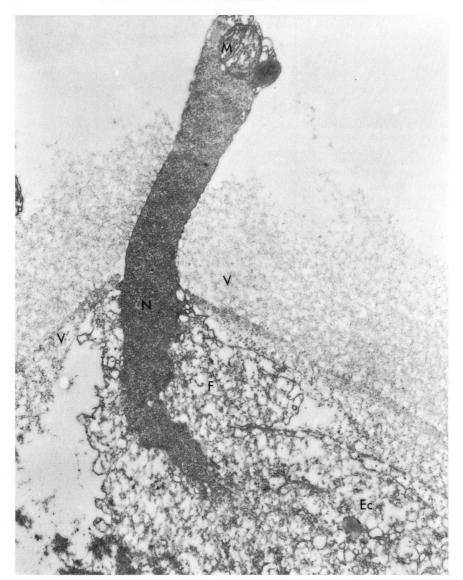

Figure 72. Spermatozoon of the enteropneust *Saccoglossus kowalevskii* being drawn into the egg cytoplasm by the fertilization cone (electronmicrograph). Ec, Egg cytoplasm; F, fertilization cone; M, mitochondrial body; N, nucleus of spermatozoon, greatly elongated as it is being drawn into the egg cytoplasm; V, vitelline membrane. (Courtesy of Dr. L. H. Colwin and Dr. A. L. Colwin, 1963.)

be affected by the attachment and penetration of the spermatozoon; in addition, the contents of the granules are not released to the exterior but into the egg cytoplasm (Pasteels and Harven, 1962).

Lastly, there are many animals which do not possess cortical granules. In these animals, such as urodele amphibians, insects and others, there do not seem to occur at fertilization any morphological changes comparable to the "cortical reaction" of sea urchin eggs.

Normally only one spermatozoon penetrates into the egg in most classes of the animal kingdom (in particular, in coelenterates, annelids, echinoderms,

Figure 73. Spreading of cortical change (black) in a sea urchin egg after fertilization. The figure at the left represents the moment when the spermatozoon contacts the egg surface. (From Rothschild, 1956.)

bony fishes, frogs and mammals). Fertilization performed by the penetration of one spermatozoon only is called **monospermic**. Under abnormal conditions, when the egg is adversely affected in any way or if there is an abnormally high concentration of the spermatozoa around the egg, more than one spermatozoon may establish contact and penetrate into the egg. The development resulting from such **polyspermic** fertilization is inevitably abnormal (**pathological polyspermy**) and the embryo is not viable.

It has often been said that the cortical reaction of the egg and, in particular, the lifting of the fertilization membrane are defense reactions which prevent the penetration of additional spermatozoa after the first one has established contact with the egg. This explanation does not seem to be entirely valid. First of all, the cortical reaction as described above is too slow to account for the exclusion of additional spermatozoa contacting the egg. We have seen that in sea urchin eggs it takes 20 seconds for the first detectable cortical reaction (color change) to spread over the whole surface of the egg.

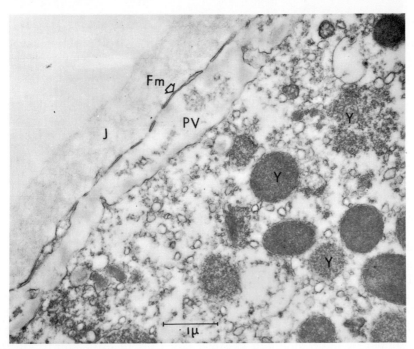

Figure 74. Electronmicrograph of surface of sea urchin egg 2 minutes after fertilization, showing absence of cortical granules and formation of the fertilization membrane. Fm, Fertilization membrane; J, jelly coat; Y, yolk; PV, perivitelline space.

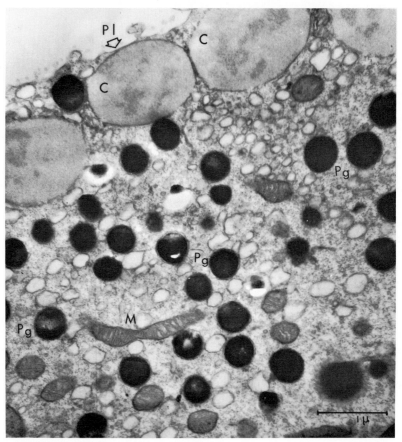

Figure 75. Surface of ripe unfertilized frog's egg showing cortical granules (electronmicrograph). C, Cortical granule; Pg, pigment granule; M, mitochondrion; Pl, plasmalemma. The surface of the cytoplasm is extended in short processes.

It has been calculated that very numerous "collisions" of additional spermatozoa with parts of the eggs which have not yet reacted could have occurred during this period. The elevation of the fertilization membrane takes even more time to complete ($\pm$ 60 seconds). Nevertheless, in nature and under favorable experimental conditions, practically all fertilized eggs are monospermic. Furthermore, in most animals there is no fertilization membrane formed, and in many there occurs no detectable change in the cortex or the egg membranes on the attachment of the spermatozoon (apart from the formation of the fertilization cone). It appears therefore, that a more subtle mechanism is involved in preventing pathological polyspermy. This mechanism is still to be investigated.

There are certain groups of animals, mainly those having yolky eggs, such as some molluscs, selachians, urodeles, reptiles and birds, in which several spermatozoa enter the egg as a rule (**physiological polyspermy**), but of these only one participates fully in the development of the embryo; the rest degenerate sooner or later, although in some cases (as in birds and reptiles) the nuclei of the accessory spermatozoa may undergo several abortive divisions in the cytoplasm of the egg. The egg in these animals thus possesses some

Figure 76. Surface of fertilized uncleaved frog's egg; the cortical granules have disappeared (electronmicrograph). Pl, Plasmalemma; L, lipochondrion; M, mitochondrion; Ec, vesiculated ectoplasm; Pg, pigment granules.

mechanism which serves to eliminate additional spermatozoa and ensures that only one remains fully active.

6–3 THE ESSENCE OF ACTIVATION

If the condition of the egg before fertilization is compared with that after fertilization, it becomes clear that the system is brought from a quasi stationary state to a condition characterized by a series of rapid changes. If it is not fertilized, the ripe egg remains quiescent for some time and eventually becomes subjected to degenerative processes, and in the end it becomes necrotic. If the egg is fertilized, it goes into action, as it were: the reduction divisions, if not performed before, are brought to completion; the male and female pronuclei fuse; complicated dislocations of cytoplasmic substances of the egg may take place (see section 6–6); and the egg enters into a period of rapid divisions (cleavage).

What is the physiological mechanism of this activation of the egg, and how does the spermatozoon produce the profound change in the egg's condition? The answer to this question has been sought by comparing the processes of metabolism and other physicochemical properties of the unfertilized and the fertilized eggs. The results of these studies have been far from satisfactory. In 1908 Warburg measured the oxygen consumption of unfertilized and fertilized sea urchin eggs and found that immediately after fertilization there was a sharp increase of oxygen consumption of up to 600 per cent as compared with unfertilized eggs. It would have been tempting to suggest that the primary action of the spermatozoon consists in release or activation of the oxidative enzymes of the egg, and that the ensuing increase of oxidation provides the energy necessary for the performance of the other changes in the egg, as outlined above, and for the development of the egg in general. It was soon discovered, however, that the increase of oxidation rate in eggs is by no means a general rule: although the oxygen uptake increases in sea urchins and some annelids (Nereis), it does not change appreciably in starfish and amphibians, and it actually decreases after fertilization in the eggs of the mollusc Cumingia and the annelid Chaetopterus (J. Needham, 1942, and Rothschild, 1956).

Obviously, the increase of oxidation rate cannot be considered as the "key reaction" of fertilization. Other metabolic changes found after fertilization in some, though by no means all, animals are: (1) production of considerable amounts of acid during first several minutes after fertilization, (2) increase of permeability of the egg membrane, (3) slight shrinkage of the egg (decrease in volume), which has been mentioned earlier, (4) increased exchange of phosphate with the surrounding medium (it was found that the rate at which labeled radioactive phosphorus, P^{32}, was taken into the fertilized eggs was in some experiments up to 160 times greater than in the case of unfertilized eggs), (5) acceleration (up to 16 times) of potassium exchange between the egg and the environment, (6) diffusion of calcium out of the eggs, (7) increase in the activity of proteolytic enzymes, and (8) changes in the birefringence of the cortical layer of the egg cytoplasm, which may be interpreted to mean that the predominantly radial arrangement of the structural constituents of the cortex found in the unfertilized egg is replaced by a tangential arrangement of the cytoplasmic micellae soon after fertilization.

The chemical changes in the egg following fertilization indicate in general a trend toward a higher rate of metabolism, but this hardly adds much to already existing knowledge that the egg is "activated," and it does not give any clue as to how the spermatozoon achieves this change.

A rather logical hypothesis would be that the action of the spermatozoon rests on the introduction of some special substance into the egg which triggers off all the other reactions, of which the changes in the metabolism of the egg are visible expressions. In view of the importance of the fertilizin–antifertilizin reaction for the entry of the spermatozoon into the egg, it has been suggested by Lillie (1919a) that the activation of the egg is also due to the action of the same substances. The combining of the fertilizin of the egg with the antifertilizin of the sperm would then be the beginning of the changes in the physicochemical system of the egg—the key reaction of fertilization.

We shall not go into the further assumptions of the theory, as in any case it cannot be accepted for quite a number of reasons. One reason is that no plausible explanation has been given as to how the binding of fertilizin and antifertilizin is connected with the other processes involved in the activation of the egg. Antifertilizin, as we have seen, can be extracted from the spermatozoa and added to the water surrounding ripe eggs. The presence of the antifertilizin can be ascertained by the sticking together of the eggs— an exact counterpart of the agglutination of the spermatozoa by the fertilizin contained in egg water—but there is observed no trace of activation of the egg by this treatment (Metz, 1957).

A new opening for understanding the essence of fertilization has been provided by the studies on the mechanism of gene action and protein synthesis (sections 2–3 and 2–4). It has been shown that the ability of an unfertilized egg to incorporate radioactively labeled precursors into proteins is very low, but that the fertilization of the egg is almost immediately followed by an increase of protein synthesis. The reason for the change cannot lie in the lack of amino acids which are necessary for protein synthesis, as these are available both in the fertilized and the unfertilized egg. The ribosomes are also present in unfertilized eggs and can be shown to be able to participate in protein synthesis. It would be attractive to think that messenger RNA is lacking in the unfertilized egg and that after fertilization the nucleus emits new quantities of messenger RNA. It has been shown, however, that enucleated fragments of the egg may be activated to parthenogenetic development (see next section), and that in these fragments an increase of protein synthesis occurs as in normal fertilized eggs (see Monroy and Tyler, 1963). As the fragments do not possess nuclei, the necessary messenger RNA in this case could not be produced on chromosomal DNA and thus must have been present, though inactive, in the cytoplasm of the unfertilized egg. The link that seems to be missing in the unfertilized egg and which becomes filled in after fertilization is the activation of the amino acids. The free amino acids of the unfertilized egg are not activated (i.e., not linked with transfer RNA). After fertilization, quantities of activated amino acids can be recorded, and the increase in activated amino acids is proportional to the increase in incorporation of amino acids into proteins, that is, proportional to the synthesis of new protein (Maggio and Catalano, 1963). It is important to note that if this interpretation is correct, the new protein is synthesized on the information provided by the messenger RNA already in the egg cytoplasm before fertilization; that is, messenger RNA produced by the chromosomes of the oocyte.

Before fertilization, the ribosomes in the egg cytoplasm are single. After fertilization, increasing quantities of ribosomes are joined in groups (Monroy and Tyler, 1963), which shows that they are actively engaged in protein synthesis. As both ribosomes and messenger RNA are present in the cytoplasm of the unfertilized egg, their lack of interaction may be the result of the absence of activated amino acids, without which synthesis cannot take place. Alternative explanations are that either the ribosomes or the messenger RNA or both are inhibited or bound in some way in the unfertilized egg, and that fertilization removes the inhibiting factor. Although the final solution of the problem of fertilization is not yet available, it is evident that some narrowing of the possibilities has been achieved, and that the questions can now be set in a more precise form, which can lead to some fruitful experimental investigations in the near future.

6—4 PARTHENOGENESIS

A different approach to the solution of the problem of fertilization lies in attempting to imitate the action of the spermatozoon by some known agent. Now it has long been known (see p. 12) that in some animals an egg can develop without fertilization, as in the aphids, phyllopods and rotifers at some times of the year, or as in bees and wasps in which a fertilized egg produces a female individual and an unfertilized egg develops into a male. These are cases of **natural parthenogenesis** (virginal reproduction). In other animals, such as most of the echinoderms and many others, the eggs under natural conditions do not develop unless they are fertilized. It has been found, however, that certain treatments of the ripe eggs may incite them to develop, and this phenomenon is known as **artificial parthenogenesis**.

A great amount of work on artificial parthenogenesis has been done with sea urchin eggs. O. Hertwig and R. Hertwig discovered that ripe sea urchin eggs may be caused to start developing by treatment with chloroform or strychnine (R. Hertwig, 1896). Later it was found that the same and even better results may be obtained by treating the eggs with a variety of substances: hypertonic or hypotonic sea water; various salts, such as the chlorides of potassium, sodium, calcium, magnesium, etc.; weak organic acids — butyric acid, lactic acid, oleic and other fatty acids; fat solvents — toluene, ether, alcohol, benzene and acetone; and urea and sucrose. Similar results are obtained by temperature shocks — that is, by transferring the eggs for a short time to warm (32° C.) or cold (0° to 10° C.) water; by electric induction shocks; by ultraviolet light; and even by shaking the eggs in ordinary sea water (see Loeb, 1913, and Harvey, 1956). This long list of agents (it is by no means exhaustive) clearly shows that there is no one agent which can be recognized as the specific cause of the activation of the egg, the cause which determines the nature of the processes that are to take place. Obviously, factors determining the nature of the reaction of the egg are contained in the egg itself. The agents causing the artificial parthenogensis of the egg are instrumental only as factors triggering off this reaction of the egg, and if this is so it becomes plausible that the spermatozoon itself exercises only a similar triggering action.

Something further may be deduced, however, from the array of agents causing artificial parthenogenesis. Most of the agents used are of such a, nature that they damage the cells to a greater or lesser degree, and if applied in greater intensity, or for a longer time, they can cause the death of the cells. It is reasonable to suppose, then, that activation of the egg involves some type of sublethal damage to the egg cytoplasm. Furthermore, some of the agents used, such as fat solvents, may be expected to affect primarily the cell surface, which is known to consist partly of lipoids; and all other chemical agents may likewise primarily affect the surface of the cytoplasm, which would also not be immune from the action of physical agents.

We may therefore take one step further and suggest that the activation of the egg is connected somehow with a damage to the cortical layer of the egg cell cytoplasm. This is the more likely because (1) the reaction of the egg is started as soon as the spermatozoon comes in touch with the surface of the egg, and (2) the first detectable reactions of the egg occur in the cortical layer, and actually involve the breakdown of parts of the cortex (the cortical granules). It must be recognized, on the other hand, that even if it were proved that sublethal damage to the egg cortex is essential for activation, it would not yet be explained how this damage causes the other progressive changes in the egg. One must agree that "the activation of the egg cannot as yet be described completely in terms of the interaction of known specific egg and sperm substances." (Metz, 1957, p. 59.) It may be assumed, however, that the cortical damage is somehow transformed so as to set in motion the mechanism of protein synthesis, as has been indicated on p. 119.

It will be interesting to conclude this section by adding some information on natural and artificial parthenogenesis in some vertebrates.

In frogs, artificial parthenogenesis may be achieved by some of the methods used on echinoderm eggs, such as the use of hypertonic and hypotonic solutions, some poisons (corrosive sublimate) and electric shock. The activation achieved by these methods is incomplete, however, and the development does not go beyond abortive cleavage. A more efficient method is pricking the eggs with a fine glass needle (a method also used successfully with echinoderm eggs). However, for the full success of this method it is necessary that the needle be smeared with blood or be contaminated by cells or cellular particles from other tissues. If particles from foreign cells are thus introduced into the ripe egg cell, the cleavage is greatly improved, and a small percentage of the treated eggs may go through the whole development apparently quite normally (Bataillon, 1910). Instead of pricking the eggs with a contaminated needle, constituent parts of cells may be also introduced into the egg with a micropipette. In this way it has been possible to investigate what fractions of cell constituents are most active in causing parthenogenesis, and it has been found that "large granules" of a centrifuged tissue homogenate (this fraction includes the mitochondria) have the strongest effects, while the liquid supernatant had no more effect than did the pricking with a clean needle or a needle wetted with a buffer saline solution (Shaver, 1953—see Table 5).

TABLE 5. ACTIVATION OF FROG EGGS BY INJECTING THEM WITH TISSUE (TESTIS) EXTRACT AND VARIOUS FRACTIONS OF THE SAME OBTAINED BY CENTRIFUGATION (FROM SHAVER, 1953)

Preparation	% of Eggs Reaching Blastula Stage
Whole tissue extract	9.7
Large granules	35.2
Medium and small granules	19.5
Supernatant	0
Phosphate buffer	0.3
Pricked "dry"	0

So far no successful experiments have been reported in producing artificial parthenogenesis in birds, but in connection with other work it may be of interest to note that spontaneous parthenogenetic development has been observed in one representative of the class, the domestic turkey. Eggs laid by females which had been isolated from males start developing in a fairly high percentage of cases (up to 41.7 per cent in some recent experiments—Olsen, 1960a); although there is still a high percentage of abnormal development, a small number of embryos reaches the hatching stage. All the poults, the sex of which could be determined, were males. A few of these reached maturity and one was used, with success, to fertilize eggs of normal females (Olsen, 1960b).

In mammals the possibility of artificial parthenogenesis was discovered in connection with experiments cultivating unfertilized eggs *in vitro* which had been collected from the fallopian tubes. Extensive investigations in this field were undertaken by Pincus and his collaborators. Most of the experiments were done with rabbits' eggs (Pincus, 1936). It was found that if the eggs are simply kept for up to 48 hours in the ordinary tissue culture medium (blood plasma plus embryo extract), some of them become activated. The first sign of activation in this case is the completion of the second meiotic division and extrusion of a second polar body. Some of the eggs go even beyond that and start cleaving. Chemical treatment (with butyric acid, which has been used for activating sea urchin eggs) does not seem to give any better results. However, a temperature shock, in particular a treatment with cold, is more effective.

To allow the activated eggs to develop further, they have been in some experiments injected into the fallopian tubes of rabbit does, which were made "pseudopregnant" by mating with a sterile buck or by injection of hormones (the luteinizing hormone). In the body of the female the development progressed further, and quite a number of embryos reached the blastocyst stage (18 per cent in one experiment in which the eggs were activated by cooling for 24 hours at 10° C.—Chang, 1954). In two cases where the fertilization of the eggs by spermatozoa seems to have been completely excluded, the parthenogenetic embryos completed intra-uterine development, and one of the young was born alive (the other was stillborn—Pincus, 1939). In another case the eggs were given a cold shock *in vivo* by opening the body cavity of a rabbit doe which had unfertilized eggs in its fallopian tubes and cooling the fallopian tubes with cold water. One live young was born (Pincus and Shapiro, 1940). So far these are the only records of living mammalian young produced by parthenogenesis, and in view of the importance of the results it would be highly desirable that the experiments should be corroborated independently by other workers in this field. (See also Beatty, 1957.)

6—5 THE SPERMATOZOON IN THE EGG INTERIOR

There is some variation in different animals as to how much of the spermatozoon is taken into the interior of the egg. In many animals, notably in the mammals, the whole of the spermatozoon head, middle piece and tail penetrates into the cytoplasm and for a short time may be seen lying intact in the interior of the egg. In some animals (echinoderms), however, the tail of the spermatozoon breaks off and is left outside the vitelline membrane, and even the middle piece of the spermatozoon may be left without, so that only the head and the centrosome enter the egg (*Nereis*). That the tail of the spermatozoon often does not enter the egg gives additional proof that its functions are purely locomotive.

The information concerning the middle piece of the spermatozoon is not unequivocal. On the one hand, the middle piece appears to enter the egg cytoplasm in most cases; on the other hand, there is no definite proof that any constituents of the spermatozoon except for the nucleus and the centrosome play any active part in subsequent development. The mitochondria contained in the middle piece have been observed in some cases to scatter in the cytoplasm of the egg, but it is not known how long they maintain their existence there.

The subsequent behavior of the spermatozoon, or rather its head, is dependent on the stage of maturation (reduction divisions) which the egg has reached at the time of fertilization. In the sea urchins the eggs are shed and become fertilized after the reduction divisions have been completed and both polar bodies have been extruded from the egg. This is, however, by no means a general occurrence. In vertebrates the rule is that the egg completes its first reduction division in the ovary and reaches the metaphase stage of the second meiotic division. In this stage all further progress is arrested, ovulation takes place and the egg may become fertilized. The second reduction division is completed and the second polar body extruded only if the egg is fertilized by a spermatozoon or activated in some other way (see p. 122). In ascidians, some molluscs and annelids the egg reaches only the metaphase of the first meiotic division when it becomes ripe and is fertilized; only then does the egg complete the first reduction division and carry out the second. Lastly, in some annelids, in nematodes and in chaetognaths the eggs are fertilized even before the beginning of meiotic division, while the oocyte nucleus is still intact.

It follows that although in animals like the sea urchins the spermatozoon nucleus may immediately proceed to join the egg nucleus, in other cases the immediate effect of the fertilization, so far as the nuclear apparatus is concerned, is the completion of the meiotic divisions, only after which may the fusion of the male and female pronuclei take place.

When the spermatozoon first penetrates into the egg cytoplasm it moves with the acrosome (or acrosomal filament) at its front. The nucleus and the centrosome are arrayed behind the acrosome in that order. Soon, however, a rotation of the nucleus and the centrosome can be observed in many, though not in all, animals, the centrosome coming ahead of the nucleus, and the nucleus turning through 180°, so that its original posterior end turns forward. The other parts of the spermatozoon, if still discernible by this stage, lose connection with the nucleus and the centrosome. Both the nucleus and the centrosome change their appearance. The nucleus, which is now referred to as the **male pronucleus**, starts swelling, and the chromatin, which is very closely packed in the spermatozoon, becomes again finely granular. By imbibition of fluid from the surrounding cytoplasm the pronucleus becomes vesicular. The centrosome at the same time becomes surrounded by an aster, similar to that of the centrosome in the early stages of an ordinary mitosis. While these changes are going on, the sperm nucleus, together with the centrosome, moves through the egg cytoplasm toward the area where the fusion with the nucleus of the egg, the **female pronucleus**, is to take place. This area is generally near the center in holoblastic eggs having a fairly small amount of yolk, but in telolecithal eggs it is in the center of the active cytoplasm at the animal pole of the egg. As the sperm head moves inward it may be accompanied by some cortical and subcortical cytoplasm. If the latter

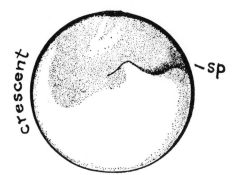

Figure 77. Penetration path of the spermatozoon (*sp*), seen in a section through a fertilized egg of a frog, and its relation to the gray crescent. (After Schultze, from Morgan, 1927.)

is heavily pigmented, as in amphibian eggs, the trajectory of the sperm head may be marked by pigment granules trailing along its path. This is sometimes referred to as the **penetration path** (Fig. 77).

The female pronucleus also has to traverse a greater or lesser way before it reaches the male pronucleus. At the beginning of its migration the female pronucleus is invariably at the surface of the egg, where the second meiotic division has been taking place, since it is only after the completion of the meiotic division that the nucleus of the egg may fuse with the nucleus of the spermatozoon. The haploid nucleus of the egg, after the completion of the second meiotic division, is often in the form of several vesicles known as the **karyomeres**. These fuse together to form the female pronucleus, which swells and increases in volume as it approaches the male pronucleus. In the last stage before they meet, the male and female pronucleus may become indistinguishable.

The actual fusion of the male and female pronuclei may differ in detail. In some animals the two pronuclei actually fuse together; that is, the nuclear membranes become broken at the point of contact and the contents of the nuclei unite into one mass surrounded by a common nuclear membrane. At the approach of the first cleavage of the fertilized egg of sea urchins and vertebrates the nuclear membrane dissolves and the chromosomes of maternal and paternal origin become arranged on the equator of the achromatic spindle. In other cases, however, the male and female pronuclei do not fuse as such, but the nuclear membranes in both dissolve and the chromosomes become released. In the meantime the centrosome has divided in two and an achromatic spindle has been formed to which the chromosomes derived from the male and the female pronucleus become attached. Only after the completion of the first division of the fertilized egg do the paternal and maternal chromosomes become enclosed by common nuclear membranes in the nuclei of the two daughter cells into which the egg has become divided (*Ascaris*, some molluscs, and annelids).

In both types the chromosomes of the maternal and paternal set retain, of course, their individuality. Lastly, in some animals, of which the copepod *Cyclops* is a well-known example, the paternal and maternal nuclear components remain separate for some time even after cleavage has started, so that each blastomere has a double nucleus consisting of two parts lying side by side, but each surrounded by its own nuclear membrane.

A closer union of the homologous chromosomes takes place much later in preparation for meiosis in the gonads of the new individual and also in cases of somatic conjugation of chromosomes, as in the salivary gland chromosomes of *Drosophila*.

6—6 CHANGES IN THE ORGANIZATION OF THE EGG CYTOPLASM CAUSED BY FERTILIZATION

In addition to activating the egg and providing an opportunity for amphimixis, the penetration of the spermatozoon into the egg (or the parthenogenetic activation of the egg) causes in many animals, perhaps in all, far-reaching displacements of the cytoplasmic constituents of the egg. As a result of this, the distribution of various cytoplasmic substances and inclusions in the egg at the beginning of cleavage may be very considerably different from that in the unfertilized egg, and even qualitatively new areas may sometimes appear. It will be evident later that these changes in the organization of the egg at fertilization may be of a most profound importance for further development of the fertilized egg.

One result of the extrusion of the cortical granules is that a large part of the original outer egg cell surface becomes replaced by the inner surfaces which surrounded the cortical granules and now are everted onto the exterior (Afzelius, 1956). In view of the importance of the cell surfaces for morphogenetic processes (see further, sections 7–7 and 9–1), this change in the composition of the surface layer of the egg may have a considerable significance, though at present it has not been actually shown in what degree the changes in the physiological properties of the fertilized egg, as compared with the egg before fertilization, are due to the replacement of part of its outer surface.

Displacements of cytoplasmic substances may be observed best in those eggs in which easily distinguishable kinds of cytoplasm have been evolved during the growth and maturation of the oocyte.

We have seen that in the ascidian *Cynthia partita* the surface of the mature egg is covered by a layer of cortical cytoplasm containing yellow granules. The position of the egg nucleus close to the animal pole stresses the polar organization of the egg, but there is no trace of a bilateral organization: all meridians of the egg are exactly alike. The spermatozoon penetrates into the egg at any meridian and nearer to the vegetal pole.

As soon as the spermatozoon enters the egg, the yellow cortical cytoplasm falls into violent commotion (Fig. 78). First of all, the yellow cytoplasm begins to stream down along the surface of the egg toward the vegetal pole, and for a time it accumulates as a cap on the vegetal pole. As the spermatozoon pronucleus penetrates deeper into the cytoplasm on its course toward the egg pronucleus, the yellow cytoplasm reverses its movement and streams upward but this time on one side of the egg only — namely, on the side where the spermatozoon entered the egg. Shortly before the first cleavage the yellow cytoplasm takes up a position just below the equator of the egg, forming there a crescentic area which later gives rise to mesoderm and may be called the **mesodermal crescent**. At the same time a crescent of light gray cytoplasm appears subequatorially on the opposite side of the egg. The origin

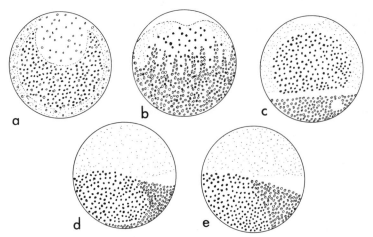

Figure 78. Displacements of cytoplasmic substances in the egg of the ascidian *Cynthia partita* following fertilization. *a*, Ripe unfertilized egg; *b*, egg immediately after entry of spermatozoon; *c, d*, two successive stages of the egg at the time when ♂ pronucleus moves to meet ♀ pronucleus; *e*, egg just before first division. Yolk granules are represented by black dots, yellow granules by circles. (After Conklin, from Huxley and de Beer, 1934, and Morgan, 1927.)

of this cytoplasmic substance has not been traced, but it is found to give rise later to the notochord and may therefore be denoted as the **notochordal crescent**. Thus the cytoplasmic displacements following fertilization not only bring some kinds of cytoplasm to more strictly defined, restricted areas, but also in this case give the egg a distinct bilateral structure (Conklin, 1905). Four different kinds of cytoplasm are now present in the egg: the yellow cytoplasm on one side and the light gray cytoplasm on the other side form together a belt surrounding the egg just below the equator. Below this subequatorial zone, toward the vegetal pole, the cytoplasm contains abundant yolk granules, and, in the subcortical layer, also large numbers of mitochondria (Mancuso, 1964). This *vegetal cytoplasm* is slaty gray in color. Above the equator, in the animal hemisphere, the cytoplasm contains less yolk and few mitochondria and appears more transparent than the rest of the egg. As we will see later, during development the different kinds of cytoplasm give rise to specific parts of the embryo.

Displacements of cytoplasmic substances follow fertilization in other animals also. In the sea urchin *Paracentrotus lividus* the mature egg contains red granules in the cortical cytoplasm, evenly distributed over its whole surface. After fertilization, streaming movements of the surface layer bring the pigmented granules into a subequatorial zone, leaving the whole of the animal hemisphere clear of pigment and also removing pigment from a smaller area at the vegetal pole (Fig. 79).

The structure of the amphibian egg at the time of fertilization was described on p. 77. Only a few minutes after the sperm has penetrated the egg, the surface layer of protoplasm starts contracting toward the animal pole of the egg, and in the course of this contraction the pigmented protoplasm covers up the gap in the pigment layer at the animal pole, where the first polar body has been given off. Considerably later (10 minutes after insemina-

Figure 79. Displacement of pigment in the egg of the sea urchin *Paracentrotus lividus* following fertilization. *a*, Oocyte; *b*, ripe unfertilized egg; *c*, fertilized egg. (After Boveri, from Morgan, 1927.)

tion of a *Rana temporaria* egg at 18° C.) a much more extensive movement of the cytoplasm begins. This involves practically the whole cortical layer of the egg, which is rotated in respect to the internal mass of cytoplasm (Ancel and Vintemberger, 1948). At the future dorsal side of the egg, the cortical cytoplasm moves upward toward the animal pole, and at the opposite, future ventral, side of the egg the cortical cytoplasm moves downward toward the vegetal pole (Fig. 80). As the edge of intensely pigmented cortical cytoplasm rises above the equator on the dorsal side, it reveals the deeper lying ring of marginal cytoplasm. The marginal cytoplasm, although bearing some pigment, is much lighter colored than the cortical cytoplasm. The result is that there appears on the dorsal side of the egg a subsequatorial, lightly pigmented, crescentic area known as the **gray crescent**.

The gray crescent presents an arrangement of cytoplasmic constituents which had not occurred in the egg previously. Owing to the sliding upward of the cortical layer, not only is the heavily pigmented surface protoplasm removed from this area but the cortical layer of the vegetal field is drawn over it, with some of the yolky cytoplasm of that part of the egg superimposed over the marginal cytoplasm. The superimposed layer is sufficiently thin not to conceal the pigment of the deeper-lying marginal cytoplasm. On the ventral side of the egg the reverse occurs; the marginal cytoplasm is partly covered by the layer of pigment.

As a result of these displacements, the egg acquires a very well-defined

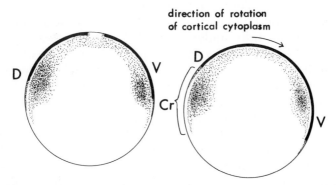

Figure 80. Diagrammatic median sections showing displacement of the cortical cytoplasm in the frog's egg following fertilization, with the formation of the gray crescent (*Cr*). *D*, Dorsal surface; *V*, ventral surface of the egg. (According to Banki, 1929, and Ancel and Vintemberger, 1948.)

bilateral symmetry, with the median plane bisecting the gray crescent. It is in this condition that the cytoplasm of the egg is found at the beginning of cleavage.

The new distribution of cytoplasmic substances of the egg is immediately followed by changes in the physiological properties of the surface layer of the egg. Before the appearance of the gray crescent the permeability of the cortical cytoplasm for vital dyes is the same over the whole of the surface of the egg, but after the rotation of the cortical cytoplasm differences become discernible. The permeability to vital dyes becomes decreased around the animal pole and on the ventral surface of the egg, but in the gray crescent area this decrease does not take place. The permeability at the gray crescent thus becomes relatively higher than at other parts of the egg's surface (Dollander, 1953). Further physiological distinctions follow in later stages, and at the approach of gastrulation the gray crescent takes the lead in the formation of the blastopore, as will be explained in section 8–4.

There is some experimental evidence that factors external to the egg may decide on which side of the amphibian egg the layer of cortical cytoplasm moves upward, and on which side, therefore, the gray crescent will develop. In 1885 W. Roux attempted to control the point of entry of the spermatozoon into the frog egg by applying a sperm solution on one side of the egg only, and he found that the gray crescent appeared on the side opposite to that of the point of entry into the egg. This was confirmed by some more recent work (Ancel and Vintemberger, 1948). The arrangement of the cytoplasmic substances in the egg of an ascidian follows, as we have seen, the same course. However, if the frog's egg is stimulated to parthenogenetic development by pricking, the gray crescent appears without any relation to the point at which the egg was pricked. In the egg of the sturgeon there appears after fertilization and before the beginning of cleavage a "gray crescent" very similar to that of the amphibian egg and bearing the same relationship to the later formation of the blastopore. In the sturgeon, however, the spermatozoon enters the egg through a micropyle exactly at the animal pole; it can therefore in no case determine the position of the gray crescent or the plane of symmetry of the embryo (Ginsburg, 1953).

From this it is obvious that the direction of the rotation of the cortex of the frog's egg, and the development of the gray crescent in a frog's or in a sturgeon's egg, can be determined by some special properties of the cytoplasm of the egg and independently of the entry of the sperm. What these properties are is not fully understood. In this connection it is noteworthy that if the unfertilized egg of a frog is allowed to rotate freely, it takes up a position with its main axis not strictly vertical but slightly oblique. The part of the equator which is raised in this position is that part where the gray crescent will later develop and which corresponds later to the dorsal side of the embryo. The fact that the dorsal side tends to be raised and that the opposite ventral side sinks down indicates that the cytoplasm on the dorsal side has a slightly lower specific gravity. This may mean that there is less yolk on this side (though of course the greatest concentration of yolk is toward the vegetal pole of the egg). It is doubtful, however, whether the amount of yolk is the decisive factor in determining the position of the gray crescent.

It has been mentioned before (p. 77) that the unfertilized egg of a frog may show some traces of bilateral symmetry: the ring-shaped zone of marginal cytoplasm has been found to be slightly thicker on one side, and this is the side that may well be the one on which the gray crescent develops in a parthenogenetically activated egg.

On the other hand, the possibility of determining the plane of bilateral symmetry of the egg by the point of entry of the spermatozoid shows that the inherent differences in the egg may be overridden by an external factor. In other words, any part of the marginal zone which lies opposite the point of entry of the spermatozoon may be transformed into the gray crescent. In respect to the development of its bilateral symmetry, the egg appears to have a very considerable amount of flexibility.

7

Cleavage

One of the peculiarities of sexual reproduction in animals is that the complex multicellular body of the offspring originates from a single cell—the fertilized egg. It is necessary, therefore, that the single cell be transformed into a multicellular body. This transformation takes place at the very beginning of development and is attained by means of a number of cell divisions following in rapid succession. This series of cell divisions is known as the process of **cleavage**.

Cleavage can be characterized as that period of development in which:
1. The unicellular fertilized egg is transformed by consecutive mitotic divisions into a multicellular complex.
2. No growth occurs.
3. The general shape of the embryo does not change, except for the formation of a cavity in the interior—the blastocoele.
4. There is no qualitative change in the chemical composition of the egg, though a transformation of the food reserves into active cytoplasm and of cytoplasmic substances into nuclear substance does take place.
5. The constituent parts of the cytoplasm of the egg are not displaced to any great extent and remain on the whole in the same positions as in the egg at the beginning of cleavage.
6. The ratio of nucleus to cytoplasm, very low at the beginning of cleavage, is, at the end, brought to the level found in ordinary somatic cells.

7 — 1   PECULIARITIES OF CELL DIVISIONS IN CLEAVAGE

The cleavage of the fertilized egg is initiated by the division of the nucleus (the synkaryon), and, as a general rule, the division of the nucleus is followed by the division of the cytoplasm, so that the egg cell divides into two daughter cells. The daughter cells are termed the **cleavage ceils** or the **blastomeres**. The first two blastomeres divide again, thus producing four blastomeres, then 8, 16, 32 and so on. The first cleavages tend to occur simultaneously in all the blastomeres but sooner or later the synchronization is lost and the blastomeres divide at different times, independently of one another.

The division of the blastomeres is essentially a typical mitosis, and the chromosomes have the appearance and structure of somatic chromosomes. There is, however, one very important difference between the cell divisions in cleavage and the cell divisions in later stages of development and in the adult organism. In the later stages and in the adult, the cell division is intimately connected with growth. After each division the daughter cells grow, and when they are approximately doubled in size they divide again. The cells thus maintain an average size in every type of tissue. During cleavage this is not so. The consecutive divisions of the blastomeres are not separated by periods of growth. A blastomere does not increase in size before the next division begins. Consequently, with each division the resulting blastomeres are only half the original size. Thus cleavage begins with one very large cell and ends with a great number of cells, each of which is no longer very much larger than the tissue cells of the adult animal. Indeed, at the end of cleavage, the cells are usually even smaller than most of the differentiated cells of an adult animal, because cellular differentiation is often accompanied by an increase in the size of an individual cell.

The nuclei of the early cleavage cells are considerably larger than they are in ordinary somatic cells of the same animal. This is, however, mainly due to the presence of larger amounts of nuclear sap and not to chromosomal material. The amount of nucleic acid in individual nuclei may be determined by using the property of these acids of absorbing ultraviolet light at a wavelength of 2600 Ångströms. If a very narrow beam of light of this wavelength is passed through a nucleus in a microscopic preparation, the light absorbed by the nucleus may be measured and the actual content of the nucleic acid may then be calculated. Alternatively, the nuclei may be stained in the preparation by the Feulgen method which is specific for deoxyribonucleic acid, and the absorption of light by the fuchsin fixed in the nucleus may be taken as an estimate of the nucleic acid present.

Since the chromosomal material in the cleavage cells is being doubled at each mitotic division, one would expect the amounts of deoxyribonucleic acid to vary from a diploid amount in cells that have just undergone mitosis to a tetraploid amount in cells ready to divide again. This has actually been found in the embryo of the sea urchin *Lytechinus*, from the one-cell stage (zygote nucleus) to the larval stage (McMaster, 1955 – see Table 6).

As an example we may also quote results obtained by measurement of the deoxyribonucleic acid content in nuclei during fertilization and cleavage in an annelid, *Chaetopterus* (Alfert and Swift, 1953 – see Table 7).

In spite of the greater volume of the cleavage nuclei, these are small in proportion to the volume of the cells. In a mature sea urchin egg before fertilization the ratio $\dfrac{\text{volume of the nucleus}}{\text{volume of cytoplasm}}$ is 1/550 (Brachet, 1950). At the end of cleavage (in the blastula stage) the same ratio is 1/6.

If the numbers of cells in a developing embryo at various stages are counted, the change in the rate of reproduction of cells between the period of cleavage and the later development becomes very obvious. In Figure 81 the logarithm of the number of cells in a frog embryo is plotted against time, and it is seen that the curve shows a very distinct bend at about 40 hours,

TABLE 6. Mean Amounts of Deoxyribonucleic Acid per Nucleus in Arbitrary Units in Early Development of the Sea Urchin *Lytechinus variegatus* (From McMaster, 1955)

Stage		DNA	Condition of Nucleus
1-cell		1.11 ± .06	near 4n
2-cell		1.02 ± .04	"
4-cell		1.09 ± .04	"
8-cell		1.08 ± .07	"
16-cell	micromeres	0.82 ± .06	2n < 4n
	mesomeres	1.04 ± .04	near 4n
	macromeres	1.02 ± .04	"
28-cell	micromeres	1.10 ± .05	"
	mesomeres	0.95 ± .06	"
	macromeres	1.01 ± .03	"
blastula ectoderm		0.68 ± .04	2n < 4n
gastrula ectoderm		0.60 ± .03	2n +
early pluteus ectoderm		0.62 ± .03	"
late pluteus ectoderm		0.60 ± .03	"

which is just at the end of cleavage (between the blastula stage and the beginning of gastrulation), if development has been proceeding at 15° C. Before this time the rate of increase is far more rapid than afterwards (Sze, 1953).

The rhythm of cleavage as measured by the time interval between two consecutive divisions is not quite the same in different animals. In the goldfish, divisions follow each other continuously at rather regular intervals of about 20 minutes. The interval is nearer one hour in the case of the frog, though it depends very much on temperature. The eggs of mammals cleave very much more slowly, about 10 to 12 hours elapsing between consecutive cell divisions in the mouse at 37° C. (Kuhl, 1941).

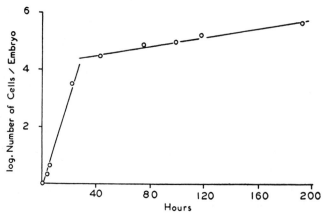

Figure 81. Increase of number of cells during early development of the frog's egg. (From Sze, 1953.)

TABLE 7. NUCLEIC ACID CONTENT IN NUCLEI DURING GAMETOGENESIS AND CLEAVAGE IN *Chaetopterus* (DEOXYRIBONUCLEIC ACID IN ARBITARY UNITS – AVERAGE FROM SEVERAL DETERMINATIONS)

Stage	Amount of DNA	Condition of nucleus
1st polar body	127 ± 3	2n
Spermatozoid	61 ± 1	1n
Cleavage, interphase	210 ± 9	2n ——— 4n
Cleavage, prophase	263 ± 10	4n
Cleavage, telophase	124 ± 3	2n

7–2 CHEMICAL CHANGES DURING CLEAVAGE

Although there is no growth during the period of cleavage, certain limited chemical transformations are going on. These may be classed under two headings. One is the utilization of yolk or other food reserves. This consumption is necessary to cover the energy requirements of the cleaving egg. But it has also been observed that the amount of active cytoplasm increases throughout the period of cleavage. This can best be seen in microscopic sections, since it is difficult to differentiate chemically between active cytoplasm and reserve protein. Furthermore, the respiration increases steadily throughout the period of cleavage, and this is generally attributed to an increase in the amount of active cytoplasm (Boell, 1945; Weber and Boell, 1955).

The second type of change that is observed during cleavage is a steady increase of nuclear material at the expense of cytoplasm. The number of nuclei is of course doubled with every new division of the blastomeres, and this increase is accompanied by an increase of nuclear substance, which involves an increase of deoxyribonucleic acid – the amount per nucleus of the latter remaining constant (McMaster, 1955 – see Table 6).

The increase of the chromosomal deoxyribonucleic acid, at least during the earlier phases of development, must be at the expense of materials contained in the egg. There are several possible sources of such materials. In the first place, one should mention the nucleic acids present in the cytoplasm of the eggs. In the sea urchin eggs there is a large amount of ribonucleic acid in the egg cytoplasm, and this gradually disappears later in development (Brachet, 1950b). Of particular interest is the presence of deoxyribonucleic acid in the cytoplasm of amphibian eggs (Sze, 1953; Brachet and Quertier, 1963). To check the origin of deoxyribonucleic acid in cleavage cells, DNA precursors labeled by radioactive atoms were supplied to eggs of sea urchins and amphibians. When cleaving sea urchin eggs were kept in sea water containing C^{14} labeled glycine (which may be used for the synthesis of purine groups in the nucleic acid molecule), it was found that the radioactive carbon atoms were incorporated in large amounts into the deoxyribonucleic acid, bypassing the cytoplasmic ribonucleic acid (Abrams, 1951). Also, when C^{14} labeled glycine was injected into fertilized frog eggs, some of it was incorporated into deoxyribonucleic acid (Grant, 1958b).

The amounts of small molecular precursors incorporated into deoxyribonucleic acids in cleaving frog eggs were not quite large enough to account for the increase of the nuclear material during cleavage. It has been concluded therefore that the rapid formation of new chromosomes during cleavage probably makes use of cytoplasmic deoxyribonucleic acid (Grant, 1958a; Moore, 1962). It remains to be seen whether the cytoplasmic ribonucleic acid is incorporated into chromosomes in large enough units which might contain genetic information, or whether it is broken down into mononucleotides before incorporation (Moore, 1962). So far there is no satisfactory evidence that the cytoplasmic deoxyribonucleic acid carries genetic information which is incorporated into the chromosomes.

The yolky eggs of birds, reptiles and also of insects contain very little nucleic acid, and the synthesis of deoxyribonucleic acid must be derived from the foodstuffs contained in the yolk. In mammals, nucleic acids are built up from substances taken up by the embryo from without (Brachet, 1950).

The changes taking place during cleavage seem to be predominantly quantitative, no new substances appearing during this phase.

7−3 PATTERNS OF CLEAVAGE

The way in which the egg is subdivided into the daughter blastomeres is usually very regular. The plane of the first division is as a rule vertical; it passes through the main axis of the egg. The plane of the second division is also vertical and passes through the main axis, but it is at right angles to the first plane of cleavage. The result is that the first four blastomeres all lie side by side. The plane of the third division is at right angles to the first two planes and to the main axis of the egg. It is therefore horizontal or parallel to the equator of the egg. Of the eight blastomeres four lie on top of the other four, the first four comprising the animal hemisphere of the egg, the second the vegetal hemisphere.

If each of the blastomeres of the upper tier lie over the corresponding blastomeres of the lower tier, the pattern of the blastomeres is radially symmetrical (Fig. 82). This is called the **radial type** of cleavage. In many

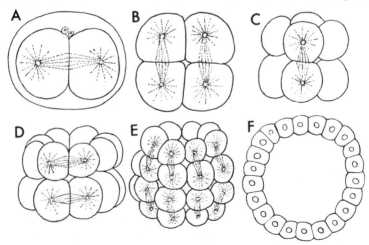

Figure 82. Radial cleavage with almost equal size of blastomeres in sea cucumber *Synapta digitata*. *A*, 2 cell stage. *B*, 4 cell stage (viewed from animal pole). *C*, 8 cell stage, lateral view. *D*, 16 cell stage. *E*, 32 cell stage. *F*, Blastula, vertical section. (After Selenka, from Korschelt, 1936.)

animals, however, the upper tier of blastomeres may be shifted with respect
to the lower tier of blastomeres, and the radially symmetrical pattern becomes
distorted in various degrees. The distortion may be due sometimes to individual variation, but there are certain groups of animals in which distortion
always takes place and is due to a specific structure of the egg.

In the annelids, molluscs, nemerteans and some of the planarians (the
Polycladida) all of the blastomeres of the upper tier are shifted in the same
direction in relation to the blastomeres of the lower tier, so that they come to
lie not over the corresponding vegetal blastomeres, but over the junction
between each two of the vegetal blastomeres (Fig. 83). This comes about not
as a result of secondary shifting of the blastomeres but because of oblique
positions of the mitotic spindles, so that right from the start the two daughter
cells do not lie above one another. The four spindles during the third cleavage
are arranged in a sort of spiral. This type of cleavage is therefore called the
spiral type of cleavage.

The turn of the spiral as seen from above may be in a clockwise direction
or in a counterclockwise direction. In the first case the cleavage is called
dextral; in the second case it is called **sinistral**. Since the cleavage planes are
at right angles to the spindles, they also deviate from the horizontal position
found in radial cleavage, and each cleavage plane is inclined at a certain
angle. The spiral arrangment of the mitotic spindles can be traced even in the
first two divisions of the egg; the spindles are oblique and not vertical as in
radial cleavage. However, the resulting shifts in the position of the blastomeres are not so obvious as after the third cleavage. During the subsequent
cleavages the spindles continue to be oblique, but the direction of spiraling
changes in each subsequent division. Dextral spiraling alternates with sinistral, so that the spindle of each subsequent cleavage is approximately at
right angles to the previous one.

It will be noticed that the type of cleavage of the egg as a whole, whether

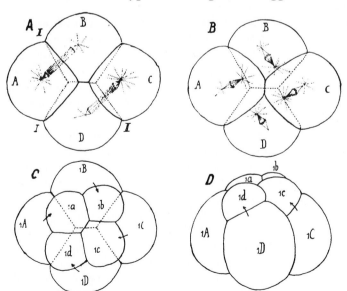

Figure 83. Spiral cleavage in the mollusc *Trochus A*, 4 cell stage, just after second division
(spindles of second division still visible). *B*, 4 cell stage, but in preparation for third division
(metaphase). *C*, 8 cell stage, viewed from animal pole. *D*, 8 cell stage, lateral view. (After Robert,
from Korschelt, 1936.)

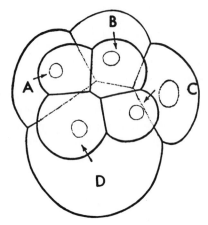

Figure 84. Spiral cleavage in the mollusc *Unio* with blastomere *D* distinctly larger than blastomeres *A*, *B*, and *C*. (After Lillie, from Kellicott, General Embryology, 1914.)

dextral or sinistral, depends on the direction of spiraling occurring during the third division of the egg.

Peculiarities of the cleavage pattern can also be introduced by differences in the size of the blastomeres. Of the four blastomeres in the four-cell stage of eggs having a spiral type of cleavage, it is often found that one blastomere is larger than the other three (Fig. 84). This allows us to distinguish the individual blastomeres. The four first blastomeres are denoted by the letters *A, B, C, D,* the letters going in a clockwise direction (if the egg is viewed from the animal pole) and the largest blastomere being denoted by the letter *D*. In some animals having otherwise an approximately radial type of cleavage, two of the first four blastomeres may be larger than the other two, thus establishing a plane of bilateral symmetry in the developing embryo. Subsequent cleavages may make the bilateral arrangement of the blastomeres still more obvious (as in tunicates and in nematodes, although in a different way). The resulting type of cleavage is referred to as the **bilateral type.** (See Fig. 102, p. 154.)

The yolk, which is always present in the egg at the beginning of cleavage in greater or lesser quantities, exerts a very far-reaching effect on the process of cleavage. Every mitosis involves movements of the cell components—the chromosomes, parts of the cytoplasm constituting the achromatic figure, the mitochondria and the surface layer of the cell—the activity of which along the equator of the maternal cell leads to the eventual separation of the daughter cells. During these movements, the yolk granules or platelets behave entirely passively and are passively distributed between the daughter blastomeres. When the yolk granules or platelets become very abundant, they tend to retard and even inhibit the process of cleavage. As a result, the blastomeres which are richer in yolk tend to divide at a slower rate and consequently remain larger than those which have less yolk. The yolk in the uncleaved egg is more concentrated toward the vegetal pole of the egg. It is therefore at the vegetal pole of the egg that the cleavage is most retarded by the presence of yolk, and where the blastomeres are of the largest size.

A good example of the effect of the yolk on cleavage is given by the frog's egg (Fig. 85). The influence of the yolk on cleavage may be detected even during the first division of the fertilized egg. During the anaphase of the mitotic division, a furrow appears on the surface of the egg which is to separate the two daughters blastomeres from one another. This furrow, however,

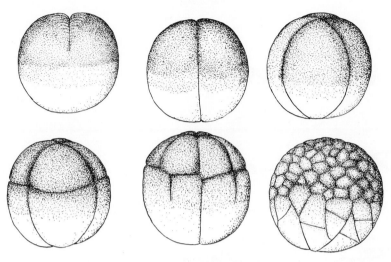

Figure 85. Cleavage in the frog, semidiagrammatic.

does not appear simultaneously all around the circumference of the egg, but at first only at the animal pole of the egg, where there is less yolk. (It has been indicated that the first cleavage plane is vertical and therefore passes through the animal and vegetal poles of the egg.) Only gradually is the cleavage furrow prolonged along the meridians of the egg, until, cutting through the mass of yolk-laden cytoplasm, it eventually reaches the vegetal pole and thus completes the separation of the two first blastomeres. The same process is repeated during the second cleavage. During the third cleavage, when the plane of separation of the daughter blastomeres is horizontal, the furrow appears simultaneously over the whole circumference of the egg, for it meets with an equal resistance from yolk everywhere.

A further accumulation of the yolk at the vegetal pole of the egg causes still greater delay in the cell fission at this pole, so that the cleavage becomes inhibited more and more. This can be traced very well in a series of various ganoid fishes, whose eggs possess an increasing amount of yolk. In *Acipenser* the cleavage is complete, as in the amphibians, but the difference between the micromeres of the animal hemisphere and the macromeres of the vegetal hemisphere is much sharper than in amphibians. In *Amia* (Fig. 86) cleavage starts at the animal pole, and the cleavage furrows reach the vegetal pole, but they are so retarded that subsequent divisions begin at the animal pole before the preceding furrows cut through the yolk at the vegetal pole. In

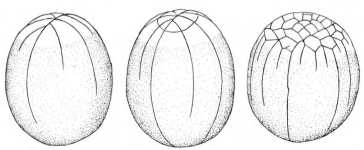

Figure 86. Cleavage in the ganoid fish *Amia*. (After Whitman and Eyklesheimer, from Korschelt, 1936.)

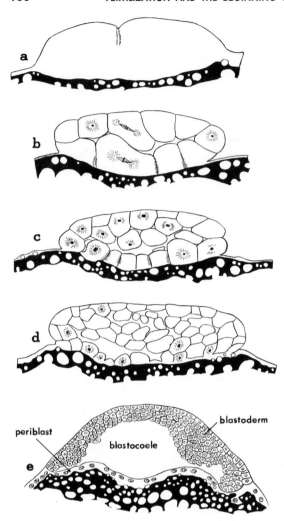

Figure 87. Cleavage and blastula of bony fish. *a, b, c, d,* Trout (after Kopsch); *e, Muraena* (after Bocke). (From Brachet, 1935.)

Lepidosteus the cleavage starts at the animal pole as in *Amia,* but the cleavage furrows never reach the vegetal pole, so that the vegetal hemisphere of the egg remains uncleaved. This results in what is called **incomplete cleavage**. The eggs which are completely divided into blastomeres are called **holoblastic**, those with incomplete cleavage **meroblastic**. As a result of incomplete cleavage the egg is divided into a number of separate blastomeres and a residue, which is an undivided mass of cytoplasm with numerous nuclei scattered in it.

In eggs in which the yolk is segregated from the active cytoplasm (elasmobranchs, bony fishes, birds and reptiles), the cleavage is distinctly recognizable as meroblastic or incomplete right from the start (Figs. 87, 88 and 89). At first, all the cleavage planes are vertical, and all the blastomeres lie in one plane only. The cleavage furrows separate the daughter blastomeres from each other but not from the yolk, so that the central blastomeres are continuous with the yolk at their lower ends, and the blastomeres lying on the circumference are, in addition, continuous with the uncleaved cytoplasm at their outer edges. As the nuclei at the edge divide, more and more cells become cut off to join the ones lying in the center, but the new blastomeres are also in continuity with the uncleaved yolk underneath.

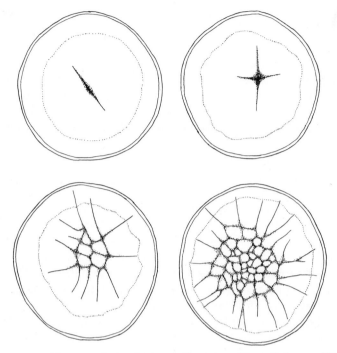

Figure 88. Cleavage of a hen's egg, surface view. (From Patterson, 1910.)

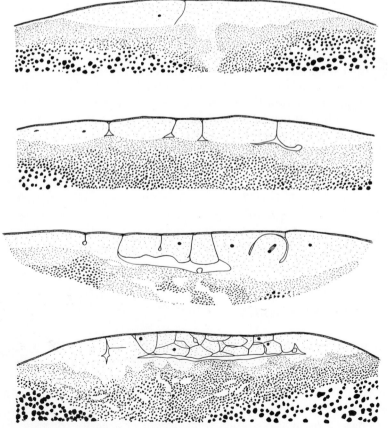

Figure 89. Cleavage of a hen's egg (sections). (From Patterson, 1910.)

In a later stage of cleavage, the blastomeres of the central area become separated from the underlying yolk in one of two ways: either slits may appear beneath the nucleated parts of the cells, or else the cell divisions may occur with horizontal (tangential) planes of fission. In the latter case one of the daughter cells, the upper one, becomes completely separated from its neighbors, while the lower blastomere retains the connection with the yolk mass. The marginal cells, which remain continuous with each other around their outer edges, are also continuous with the mass of yolk and hence with the lower cells resulting from tangential divisions. All these blastomeres eventually lose even those furrows which partially separated them from one another, and fuse into a continuous syncytium with numerous nuclei but no indication of individual cells.

The cytoplasmic cap on the animal pole of the egg is now, in its central part, subdivided into a number of "free" blastomeres, while around the outer margin of the mass of blastomeres, and underneath, closely adhering to the yolk, is the syncytial layer which is called the **periblast**. The periblast is not destined to participate directly in the formation of the embryonic body, but it is supposed to be of some importance in breaking down the yolk and making it available for the growing embryo.

Another type of incomplete cleavage is found in centrolecithal eggs. At the beginning of cleavage the nucleus (synkaryon) lies in the center of the egg surrounded by a small amount of cytoplasm. The mitotic division of the nucleus starts in this position, but at first it is not followed by a division of cytoplasm (Fig. 90). As a result, a number of nuclei are formed all embedded in the undivided central mass of cytoplasm. After several divisions have taken place (the actual number of divisions varies in different animals), the nuclei start moving away from the center of the egg. Each nucleus, surrounded by a small portion of the original central cytoplasm, travels outward toward the surface of the egg. The central mass of cytoplasm is thus broken up and disappears. When the nuclei reach the surface of the egg, the cytoplasm surrounding them fuses with the superficial layer of cytoplasm. The surface layer of the embryo is then a syncytium with numerous nuclei embedded in an undivided layer of cytoplasm. In the next stage the cytoplasm becomes subdivided, by furrows going inward from the surface, into as many sections as there are nuclei. The sections can now be called cells, even though these are at first still connected to the yolk mass. Sooner or later the cells become completely separated from the yolk. The latter persists as a compact mass until it is gradually used up as a food reserve by the developing embryo. This type of cleavage is called **superficial cleavage**. It is the usual type of cleavage in insects and many other arthropods.

7–4 MORULA AND BLASTULA

The blastomeres in the early cleavage stages tend to assume a spherical shape like that of the egg before cleavage. Their mutual pressure flattens the surfaces of the blastomeres in contact with each other, but the free surfaces of each blastomere remain spherical, unless these outer surfaces are also compressed by the vitelline membrane. The whole embryo acquires, in this stage, a characteristic appearance reminiscent of a mulberry. (See Fig. 82,*e*

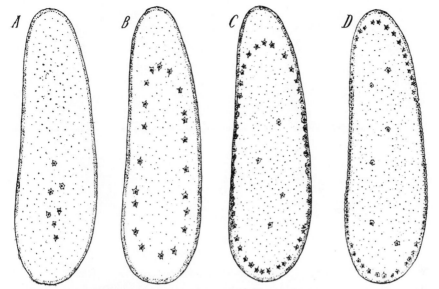

Figure 90. Superficial cleavage of a beetle (*Hydrophilus*). (After Heider, from Korschelt, 1936.)

p. 134.) Because of this superficial similarity, the embryo in this stage is called a **morula** (Latin for mulberry).

The arrangement of the blastomeres in the morula stage may vary in the different groups of the animal kingdom. In coelenterates it is often a massive structure, blastomeres filling all the space that had been occupied by the uncleaved egg. Some of the blastomeres then lie externally, others in the interior. (Some embryologists apply the name morula to this type of embryo only.) More often, as the egg undergoes cleavage, the blastomeres become arranged in one layer, so that all the blastomeres participate in the external surface of the embryo. In this case a cavity soon appears which at first may be represented just by narrow crevices between the blastomeres, but which gradually increases as the cleavage goes on. This cavity is called the **blastocoele**.

As the cleavage proceeds, the adhesion of the blastomeres to each other increases, and they arrange themselves into a true epithelium. In cases where a cavity has been forming in the interior of the embryo, the epithelial layer completely encloses this cavity, and the embryo becomes a hollow sphere, the walls of which consist of an epithelial layer of cells. Such an embryo is called a **blastula**. The layer of cells is called the **blastoderm**, and the cavity is the blastocoele already mentioned (Fig. 91, *a*).

In oligolecithal eggs with complete cleavage (echinoderms, *Amphioxus*) the blastomeres at the end of cleavage are not of exactly equal size, the blastomeres near the vegetal pole being slightly larger than those on the animal pole. When the blastula is formed, the cells arrange themselves into a simple columnar epithelium enclosing the blastocoele. Because the vegetal cells are larger than the animal cells, the blastoderm is not of an equal thickness throughout; at the vegetal pole the epithelium is thicker, at the animal pole it is thinner. Thus the polarity of the egg persists in the polarity of the blastula.

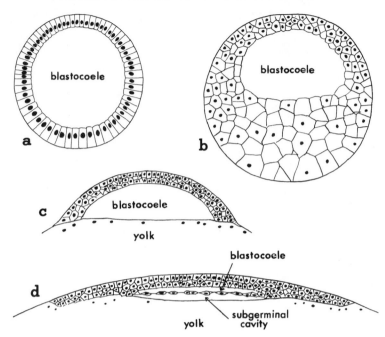

Figure 91. Diagrammatic comparison of blastulae of an echinoderm (*a*), a frog (*b*), a bony fish (*c*) and a bird (*d*).

Animals with a larger amount of yolk, such as the frog, show a difference in the size of the cells of the blastula that may be very considerable, and the blastula still further departs from the simple form of a hollow sphere. The cells here are also arranged into a layer surrounding the cavity in the interior, but the layer is of very uneven thickness. At the vegetal pole the layer of cells is very much thicker than at the animal pole, and the blastocoele is consequently distinctly eccentric, nearer to the animal pole of the embryo (Fig. 91,*b*). Furthermore, the blastoderm is no longer a simple cylindrical epithelium but is two or more cells thick. The cells in the interior are rather loosely connected to each other, but at the external surface of the blastula the cells adhere to one another very firmly because of the presence of a cementing substance joining the surfaces of adjoining cells in a narrow zone just underneath the surface of the blastoderm. (See Fig. 151, p. 216.)

A process corresponding to blastula formation occurs also in animals whose eggs have incomplete cleavage. In a bony fish or a shark the early blastomeres tend to round themselves off, thus showing that they are only loosely bound together. Later the blastomeres adhere to each other more firmly and so become converted into an epithelium. Again, as in amphibians, the superficial cells are firmly joined to one another while the cells in the interior may remain loosely connected until a later stage. The epithelium, however, cannot have the form of a sphere. Just as the cleavage is restricted to the cap of cytoplasm on the animal pole of the egg, so also the blastoderm is developed only in the same polar region. The blastoderm therefore assumes the shape of a disc lying on the animal pole. The disc, which is called the **blastodisc**, is more or less convex and encloses, between itself and the uncleaved residue of the egg, a cavity representing the blastocoele (Fig. 91,*c*).

The earlier stages of the discoidal cleavage in the eggs of reptiles and birds resemble essentially the cleavage in the meroblastic eggs of the fishes. At the time when the blastoderm is being formed, however, a very essential difference becomes apparent. In fishes, when the loosely connected blastomeres become converted into an epithelial layer, there is only one layer formed. The same is found in tortoises, but in most reptiles, especially lizards and snakes, and in birds, only some of the cells are incorporated into the superficial layer, which we will call the **epiblast**. A small number of the blastomeres remain underneath the superficial layer, lying loose in the space between the latter and the yolk. These cells subsequently unite themselves into a thin layer of flat epithelium, called the **hypoblast**, separated from the surface layer by a cavity (Fig. 92). This lower layer of cells has caused many controversies among embryologists as to its significance and homologies. It has been shown (Pasteels, 1945 and 1957) that this layer corresponds to the cells lying in the floor of the blastocoele on the vegetal side of the blastocoele cavity in animals such as amphibians. The cavity between the superficial layer and this deeper layer in birds and reptiles corresponds therefore to the blastocoele of amphibians and fishes (Fig. 91,*d*). The space between the hypoblast and the yolk may then be distinguished as the **subgerminal cavity**.

There is a further difference in that the cavity in birds and reptiles does not appear under the whole of the blastoderm but only under the central part of it. No cavity is formed under the layer of blastomeres in the periphery of the blastodisc. The blastodisc is thus subdivided into two parts: the central part, called the **area pellucida**, and the peripheral part, the **area opaca**. The names indicate that the central part appears more transparent in the living embryo, owing to the presence of the cavity under the layer of blastomeres; the peripheral area is opaque because the blastomeres rest directly on the yolk.

Only the area pellucida furnishes material for the formation of the body of the embryo. The cells of the area opaca are concerned with the breakdown of the underlying yolk and thus indirectly supply the embryo with foodstuffs.

In centrolecithal eggs having a superficial cleavage (insects), there is no cavity comparable to the blastocoele. Nevertheless, the formation of the epithelium on the surface of the egg, after the nuclei have migrated to the exterior, can be compared to the formation of the blastula. The layer of cells thus formed on the surface of the embryo is the blastoderm. Instead of surrounding a cavity, the blastoderm envelops the mass of uncleaved yolk. We may also compare this stage to an embryo whose blastocoele has been filled with yolk.

Up to the blastula stage, the developing embryo preserves the same general shape as the uncleaved egg. So far, the results achieved are the subdivision of the single cell into a multiplicity of cells and the formation of the blastocoele. In addition, the substances contained in the egg remain very much in the same position as before. The yolk remains near the vegetal pole. In pigmented eggs, such as those of amphibians, the pigment remains as before, more or less restricted to the upper hemisphere of the egg. Only a slight intermingling of cytoplasm seems to be produced by the cleavage furrows cutting through the substance of the egg.

Figure 92. Four stages in the formation of the epiblast and the hypoblast from the cleavage cells of the duck embryo. *A*, Late cleavage, all cells in one undifferentiated layer. *B*, Superficial cells join closer to form epiblast (*ep*). Underneath this there remain numbers of loose cells. *C* and *D*, Loose cells join to form hypoblast. (From Pasteels, 1945.)

It has been pointed out that during cleavage no qualitative changes can be discovered in the chemical composition of the developing embryo. No new substances, either chemically defined or microscopically detectable, have been found to appear during cleavage. It is conceivable, however, that the substances present in the egg may be redistributed in some way during cleavage and that such a redistribution may be essentially important for further development.

In this connection we shall examine first of all whether the numerous nuclei produced during the mitotic divisions of the egg are all alike in their properties, or whether any differences may be discovered among them.

7−5   THE NUCLEI OF CLEAVAGE CELLS

In his "germ plasm theory," A. Weismann presented a hypothesis to explain both heredity and the ontogenetic development of organisms. According to Weismann (1904), every distinct part of an organism (animal or plant) is represented in the sex cell by a separate particle: a **determinant**. The sum total of determinants would represent the parts of the adult organism with all their peculiarities. The complete set of determinants would be handed down from generation to generation, which would account for hereditary transmission of characters. The determinants, according to Weismann, are localized in the chromosomes of the nucleus, just as are the genes of modern genetics. However, there is this difference, that the genes are not supposed to represent *parts* of the organism but rather properties which may sometimes be discernible in all the parts of the body.

During the cleavage of the egg, the various determinants, according to Weismann, become segregated into different cells. The blastomeres would get only some of the determinants; namely, those which correspond to the fate of each blastomere. The successive segregation of the determinants would eventually result in each cell's having only determinants of one kind, and then nothing would be left to the cell but to differentiate in a specific way in accordance with the determinants present. Only the cells having the sex cells among their descendants, Weismann held, would preserve the complete set of determinants, since these would be necessary for directing the development of the next generation.

Even though Weismann's conception of the properties of determinants is not tenable from the genetic viewpoint, it is still important to know whether the difference in the fate of the blastomeres and parts of the embryo may be attributed to differences in the nuclei of the cleavage cells. Experiments now give convincing information on this point.

Our knowledge of the development of complete embryos from one of the two daughter blastomeres of the egg (as a result of either separating the two first blastomeres or killing one of the first two blastomeres−see section 1–3) contradicts Weismann's hypothesis about the segregation of determinants during cleavage. The evidence becomes still more conclusive because it has been found that not only are the first two blastomeres capable of developing into complete embryos, but that the blastomeres in later cleavage stages sometimes possess the same ability. In the case of sea urchins one of the first four blastomeres, and even occasionally one of the first eight blastomeres, may develop into a whole embryo with all the normal parts but reduced in size (see Fig. 93−Hörstadius and Wolsky, 1936).

However, the method of isolating blastomeres does not permit one to test the properties of nuclei of later generations of cells. In the four-cell stage, the quantity of cytoplasm contained in one blastomere may already be too small for development to take place in an approximately normal fashion.

Figure 93. Results of separation of the first four blastomeres of a sea urchin's egg. *a*, Normal pluteus; *b*, *c*, *d* and *e*, plutei of normal structure but diminished size, each developed from one of the blastomeres of the four-cell stage. All drawn to the same scale. (From Hörstadius and Wolsky, 1936.)

This is true in increasing degree as cleavage proceeds and the individual blastomeres become smaller and smaller.

To push the investigation further, a different method has been devised. A most elegant experiment in this field was carried out by Spemann (1928). Spemann constricted fertilized eggs of the newt *Triturus* (*Triton*) into two halves with a fine hair, just as they were about to begin to cleave. The constriction was not carried out completely, so that the two halves were still connected to each other by a narrow bridge of cytoplasm. The nucleus of the fertilized egg lay in one half, and the other half consisted of cytoplasm only. When the egg nucleus began to divide, the cleavage was at first restricted to that half of the egg which contained the nucleus (Fig. 94). This half divided into two, four, eight cells, and so on, while the nonnucleated half remained uncleaved. At about the stage of 16 blastomeres, one of the daughter nuclei, now much smaller than at the beginning of cleavage, passed through the cytoplasmic bridge into the half of the egg which had hitherto no nucleus (Fig. 94,*c*). Forthwith this half also began to cleave. After both halves of the egg were thus supplied with nuclei, Spemann drew the hair loop tighter and separated the two halves of the egg completely from each other. They were now allowed to develop into embryos. In a number of cases two completely normal embryos developed from the two halves of the egg as a result of this experiment.

Of the two embryos, each started by having one half of the egg cytoplasm, but as to the nucleus they were in a very different position. While one of the embryos possessed 15/16 or even 31/32 of all the nuclear material of the egg, the other got only 1/16 or 1/32 of the nuclear material. This proves conclusively that even in the 32-cell stage every nucleus has a complete set of hereditary factors necessary for the achievement of normal development. All the nuclei in this stage are completely equivalent to one another and to the nucleus of the fertilized egg. The hypothesis of an unequal division of the hereditary substance of the nucleus, of the segregation of determinants or

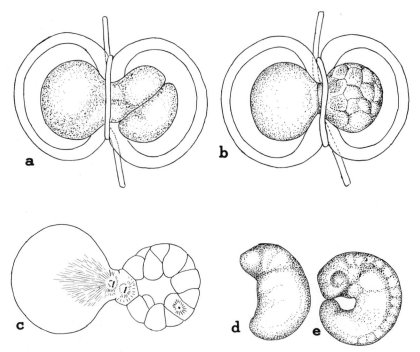

Figure 94. Spemann's experiment of delayed supply of the nucleus to one half of a newt's egg. *a*, Beginning of cleavage in nucleated half. *b*, One of the nuclei has penetrated into the uncleaved half, and a cell boundary appears between this and the half which originally contained the zygote nucleus. *c*, Same stage in section. *d*, Embryo from the half with delayed nuclear supply. *e*, Embryo from the half which contained the zygote nucleus. (From Spemann, 1938.)

genes to the different cleavage cells, is thus disproved. It is now assumed that every cell of the metazoan body has a complete set of nuclear factors necessary for development (a complete set of genes, in the terminology of modern genetics).

The experiments on the delayed nuclear supply to one half of an amphibian egg has been corroborated by experiments on the eggs of other animals. It will be useful to relate here a corresponding experiment carried out on a very different kind of animal: the dragonfly *Platycnemis pennipes* (Seidel, 1932). In the dragonfly the cleavage is incomplete, and only the nucleus divides at first, the cytoplasm remaining uncleaved. The egg is elongated, and after the first division the daughter nuclei move, one into the anterior and the other into the posterior half of the egg. When eight nuclei are available, these are spaced along the length of the egg. By further divisions nuclei are provided for all cells in the respective regions (Fig. 95, *a–d*). In the stage when two nuclei are present, either of them may be killed by a short exposure to a narrow beam of ultraviolet light, which does not damage the cytoplasm to any great extent (Fig. 95, *e*). The remaining nucleus continues to divide, and its daughter nuclei are distributed to all parts of the egg instead of supplying only one half of it. Completely normal embryos develop, no matter which of the two nuclei is allowed to survive (Fig. 95, *f*). The two nuclei prove to be completely equivalent for development, although normally they would have supplied very different parts of the embryo.

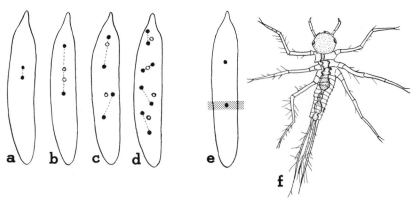

Figure 95. *a, b, c,* and *d,* Early cleavage in the dragonfly *Platycnemis pennipes.* Hollow circles indicate the previous position of the nuclei in each case. *e,* Killing one of the first two cleavage nuclei by ultraviolet irradiation. Irradiated area is stippled. *f,* Larva which developed from an egg treated as in *e.* (Adapted from Seidel, 1932.)

The methods used in the above experiments in testing the properties of the cleavage nuclei are of necessity confined to the earlier stages of cleavage. At present a more universal method is available which allows the investigation to be extended to nuclei of cells of much more advanced embryos, and possibly it may ultimately be applied even to fully differentiated cells of an adult organism. This is the method used for transplantation of nuclei. The transplantation of nuclei from one cell to another was first carried out sucessfully on *Amoeba,* and the method was then applied to test the properties of nuclei in developing frog embryos (Briggs and King, 1952, 1953 and 1957; King and Briggs, 1954 and 1956). The method, as applied to the frog embryo, consists essentially in taking the nucleus of any cell from an embryo, during the stages from blastula to tailbud, and injecting it into an enucleated uncleaved egg.

The egg receiving the nucleus must be specially prepared. The ripe eggs are removed from the oviducts and activated by pricking with a glass needle (see section 6–3). The egg nucleus then approaches the surface of the cytoplasm in preparation for the second maturation division and is removed by a second prick with a glass needle at the exact spot where the nucleus is located. Next, a cell of an advanced embryo is separated from its neighbors and sucked into the tube of an injection pipette. The diameter of the pipette is smaller than that of the cell and as a result the surface of the cell is broken. The contents of the pipette, consisting of the nucleus and the debris of the cytoplasm, are injected deep into the enucleated egg. When the pipette is withdrawn, the egg cytoplasm tends to escape through the hole in the egg membranes, forming an extraovate protrusion. This has to be cut off by a pair of glass needles to prevent further loss of egg substance (Fig. 96).

As a result of these procedures, up to 80 per cent (King and Briggs, 1956) of the eggs operated on start cleaving and producing numerous cells, the nuclei of which are derived from the injected nucleus, and the cytoplasm of which is from the enucleated egg (the small amount of cytoplasm injected with the nucleus, comprising less than 1/40,000 of the volume of the egg cytoplasm, may be ignored). Not all eggs which start cleaving develop normally later, but at least a small proportion do so and may go through all the

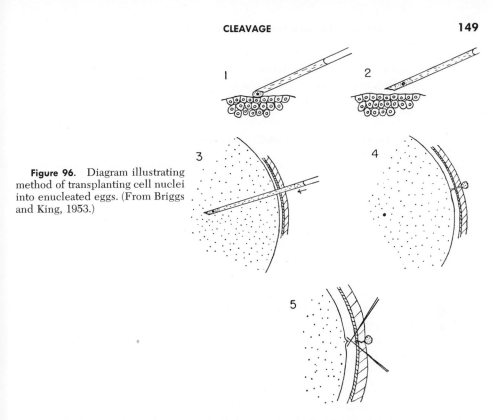

Figure 96. Diagram illustrating method of transplanting cell nuclei into enucleated eggs. (From Briggs and King, 1953.)

stages of embryonic and postembryonic development up to metamorphosis (Fig. 97). In other cases the development is arrested or becomes abnormal in various stages. These cases of abnormal development do not concern us in the present instance, but the cases of complete development show that the nuclei of embryos in advanced stages, particularly in the late blastula and the early gastrula stages, can provide everything necessary for the differentiation of all types of cells of a normal embryo, whereas they would have normally participated in only one type of differentiation. In the late blastula, the stage used for some of these nuclear transplantations, there are 8,000 to 16,000 cells, which means that about 13 to 14 divisions (or generations) of the original nucleus of the fertilized egg have been performed without diminishing the power of the nucleus to support every type of differentiation provided for by

Figure 97. Metamorphosing tadpole developed from an egg with transplanted nucleus. (From King and Briggs, 1954.)

the specific genotype. Nuclei of cells of an early gastrula show the same properties, although the subdivision of the embryo into areas with different roles in development is well on the way at that stage, as will be shown in subsequent sections (Chapter 8).

7–6 DISTRIBUTION OF CYTOPLASMIC SUBSTANCES OF THE EGG DURING CLEAVAGE

The fact that the nuclei of the developing embryo are fully equivalent to each other does not allow us to ascribe to the nucleus the origin of differences in the fate of the cells during development of the embryo. What then is the cause of the observed differences in the developmental behavior of cells? By exclusion, we may suppose that the cause of the differences lies in the cytoplasm, and that the cells produced during cleavage do not receive the same cytoplasmic substances. There is direct experimental support in favor of this supposition.

Curiously enough, a further elaboration of Spemann's experiment of delayed nuclear supply to one half of the *Triturus* egg can be brought to bear on this problem (Spemann, 1928).

It has already been mentioned that pigment is unequally distributed over the surface of amphibian eggs (sections 4–3 and 6–6). The animal hemisphere of the egg is more or less heavily pigmented; the region around the vegetal pole is poor in pigment or completely white; the equatorial, or rather sub-equatorial, marginal zone is more lightly pigmented than the animal hemisphere but more darkly pigmented than the vegetal region. On one side of the egg the marginal zone is broader than on the other, and this region is known as the **gray crescent** (from the color of this region in the common European frogs). The gray crescent indicates the future position of the dorsal lip of the blastopore and also corresponds to the **dorsal** region of the embryo (see section 8–4).

In the egg of the newt the pigment is not very abundant, but the gray crescent is readily distinguishable in the uncleaved egg. It is therefore possible to determine the position of the ligature in respect to the gray crescent (Fig. 98). If the ligature subdivides the gray crescent cytoplasm equally between the two halves of the egg, two more or less normally developed embryos are found to develop (Fig. 98, *b, e*). If the ligature comes to lie so that all the gray crescent cytoplasm is contained in one half of the egg, whereas the other half does not get any of it, then a complete embryo is developed only from the first half. The second half remains highly abnormal; it does not develop a nervous system, a notochord or segmented muscle; the only parts that can be discerned are epidermis, unsegmented (lateral plate) mesoderm and yolk endoderm. All these are parts of the ventral region of the body, thus justifying the name "belly" (Bauchstück) given by Spemann to the defective embryos (Fig. 98, *a, c, d*).

Now it is found that the fate of the egg half, whether it develops into a complete embryo or into a "belly," does not depend on which of the two halves had retained the egg nucleus originally and which was delayed in receiving a nucleus. A half with a delayed nuclear supply will develop into

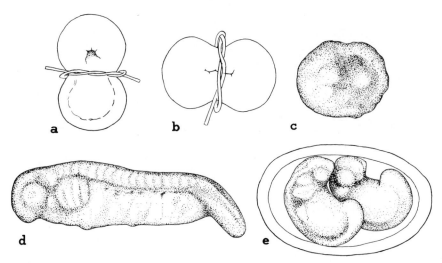

Figure 98. Constriction of a newt's egg in the frontal (*a*) and medial (*b*) plane. After frontal constriction the ventral half developed into a "belly" (*c*), the dorsal half into a complete embryo (*d*). After medial constriction (*b*) both halves developed into complete embryos (*e*). (From Spemann, 1938.)

a complete embryo if it contained the gray crescent cytoplasm. On the other hand, the egg half without gray crescent cytoplasm will become a "belly" even if it contained the egg nucleus right from the beginning. The difference in the time of nuclear supply and the amount of nuclear material received is completely overridden by differences in the cytoplasmic composition of the two egg halves.

The importance of cytoplasmic substances in the egg for the differentiation of parts of the embryo is further proved by a number of experiments carried out on the eggs of various animals. The following will be chosen as examples:

In the egg of the mollusc *Dentalium* (Wilson, 1904), there may be distinguished three layers of cytoplasm: a layer of clear cytoplasm at the animal pole of the egg, a broad layer of granular cytoplasm in the equatorial zone (actually forming the bulk of the egg substance), and a second layer of clear cytoplasm at the vegetal pole of the egg (Figs. 49 (p. 78) and 99). When the egg begins to cleave, the clear cytoplasm at the vegetal pole is pushed out in the form of a **polar lobe**. As the division of the egg draws to its conclusion, the polar lobe is rounded off and remains connected to the rest of the egg only by a narrow cytoplasmic bridge. When the division is completed, the polar lobe is found to be connected with one of the daughter cells, namely cell *CD* of Figure 99 (the cleavage of *Dentalium* is spiral), and at the end of mitosis it is fused with this cell. In this way cell *CD* gets all the three types of cytoplasm, while the other daughter cell, cell *AB*, gets a half of the animal pole's clear cytoplasm, a half of the granular cytoplasm, but no vegetal cytoplasm. Cell *CD* is consequently slightly larger than cell *AB*.

The formation of the polar lobe is repeated when the second cleavage begins; that is, when the egg divides into four blastomeres. Of the two daughter cells of blastomere *CD*, the polar lobe passes to blastomere *D*, while blastomere *C* receives only the clear cytoplasm of the animal pole and the granular cytoplasm.

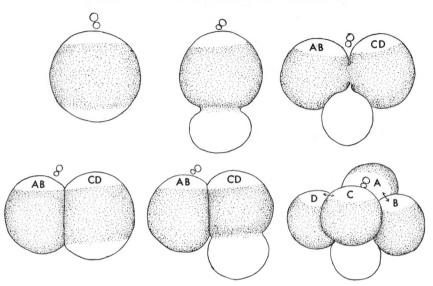

Figure 99. Cleavage of the mollusc *Dentalium*. (From Wilson, 1904.)

The two blastomeres of the two-cell stage and the four blastomeres of the four-cell stage are therefore not equivalent as to their cytoplasmic composition, only one blastomere (*CD* or *D*, respectively) containing the whole of the vegetal polar lobe material. The behavior of the blastomeres is also found to be different. If the first two blastomeres are separated and allowed to develop, blastomere *CD* is found to produce a complete larva (a **trochophore** in this case), though of diminished size. Blastomere *AB* also develops into a larva, but the larva is defective in some respects, the most significant defect being that it completely lacks the rudiment of the mesoderm normally contained in the posterior or "post-trochal" part of the larva (Fig. 100).

If the blastomeres are isolated in the four-cell stage, they are again found to differ in their development. Only blastomere *D*, which possesses the clear

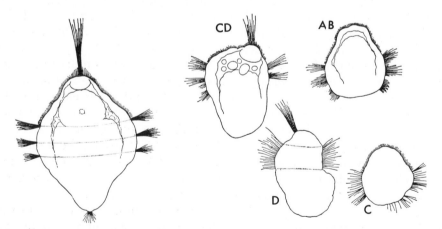

Figure 100. Larvae of *Dentalium* developing from a whole egg (left) and from separated blastomeres (right). The letters indicate from which blastomere each larva has developed. (From Wilson, 1904.)

cytoplasm of the vegetal pole, develops into a complete, though smaller, trochophore larva; the other three blastomeres develop into defective larvae lacking the mesoderm rudiment. It has been concluded, therefore, that the clear cytoplasm of the vegetal pole is necessary for the development of the mesoderm.

This conclusion is further supported by the following experiment:

At the time of the first or second cleavage the polar lobe containing the clear cytoplasm of the vegetal pole can be nipped off. The remainder then contains all the clear cytoplasm of the animal pole and the granular cytoplasm. It also contains all the nuclear material but no vegetal polar lobe material. The result is that the larva developed from such an egg is defective and lacks the mesoderm rudiment. This is a very clear proof that it is the cytoplasm and not the nucleus that makes blastomere D different from the three others and able to produce a certain differentiation (the mesoderm rudiment) which the other blastomeres are incapable of producing.

The egg of the oligochaete *Tubifex* contains polar plasms that are very similar to those of *Dentalium*. There is a cap of transparent cytoplasm at the animal pole of the egg—the animal polar plasm. A broad equatorial zone of the egg consists of granular cytoplasm. At the vegetal pole there is again a cap of transparent cytoplasm—the vegetal polar plasm. No polar lobe is formed, but nevertheless both polar plasms are passed to blastomere CD, during the first cleavage of the egg, and to blastomere D during the second cleavage (Fig. 101). The potentialities of the individual blastomeres may be tested by killing the other blastomeres by means of a localized exposure to ultraviolet rays (Penners, 1925). The survival of blastomere D in this animal is essential not only for the development of mesoderm but also for the development of the nervous system and the segmentation of the body. If blastomere D is killed, the remainder develops into ectoderm and endoderm, but no further differentiation is produced. If blastomeres A, B and C are killed, the remaining blastomere D may develop into a complete embryo. This it does the more easily because it is very much bigger than the other blastomeres.

That the difference between blastomere D and the other blastomeres is due to the presence of the vegetal polar plasm is shown by the following experiment (Penners, 1924). If the fertilized egg is exposed for a short time to an excessively high temperature, the first division of the egg is abnormal: the vegetal polar plasm, instead of passing to one of the daughter blastomeres, is equally divided between the two. The result is that both the first two blastomeres have the properties of the CD blastomere. Each of them

Figure 101.   Cleavage of the egg of *Tubifex*. The animal (*an.*) and vegetal (*veg.*) polar plasms are indicated by stippling. (After Penners, from Morgan, 1927.)

is now capable of developing into a normal embryo with segmented mesoderm and a nervous system. In fact, if the egg is allowed to develop without
further interruption, each of the first two blastomeres gives rise to a complete
set of organs (segmented mesoderm, nervous system), so that a twinning from
one egg is the result. The twins may be fused with each other to a varying
degree.

In the egg of the ascidian *Cynthia partita,* no less than four cytoplasmic
substances may be distinguished because of differences in the color of these
substances (Conklin, 1905). In the egg at the beginning of cleavage, the
animal hemisphere consists of clear transparent cytoplasm. The vegetal pole
of the egg is taken up by a slaty gray cytoplasm, rich in yolk. In between,
slightly below the equator, may be discerned two crescentic areas on opposite sides of the egg. One crescentic area consists of light gray cytoplasm,
and the other consists of yellow cytoplasm, the yellow color due to the
presence of yellow granules (Fig. 102).

During cleavage the four kinds of cytoplasm are distributed to different
cells. Later the cells containing clear cytoplasm give rise to ectoderm; the
cells containing slaty gray cytoplasm become endoderm; the cells containing
yellow cytoplasm develop into mesoderm; and the cells containing light
gray cytoplasm become neural system and notochord. The assumption may
be made, therefore, that the development of the parts of the embryo enumerated is caused by the kind of cytoplasm that is contained in the cells.
This can actually be proved by centrifuging the eggs before they have begun
cleaving (Conklin, 1931). In this way the cytoplasmic substances within
the egg may be displaced, and when the eggs begin to cleave, the various
kinds of cytoplasm are held in abnormal positions when the substance of
the egg is subdivided into cells. An embryo may develop from a centrifuged
egg, possessing recognizable tissues and rudiments of organs, but these are
arranged in a chaotic way. As the distinctions between the various cytoplasmic substances can still be discerned, it is discovered that each organ
and tissue develops in that position where the respective cytoplasmic substance came to lie as the result of centrifugation (Fig. 103). The results of
these experiments support the assumption made above about the decisive
part played by the cytoplasmic substances in differentiation.

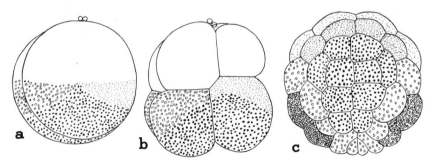

Figure 102. Three cleavage stages of the ascidian *Cynthia partita. a,* 2-cell stage. *b,* 8-cell
stage. *c,* 64-cell stage. Large black dots represent slaty gray cytoplasm; circles represent yellow
cytoplasm; loosely arranged circles represent mesenchyme cells; closely spaced circles represent
muscle cells; heavy stippling represents presumptive notochord; light stippling represents
presumptive neural plate. (After Conklin, 1905, redrawn from Korschelt, 1936.)

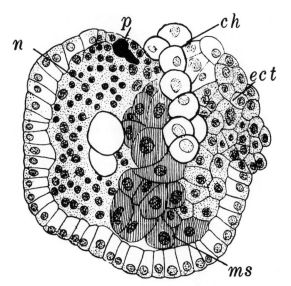

Figure 103. Displacement of organ rudiments in an embryo of *Cynthia partita* as a result of the centrifugation of the egg. *n*, Neural system; *p*, eye pigment; *ch*, notochord; *ect*, ectoderm; *ms*, muscle cells. (From Conklin, 1931.)

7—7 ROLE OF THE EGG CORTEX

Distribution of visible materials in the egg and in the embryo during cleavage is, however, not always of crucial importance for the localization of parts in the developing embryo. Some substances and cellular inclusions may be displaced without disturbing the normal segregation of the embryo into its subordinate parts. This can most conveniently be done by centrifugation of the uncleaved eggs. Centrifuging the eggs of most animals for a few minutes with moderate speeds, giving an acceleration of several thousand times gravity, is sufficient to rearrange various cellular inclusions in the interior of the egg according to their specific gravity.

After sufficiently strong centrifugation, the eggs become stratified and show at least three typical layers. At the centripetal pole there is usually an accumulation of fat or lipoid droplets, which are the lightest constituents of the egg cytoplasm. There follows a layer of hyaline cytoplasm, which is the ground substance of the egg. The nucleus, or asters with chromosomes (if the centrifuged egg was in meiosis or mitosis), are also found in the hyaline layer. The yolk, as the most dense and heavy constituent of the egg, accumulates at the centrifugal pole.

In the eggs of some animals the vegetal pole is so much heavier, owing to the presence of yolk, that it becomes oriented centrifugally during centrifugation. In this case the yolk is not displaced from its normal site at the vegetal pole but is only more concentrated. To displace the yolk in these cases the eggs have to be fixed in a desired position, so that they cannot freely rotate. This can be done sometimes by sucking them into narrow capillaries or by embedding the eggs in gelatin prior to centrifugation.

If the main axis of the embryo lies at random to the centrifugal force, as often happens, cellular inclusions will be dislocated to different parts in individual eggs. Figure 104 shows the results of centrifuging eggs of the sea urchin *Arbacia*. The red pigment granules present in these eggs are concentrated at the centrifugal end of the egg (Fig. 104, *a*). Some scattering of the granules occurs after the centrifuging is stopped and before cleavage progresses sufficiently to prevent further redistribution of the granules by subdividing the egg into blastomeres. It now becomes evident that the granules are concentrated in different positions in respect to the egg axis: near the vegetal pole (Fig. 104, *b*), near the animal pole (Fig. 104, *c*), or toward one side (Fig. 104, *d*). Independently of the position of the granules, the invagination of the blastopore occurs at the vegetal pole, so that the region of the blastopore will contain the pigment granules in some embryos but not in others (Fig. 104, *e, f*) (Morgan, 1927).

It has often been found that the pattern of cleavage may be highly independent of the distribution of cytoplasmic substances inside the egg. We have already described the cleavage of the mollusc *Dentalium,* in which a polar lobe appears at the vegetal pole during the first and second divisions of the egg and contains the cytoplasm necessary for the development of the mesoderm in the larva. A similar polar lobe is observed during cleavage of another mollusc, *Ilyanassa.* The polar lobe in this species is normally filled with yolky cytoplasm, while at the animal pole the egg cytoplasm is fairly free from yolk. Eggs of *Ilyanassa* have been centrifuged "in reverse"; that is, with the vegetal pole fixed in position facing the axis of the centrifuge. As a result the heavy yolk is thrown into the animal hemisphere (still marked by the position of the polar bodies), and the hyaline cytoplasm and lipoid droplets are concentrated at the vegetal pole. Nevertheless, the polar lobe appears at the vegetal pole when the egg starts cleaving, although the lobe now contains mainly hyaline cytoplasm and lipoid instead of the yolk granules (Fig. 105). It is obvious that the formation of the polar lobe is not dependent on the yolk normally located at the vegetal pole, but on something that is not displaced by the centrifugal force (Morgan, 1927).

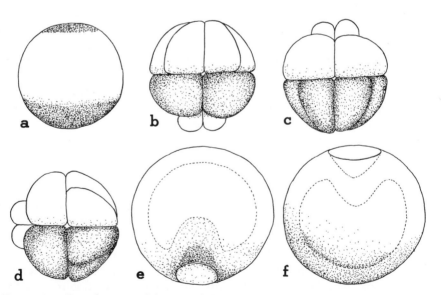

Figure 104. Centrifugation of the egg of the sea urchin *Arbacia. a,* Egg immediately after centrifugation: red pigment (stippling) thrown to centrifugal pole, oil droplets assembled at the centripetal pole. Drawings show position of red pigment in respect to the main axis during cleavage (*b, c, d*) and at the beginning of gastrulation (*e, f*). (From Morgan, 1927.)

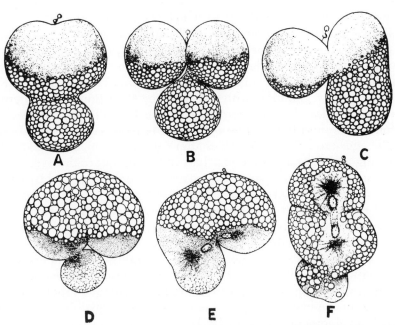

Figure 105. *A, B, C,* Normal cleavage of the mollusc *Ilyanassa. D, E, F,* Cleavage stages after centrifugation "in the reverse," with the heavy yolk displaced toward the animal pole. (From Morgan, 1927.)

What can this something be? There are two possibilities. The first is that there exists in the cytoplasm some fixed network with sufficiently broad meshes to allow for the free movement of yolk granules and other inclusions without itself being torn or distorted. The existence of such a network cannot, however, be supported by any observation on the physical state or ultramicroscopic structure of cytoplasm. There remains the other alternative that the fixed system which is not displaced by centrifugation is the cortical layer of cytoplasm, or the **cortex** of the egg. This is in conformity with direct observation; the cortical granules (see section 4–3) are not displaced by centrifugation (E. B. Harvey, 1946). The layer of cytoplasm in which they are embedded is therefore sufficiently viscous to resist the forces usually generated in centrifugation experiments.

Since the immovable cortex of the egg appears to determine the point at which invagination begins in centrifuged *Arbacia* eggs, as well as to determine the position of the vegetal polar lobe in *Ilyanassa,* the further suggestion may be made that the cortex is the actual carrier of the polarity of the egg, or that the polarity of the egg is ingrained in its cortex. If this were correct, the distribution of the substances in the interior of the egg might be expected to be controlled or determined by the egg cortex. This suggestion finds support in some further results of centrifugation experiments; namely, the fact that cell constituents tend to return to their normal positions after the cessation of centrifuging. A scattering or mixing up of the strata into which the egg contents had been arranged by centrifugation could be a result of random movement of particles. But this explanation does not apply to cases in which after centrifugation certain particles not only move out from the position to which they were brought by the centrifugal force but take up a very definite location in the egg.

We have seen that in the egg of the ascidian *Cynthia* different kinds of egg cytoplasm may be displaced by centrifugation. Immediately after centrifugation the eggs show a very clear stratification, as can be seen in Figure 106, *a*. The yellow granules, which go into the formation of mesoderm (see p. 154), are displaced to the centripetal pole; the yolk is displaced to the centrifugal pole; and the hyaline cytoplasm remains as a layer in between. When the eggs are left to themselves after centrifugation, the egg substances start flowing and rearranging themselves in the interior of the egg. If the cell divisions set in sufficiently soon, this rearrangement is stopped by partitions appearing between the cleavage cells, and the result is the formation of the abnormal embryos dealt with earlier. If, however, the eggs are centrifuged well in advance of the beginning of cleavage, or if the first divisions of the egg are delayed, the redistribution of the egg contents may proceed so far that normal conditions are attained. Figure 106, *b* shows the end result of such a redistribution: the yolk is at the vegetal pole, the animal hemisphere is filled with hyaline cytoplasm, and the yellow granules take up a subequatorial area on one side of the egg, corresponding to the mesodermal "yellow crescent" of normal development (Conklin, 1931).

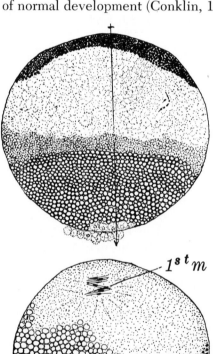

Figure 106. Redistribution of cytoplasmic inclusions in the egg of *Cynthia partita* following centrifugation. *a*, Egg immediately after centrifugation; *b*, centrifuged egg 22 hours later (the yellow granules, shown black, have taken up a subequatorial position on one side of the egg). *1st m*, Spindle of first meiotic division. (From Conklin, 1931.)

Another and perhaps even more impressive example is that of the egg of the mollusc *Aplysia limacina*. In the eggs of this animal there are to be found granules containing ascorbic acid (vitamin C), probably connected with the Golgi bodies. In immature oocytes the ascorbic acid granules are uniformly distributed throughout the egg cytoplasm. During maturation the granules accumulate in a ring lying inside the cortical cytoplasm and somewhat above the equator. By centrifugation the granules are concentrated at the centrifugal pole (Fig. 107), but after cessation of centrifugation the ascorbic acid granules soon start moving and again take up their normal position as a supra-equatorial ring (Peltrera, 1940).

The most plausible explanation of the last two experiments is that the displaced cytoplasmic particles tend to return to the proximity of certain regions of the egg cortex which had remained in their respective positions all the time the egg was being centrifuged. It would follow that in normal development the cytoplasmic substances in the egg are distributed in relation to local differences in the egg cortex, and that it is the egg cortex, therefore, that foreshadows in some way the pattern of the future development of the embryo.

7–8 THE MORPHOGENETIC GRADIENTS IN THE EGG CYTOPLASM

While we have learned that the cytoplasm of the egg, and in particular its cortex, starts the chain of reactions which eventually leads to the differentiation of parts of the embryo, it should not be imagined that the structure of the future embryo is rigidly determined by local differences in the cytoplasm of the egg. The local peculiarities of the egg cytoplasm are only some of the factors necessary for the formation of organ rudiments. That this is so can be shown by examining the development of the sea urchin, for instance.

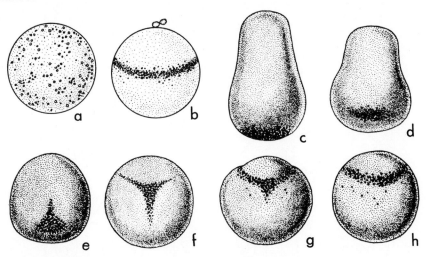

Figure 107.   Redistribution of vitamin C granules in eggs of *Aplysia limacina* during maturation and following centrifugation. *a*, Immature egg (oocyte); *b*, mature egg; *c*, egg immediately after centrifugation. *d–h*, Consecutive stages of recovery of the centrifuged egg, with the vitamin C granules returning to their normal position. (After Peltrera, from Raven, 1958.)

In the 16-cell stage of the sea urchin, the blastomeres are of three different sizes. The animal hemisphere consists of eight blastomeres of medium
size, the **mesomeres**, which are destined to produce most of the ectoderm of
the larva. The vegetal hemisphere consists of four very large blastomeres, the
macromeres, and of four very small blastomeres, the **micromeres**, which lie
at the vegetal pole of the egg. The macromeres contain some more material
for the ectoderm and all the material for the endoderm. In a subsequent
cleavage the future ectoderm and endoderm are segregated from each other
into an upper tier of macromeres and a lower tier of macromeres. The upper
tier of macromeres lying immediately under the equator of the embryo contains the ectodermal material; the lower tier of macromeres, lying nearer to
the vegetal pole, contains the endodermal material. The micromeres develop
into mesenchyme, which later produces the larval skeleton consisting of
calcareous spicules (Hörstadius, 1935). In the sea urchin *Paracentrotus
lividus*, the cytoplasm of the macromeres possesses a surface layer of red
pigment granules, making the macromeres easily distinguishable from the
other cleavage cells. The red pigment is already present in the egg at the
beginning of cleavage as a broad subequatorial zone (Fig. 108).

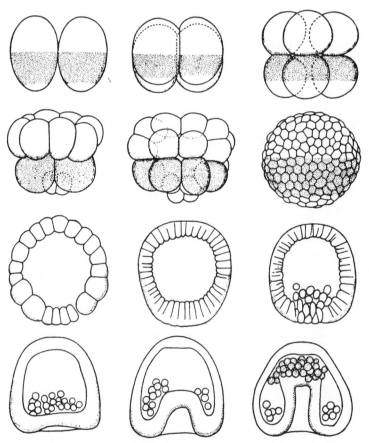

Figure 108.   Cleavage and gastrulation of the sea urchin *Paracentrotus lividus*. (After Boveri,
from Spemann, 1936.)

In the blastula stage, the cytoplasmic substances are found in the same arrangement as at the beginning of cleavage. Subsequently, the descendants of the micromeres migrate into the blastocoele where they develop the skeletal spicules; the descendants of the lower tier of macromeres invaginate, forming a pocketlike cavity—the gut; and the ectoderm produces a ciliary band, serving for locomotion, and a tuft of rigid cilia at the former animal pole. The ectoderm also sinks inward to produce a stomodeum, coming into communication with the endodermal gut at its anterior end, while the original opening of the pocketlike invagination (the blastopore) becomes the anal opening (Fig. 109).

The embryo of the sea urchin develops into a larva called a **pluteus** (Fig. 63, p. 95). If the blastomeres of the sea urchin are separated in the two-cell stage or in the four-cell stage, each of them develops into a complete pluteus of diminished size. This may be related to the fact that the first two cleavage planes are meridional, passing through the main axis of the egg. All of the first four blastomeres therefore get equal portions of the three cytoplasmic regions of the egg (ectodermal, endodermal and mesenchymal). A different result is observed if the egg is separated into the animal and vegetal

Figure 109. Early larvae of the sea urchin *Parechinus* showing development of skeleton. *pM*, Primary mesenchyme; *sM*, secondary mesenchyme; *A*, apical tuft of ciliae; *VW* and *DW*, ventral and dorsal body walls. (After Schmidt, from Spemann, 1936.)

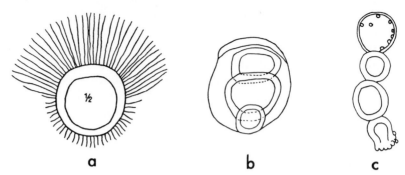

Figure 110. Animalized (a) and vegetalized (b, c) larvae of a sea urchin. (After Hörstadius, from Lehmann, 1945.)

halves after the third cleavage, the third cleavage plane being equatorial. In this case both halves produce, as a rule, defective embryos (Fig. 110). The animal half differentiates as an ectodermal vesicle; it does not produce a gut. Even purely ectodermal structures are abnormally differentiated (i.e., the ciliary band is not developed; the tuft of long cilia on the animal pole, on the other hand, develops excessively, growing over a much greater surface than it does normally — Fig. 110, a). The vegetal half is differentiated into an ovoid embryo with a disproportionately large endodermal gut but without a mouth. There may be a few irregular skeletal spicules but no arms and no ciliary band (Fig. 110, b).

In later cleavage stages, it is possible to cut the morula transversely below the equator. In such cases the vegetal part develops still more abnormally: it produces a large endodermal gut and a small ectodermal vesicle (Fig. 110, c). The gut does not lie inside the ectodermal vesicle but is evaginated to the exterior (turned inside out), due to an interference with the normal processes of gastrulation. This phenomenon is known as **exogastrulation**. The mesenchyme cells migrate into the interior, but they usually produce no skeletal spicules or only very small and abnormal ones (Hörstadius, 1928, 1935).

The result of this experiment is obviously due to the fact that each of the two halves lacks some parts contained in the other half. However, each half does not simply produce what would normally have been the fate of the respective part. Instead, the differentiation of each half seems to be "exaggerated" as compared with its normal fate. This is especially clear in the the case of the increased animal tuft of cilia.

The same "exaggeration" of the ectodermal or of the endodermal differentiations can be achieved by exposing the developing eggs to certain chemical substances, even without removing any parts of the egg or embryo. If the fertilized sea urchin egg is exposed to sea water containing some lithium salts in solution, the embryo develops just as if it were only the isolated vegetal half. The gut is increased and tends to exogastrulate instead of invaginating toward the interior (Herbst, 1893). The skeleton is absent or abnormal; the ectoderm is represented by an epithelial vesicle and fails to differentiate further. The increase in the size of the gut occurs at the expense of the ectoderm, and in extreme cases most of the embryo differentiates as an enormous everted gut, with the ectodermal vesicle reduced to a tiny appendage. The opposite effect is achieved if, before fertilization, the egg is exposed to artificial sea water lacking calcium ions but with sodium thiocyanate (NaSCN) added to it. In this case the gut is diminished or completely absent, the ciliary bands in the ectoderm fail to develop, and the tuft of stiff cilia at the animal pole is increased in size (Lindahl, 1933).

It appears that all these phenomena may be accounted for by assuming that there exist in the sea urchin's egg two factors or principles which are mutually antagonistic yet interact with each other at the same time, and that the normal development is dependent on a certain equilibrium between the two principles. Each has its center of activity at one of the poles of the egg. The activity diminishes away from the center, producing a **gradient** of activity. The two gradients of activity decline in opposite directions: the one from the animal pole, the other from the vegetal pole. Taking into account this type of distribution of activities, the factors or principles have themselves been called **gradients**. The two gradients are therefore the **animal gradient**, with a center of activity at the animal pole, and the **vegetal gradient**, with a center of activity at the vegetal pole.

According to this theory (originally suggested by Boveri, in 1910, and developed in application to the sea urchin egg by Runnström, 1928, and Hörstadius, 1928) normal development depends on the presence of both gradients and an equilibrium between them. If the animal gradient is weakened or suppressed, the vegetal gradient becomes preponderant and the embryo is **vegetalized**; i.e., it develops to excess parts pertaining to the vegetal gradient, such as the gut. If the vegetal gradient is weakened or suppressed, the animal gradient becomes preponderant and the embryo is **animalized**; i.e., it develops to excess parts pertaining to the animal gradient, such as the tuft of stiff cilia at the animal pole. Other structures of the embryo, such as the ciliary bands and the skeleton, can only develop if both gradients are active, and the development is the more nearly normal the more the two gradients approach a correct equilibrium.

The equilibrium between the two gradients may be upset in various ways. The animal gradient may be weakened, with concomitant vegetalization of the embryo, by removing its center of activity (the blastomeres at the animal pole of the egg) or by the action of lithium salts. The vegetal gradient may be weakened by removing its center of activity (the vegetal part of the egg) or by the action of sodium thiocyanate.

The gradient concept aptly covers the result of various experiments on sea urchin's eggs. In addition we shall consider the following experiments. It is possible to separate from each other the three groups of blastomeres in the 16-cell stage—the mesomeres, the macromeres and the micromeres—and then recombine them at will (Hörstadius, 1935). In isolation the three groups develop as follows:

Isolated mesomeres develop into a vesicle with a tuft of cilia (as mentioned before), due to a preponderance of the animal gradient and animalization.

Isolated macromeres plus micromeres develop into an extremely vegetalized embryo with evaginated gut, the result of a preponderance of the vegetal gradient.

Mesomeres plus macromeres develop into a practically normal embryo; the macromeres bear a sufficiently strong vegetal gradient to counterbalance the animal gradient. Mesenchyme and skeleton develop in such embryos in spite of the absence of micromeres.

Micromeres alone are not capable of any development, since they do not keep together but fall apart.

Mesomeres (ectoderm) plus micromeres (mesenchyme) develop into a complete and more or less normal pluteus. This combination is especially illuminating since the gut of such embryos develops in spite of the absence of the macromeres which should normally have supplied the material for the gut. However, the embryo possesses the two gradients, the animal gradient borne by the mesomeres and the vegetal gradient borne by the micromeres, and the possession of the two gradients seems to create the necessary conditions for normal development.

What has been said is sufficient to show that the presence of different cytoplasmic substances in the egg does not necessarily mean that there is a direct relation between the substances in the cytoplasm of the egg and certain specific organs, in the sense that the cells containing the particular kind of cytoplasm develop directly into the corresponding organ. In the last experiment quoted, the absence of the cytoplasm with red pigment did not prevent the development of the gut because the necessary conditions for the gut development were provided for in another way.

Physicochemical Nature of the Animal-Vegetal Gradient System in Sea Urchin Eggs.   The existence of animal and vegetal gradients is proved not only by the patterns of morphogenetic processes occurring after certain interventions in the normal development of the egg, but also by the direct demonstration of the gradients as peculiar physicochemical states of the cells of the developing embryo. One way of proving their existence is to study the reduction of dyes by the embryo under conditions of anaerobiosis. Sea urchin embryos (or embryos of other animals for that matter), slightly stained with the vital dye Janus green (diethylsafraninazodimethylaniline), are placed in a small chamber sealed off with petroleum jelly. After some time all the free oxygen contained in the chamber is used up as result of the respiration of the embryos. After that the embryos respire using Janus green as an acceptor of hydrogen, which is first reduced to a red dye, diethylsafranin, and further to a colorless substance, leucosafranin. The light grayish blue color of Janus green first changes into red, and then, as a second step in the reduction of the dye, the color disappears completely.

The reduction of Janus green, shown by the color change, does not occur simultaneously in the whole embryo but follows a very characteristic sequence. In the late blastula and early gastrula of the sea urchin, the change in color is first noticeable at the vegetal pole, at the point where the primary mesenchyme is given off (Fig. 111). Then the color change spreads out, involving the whole vegetal hemisphere, and reaches the equator. At this stage a spot of changed color appears at the animal pole and also gradually increases, so that the bluish color remains only in the form of a ring lying well above the equator in the animal hemisphere. Even this ring eventually disappears. The red color now begins to fade in the same sequence, starting first from the vegetal pole and then from the animal pole (Child, 1936; Hörstadius, 1952).

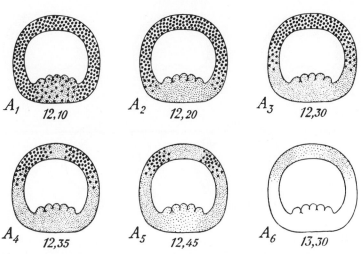

Figure 111. Reduction of Janus green in a late blastula of a sea urchin. Large dots represent blue color; small dots, red; no dots show a complete fading of the stain. Figures indicate time of observation. (From Hörstadius, 1952.)

The order in which the dye is reduced in the embryo shows such a nice correspondence to the postulated animal and vegetal gradients that this alone would justify our mentioning these experiments. However, the connection goes much further. Where either the animal or vegetal gradient is suppressed, the corresponding gradient of reduction also disappears. In isolated animal halves of sea urchins' eggs the animal tendencies of development are predominant, and it is found that such animalized embryos start reducing

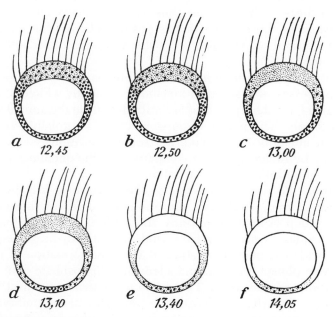

Figure 112. Reduction of Janus green in animalized sea urchin embryo (isolated animal half). (From Hörstadius, 1952.)

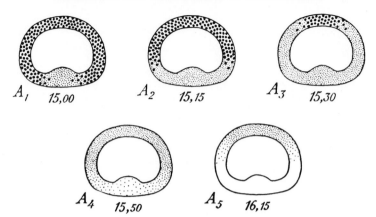

Figure 113. Reduction of Janus green in vegetalized sea urchin embryo (isolated vegetal half). (From Hörstadius, 1952.)

Janus green at the animal pole only; there is no center of reduction at the vegetal pole (Fig. 112). In isolated vegetal halves the animal tendencies of development are suppressed and the vegetal tendencies are supreme. Correspondingly, the only center of reduction is at the vegetal pole; no center of reduction appears at the animal pole (Fig. 113). Embryos animalized or vegetalized chemically show reduction gradients similar to isolated animal and vegetal halves of the egg (Hörstadius, 1955).

We have seen that the micromeres are carriers of the highest point of the vegetal gradient, and they preserve this property after transplantation. Accordingly, the micromeres can also serve as a center of a reduction gradient. If a group of four micromeres is implanted laterally, and the embryo is tested for reduction of Janus green, it can be seen that in addition to the two normal gradients, one from the vegetal pole and one from the animal pole, a third gradient appears, having the implanted micromeres as its center but spreading out from these to the adjacent cells. In short, every modification of the gradient system of the embryo that is postulated from the morphogenetic behavior of the embryo is reflected in the gradients of reduction of Janus green (Hörstadius, 1952).

The animal and vegetal gradients can thus be considered to be definite metabolic processes or systems of metabolic reactions which involve oxidation and which have their points of highest intensity at the animal and vegetal poles respectively. The nature of these reactions is probably very complex and is as yet not fully understood, but some indications concerning these reactions may be deduced from a comparison of the chemical agents which may cause vegetalization or animalization.

Apart from the use of lithium ions, vegetalization may be caused by sodium azide (Child, 1948) and dinitrophenol. Both of these substances belong to a group of enzyme poisons; the azide is known to inactivate the cytochrome oxidase system, and the dinitrophenol disturbs respiration by preventing oxidative phosphorylation, that is, the formation of energy-rich bonds between phosphoric acid and adenosine diphosphate (with the formation of adenosine triphosphate). This might mean that vegetalization is based essentially on a disturbance of oxidative processes in the embryo (Lindahl, 1936) and, perhaps even more specifically, a disturbance of the processes of phosphorylation (Hörstadius, 1953b).

That the action of lithium ions is along the same lines may be deduced from a number of observations of which we shall single out the following. Lithium salt treatment suppresses the rise of oxygen consumption which occurs normally at the beginning of gastrulation, that is, at the same time as the morphological effects of vegetalization begin to be apparent (Lindahl, 1936). Furthermore, inorganic phosphate accumulates in the sea water during development of lithium ion-treated embryos—again a hint that these embryos are incapable of utilizing the energy of oxidation for phosphorylation and synthesis of adenosine triphosphate.

The whole sequence of reactions involved in vegetalization must, of course, be far more complicated. Thus it has been found that the relative amounts of various amino acids change as a result of vegetalization in lithium ion-treated embryos (Gustafson and Hjelte, 1951). Furthermore, if a modification of the respiratory system of the embryo is the essential feature of vegetalization, it remains to be discovered why the processes of morphogenesis at the animal pole of the embryo (essentially the ectodermal organs) are more severely affected than those of endodermal parts developing at the vegetal pole.

In this connection it may prove important that the distribution of mitochondria in a sea urchin blastula and early gastrula conforms to the animal–vegetal gradient, i.e., mitochondria are found in larger numbers in cells near to the animal pole and in smaller numbers toward the vegetal pole. Furthermore, the gradient of mitochondrial distribution closely follows the changes in the whole system of the embryo produced by animalization and vegetalization. For instance, the numbers of mitochondria in the animal hemisphere are decreased by lithium salt treatment or by implantation of micromeres (Lenicque, Hörstadius and Gustafson, 1953). Now it is known that the mitochondria are the main sites of oxidative phosphorylation, which seems to be the reaction most affected by vegetalizing agents. It may then be that the mitochondria are the immediate site of action of these agents.

As to animalizing agents, the first of those mentioned above, sodium thiocyanate, has been found to be rather unreliable. Some batches of eggs treated by this chemical do not react at all. In other batches individual embryos become animalized to greatly varying degrees. Subsequently, many other substances were found whose animalizing action is much more predictable. These belong to several distinct groups:

1. Some metals: zinc, mercury.

2. Some proteolytic enzymes: trypsin, chymotrypsin.

3. Many acidic dyes: in particular some possessing sulfonic (HSO_3) groups in their molecules, such as Evans blue, chlorazol sky blue, trypan blue, Congo red, and others possessing carboxyl groups ($COOH$), such as uranin and rose bengal.

4. Some other sulfonated organic compounds: germanin and others.

5. Some anionic (acid) detergents.

Animalization may be achieved by extreme dilutions of a chemical; for instance, 1:50,000 in the case of Evans blue.

It seems that the common property of most if not all the above agents is their ability to attack proteins or to form compounds with proteins, especially with basic proteins. In the case of the very large number of sulfonated and carboxylated dyestuffs, it is fairly certain that their acidic groups become attached 'to the functional side groups of protein molecules. The two metals mentioned above, zinc and mercury, also become easily bonded to side groups of protein molecules. The case of mercury is very remarkable: mercuric chloride, a powerful poison used therefore as a fixative for proteins, causes animalization when applied for a very short time in great dilutions (1:90,000). It is probable that by blocking the active side groups of the protein molecules, the agents referred to "immobilize" these molecules, preventing them from interacting normally with other cell constituents. Even the steric configurations of protein molecules may thus be altered, since these are based on lateral bonding between molecules and their parts. A far-reaching change of the properties of proteins may thus be brought about (Lallier, 1956 and 1957).

In the case of animalizing agents, we are in the fortunate position that their point of attack can be clearly demonstrated. The dyes which have been used for this purpose stain the cells of the embryo, and it can be seen that the first cells to be stained are the primary mesenchyme cells at the vegetal pole. With higher concentrations of the dye or with a longer duration of the treatment, the adjoining presumptive endodermal cells show the staining too. The zinc taken up into the cells of embryos may be made visible because it gives a pink coloration with dithizone. In embryos first treated with zinc and later immersed in a dithizone solution, the pink color is detectable in the same position as in the case of animalizing dyes (Lallier, 1956 and 1957). It is thus quite clear that animalization is due to damage to the center of the vegetal gradient.

Considering what has been said about the mechanism of action of the vegetalizing and animalizing agents, we may conclude that neither animalization nor vegetalization is ever achieved by a stimulation of one of the gradients, but always by a depression of the opposite gradient (or of the metabolic system which is responsible for the gradient). The increased development of any of the structures is then brought about by the alternative morphogenetic system expanding when the one is reduced in vigor. The competitive relation between the two gradients is thus demonstrated in a most convincing way.

7−9 MANIFESTATION OF MATERNAL GENES DURING THE EARLY STAGES OF DEVELOPMENT

In the previous sections evidence has been presented that: (1) The differences between the various parts of the embryo are not due to differences in their nuclei but to differences of the cytoplasm. From this it may be inferred that (2) the nuclei of the cleavage cells and the genes contained therein do not control the earliest stages of development of the animal egg.

This does not mean, however, that genetic factors have nothing to do with the early stages of development. The genetic factors, the genes, do play a part in this period but in a very special way. It is not the genes contained in the nuclei of the blastomeres but the genes in the cells of the maternal body that determine the peculiarities of the egg and its early development. The best-known example of this type of gene action is concerned with the inheritance of coiling in gastropod molluscs.

In the snails, as a rule, the shell is coiled spirally, and the internal organization of the animal shows a corresponding dislocation, some of the organs (heart, kidney and gills) being twisted around through an angle of nearly 180°. The direction of coiling of the shell is clockwise, if viewed from the apex of the shell. This type of coiling is called **dextral**. As an exception, the coiling may be counterclockwise, or **sinistral**. Individuals having a sinistral coiling of the shell have the internal organs dislocated in the opposite direction from that in dextral individuals. In short, dextral and sinistral individuals comport themselves in every detail of organization as mirror images of each other.

The eggs of gastropod molluscs show a spiral type of cleavage (see section 7–3), and it has been noted that the type of cleavage of the egg has a definite relation to the type of coiling of the adult. If the cleavage is dextral — that is, if the cleavage spindles show a clockwise spiraling — the adult snail also has a dextrally coiled shell. If the cleavage is sinistral, the coiling of the shell is likewise sinistral (Fig. 114). The connection between the type of cleavage and the coiling of the shell is established through the position of blastomere *D* in respect to the other blastomeres. Since it is from blastomere *D* that the mesoderm develops, its situation is reflected in the position of the internal organs, and the coiling of the shell is one of the secondary expressions of this asymmetry.

There are some species of gastropods in which all the individuals are sinistral, but the main interest attaches to a species in which sinistral individuals occur as a mutation among a population of normal dextral animals. Such a mutant was discovered in the fresh-water snail *Limnaea peregra* (Boycott, Diver, Garstang and Turner, 1930). Breeding and cross breeding of dextral and sinistral snails showed that the difference between the two forms is dependent on a pair of allelomorphic genes, the gene for sinistrality being recessive (1), and the gene for the normal dextral coiling being dominant (L). The two genes are inherited according to mendelian laws, but the action of any genetic combination is manifested only in the next generation after the one in which a given genotype is found.

Thus, if the eggs of a homozygous sinistral individual are fertilized by the sperm of a dextral individual, the eggs cleave sinistrally, and all the snails of this F$_1$ generation show a sinistral coiling of the shell. The genes of the sperm

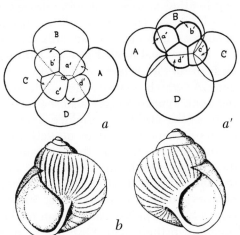

Figure 114. Correlation of sinistral (*a*) and dextral (*a'*) cleavage with sinistral (*b*) and dextral (*b'*) coiling of the shell in gastropods. (After Conklin, from Morgan, 1927.)

do not manifest themselves, although the genotype of the F_1 generation is Ll.

If a second generation (F_2) is bred from such sinistral individuals, it is all dextral, instead of showing segregation as would be expected in normal mendelian inheritance. In fact, segregation does take place in the F_2 generation so far as the genes are concerned, but the new genic combinations fail to manifest themselves, since the coiling is determined by the genotype of the mother. The genotype being Ll, the gene for dextrality dominates and is responsible for the exclusively dextral coiling of the second generation. Only in the third generation (F_3) does segregation in the proportion of 3 to 1 become apparent, and then not as segregation between individuals in each brood, but as a segregation of broods. Each brood—that is, the offspring of an individual of the F_2 generation—shows a coiling that is determined by the maternal genotype. Since the individuals of the F_2 generation had the genotypes 1 LL, 2 Ll, 1 ll, three quarters of them, on the average, produce eggs developing into dextral snails, and one quarter produce eggs developing into sinistral individuals. Of the dextral broods, one third breed true, giving only dextral offspring, and two thirds show further segregation among the broods of the next generation.

It is easy to understand that the results of a reciprocal cross—that is, of the fertilization of the eggs of a homozygous dextral individual by the sperm of a sinistral individual—will lead to a somewhat different type of pedigree: the F_1 generation will be all dextral (with genotype Ll) and the F_2 generation again all dextral (with genotypes LL, Ll, lL and ll). The F_3 generation will show segregation among broods, just as in the cross examined first.

The whole case becomes clear if it is realized that the type of cleavage depends on the organization of the egg which is established before the maturation divisions of the oocyte nucleus. The type of cleavage is therefore under the influence of the genotype of the parent (the mother). The haploid state of the egg nucleus continues for only a very short time and cannot materially affect the organization of the egg. The sperm enters the egg after this organization is already established. Similarly, we should expect that the elaboration of cytoplasmic organ-forming substances is under the control of maternal genes, even though this cannot be proved because no mutants are known which produce a difference in these substances.

It is conceivable that maternal genes might produce conditions in the egg leading to morphogenetic processes, which take place at a later stage of development, without visibly modifying the cleavage pattern. Several cases of such an influence are actually known.

In the meal moth *Ephestia kühniella*, the dark pigmentation of the eyes, both in the adult moth and in the caterpillar, depends on the presence of a gene A, which controls the production of one of the precursors of the eye pigment, kynurenin (see also section 16–6). In the allelomorph with recessive gene a, the ability to produce kynurenin is lost, and the eyes of the caterpillars and moths contain no dark pigment. In crosses between the normal moth and the a mutant, the pigmentation of the larval eyes is determined by the genotype of the mother, exactly as is the case with the coiling of the shell in *Limnaea peregra*. In a back cross between a heterozygous Aa female and a homozygous recessive aa male, 50 per cent of the offspring have the genotype aa; nevertheless, all the caterpillars that emerge from the eggs have dark pigment in their eyes. Only later, in the fourth instar, a difference becomes

apparent between the *Aa* caterpillars and the *aa* caterpillars: in the *Aa* caterpillars the eye pigmentation persists, and the moths have black eyes; in the
aa caterpillars the dark pigment gradually fades and eventually disappears
altogether—the adult moths lack the dark pigment in their eyes.

The explanation of this is that the eggs which will have the genotype *aa*
after fertilization will accumulate a certain amount of kynurenin while still
in the ovaries. Before maturation, the genotype of all the oocytes is of course
the same as the genotype of the somatic cells of the mother, *Aa* in this case,
and the presence of the *A* gene in the oocyte accounts for the elaboration of
the eye pigment precursor. Besides, kynurenin is diffusible, and when produced by some cells of the mother it may diffuse into other cells and so
augment their supply. This latter circumstance has been cited as a direct
proof of the mechanism by means of which the maternal genotype can influence the color of eyes of caterpillars (Kühn, 1936). Organs (testis, brain)
from a normal caterpillar (*AA*) have been transplanted into caterpillars of the
aa mutant. When the caterpillars metamorphosed into moths, the treated
females were paired with *aa* males. The offspring from such a mating consisted of individuals with a purely recessive (*aa*) genotype. Nevertheless, the
young caterpillars had pigmented eyes, just as if they had developed from
eggs of a female bearing the gene *A* (Fig. 115). Since the gene *A* was actually
absent both from the somatic cells of the mother and from the cells of the
offspring, the explanation for the experimental results is as follows: the
precursor of the pigment, the kynurenin, was elaborated by the transplanted
testis or brain, and by diffusion it penetrated into the oocytes of the female
and was stored there. In the developing caterpillar the kynurenin was further
processed into the eye pigment.

Kynurenin is of course not the only substance produced under the influence of the maternal genes while the egg is developing in the ovary. Very
many, if not all, of the cytoplasmic substances in the egg mentioned in section
4–3 must have a similar origin. The cytoplasmic substances determining the
properties of blastomeres during cleavage may thus be an after-effect of the
action of genes at a previous stage of the reproductive cycle.

Figure 115. Effect on the eye pigmentation of the next generation when
the testis from an *AA* caterpillar of the
meal moth *Ephestia kühniella* is
transplanted onto an *aa* caterpillar.
Eye pigmentation of untreated *AA* and
aa caterpillars is shown for comparison. (Modified after Kühn, 1941.)

PART IV

GASTRULATION AND THE FORMATION OF THE PRIMARY ORGAN RUDIMENTS

The process of gastrulation is one of displacement of parts of the early embryo. As a result the endodermal and mesodermal organ rudiments are removed from the surface of the embryo, where the presumptive material for these rudiments is to be found in the blastula stage, and brought into the interior of the embryo, where the respective organs are found in the differentiated animal. At the same time the single layer of cells, the blastoderm, gives rise

173

to three germinal layers—the ectoderm, the endoderm and the mesoderm.

The most prominent features of gastrulation are, thus:

1. A rearrangement of cells of the embryo by means of **morphogenetic movements**.
2. At the same time, the rhythm of cellular divisions is slowed down.
3. Growth, if any, is insignificant.
4. The type of metabolism changes; oxidation is intensified.
5. The nuclei become more active in controlling the activities of the embryonic cells. The influence of the paternal chromosomes becomes evident during gastrulation.
6. Proteins of new kinds, that were not present in the egg, begin to be synthesized.

Morphological Aspects of Gastrulation and Primary Organ Formation

8 – 1 FATE MAPS

A correct interpretation of gastrulation is impossible without a knowledge of the position which the presumptive germinal layers occupy in the blastula. This position may be ascertained in various ways. A chart, showing the fate of each part of an early embryo, in particular, a blastula, is called a **fate map**.

In tracing the fate of the various parts of the blastoderm, it is sometimes possible to make use of the peculiarities of the cytoplasm in various parts of the egg, such as the presence of pigment granules, etc. In the developing amphibian egg, for instance, one may trace in which part of the differentiated embryo the black pigment comes to lie. Originally this pigment is restricted to the animal hemisphere of the egg. However, peculiarities of pigmentation are seldom sufficient to make it possible to reconstruct the fate map in any great detail. Recourse must be made to artificial marking of parts of the blastoderm.

A satisfactory method of marking was devised for this purpose by Vogt (1925). The method consists in soaking a piece of agar in a vital dye (Nile blue sulfate, neutral red, Bismarck brown) and then applying the piece of agar to the surface of the embryo in the necessary position. The dye diffuses from the agar, and in a matter of minutes the cells of the embryo to which the agar has been applied take up sufficient dye to produce a stain on the surface of the embryo. This marking can be done without removing the vitelline membrane, since it is permeable to the vital dyes, and so the embryo continues to develop normally. The presence of the stain does not change the normal development of the embryo, and the position of the stained cells in the differentiated embryo clearly shows the fate of the stained area. It has been established by trial that the vital dye remains, on the whole, restricted to the cells which had originally taken up the dye and to their descendants. The diffusion of the stain, if the staining has been done correctly, is negligible, and does not interfere with interpreting the results. Several stain marks may be made on the surface of the same embryo, using different colors (red, blue, brown). In this way one experiment may disclose the fate of many parts of the early embryo at the same time.

It was later found that cellophane can be also used as stain carrier instead of agar, and that it is actually a more convenient one, as cellophane comes in thin sheets from which it is easy to cut out pieces of the desired size and shape. All vital staining is now done with cellophane as stain carrier.

Independently of vital staining, another method has also been devised for marking cells of a developing embryo. This consists in applying tiny particles of carbon to the surface of the embryo. Carbon particles stick to the surface of the cells and can thus be used as markers enabling the investigator to follow the movements of the cells and draw up fate maps (see Spratt, 1946).

The vital stain marking method was in the first place applied to the reconstruction of the fate map in the amphibian embryo, and the original investigations have been subsequently checked by many embryologists. It is most advantageous, therefore, that the fate map of an amphibian embryo, such as the embryo of a newt *(Triturus)* or axolotl *(Ambystoma)*, should be dealt with first in this description.

The Fate Map of an Amphibian Embryo.   The whole surface of the blastula of an amphibian may be roughly divided into three main regions (Vogt, 1925): (1) a large area on and around the animal pole, (2) an intermediate zone, also known as the **marginal zone**, going all around the equator of the blastula, (3) the area on and around the vegetal pole (Fig. 116). These three main regions coincide approximately with areas which differ in their pigmentation. The animal region is all deeply pigmented. The marginal zone, which is much broader on one side of the embryo, is pigmented but not so deeply as

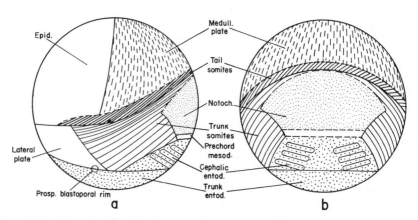

Figure 116.   Fate maps of the early gastrula of the axolotl. *a,* Lateral view; *b,* dorsal view. (After Pasteels, from Willier, Weiss and Hamburger, 1955.)

the region around the animal pole. The vegetal region is more or less devoid of pigment.

Inside each region, we find areas corresponding to the future organs of the animal. The **animal region** consists of two main areas: the area whose fate is to develop into the nervous system of the embryo, and the area which is to become the skin epidermis of the embryo. The material for the sense organs is also contained in these two areas. Inside the nervous system area, a small sub-area may be traced which is to participate in the formation of the eyes of the embryo; inside the epidermis area, the material for the nose and the ears and the ectodermal part of the mouth may similarly be traced. In the intermediate or **marginal zone**, we find the material for the notochord occupying a large area on the dorsal side of the blastula. This is followed by an area lying nearer to the vegetal pole and containing the material for the pre-chordal connective tissue; this area is known as the prechordal plate. Farther down, toward the vegetal pole but still inside the marginal zone, lies the material for the anterior parts of the alimentary canal: the endodermal lining of the mouth, gill region and pharynx. The parts of the marginal zone on both sides of the notochordal area are taken up by the material for the segmental muscles of the body. The lateral and ventral parts of the marginal zone give rise to the mesodermal lining of the body cavity, the kidneys, etc. (ventro-lateral mesoderm). The **vegetal region** is composed of cells which are later found in the midgut and hindgut.

It will be noticed that the areas destined to develop into the organs of the mid-dorsal part of the animal lie on one side of the blastula, on that side where the marginal zone is taken up by the notochord area. Nearer to the animal pole is situated the area of the neural system. This side of the blastula corresponds therefore to the dorsal side of the embryo. Similarly, parts of the head (eye, nose, ears) develop from areas near the animal pole of the blastula, which therefore corresponds to the anterior end of the embryo. Since the materials of the egg have not been displaced to any great extent during the cleavage, it may be inferred that the animal pole of the fertilized egg corresponds to the anterior end of the embryo. Where the marginal zone is the broadest is the dorsal side; the opposite side may be considered as ventral, and the vegetal pole as the posterior. We find, however, that the foregut area (pharynx, part of the epithelium of the mouth) is also situated on what we have agreed to call the dorsal side of the egg. The explanation of this fact will be found later (section 8–4).

On the whole, however, the location of the areas destined to develop into most of the organs does not seem to have anything in common with the position of the same organs in the adult animal. Organs which later are situated in the interior of the animal's body—such as the notochord, the gut or the brain—are represented by areas laid out on the surface of the blastula. The cells destined to cover the whole of the animal's body, such as the epidermis of the skin, occupy only a limited area on the surface of the blastula. Parts of the three germinal layers—ectoderm, endoderm and mesoderm—are all located on the surface of the embryo, instead of being in a concentric arrangement, with the ectoderm on the outside, endoderm in the middle and the mesoderm between (see p. 6). It is obvious that a far-reaching displacement or reshuffle of the parts of the blastoderm must take place before every cell can arrive at its final position.

This displacement of parts of the blastoderm, which are eventually re-arranged in a system of concentric layers of cells, is the essence of the process of **gastrulation**. We shall now for a time leave the amphibians and consider the process of gastrulation in an animal with a more simple organization, a representative of lower chordates, the *Amphioxus*. Later we will describe gastrulation as it occurs in amphibians and, lastly, in the meroblastic eggs of the fishes and birds.

8−2   GASTRULATION IN *AMPHIOXUS*

In *Amphioxus*, there are differences in the various regions of the egg cytoplasm which permitted Conklin (1932) to trace these regions into the later stages of development and thus to reconstruct a fate map, at least in rough outlines.

At the beginning of cleavage three regions can be distinguished in the *Amphioxus* egg. Near the vegetal pole there is found a mass of cytoplasm which contains the greatest amount of yolk (although yolk in this case is not abundant and the yolk granules are relatively very small). The animal hemi-sphere of the egg consists of cytoplasm that has less yolk and is in conse-quence more transparent. On one side of the egg, in a position roughly cor-responding to the marginal zone of the amphibian egg, there is a special type of cytoplasm. This cytoplasm does not contain much yolk, but it can be dis-tinguished from the animal cytoplasm by its ability to be deeply stained by basic dyes. The mass of cytoplasm of this kind has a crescentic shape, the attenuated ends of the cresent being drawn out along the equator of the egg about halfway round (Fig. 117).

During the period of cleavage the three regions become subdivided into blastomeres without the cytoplasmic substances having been displaced to any great extent. The distinctions which could be traced in the cytoplasm of the egg now become accentuated by further distinctions in the size and shape of the blastomeres. The vegetal material is now contained in a number of rather large cells taking up the position on and around the vegetal pole of the blastula. The animal hemisphere is made up of cells containing the clear cytoplasm. The cells are columnar and form a very closely packed columnar epithelium. The cells containing the basophilic cytoplasm are clearly discernible even as to shape. They are the smallest cells in the blas-tula, smaller even than the animal cells, and they are rather loosely packed, the external surfaces bulging out, as is usually found in the earlier cleavage stages (Fig. 118).

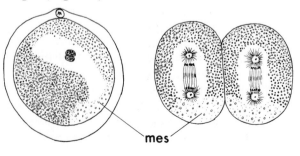

Figure 117. Medial section of uncleaved egg of *Amphioxus* (left), and an equatorial section of the two-cell stage (right), showing the position of the mesodermal crescent. (After Conklin, 1932.)

mes

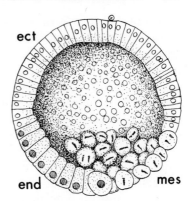

Figure 118. Blastula of *Amphioxus* showing distinction between the cells of the mesodermal crescent *(mes)* and the cells of the presumptive endoderm *(end)* and ectoderm *(ect)*. (After Conklin, 1932.)

The fate of the three regions is the following: The clear cytoplasm that later becomes the animal hemisphere of the blastula develops mainly into skin epidermis. The granular cytoplasm, which takes up the region around the vegetal pole of the blastula, develops into the lining of the alimentary canal. The crescent of basophilic cytoplasm is the material which gives rise to the muscles and the lining of the body cavity and thus represents a mesodermal area.

More recently, the method of local vital staining has been applied to the study of *Amphioxus* development (Tung, Wu and Tung, 1962a). It was found that the presumptive mesodermal area is not restricted to one half of the egg

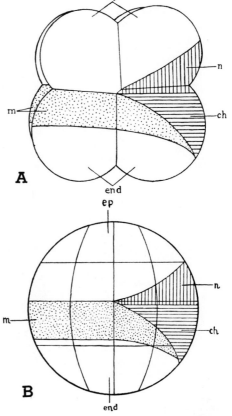

Figure 119. Fate maps of *Amphioxus* *(Branchiostoma) belcheri* at the 8-cell stage *(A)* and at the 32-cell stage *(B)*. ch, Presumptive notochord; end, presumptive endoderm; ep, presumptive epidermis; m, presumptive mesoderm; n, presumptive neural system. (From Tung, Wu and Tung, 1962a.)

only but reaches farther around the equator. On the opposite side a zone giving rise to the notochord could be detected, and above that a crescentic area which develops into the nervous system (Fig. 119). The similarity between this fate map and that of the amphibians is practically complete. There is also a striking similarity to the distribution of different kinds of cytoplasm in the ascidian embryo (see section 6–6).

As a result of cleavage in *Amphioxus,* a blastula is formed which has a large blastocoele and a blastoderm consisting of a single layer of columnar cells (Fig. 120, *a*). The cells at the vegetal pole are somewhat larger than at the animal pole and the blastoderm therefore is thicker. The various cytoplasmic substances present in the egg suffer no appreciable displacement during cleavage, and the fate map as presented in Figure 119 can equally well be applied to the blastula. The necessity of displacement of the parts so as to put them in the positions where they are situated in the adult animal is amply evident.

Gastrulation is initiated when the blastoderm at the vegetal pole becomes flat and subsequently bends inward, so that the whole embryo, instead of being spherical, becomes converted into a cup-shaped structure with a large cavity in open communication with the exterior on the side that was originally the vegetal pole of the embryo. The cup has a double wall, an external and an internal one, the latter lining the newly formed cavity. The external and internal epithelial layers are continuous with each other over the rim of the cup-shaped embryo. In this stage there is still a space between the external

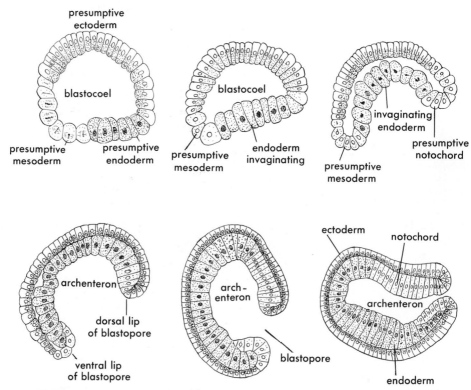

Figure 120. Gastrulation of *Amphioxus.* A series of consecutive stages (median sections). (After Conklin, 1932.)

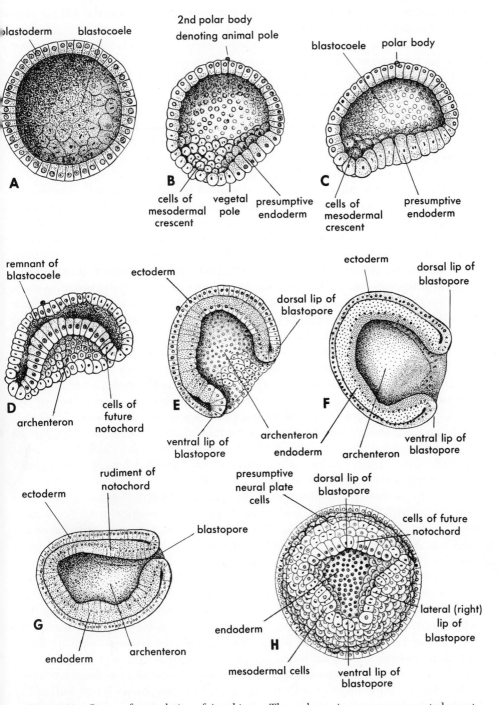

Figure 121.   Stages of gastrulation of *Amphioxus*. The embryos in *a-g* are represented as cut in the median plane. *a*, blastula; *b* and *c*, beginning of invagination; *d*, invagination advanced, the embryo attaining the structure of a double-walled cup with a broad opening to the exterior; *e*, and *f*, constriction of the blastopore; *g*, completed gastrula; *h*, middle gastrula, whole, viewed from side of blastopore. (From Conklin, 1932.)

and the internal wall representing the remnants of what was the blastocoele of the blastula (Figs. 120, 121).

The external lining consists of presumptive epidermis and presumptive nervous system. In other words, it consists of parts which have been classified as ectoderm. The internal lining consists mainly of the presumptive gut material; that is, of endoderm. The presumptive material of the notochord and the mesodermal crescent at first lie on the rim of the cup, but very soon they shift inward so as to occupy a position on the internal wall of the cup. In this way the endoderm, the mesoderm and the notochord disappear from the surface of the embryo into the interior where they belong. The external surface of the embryo now consists of ectoderm.

The embryo in this stage of development is called a **gastrula**. The movements of infolding or inward bending of the endoderm and mesoderm are known as **invagination**. The cavity arising through the invagination of the endoderm and mesoderm is called the **primary gut** or **archenteron**. The opening of the archenteron to the exterior is called the **blastopore**. At the same time the blastopore denotes the pathway by which the endoderm and mesoderm pass into the interior of the embryo. The blastopore, being the opening leading into the primary gut, has been likened to a mouth; its rims, therefore, are usually referred to as the **lips** of the blastopore. We may distinguish the dorsal lip, the ventral lip and the lateral lips of the blastopore, respectively.

The blastopore is very broad in the initial stage of gastrulation, but soon the lips of the blastopore begin to contract, so that the opening which leads into the archenteron becomes smaller and is eventually reduced to an insignificant fraction of the original orifice. This contraction of the lips of the blastopore is connected with the disappearance of the mesodermal crescent material and the presumptive notochord from the rim of the cup-shaped embryo. As more material is shifted into the interior of the gastrula, the remnants of the blastocoele become completely obliterated by the two walls of the embryo coming into contact with each other.

As the presumptive notochord and the mesodermal crescent shift into the interior of the gastrula, they also change their position relative to each other (Fig. 122). In the blastula, these two areas lie on opposite sides of the embryo. Now the lateral horns of the mesodermal crescent converge toward the dorsal side of the embryo and come to lie on both sides of the presumptive notochord. In the next stage that follows after the contraction of the rim of the blastopore, the embryo becomes elongated in the anteroposterior direction, all the various presumptive areas participating in this elongation. The elongation of the notochordal and the mesodermal material brings them into still closer contact with each other, the notochordal material shifting backward, in between the two horns of the mesodermal crescent material. The result of these movements is that the notochordal material becomes stretched into a longitudinal band of cells lying medially in the dorsal inner wall of the gastrula and flanked on both sides by bands of mesodermal cells similarly stretched in a longitudinal direction. The remainder of the lateral, ventral and anterior parts of the inner wall of the gastrula consists of endodermal cells.

The external wall of the gastrula similarly takes part in the elongation of

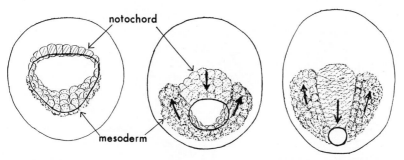

Figure 122. Change in the relative position of the presumptive mesoderm and the presumptive notochord during closure of the blastopore in *Amphioxus*. Diagrammatic. (After Conklin, 1932.)

the embryo. One of the results of this is that the presumptive material of the nervous system becomes stretched into a longitudinal band of cells lying mediodorsally over the notochordal material but being somewhat broader than the latter.

8—3 FORMATION OF THE PRIMARY ORGAN RUDIMENTS IN AMPHIOXUS

Immediately after the germinal layers have taken up their position in the inside and on the surface of the gastrula, the next phase of development sets in. The sheets of epithelium which were representative of the various parts of the future animal become broken up into discrete cell masses of diverse shape which can be called the **primary organ rudiments**. The term "primary" indicates that the structures in question are not final; they are actually complex in nature, and a further subdivision of the cell masses, or at least of most of them, is necessary before every single organ and structure of the adult animal appears as such.

In the interior of the embryo the presumptive materials of the notochord, the mesoderm and the gut become separated from each other by crevices appearing along the boundary lines of each (Fig. 123). The strip of cells lying mid-dorsally rounds itself off forthwith and becomes a cylindrical cord of cells, the **notochord**, which still differs from the same organ of the adult *Amphioxus* in the structure of its cells.

As the presumptive material of the mesoderm becomes separated both from the notochord and the endoderm, it breaks up into a series of roughly cuboidal masses of cells lying on each side, one behind the other along the length of the animal's body. These blocks of mesodermal cells are called the **mesodermal segments**. In connection with their formation, one detail should be noted. Just before the mesodermal cells become separated from the endoderm and notochord, a longitudinal groove appears on the inner surface of the mesodermal bands; that is, on the surface toward the archenteron. The groove becomes drawn out into each of the mesodermal segments, so that a pocketlike invagination is formed in each. At the same time, crevices cut in between adjoining segments from the outside, separating them from each

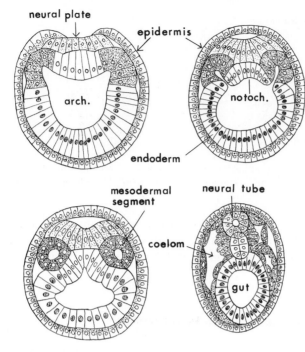

Figure 123. Formation of the primary organ rudiments in *Amphioxus*. Transverse sections. (After Hatchek, from Korschelt, 1936.)

other (Figs. 124, 125). When the mesodermal segments become eventually separated from the endoderm and notochord, the pocketlike invaginations in each become completely closed off from the cavity of the archenteron and become small cavities inside the mesodermal segments. In a later stage of development, these cavities expand and become the secondary body cavity or **coelom** of the adult animal. The derivation of the cavities of the mesodermal segments from the archenteric cavity is distinct in the case of the most anterior segments, but the posterior mesodermal segments are solid masses of cells at first and acquire cavities later as a result of the separation of the cells in the middle.

When the notochord and the mesodermal segments dissociate themselves from the endodermal material, the free edges of the endoderm approximate each other and fuse along the dorsal midline. The endoderm thus becomes converted into a closed sac. The cavity of this sac becomes the cavity of the alimentary canal.

In the ectoderm the presumptive nervous system material becomes separated from the surrounding presumptive epidermis in the form of an elongated

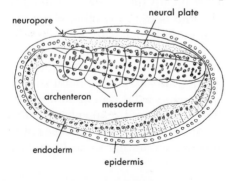

Figure 124. Embryo of *Amphioxus* in lateral view showing mesodermal segments (*mes*) overlying the notochord and neural plate. (After Conklin, 1932.)

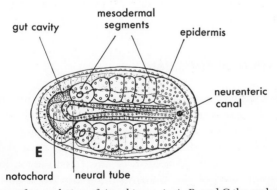

Figure 125.   Stages of neurulation of *Amphioxus*, in A, B, and C the embryos are represented as being cut in the median plane. A, Earliest stage of neurulation; C, almost completed neurula; D, slightly later stage than C but cut paramedially so that the right row of mesodermal segment can be seen; E, completed neurula whole, seen from the dorsal side. The transparency of the embryo allows one to see at the same time the various parts superimposed over one another (neural tube, notochord, mesodermal segments and gut). (From Conklin, 1932.)

plate, the **neural plate.** The neural plate sinks below the level of the remainder of the ectoderm and is then covered by the free edges of the epidermal epithelium (Fig. 123). The neural plate forthwith rolls itself into a tube, the lateral edges folding themselves upward and fusing along the midline. The neural plate is then transformed into the **neural tube**, which becomes the spinal cord of the animal. The neural tube does not close completely at the anterior end but leaves an opening, the **neuropore**, which remains patent until the later stages of development.

The epidermal epithelium which covers the neural plate by shifting over its surface is derived from the sides and from the area posterior to the neural plate. Because the hind end of the neural plate borders on the blastopore, the posterior portion of epidermis covering the neural plate is derived from the region below (ventral to) the blastopore. As the epidermis shifts forward over the surface of the neural plate, it also passes over the blastopore (Fig. 125). The blastopore becomes cut off from the exterior and opens into a space lined by the walls of the neural tube. The canal thus formed, which connects the blastopore, and therefore the archenteron, with the cavity of the neural tube, is called the **neurenteric canal**. The canal persists for only a short time, until the cavity of the neural tube (later becoming the central canal of the spinal cord) becomes completely separated from the cavity of the archenteron, which in turn becomes that of the alimentary canal. The cavity of the alimentary canal later acquires communication with the exterior by means of the oral and anal openings which break through the body wall, but this does not take place until a very much later stage of development.

After the formation of the spinal cord, the notochord, the gut and the mesodermal segments, the early embryo of *Amphioxus* possesses most of the essential features of the organization of chordate animals. The features which are still lacking are a mouth, an anus and the gill clefts. The gill clefts, as well as the mouth, are developed in all chordates at a comparatively late stage. We will see that a stage of development in which an embryo possesses a spinal cord, notochord, gut and the segmented mesoderm recurs with great tenacity in all vertebrates, and that the subsequent stages of development in all classes of vertebrates are much more similar than are the processes of cleavage and gastrulation.

8—4   GASTRULATION IN AMPHIBIANS

The purpose which gastrulation must achieve in the amphibians is the same as in *Amphioxus:* the areas of the blastoderm which are destined to become gut, notochord, muscle, etc., have to be brought into the interior of the embryo. However, in the amphibians this cannot be done by the bending inward of the vegetal region of the blastoderm, as in *Amphioxus,* because the vegetal wall of the blastula is far too thick and overladen with yolk and is therefore rather passive in its behavior. The processes leading to the disappearance of the material for the internal organs from the surface are therefore carried out mainly by the more active cells of the marginal zone. A correct understanding of amphibian gastrulation has been achieved by the method of localized vital staining—by applying marks of vital stain on the surface of the embryo and tracing the movements of the stained areas in the course of gastrulation (Vogt, 1929).

The first trace of gastrulation which can be observed in an egg of a newt or a frog is the formation of a depression or groove on the dorsal side of the embryo, at the boundary between the gray crescent (see pp. 127 and 150) and

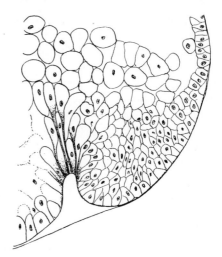

Figure 126. Median section through the blasto-pore region of an early gastrula of a newt, showing the cells at the bottom of the pit streaming into the interior. (After Vogt, 1929.)

the vegetal region. If the embryo is studied in sections in this stage, one may observe that the cells at the bottom of the groove are streaming into the interior of the embryo toward the blastocoele cavity (Fig. 126). In the next phase of gastrulation, the groove begins to spread transversely, and its lateral ends are prolonged all along the boundary between the marginal zone and the vegetal region until they meet at the opposite, ventral, side of the embryo, thus encircling the vegetal region (Fig. 127). The groove represents the blasto-pore. It is produced by the invagination of the endodermal and mesodermal material into the interior of the embryo.

The invagination in this case is not quite similar to the invagination in *Amphioxus*. The original groove may be said to have been the result of the bending inward of a portion of the blastoderm and the formation of a pocket-like depression. Once the depression has been formed, however, the further invagination can better be described as the rolling of the superficial cells

Figure 127. Changes in shape of the blastopore and closure of the blastopore during gastrulation in a frog.

over the rim of the blastopore and into its interior while new portions of the blastoderm approach the rim in their stead. While the superficial material is rolling over the rim of the blastopore, the rim itself does not remain stationary but gradually shifts over the surface of the vegetal region, moving away from the animal pole and toward the vegetal pole. By the time the blastopore has the form of a ring, the cells of the vegetal region are still to be seen filling the space enclosed by the edge of the blastopore. These cells are then called the **yolk plug** (Figs. 130, 131 and 132). The rim of the blastopore, however, continues to contract and at last covers the yolk plug altogether. In this way the material of the vegetal region disappears eventually into the interior

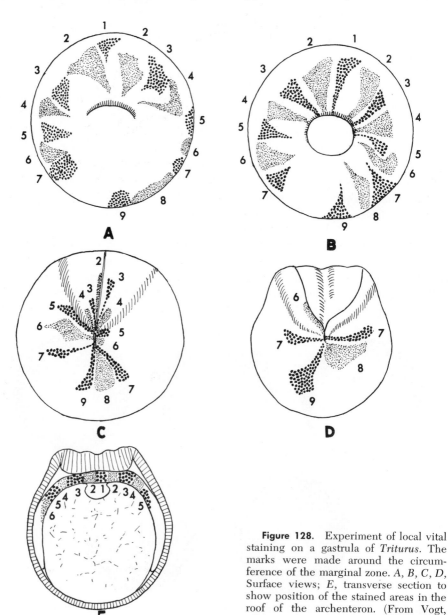

Figure 128. Experiment of local vital staining on a gastrula of *Triturus*. The marks were made around the circumference of the marginal zone. *A, B, C, D,* Surface views; *E,* transverse section to show position of the stained areas in the roof of the archenteron. (From Vogt, 1929.)

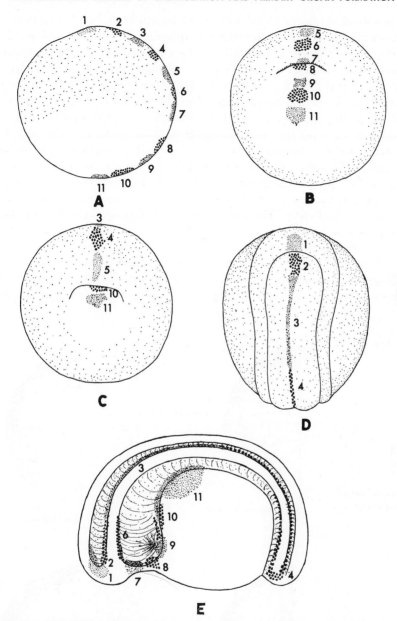

Figure 129.   Experiment of local vital staining on a gastrula of *Triturus*. The marks were made along the dorsal median surface. *A, B, C, D,* Surface views; *E,* the embryo dissected in the medial plane to show the position of the stained areas in the inferior. (From Vogt, 1929.)

of the embryo. When the blastopore contracts to such a degree that the yolk plug disappears from view, the blastopore is said to be "closed." This is not quite exact, however, since a narrow canal leading into the interior still persists (Fig. 130).

If the blastoderm above the rim of the blastopore is marked with spots of vital stain, it can easily be seen that the stained areas stretch toward the lips of the blastopore, approach its rim, roll over the edge and disappear inside (Fig. 128). Once inside, the stained material does not come to rest but continues its movements in the interior of the embryo, but this time it moves away from the blastopore in the opposite direction from that which it followed while the stained material was still on the surface of the embryo. It can also be seen that the movement of the superficial material is most rapid and extensive on the dorsal meridian of the embryo. More material is invaginated over the dorsal lip of the blastopore than over the lateral lips and least over the ventral lip of the blastopore. This accounts for the different breadth of the marginal zone around the circumference of the egg. In fact, the upper limit of the marginal zone is none other than the limit to which the blastoderm is invaginated during the process of gastrulation. The vegetal region is similarly that part of the blastoderm which is enclosed by the rim of the blastopore. The animal region is the part of the blastoderm that does not pass into the interior by way of the blastopore. The extent of the invagination can be clearly seen if a series of vital stain spots is made along the mid-dorsal meridian of the embryo, as shown in Fig. 129.

On the dorsal side of the embryo, where the groove had first appeared and where the streaming of the cells into the interior of the embryo is the most active, a cavity is soon formed leading from the groove on the surface

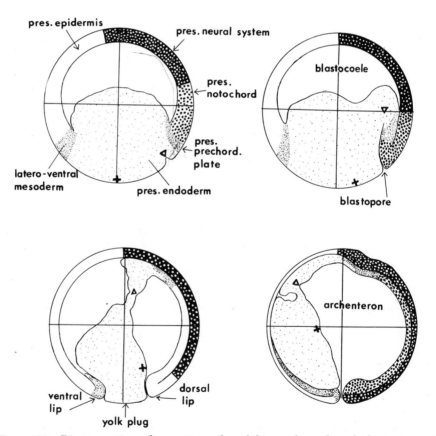

Figure 130. Diagrammatic median sections of amphibian embryos from the beginning to the completion of gastrulation. The triangle marks the cells which start invagination. The cross marks the position of the cells which were at the vegetal pole when gastrulation began. (After Vogt, 1929.)

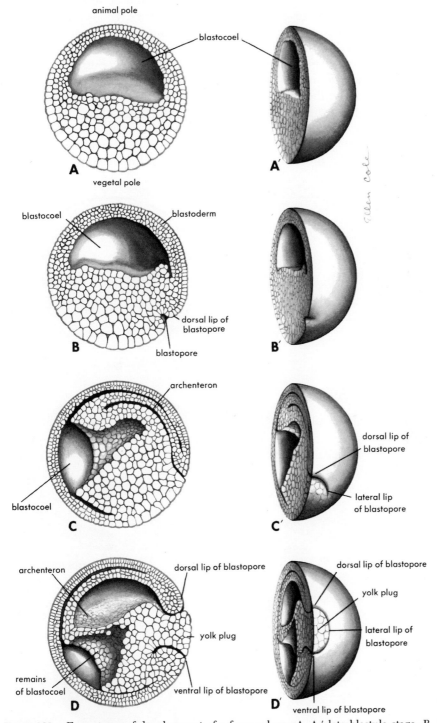

Figure 131.   Four stages of development of a frog embryo; A, A,′ late blastula stage; B, B,′ beginning of gastrulation; C, C,′ middle gastrula stage; D, D,′ late gastrula stage (semidiagrammatic). Drawings on the left represent the embryos cut in the median plane; drawings on the right represent the same embryos viewed at an angle from the dorsal side (A, B, C) or from posterior end (D).

into the interior of the embryo. This cavity is lined on all sides by the invaginated cells and represents the archenteron (Figs. 130, 131 and 132). The archenteron is at first a narrow slitlike cavity, but later, as more material becomes invaginated, it expands at its anterior end and in so doing encroaches on the blastocoele. The latter is eventually obliterated (Fig. 130). While the rim of the blastopore moves over the surface of the vegetal region, the vegetal region is drawn into the interior and at the same time caused to rotate, so that after the end of gastrulation it comes to lie in the ventral part of the archenteron, its originally exterior surface facing its cavity (Fig. 130). The opposite, dorsal, wall of the archenteron consists of cells of the marginal zone which have rolled into the interior over the dorsal lip of the blastopore.

Figure 132. Blastula, gastrulation and formation of primary organ rudiments in the frog. a, Late cleavage stage showing difference in the size of the blastomeres; b, late blastula; c, early gastrula; d, middle gastrula; e, neurula, transverse section; f, transverse section after completion of neurulation.

We can now trace the displacements and movements of each area of the blastula individually.

The Ectoderm.   The material of the animal region, including the presumptive epidermis and the presumptive nervous system, greatly increases its surface during gastrulation, and at the end of gastrulation it covers the whole embryo after the mesoderm and the endoderm have disappeared inside. The **expansion** of the ectoderm is an active process, and the increase of surface area goes on at the expense of a thinning out of the epithelial layer. The presumptive epidermis expands in all directions, but in the case of the presumptive nervous system the expansion is mainly in the longitudinal direction, i.e., toward the blastopore. In the transverse direction, on the other hand, the presumptive nervous system area contracts, and the material of the lateral horns of the crescentic area is drawn in toward the dorsal side of the embryo. As a result, the whole nervous system area changes its shape and becomes oval, elongated in an anteroposterior direction.

The Notochord.   The notochord rolls over the dorsal lip of the blastopore into the interior of the embryo and becomes stretched along the dorsal side of the archenteron, forming the mid-dorsal strip of the archenteron roof. As it does so, the presumptive notochord undergoes a very considerable elongation in the longitudinal direction and a corresponding contraction in the transverse direction. The notochordal material becomes concentrated on the dorsal side of the embryo, just as is the presumptive neural system but even to a much greater degree.

The Prechordal Plate.   The prechordal plate, which in the blastula lies just below the presumptive notochord, is the first mesoderm to invaginate and does so by rolling over the dorsal lip of the blastopore and becoming a part of the archenteron roof in front of the anterior end of the notochordal material.

The Mesoderm.   Of all parts of the blastula, the mesodermal area undergoes the most complicated movements. Most of the mesoderm invaginates into the interior by rolling over the lateral and ventral lips of the blastopore. Once inside the embryo, the mesoderm moves in an anterior direction as a sheet of cells, penetrating between the ectoderm on the outside and the endoderm on the inside. The mesoderm in Urodela detaches itself from the endoderm and moves forward between the ectoderm and the endoderm, having a free edge anteriorly but preserving an uninterrupted connection with the notochordal material on the dorsal side of the embryo (Fig. 133).

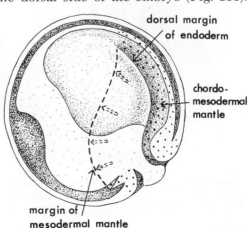

Figure 133.   Gastrula of *Triturus* cut in the median plane to show separation of the chordomesodermal mantle from the endoderm. (After Vogt, from Hamburger, 1947.)

dorsal margin of endoderm

chordo-mesodermal mantle

margin of mesodermal mantle

The notochordal and the mesodermal material in this stage are in the form of one continuous epithelial sheet, the **chordo-mesodermal mantle**. In the Anura, the mesoderm does not split off from the adjoining endoderm until gastrulation is nearly finished. The result is, however, the same: the formation of the chordo-mesodermal mantle lying between the ectoderm and the endoderm. As the mesoderm moves from the posterior end of the embryo (represented by the blastopore) toward the anterior end, there remains at the anterior end a region which the mesodermal mantle has not yet reached. This region, which is free of mesoderm, diminishes as gastrulation proceeds but does not disappear completely. It is in this mesoderm-free region at the anterior end of the embryo that the mouth is later formed.

The concentration toward the dorsal side of the embryo, noted in respect to the notochordal and nervous system material, is also very distinct in the case of the mesodermal mantle. The movement of the mesoderm inside the embryo does not follow the same path as on the surface. If the trajectories of all parts of the presumptive mesoderm are traced, it is seen that they converge toward the dorsal side where they represent the movement of the mesoderm after its invagination (Fig. 134). As a result, the mesodermal material becomes concentrated toward the dorsal side. The mesodermal layer is thickest in the roof of the archenteron, where the mesoderm adjoins the notochord; it is thinned out in the lateral part and still more so in the ventral part of the embryo. The mesoderm continues to invaginate by rolling over the rim of the blastopore, even after the endoderm has come to lie inside and the yolk plug has disappeared from the surface. The invagination of the mesoderm may therefore be considered as retarded as compared with the invagination of the endoderm. The degree of retardation is not the same in different animals. It is the least in frogs, greater in the urodeles, and greatest in the lamprey whose gastrulation is, otherwise, very similar to the gastrulation of the amphibians (Pasteels, 1940). As a result of the retardation, the presumptive mesoderm of the tail region and sometimes also the presumptive mesoderm of the posterior trunk region may still be on the surface of the embryo when the blastopore is "closed."

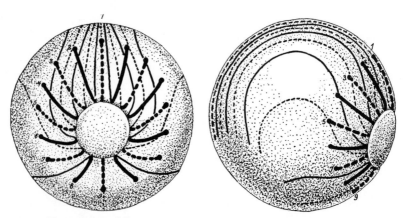

Figure 134. Trajectories of the movements of parts of the marginal zone during gastrulation in amphibians. Thick lines show movements of cells on the surface of the embryo; thin lines show movement of invaginated cells. (From Vogt, 1929.)

The Endoderm. The presumptive endoderm is found, in the blastula, partly in the marginal zone and partly in the vegetal region. The two parts of the presumptive endoderm invaginate in different manners: the part lying in the marginal zone is mainly absorbed into the original pitlike invagination of the blastopore; the vegetal region disappears from the surface when it becomes covered up by the contracting rim of the blastopore.

The blastopore first appears as a pit in the endodermal area, between the marginal zone endoderm and the vegetal endoderm. The endodermal cells lying at the bottom of the pit are later found in the duodenal region of the embryo. In the early gastrula the presumptive endoderm of the pharyngeal and oral region lies on the anterior slope of the pit and is therefore invaginated as part of the dorsal lip of the blastopore. This material later forms the most anterior part of the advancing archenteron. In the later stages of gastrulation, the oral and pharyngeal endoderm expands so as to form the spacious **foregut**, whose lateral, ventral and anterior walls then consist of a rather thin layer of endoderm. Only part of the dorsal wall of the foregut is taken up by the prechordal plate and the anterior tip of the notochord.

The endoderm of the vegetal region passes into the interior of the embryo more or less passively and there comes to lie in the floor of the archenteron. It is not pushed forward as far as the marginal zone endoderm, but remains confined to the middle and posterior parts. The layer of endoderm in the floor of the archenteron is very thick, and the cavity of the archenteron is therefore reduced posteriorly to a rather narrow canal underneath the chordo-mesodermal mantle. This narrow part of the archenteron later becomes the **midgut** of the embryo. The lateral endodermal walls of the midgut are much thinner, and dorsally they end at a free edge after the mesoderm has been split off from the endoderm.

8—5 FORMATION OF THE PRIMARY ORGAN RUDIMENTS IN AMPHIBIANS

At the time of the closure of the blastopore, the separation of the organ rudiments in amphibians has gone somewhat further than in *Amphioxus;* the chordo-mesodermal mantle has, to a great extent, separated itself from the endoderm, and the mesoderm has attained its definitive position between the endoderm and the ectoderm. To make the separation complete, the notochord becomes split at its anterior end from the prechordal plate, and the prechordal plate itself separates from the adjoining endoderm. The endoderm forthwith closes under the prechordal plate. The foregut is then surrounded on all sides by endodermal cells (Figs. 132, 135). In the midgut region the free edges of the endoderm approach each other in the midline and fuse, thus completely enclosing the midgut. The chordomesodermal mantle becomes subdivided into its two components: the notochord in the middle and the mesoderm on both sides. As the notochord is separated from the mesoderm, the strand of notochordal cells becomes converted into a cylindrical body, round in cross section. The mesoderm, at the same time, becomes subdivided into a series of mesodermal segments. Contrary to what is found in *Amphioxus*, however, not the whole of the mesoderm becomes segmented but only its dorsal part, the part adjoining the notochord. The

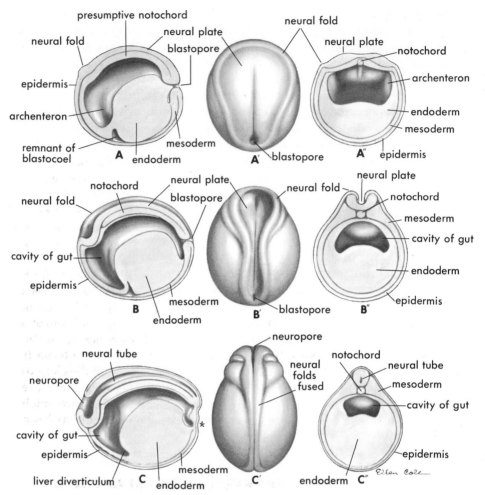

Figure 135. Three stages of neurulation in a frog embryo. The drawings in the middle show whole embryos in dorsal view. The drawings on the left show the right halves of embryos cut in the median plane. The drawings on the right show the anterior halves of embryos cut transversely. A, A′, A″, Very early neurula; B, B′, B″, middle neurula; C, C′, C″, late neurula with neural tube almost completely closed. C shows the blastopore closed; the asterisk indicates the point at which the anal opening will break through.

mesodermal layer has been thickened here owing to the convergence of the mesoderm toward the dorsal side of the embryo during gastrulation. This thickened part now becomes segmented by a series of transverse crevices cutting into the mass of mesodermal cells and separating them (Fig. 136). The thinned out lateral and ventral parts of the mesodermal mantle on each side do not become subdivided into segments, and these parts of the mesoderm are known as the **lateral plates.** The mesodermal segments in amphibians are not fully homologous to the primary mesodermal segments of *Amphioxus*; they are given the name of **somites.** Each somite is separated from the adjoining somites but remains connected to the dorsal edge of the lateral plate. The strand of cells connecting the somite to the lateral plate is known as the **stalk** of the somite, and these cells, as will be shown later, give rise to the excretory system of the embryo.

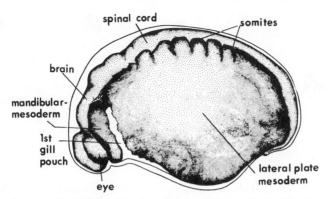

Figure 136. Segmentation of the dorsal mesoderm in an embryo of a salamander (*Ambystoma punctatum*). (Modified from Adelmann, 1932.)

At about the same time as the segmentation of the mesoderm in its dorsal part takes place, the lateral plate mesoderm becomes split into two layers, an external layer applied to the ectoderm known as the **parietal layer,** and an internal layer applied to the endoderm, the **visceral layer.** The narrow cavity between the two layers is the **coelomic cavity** or **coelom.** In later stages the cavity expands and becomes the body cavity of the adult animal (see Fig. 310, p. 405). Small cavities also appear in the somites, but these are obliterated later and disappear without a trace. There is never any connection between the coelomic cavities in the mesoderm of the amphibians and the archenteric cavity.

The presumptive nervous system has been traced previously to the stage when it forms an approximately oval-shaped area on the dorsal side of the embryo. The neural area covers the areas of the notochord and the somites in the middle and posterior parts of the embryo and the prechordal plate in front. The anterior end of the neural area is underlain by a part of the endodermal lining of the foregut. After the closure of the blastopore, the presumptive area of the nervous system becomes differentiated from the rest of the ectoderm in the form of the **neural plate** (Fig. 135). The ectodermal epithelium of the neural plate becomes thickened by the further concentration of the epithelium toward the dorsal side of the embryo. At the same time, the cells of the neural plate change in shape; they become elongated and arrange themselves into a columnar epithelium. Thus they are different from the cells of the epidermis, which remain more or less flat and arranged as a stratified epithelium usually two cells thick.

Superficially the neural plate becomes visible because of a concentration of pigment at the edges of the plate. Soon, however, the edges of the neural plate become thickened and raised above the general level as **neural folds.** A shallow groove may be seen at the same time along the midline of the neural plate, separating it into right and left halves. The neural plate continues to contract in a transverse direction, especially in its posterior parts. The neural folds become higher, so that eventually the neural plate is converted into a longitudinal depression, bordered laterally and in front by the neural folds (Fig. 135). Subsequently the folds make contact in the midline and fuse, beginning from the point corresponding to the occipital region of

Figure 137. Stages in the formation of the neural plate and neural tube in amphibians. Transverse sections (diagrammatic). Neural crest cells are shown in black.

the embryo and progressing forward and backward. In this way the neural plate is transformed into the neural tube (Figs. 132, 137). The cavity of the neural tube is broadest in the anterior part of the tube, and this part later develops into the brain with the brain cavities. In the posterior part of the neural tube, the cavity is much narrower. It will later become the central canal of the spinal cord. Sometimes the central canal is not found in the posterior part of the neural tube at the time of the closure of the neural folds, and in that case the tube is hollowed out later by the separation of the cells in the middle of the organ.

The formation and closure of the neural plate is known as **neurulation**, and the embryo, in the stages when it possesses a neural plate, is called a **neurula**.

In frogs, the neural folds reach posteriorly to the level of the blastopore or even slightly beyond it. As a result the blastopore, now reduced to a narrow canal, is surrounded by the neural folds. When the folds fuse, the external end of this canal is to be found in the floor of the neural tube. In most frogs, by the time the neural tube is formed the blastopore becomes completely occluded by the fusion of its edges. In some amphibians, however, in particular in the clawed toad, *Xenopus,* the canal remains open and becomes the canalis neurentericus, which for some time provides a direct communication between the posterior end of the archenteron and the neural tube (Fig. 138). (Compare the same formation in *Amphioxus,* Fig. 125 and p. 186.) The canalis neurentericus is later interrupted and disappears without a trace.

After the blastopore ceases to provide an opening for the gut to the exterior, a new opening breaks through at the posterior end of the embryo, slightly below the position of the blastopore. This opening becomes the anus (see Tahara and Nakamura, 1961). In urodeles, however, the blastopore remains outside the neural folds and becomes directly transformed into the anal opening.

After the neural folds have fused in the midline, the neural tube separates itself completely from the overlying epidermis. The free edges of the epidermis fuse, so that the epidermis becomes continuous over the back of the embryo. A certain number of cells, however, do not become included either in the neural tube or in the epidermis. These cells can be traced back

A

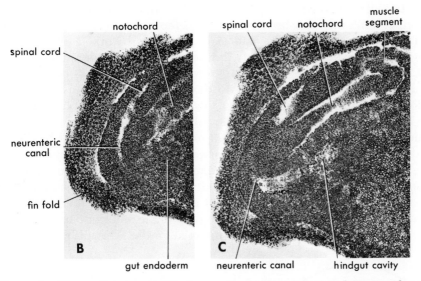

Figure 138.   The canalis neurentericus in an embryo of the clawed toad, *Xenopus laevis. A,* Reconstruction of a median section through the embryo, showing the continuity of the gut cavity and of the central canal of the neural tube at the posterior end of the embryo. *B* and *C,* Photographs of two of the sections used for the reconstruction; owing to a slight curvature of the neurenteric canal only part of it is visible in any one section.

to strips running all along the crest of the neural folds (Fig. 137). After the neural tube has become separated from the epidermis, these cells are found as an irregular flattened mass between the neural tube and the overlying epidermis. This mass of cells is the **neural crest.** The neural crest may be continuous across the midline at first, but very soon the mass of cells separates into a right and a left half, lying dorsolaterally to the neural tube. The neural crest cells have been found to play a very special part in the development of the embryo, as will be indicated later (section 13–3).

During neurulation, the embryo already begins to stretch in length. At the same time it is flattened from side to side and also becomes smaller in a dorsoventral direction. The volume of the embryo does not change appreciably. The stretching is greatest in the posterior part of the embryo. As the neural tube takes part in this general stretching, it becomes still more attenuated in its posterior parts, so that the difference between the presumptive brain and the presumptive spinal cord is increased. The part of the embryo above the blastopore becomes elongated beyond the blastopore and this elongation becomes the rudiment of the tail. It is known as the **tailbud** (see Fig. 215, p. 313). The gill pouches are formed as lateral outpushings of the foregut, and in later development these give rise to the gill clefts. The mouth later breaks through at the anterior end of the foregut.

8–6 GASTRULATION AND FORMATION OF THE PRIMARY ORGAN RUDIMENTS IN FISHES

In vertebrates which have meroblastic eggs, the fate map must necessarily be different, owing to the presence of the uncleaved yolk. Nevertheless, a distinct similarity can be discovered in the position of the various areas relative to one another. The fate maps have been worked out for elasmobranchs and the bony fishes. Only the latter will be considered here in detail (Fig. 139).

In fishes, the areas destined to develop into the organs of the dorsal region of the animal are concentrated toward one edge of the blastodisc which can be denoted as posterior. At the edge of the disc lies the area for the alimentary canal; in front of the area for the alimentary canal lies the area for the notochord; and still farther forward, toward the center of the blastodisc, lies the area for the neural system. The material for the mesodermal muscles and the lining of the body cavity is situated on both sides of the gut and notochord areas and is drawn out along the edge of the blastodisc. In *Fundulus*, the mesoderm area is interrupted in the anterior part of the blastodisc, and here lies the presumptive material for the skin epithelium (Oppen-

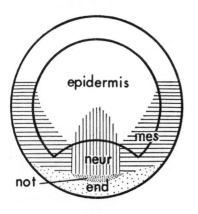

Figure 139. Fate map of a bony fish *Fundulus*, after Oppenheimer. *neur*, Presumptive neural system; *mes*, presumptive mesoderm; *end*, presumptive endoderm; *not*, presumptive notochord. (After Oppenheimer, 1947.)

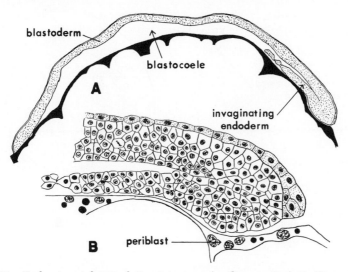

Figure 140. Early stage of gastrulation in a trout (median section). *A*, View of the whole blastodisc under low magnification; *B*, part adjoining the blastopore (posterior edge of blastodisc) at higher magnification.

heimer, 1947). In *Salmo,* however, the mesodermal area reaches all around the circumference of the blastodisc (Pasteels, 1940).

The invagination of the mesoderm and the endoderm proceeds around the circumference of the blastodisc. There is no inpushing of epithelial layers, however, and no archenteron is formed. The endoderm, which was located around the posterior half of the circumference of the blastodisc in the blastula stage, shifts into the interior along the surface of the yolk or, to be more exact, over the surface of the periblast (see section 7–3). As the cells move inward they are also concentrated toward the midline of the embryo. They eventually form a thin layer or plate underneath the blastodisc (Fig. 140).

The mesoderm invaginates in the same way at first, but later the invagination is continued as a process of rolling over the edge of the blastodisc. Although no archenteron is formed, the edge of the blastodisc must be recognized as the blastopore, because it is the pathway by which the endoderm and the mesoderm pass into the interior of the embryo. The concentration of the material toward the dorsal side of the embryo is, in the case of the mesoderm, even more pronounced than in the case of the endoderm. The mesodermal cells begin to converge toward the midline even before they invaginate. By applying vital staining, it has been ascertained that the mesodermal material lying around the rim of the blastopore (the edge of the blastodisc) streams along the edge of the blastodisc toward the posterior end, where the body of the embryo begins to be formed. Once invaginated, the mesodermal cells move obliquely forward and toward the midline, converging in the midline where the axial organs of the embryo will be formed.

The presumptive notochordal area, which is elongated transversely in the blastula, is, during the process of invagination, concentrated toward the midline and stretched in a longitudinal direction, so that eventually it is converted into a narrow strip of cells lying in the midline of the embryo, above the endodermal plate and under the ectoderm. The notochord, as well as the

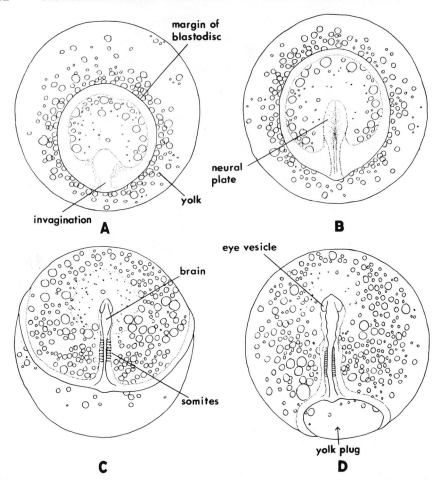

Figure 141.   Stages of development of the trout. *A*, Blastodisc in the stage of gastrulation; *B*, neural plate stage; *C*, formation of the brain, eye vesicles, and somites; *D*, overgrowth of yolk almost completed.

prechordal plate, invaginates by rolling over the posterior edge of the blasto-disc, which corresponds, of course, to the dorsal lip of the amphibian blasto-pore. Notochord, prechordal plate and mesoderm are continuous with each other, forming a chordo-mesodermal mantle. The neural system area is stretched toward the posterior edge of the blastodisc (to the dorsal lip of the blastopore), and thus it takes the place of those parts which had disappeared from the surface. At the same time, the presumptive nervous system area concentrates toward the midline and becomes a strip of tissue lying over the presumptive notochord but reaching considerably farther forward from the posterior edge of the blastodisc.

In the fishes the formation of the primary organ rudiments in the anterior part of the embryo begins long before the invagination has been accomplished in the posterior part (Fig. 141). The first to appear is the anterior end of the neural plate, corresponding to the prechordal part of the brain. Next in suc-cession appears the neural plate of the hindbrain region and of the anterior trunk region. At the same time the notochord starts separating from the mesoderm, with which it has previously been united into a continuous layer. The mesodermal mantle had already been thickened all along the presumptive notochord, owing to the concentration toward the midline during gastrulation. These thickened parts of the mesoderm adjoining the notochord are now sub-divided into segments—the somites. The remainder of the mesodermal mantle stays unsegmented and represents the lateral plate mesoderm. The endodermal plate now concentrates toward the midline and consequently becomes thicker, but the cavity of the alimentary canal does not appear until a very much later stage. When it does appear, it is formed by a separation of the cells along the middle of the endodermal cord of cells.

The process of neurulation in the bony fishes differs considerably from that in amphibians. Although a neural plate is found, the neural folds are only slightly indicated. The neural plate does not roll into a tube but nar-rows gradually, at the same time sinking deeper and deeper into the under-lying tissues. Eventually it separates from the epidermis, which becomes con-tinuous over the dorsal surface of the embryo. No cavity appears in the nervous system rudiment while it is being separated from the remainder of the ectoderm. The ventricles of the brain and the central canal of the spinal cord are formed later by the separation of cells in the middle of the brain and spinal cord.

While the invagination of the endoderm and mesoderm and later the for-mation of the primary organ rudiments of the anterior part of the body are going on, the blastodisc as a whole is spreading to cover an ever-increasing part of the yolk. The rim of the blastodisc shifts over the surface of the yolk in a centripetal direction. This movement of the blastodisc rim may be com-pared to the movement of the rim of the amphibian blastopore away from the animal pole and toward the vegetal pole of the embryo. Eventually the rim of the blastodisc converges at or near the opposite side of the yolk, and the opening closes by constriction of the rim.

We have seen that the rim of the blastodisc corresponds to the lips of the blastopore. The process described just now is therefore equivalent to the closure of the blastopore in the amphibians and *Amphioxus*. Incidentally, it ends up by having all the yolk covered by the blastodisc. Just before the blastopore closes, a yolk plug may be seen projecting from the blastopore. This yolk plug looks very much like the yolk plug in the amphibians, but it differs from it in so far as it consists only of nonsegmented yolk, whereas the yolk plug in the amphibians consists of cells of the vegetal region. At the time when the lips of the blastopore move over the surface of the yolk, they do not contain presumptive endoderm except at the posterior edge of the blasto-disc. The endoderm, therefore, does not form a continuous sheet all around the yolk which in the lateral and ventral parts of the embryo is in direct con-tact with the lateral plate mesoderm.

Gastrulation and the formation of the primary organ rudiments in elasmo-branchs follow the same pattern as in the bony fishes—with the difference, however, that an archenteron is formed at the posterior edge of the blastodisc by the invagination of the presumptive notochord and endoderm. Likewise the rudiment of the nervous system is not solid, as in bony fishes, but the neural plate is rolled into a tube having a distinct cavity right from the start.

8−7   GASTRULATION AND THE FORMATION OF THE PRIMARY ORGAN RUDIMENTS IN BIRDS

The fate map in birds presents a new feature as compared with the fate map in fishes. It has already been indicated that the blastoderm in birds consists of two parts: the area pellucida and the area opaca. The area opaca is completely excluded from the formation of the body of the embryo, and the fate map, in so far as the parts of the embryo are concerned, is restricted to the area pellucida. Furthermore, since the blastoderm is bilaminar, consisting of epiblast and hypoblast, fate maps have to be made out for each of the two layers separately. The fate map as described below is the outcome of numerous experiments carried out by different investigators. Some of these have consisted of marking the blastoderm by vital staining (Wetzel, 1929, and Pasteels, 1940), others of marking with carbon particles (Spratt, 1946). The marking was done either *in situ* in the egg, after a window was cut in the shell, or on blastoderms cultivated *in vitro*. We shall first deal with the fate map for the epiblast (Fig. 142).

Roughly, the anterior half of the epiblast of the area pellucida contains material for the skin epithelium and also for the embryonic membranes (see section 11–1). Almost in the middle of the area pellucida, or slightly anterior to the middle, lies the presumptive neural plate in the form of a transverse crescentic area, broadest in the middle and tapering to the sides. Behind the neural plate area, in the middle, lies the presumptive notochord; neither of these areas reaches far out to the sides. The area containing material for segmented muscle is situated in the midline behind the notochordal area. Most of the posterior half of the area pellucida is taken up by the material producing the mesodermal lining of the body cavity (the ventrolateral mesoderm) and by the extraembryonic mesoderm, which will not participate in the formation of the embryo (see Pasteels, 1940, Spratt, 1946, and Waddington, 1952).

As we shall see later, the epiblast also contains some presumptive endoderm. The cells which go into the formation of the endoderm, however, are few in number and apparently are not concentrated as a separate area but are derived from a fairly large field along the midline, mainly in the posterior part of the area pellucida.

The hypoblast is less accessible for local marking, since it is covered by the epiblast, but it has been possible to mark it with carbon particles when the blastoderm is excised from the egg and cultivated *in vitro* upside down

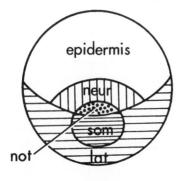

Figure 142.   Fate map of bird. *neur*, Presumptive neural system; *not*, presumptive notochord; *som*, presumptive somites; *lat*, presumptive lateral mesoderm. (From Waddington, 1952.)

(R. Fraser, 1954). In this way it was found that some of the hypoblast cells contribute to the formation of the notochord. Most of the hypoblast, however, is presumptive endoderm, though only a small part of it will become incorporated into the gut of the embryo. The remainder is destined to become the lining of the yolk sac (see further, section 11–1). It must be noted that, owing to difficulties of work with the avian blastoderm, the boundaries of the various areas in the fate map should be considered as being only approximate (Rudnick, 1948).

The organ-forming part of the blastoderm in the birds takes up only a limited area inside the blastodisc (the area pellucida). The invagination cannot therefore proceed on the edge of the blastodisc. Instead, the invagination takes place in a special region inside the area pellucida. This region is a narrow strip of blastoderm starting from the posterior edge of the area pellucida and running forward along the midline of the embryo for about three fifths of the entire length of the area pellucida. This strip of blastoderm becomes thickened during the stages of gastrulation and is known as the **primitive streak**. Along the middle of the primitive streak, when it is fully developed, there runs a narrow furrow, the **primitive groove**. At the anterior end of the primitive streak there is a thickening, the **primitive knot** or **Hensen's node** (Fig. 143, *B*). The center of Hensen's node is excavated to form a funnel-shaped depression. In some birds (the duck, for instance) this depression is continued forward into a narrow canal which will be referred to later.

The thickening of the blastoderm is brought about by a convergence of the surface layer of the blastoderm, the epiblast, toward the midline in the posterior half of the area pellucida. As the cells nearest the midline become concentrated to form the early primitive streak, the parts of the epiblast lying farther out laterally and anterolaterally swing in a curve backward and inward to take the place of parts of the blastoderm shifting toward the midline (Fig. 144). The primitive streak first becomes visible in the hindmost part of the area pellucida – the **short primitive streak** (Fig. 143, *A*).

The primitive streak now elongates by the concentration of more and more material from the sides toward the midline in front of the original short primitive streak. The early primitive streak is broad and its edges are rather vaguely indicated. In later stages it contracts in a transverse direction, becoming narrower and quite sharply delimited. This is the **definitive primitive streak** (Fig. 143, *B*). In the process of this transformation, the primitive streak elongates and its anterior end is pushed even farther forward, though the amount of this forward thrust has been a matter of controversy among embryologists (see Waddington, 1952).

While the movements in the epiblast lead to the formation of the primitive streak, there is some indication that the cells of the lower layer of the blastoderm, the hypoblast, also do not remain quiescent but shift in an anterior direction. The hypoblast first becomes a continuous layer in the posterior part of the blastoderm, and is only later found to be present in the anterior half. It is possible that the forward shift of the hypoblast contributes to the completion of this layer anteriorly.

The movements in the blastoderm leading to the formation of the primitive streak may be called **pregastrulation movements**, to distinguish them from the gastrulation movements proper.

Figure 143. Gastrulation and formation of primary organ rudiments in a chick embryo (surface views). *A*, Short primitive streak (stage 3) (from Hamburger and Hamilton, 1951); *B*, definitive primitive streak (stage 4); *C*, head process stage (stage 5); *D*, retreating primitive streak (stage 6); *E*, neural plate (stage 6 +); *F*, closure of neural tube and formation of somites (stage 9 −). (Numbers of stages after Hamburger and Hamilton, 1951.)

Figure 144. Movements in the epiblast during the formation of the primitive streak in a chick embryo as shown by displacement of vitally stained areas (A, B, C). D, Diagram of movements based on this and similar experiments. (From Wetzel, 1929.)

At the stage of the short primitive streak, the cells of the blastoderm already begin to invaginate into the space between the epiblast and the hypoblast (see section 7–4). The process of invagination is different from all that has been seen in *Amphioxus,* in the amphibians and in the bony fishes. There is no infolding of the epithelial layer of the blastoderm; neither does a sheet of cells shift from the surface to the interior, as in bony fishes. In the birds, the cells seem to be moving downward singly, even if there are many cells moving in the same direction. The regular epithelial arrangment of cells found in the epiblast becomes lost (Figs. 145, 146 and 148). This type of gastrulation movement bears the name of **immigration.**

Very soon the migrating cells reach the hypoblast and establish an intimate contact with the cells of this layer. Henceforward the whole of the primitive streak is a mass of moving cells. The direction of movement is mainly downward from the surface of the blastoderm toward the hypoblast, but the mass of migrating cells also spreads out sideways and forward from the anterior end of the primitive streak. By marking cells of the hypoblast underneath the primitive streak with carbon particles, it was found that

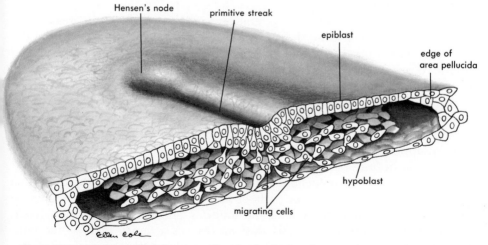

Figure 145. Anterior half of the area pellucida of a chick embryo cut transversely to show the migration of mesodermal and endodermal cells from the primitive streak.

Figure 146. Cells in the zone of migration underneath the primitive streak of a chick embryo, electronmicrograph. N, Nuclei of mesenchyme cells; Y, yolk granule. (From Balinsky and Walther, 1961.)

these cells also become a part of the shifting migrating mass, and some of the cells originally belonging to the hypoblast move into the midst of the primitive streak cells and are carried with them, especially in an anterior direction (Fraser, 1954).

Although the cells of the chick blastoderm move individually, their movements are obviously directed by common causes, and therefore the whole mass of cells moves in a coordinated fashion. The formation of depressions on the surface of the blastoderm, the furrow along the midline of the primitive streak and the funnel-shaped depression in the center of Hensen's node are due to this mass movement of cells from the surface of the blastoderm into the interior (just as in the case of a vortex appearing on the surface of water).

As the cells of the epiblast migrate into the interior, whole areas of the blastoderm disappear from the surface. They are replaced, however, by the adjoining areas moving toward the midline and taking their place in the primitive streak. The newly arrived cells in their turn migrate down into the interior. Thus the primitive streak persists, although the cells of which it is made up do not stay in the same place but are replaced all the time. The first areas to start invaginating are the presumptive prechordal plate, the notochord and the presumptive lateral mesoderm. The prechordal plate soon disappears from the surface through Hensen's node and spreads under the epiblast in front of the primitive streak.

The presumptive notochord cells become concentrated in the definitive primitive streak in the deeper parts of Hensen's node. After the prechordal plate has spread out in front of the anterior end of the primitive streak, the presumptive notochord cells start moving as a dense mass in the midline straight forward from Hensen's node underneath the surface of the epiblast (Fig. 147).

Figure 147.   Longitudinal medial section of a chick embryo in the head process stage. (After Wetzel, 1929.)

The mass of notochordal cells can be distinguished from the surrounding (mainly mesodermal) cells, and is called the **head process**, or, more correctly, the **notochordal process** (see Fig. 143, *C*). The narrow canal mentioned above and found in some birds (e.g., the duck) penetrates into this notochordal process. Since the formation of the canal is due to the movement of the invaginating cells of the gastrula, the cavity of the canal must be recognized as corresponding to a part of the archenteron, even though the lining of the canal consists exclusively of presumptive notochordal cells. There is no other cavity in the development of birds that could be considered as a homologue of the archenteron. The invagination of the mesoderm or the endoderm does not lead to the appearance of a cavity. We have already seen that in other vertebrates the archenteron may also be completely absent (pp. 201–203).

Presumptive lateral plate mesoderm is contained throughout gastrulation in the posterior part of the primitive streak, and from this position cells of the presumptive lateral plate mesoderm migrate downward, outward and forward. Indeed, no other kinds of mesodermal cells are ever found in the posterior half of the primitive streak. This part of the primitive streak can therefore be compared with the lateroventral and ventral lips of the blastopore of a frog.

The area of presumptive somites lies in the anterior part of the primitive streak. From this part of the streak, therefore, the somite material invaginates into the interior. After having passed into the interior, the cells of the presumptive somites migrate outward and forward and become distributed in a strip on each side of the notochordal process. The presumptive lateral mesoderm cells move still farther outward and are later found as sheets of cells on each side of the embryo as a lateral continuation of the dorsal mesoderm.

After its first appearance, the primitive streak increases somewhat in length, mainly owing to a longitudinal stretching of its posterior half. The adjoining part of the area pellucida is also involved in the stretching, so that the area pellucida loses its circular shape and becomes more or less pear-shaped, the attenuated end directed posteriorly. The elongation of the primitive streak is, however, only temporary. As the cells destined to become notochord, mesoderm and so on migrate into the interior of the embryo, the material of which the primitive streak consists becomes gradually exhausted. The influx of cells from the sides becomes retarded and can no longer compensate for the expenditure of cells due to immigration. The whole primitive streak begins to shrink, the anterior end receding backward, while the posterior end remains more or less stationary (Fig. 143, *D*, *E*). It has been ascertained by marking with carbon particles that Hensen's node is carried bodily backward during this recession of the primitive streak (Spratt, 1947). The presumptive notochord cells contained in Hensen's node one after another continue migrating downward and forward, so that the notochordal process is prolonged backward, owing to continual apposition of new cells. In the same way, the strip of somite mesoderm and the sheets of lateral plate mesoderm are continued backward from parts of the primitive streak which retain their properties although the whole structure is reduced in scale. By the end of gastrulation, the primitive streak has shrunk almost to nothing (Fig. 143, F); the residue becomes partly incorporated into the tailbud, which is formed at the posterior end of the body of the embryo, and partly into the cloacal region of the embryo.

As the primitive streak recedes backward, the neural system area, which lies just in front of Hensen's node and even forms the most anterior half of the node itself, stretches backward, while the lateral horns of the area are drawn in toward the midline. As a result, a strip of presumptive neural plate is left in the wake of the receding primitive streak. A part of the neural plate area is also found in front of the place where Hensen's node was located originally. This part will become the prechordal part of the brain.

The primitive streak, being the path by way of which the presumptive internal organs are invaginated into the interior of the embryo, must be considered as the blastopore, even if it does not lead into an archenteron. We have met with this situation in the bony fishes where, notwithstanding the fact that no archenteron is to be found, the edge of the blastodisc was recognized as the blastopore. The recession and disappearance of the primitive streak corresponds therefore to the closure of the blastopore. The remnant of the blastopore, as in the amphibians, is to be found in association with the anus (or cloaca).

We have seen that the primitive streak, while it is active, is a mass of cells, continuous with both the epiblast and the hypoblast, as well as with the sheets of mesodermal cells migrating in between the two, into the blastocoele (Fig. 148, a). In the part of the embryo from which the primitive streak has receded, the continuity of all three layers no longer occurs. The sheet of mesodermal cells, together with the notochordal process, is separated from the overlying epithelium, which no longer contains presumptive mesoderm or endoderm and from now on is pure ectoderm. Likewise, the chordo-mesodermal mantle has been split off from the underlying layer of cells, the former hypoblast (Fig. 148, b). This underlying layer is, however, no longer identical with the original hypoblast. Cells from the primitive streak, originally situated in the surface layer of the blastoderm (in the epiblast), have found their way into the lower layer. These are the cells of the presumptive alimentary canal (Hunt, 1937). The lower layer of cells from now on will be referred to as the endoderm. It is seen that in birds the endoderm has a double origin: some of the cells are derived from the hypoblast, a layer corresponding to the floor of the blastocoele in the amphibians. These cells are used only to a limited extent for the formation of the actual alimentary canal of the embryo; most of them become the endodermal lining of the **yolk sac** (see section 11–1). Other endodermal cells are derived from the primitive streak and join up with the first kind after

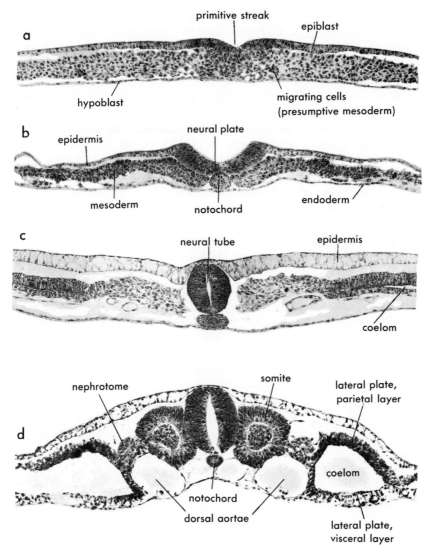

Figure 148. Stages of early development of the chick (transverse sections). *a*, Primitive streak; *b*, neural plate stage; *c*, neural tube stage; *d*, primary organ rudiments.

a process of invagination. These cells remain in the median strip of the endodermal layer, in that area of it which is actually used up for the formation of the walls of the alimentary canal.

That a certain number of endodermal cells reach their destination by invaginating through the primitive streak gives a further justification for regarding the primitive streak as the blastopore.

The neurulation and the formation of the other primary organ rudiments proceed in an anteroposterior direction, just as in the fishes. The neural plate appears in the brain region while the gastrulation movements are still in full swing (see Fig. 143, *E*). As Hensen's node recedes, farther and farther parts of the neural plate become differentiated, and the anterior parts of the neural plate proceed to close into a tube, the neural tube. The neural tube is formed in a very typical way, with a large cavity enclosed by the walls of the tube (Fig. 148, *b, c*). The notochord becomes separated from the adjoining sheets of mesoderm, and the dorsal mesoderm becomes subdivided into segments — the somites (Fig. 148, *d*).

The presumptive alimentary canal of the embryo is represented by a narrow median part of the endodermal layer. This strip of epithelium later forms a fold, with the apex of the fold directed **upward**, i.e., toward the notochord. The margins of the fold then approximate to each other and fuse, enclosing a cavity which will be the cavity of the alimentary canal. This process, however, does not take place along the whole length of the embryo but only at its anterior and posterior ends. In the middle part, although a fold of the endodermal epithelium may be present connecting the anterior and the posterior portions of the alimentary canal, this fold continues to be open towards the underlying yolk. The fate of this opening will be considered later in another connection (section 15–1).

The sheet of mesoderm invaginated through the primitive streak at first consists of loosely lying cells. At the stage when the segmentation of the mesoderm begins, or shortly before, the mesodermal cells reunite into an epithelial arrangement. After the somites and the lateral plates have been formed, the mesoderm of the lateral plate splits into two layers: the external or parietal layer and the internal or visceral layer. The cavity between the two layers is the coelom (Fig. 148, *c, d*). Small coelomic cavities appear also in the somites, but these cavities, as in the amphibians, soon disappear again.

Physiology of Gastrulation

9 — 1 MORPHOGENETIC MOVEMENTS

Gastrulation is essentially a process of movement of parts of the embryo. These movements are very different from the movements of parts of an adult animal. Whereas the movement of parts of an adult are usually of a reversible nature, the gastrulation movements are irreversible; each part remains in the position into which it has been brought by the preceding movement. As the result of the movements, the structure of the embryo is changed, or, in other words, new structural elements are created, such as the archenteron, the neural tube and the notochord, in place of the simple layer of cells found in the blastula stage. The movements have created new shapes, new forms. They have been therefore designated as the **morphogenetic movements** (Vogt, 1925).

The morphogenetic movements appear to be movements of large parts of the whole embryo, which stretch, fold, contract or expand. The question arises: how are these movements achieved? They cannot be ascribed to contractility in the narrow sense of muscle contractility. Neither can they be interpreted as an ameboid movement of the embryo as a whole, because each moving part consists of numerous cells, and the movement of the whole, we should expect, would be an integrated result of the movements of the individual cells.

That the gastrulation cannot be a function of the embryo as a whole has been proved by investigating isolated parts of the young gastrula. We have seen that the presumptive ectoderm contributes to gastrulation by expanding its surface. The expansion is an active process depending on the presumptive ectoderm itself. If large pieces of the animal region of an amphibian blastula or early gastrula are cut out and cultivated in a suitable medium (Holtfreter's saline solution, a modification of Ringer's solution), the presumptive ectoderm rounds itself up into a vesicle, and later the epithelium of this vesicle increases its surface greatly and is thrown into a series of irregular folds as it does so. Also, if presumptive ectoderm is combined with cells of presumptive endoderm and mesoderm in such a proportion that the ectoderm is far in excess of the endodermal and mesodermal parts which it has to cover, the ectoderm tends to be thrown into folds (Spemann, 1921). This shows that the expansion of the ectoderm is active and proceeds independently of the other movements involved in gastrulation. The increase of the surface of the ecto-derm is due partly to a flattening of the cells of the epithelial layer and partly to a rearrangement of cells, those of the lower layers becoming intercalated among the cells of the upper layers; as a result, the epithelium eventually becomes two cells thick.

Similarly, the movements of invagination can be performed by parts of the blastoderm independently of their surroundings. The most suitable method of testing this is to transplant small pieces of the dorsal lip of the blastopore into some other part of the embryo, into the animal region or into the ventral part of the marginal zone. The transplanted piece will invaginate and form an archenteric cavity which may be completely independent of the archenteric cavity of the host embryo. The mechanism by means of which the invagination is achieved is the change of shape and the movements of the cells of the marginal zone. If cells of a columnar epithelium contract at their external ends and expand at their internal ends, so that instead of being prismatic they become pyramidal, the whole epithelial layer must inevitably change its shape and become bent in toward the interior. This is what actually takes place in the blastopore region; the external parts of the cells here be-come attenuated, and the opposite ends of the cells expand. The cells acquire a bottle shape, with the neck of the bottle keeping the cells in touch with the surface, while the bodies of the cells are drawn away from the surface. The area occupied by a given group of cells on the surface of the embryo contracts to a small fraction of what it had been originally (see Fig. 126). The contraction at the external surface during the formation of the blastopore in the frog embryo is so violent that the plasmalemma of the cells is thrown into deep folds, and the deeper sections of the folds are nipped off as vesicles which sink into the cytoplasm (Balinsky, 1961b – Fig. 149).

The change in the shape of the cells is not due to a lateral compression from neighboring cells but is performed by the cells themselves. This is best seen if the cells are isolated by tearing the embryo to pieces: the cells pre-serve their shape, and, what is more, the infolding of the surface layer may even be facilitated by releasing a piece of it from its connections with the surrounding parts (Fig. 150 – Holtfreter, 1943a). The change in shape of the cells can be considered to be a form of ameboid movement; the bulk of the cell is displaced toward the interior. To understand the final result one has to consider, however, one further factor: namely, that the cells are held together at their external (superficial) ends.

As has been mentioned in section 7–4, the cells at the surface of the blastoderm are more firmly held together than the cells which do not reach to the surface. It has been claimed (Holtfreter, 1943a) that the adhesion of cells in the surface layer is due to the presence of an extracellular continuous cuticular membrane, the "surface coat," to which all the cells reaching the surface are firmly connected. With the aid of the electron microscope it can be shown (Balinsky, 1961b) that no such membrane exists, but that the cells

Figure 149. External surface of cells invaginating in the amphibian blastopore (electron-micrograph). Cr, Crypts formed at the surface of the cells; V, vesicles pinched off at the bottom of the crypts; P, pigment granules; B, cell boundaries; Y, yolk platelet.

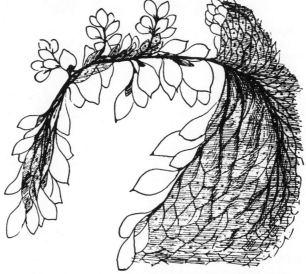

Figure 150. A fraction of an amphibian blastoporal lip with groups of cells held together by the "surface coat." (From Holt-freter, 1943a.)

reaching the surface adhere to each other very closely just at their distal ends and are probably joined by some cementing substance, which is not easily broken. (Fig. 151). As a result, when numerous cells in the blastopore region start moving inward, they cause the surface of the embryo to be pulled inward with the formation of a pocket—the rudiment of the archenteron. Similarly, when the movement of the cells is a general expansion or concentration, the cells, being joined together at their external ends, move in concord, as if borne by a common force (Holtfreter, 1943a).

Once inside, the invaginating cells push away from the rim of the blastopore with a force that can be measured. By inserting an obstacle in the form

Figure 151. Surface of the blastoderm in an early gastrula of the frog *Phrynobatrachus natalensis*. The electron micrograph shows the junction of two cells and the cell boundary reaching right to the external surface. Y, Yolk; *m*, mitochondria; *p*, pigment granules.

of a steel ball in the way of the invaginating chordo-mesoderm of an amphibian, and by measuring the force which was necessary to keep the ball in place (an electromagnet was used for this purpose), it was possible to measure the pressure developed by the migrating masses of cells (Waddington, 1939). This pressure was found to be small but measurable; it was 0.34 mg/mm².

Invagination of the endoderm and mesoderm into the interior of the embryo, as we have seen, cannot always be interpreted as the infolding of an epithelial layer. It often takes the form of immigration of individual cells into the blastocoele, as in the case of the primitive streak of amniotes. A study of the cells in the primitive streak of birds with the electron microscope shows that the behavior of migrating cells in this case is very similar to the behavior of cells in the amphibian blastopore (Balinsky and Walther, 1961). The cells of the epiblast of the chick are roughly cuboidal (or rather, low columnar). The cells participating in the downward migration start by changing their shape. The cells elongate in a vertical direction, their inner ends expand, and their outer ends become narrowed like necks of bottles reaching to the surface of the epiblast (Fig. 152).

Contrary to what happens in the amphibian blastopore, however, not all the cells in the primitive streak undergo the change in shape at the same time; while some cells become bottle-shaped, others retain the original broad columnar form. Eventually the external ends of the bottle-shaped cells lose contact with the surface and the cells slip downward, emerging on the under

Figure 152. Cells in the primitive streak of a chick embryo (electronmicrograph). Some of the cells are withdrawing from the surface of the streak, their distal ends attenuated and the proximal ends expanding. MC, Migrating cells with their distal ends (E) attenuated; SC, stationary cell, cuboidal in shape; N, nuclei; Y, yolk granules. (From Balinsky and Walther, 1961.)

(inner) surface of the epiblast. Presumably the migrating cells are not held as firmly together at their external ends as the cells of the amphibian blastopore, so, instead of pulling the surface inward, they detach themselves from the surface without causing the formation of a pocket (the archenteron). It follows that the presence or absence of an archenteric cavity may be accounted for by a different degree of mutual adhesion of cells involved in the inward movement at the time of gastrulation.

The mechanism of the migration of mesenchyme cells has also been studied in the early gastrulae of sea urchin embryos (Gustafson and Kinnander, 1956; Gustafson and Wolpert, 1961). Cinemicrography was used in these studies. Gastrulae of sea urchins were photographed at 1 to 18 second intervals. When the film, taken in this way, is projected at normal speed, the movements of the cells of the gastrula become accelerated and thus made more readily visible. Before gastrulation, the blastoderm of a sea urchin embryo is a very regular columnar epithelium, somewhat thickened (the cells being larger and taller) at the vegetal pole. The cells of the primary mesenchyme cells start "bubbling" or "pulsating" on their inner surface (the surface facing the blastocoele)—that is to say, the cytoplasm produces rounded protrusions or broad pseudopods which may collapse and then be formed again. Of course, the bulging of the cytoplasm on the inner surface cannot proceed without the cytoplasm being withdrawn from those parts of the cells which are nearer to the exterior, and this in turn means that the adhesion of the cells to one another is lost or reduced. Eventually the mesenchyme cells are squeezed out into the blastocoele, where they become spherical in shape

Figure 153. Stages of gastrulation in the sea urchin embryo, photographed in the living state. A, Immigration of primary mesenchyme. B, Beginning of invagination of the endoderm. C, Invagination of the endoderm with the formation of the archenteron. D, Mesodermal cells move away from the site of the blastopore after establishing contacts with the inner surface of the ectoderm. (Courtesy of Dr. T. Gustafson.)

—an indication of complete or almost complete loss of adhesion between them (Fig. 153). Next, however, the mesenchyme cells start a new form of activity: they send out long pseudopods into the blastocoele. These pseudopods may come into contact with the inner surface of the ectodermal cells and make firm connection with these. If this occurs, the pseudopod contracts and pulls the mesenchyme cell away from the original site of its immigration into the blastocoele. If the pseudopod fails to make a firm contact or if it does not reach an ectodermal cell but is surrounded by the blastocoele fluid, the pseudopod is withdrawn and new pseudopods are formed. By this mechanism of "trial and error" the mesenchyme cells gradually disperse from their point of origin and take up positions on the inner surface of the ectodermal layer.

9–2 SELECTIVE AFFINITIES OF CELLS AS A DETERMINING FACTOR IN CELLULAR REARRANGEMENTS

Gastrulation results in the rearrangement of cells of the embryo, the cells of different germinal layers taking up specific positions in respect of one another. We may ask what the nature of the forces which control this rearrangement is, and whether the new positions of the cells are the result of their own special properties, or whether the organization of the system as a whole (i.e., the whole embryo) is decisive in bringing each kind of cell into its appropriate position. These questions have been investigated by separating the cells of the embryo and allowing them to interact *in vitro* (see Townes and Holtfreter, 1955). The cells of amphibian embryos placed in water which had been made alkaline (*p*H 9.6 to 9.8), by adding potassium hydroxide, lose cohesion and the embryo or parts of it treated with alkali disaggregate into a mass of disconnected single cells. Masses of cells prepared in this fashion from different embryonic tissues (gastrula ectoderm, mesoderm or endoderm, neurula epidermis, neural plate and others) were then mixed together in various combinations and returned to a fresh solution of *p*H 8.0, in which the cells return to their normal state and again join together (Fig. 154).

After the original clump of cells became solid, the cells began to sort themselves out according to their properties. The ectodermal and epidermal cells combined with mesodermal or neural plate cells always ended up by assembling on the surface of the aggregate. The mesodermal and neural plate cells combined either with epidermis or with endoderm disappeared from the surface and were to be found forming solid masses in the interior. The ectodermal and epidermal cells combined with endodermal, mesodermal or neural plate cells always crawled out to the exterior. The mesodermal and neural plate cells combined either with epidermis or endoderm crawled inward and formed masses inside the aggregate. The masses of neural plate cells became hollowed out later and formed structures resembling brain vesicles. Masses of mesodermal cells arranged themselves around "coelomic cavities" (see p. 197). If epidermis, mesoderm and endoderm were present in an aggregate, the epidermis cells concentrated on the exterior, and mesodermal cells took up position between the epidermis and the endoderm; the latter, rather unexpectedly, also occupying part of the external surface of the aggregate. At a later stage, cells of different nature, while adhering to their own kind, split off from cells belonging to a different type, forming cavities between them (Fig. 155). In this way arrangements of cells similar to those produced at the end of normal gastrulation and neurulation are brought about by the activities of individual cells beginning from a completely abnormal starting point. The behavior of the cells under these conditions—and by inference also in normal development—is presumably due to their **selective affinities** (Holtfreter, 1939a, Weiss, 1947, and Steinberg, 1963). When cells touch each other as a result of their random movement, they tend to remain in

a   *b*   *c*

Figure 154. Separated cells of presumptive ectoderm and endoderm joining together into a spherical mass. (From Holtfreter, 1939b.)

Figure 155.   Rearrangement of disaggregated and reaggregated embryonic cells. *a*, Combined epidermal and neural plate cells. *b*, Combined epidermal and mesodermal cells. *c*, Combined epidermal, mesodermal and endodermal cells. (From Townes and Holtfreter, 1955.)

contact. It is supposed that the forces holding the cells together vary, depending on the kind of cells involved. The adhesion appears to be strongest between epithelial cells, much weaker between mesenchyme cells, and practically absent in cells of the macrophage type. Depending on their special properties, a cell may either adhere to another cell and stay in contact with it or may move away from a position in which the surroundings are not of such a nature that they keep the cell bound. Generally speaking, the result of these selective affinities would lead to like cells being brought together. This does not necessarily mean that the bonding between such cells is of a strictly specific nature; to allow similar cells to sort themselves out from among cells with differing properties, it would suffice that the adhesive properties of the former, at any given time, are equal in grade or intensity (see Curtis, 1962, and Steinberg, 1963).

On theoretical grounds it can be expected that cells of an aggregate, if they are free to move around (and this is the case at the time when an aggregate is formed), will eventually take up an arrangement in which the free energy of the structure is at a minimum (Steinberg, 1963). The energy with which we are concerned in this case is the power of the cells to associate themselves with other cells; that is, the power of cohesion of cells to one another. When cells are actually in contact, the energy of cohesion is no longer free; where cells are exposed to the surrounding medium, the energy of cohesion remains free. The requirements of a system with a minimum of free energy dictates that the external surface of the body formed should have the least possible area.

A body with the least possible external surface for a given volume is of course a sphere, and we see that the aggregates generally assume a spherical form (see Fig. 154). If among the cells of the aggregate some would have a stronger adhesion to one another than to others, the same requirements would dictate that the cells with a stronger mutual adhesion should not remain on the surface, but that the surface of the aggregate should be made up of cells with a weaker adhesion—in this way the free energy of the system would be at a minimum. The cells with a stronger mutual adhesion having disappeared from the surface would, in the course of their random movements, meet in the interior, and once they met they would stay together attached to one another by their strong affinities. The same would apply to aggregates consisting of more than two different types of cells; a sort of concentric arrangement might result, depending solely on the different degrees of affinity between cells moving at random.

There is one very obvious discrepancy between the results of reaggregation of isolated embryonic cells and the processes of gastrulation in intact normal embryos. In reaggregates, the endoderm in combination with mesoderm becomes arranged outside and the mesoderm takes up a position inside the endoderm, while the reverse happens in normal development. Even if cells of all three germ layers are present in the reaggregate, the endoderm does not take up a position inside but remains on the surface on one side of the newly formed complex (see Fig. 155, c).

The reason for this discrepancy is twofold. Firstly, the cells in a normal embryo do not move around at random, as do cells in reaggregates; one important condition for the sorting out of cells according to their selective affinities is therefore lacking. Secondly, the cells in the stage preceding gastrulation (the blastula stage) are in the form of an epithelium (the blastoderm) which is more or less distinctly polarized. As in typical epithelia, it has a distal surface, in contact with the external environment, which is different from the proximal surface, facing the inner milieu of the embryo. Now it has been noticed (see Gudernatsch, 1913) that when an epithelial layer is bent, or when cells escape from an epithelium as ameboid or mesenchyme cells, the direction of movement is nearly always in the proximal direction, toward the internal milieu of the embryo. It is the proximal end of the cell that is more likely to start forming pseudopods and embarking on ameboid locomotion, and that is why in an intact embryo the movement of both mesoderm and endoderm is inward and not outward. Under experimental conditions, especially if ectoderm is prevented in some way or other from covering the endoderm (as when extensive parts of the ectoderm and mesoderm are removed by an operation), the endoderm flows to the exterior, and once on the surface it remains there.

9—3 METABOLISM DURING GASTRULATION

Throughout gastrulation, the volume of the embryo does not change appreciably. Every expansion in one direction occurs at the expense of a contraction in another direction or directions. What has been said about the absence of growth during cleavage applies in the same way to the period of gastrulation. Division of cells by mitosis continues, however, throughout gastrulation, and this means that there is an increase of nuclear material at the expense of the cytoplasmic substances. Breakdown and assimilation of reserve materials are also going on, but here a new feature is observed that makes the metabolism of the gastrula different from the metabolism of a blastula.

It could be expected that the morphogenetic movements during gastrulation would cause an increased expenditure of energy and consequently an increased oxidation. This is what is actually found: the oxygen consumption during gastrulation shows a further increase as compared with the cleavage stages and with the blastula. The oxygen consumption of the frog embryo is shown in Table 8.

TABLE 8. OXYGEN CONSUMPTION DURING CLEAVAGE AND GASTRULATION IN THE FROG (AFTER COHEN FROM BARTH AND BARTH, 1954)

Stage	Oxygen Consumption (in Microliters per Milligram of dry Weight per Hour)
Cleavage (stage 6 +)	0.054
Early blastula (stage 8 +)	0.069
Late blastula (stage 9)	0.108
Mid-gastrula (stage 11 −)	0.141
Late gastrula (stage 12 +)	0.162

A similar sharp increase in total oxygen consumption is also observed in sea urchin eggs.

One of the substances particularly involved in the supply of energy during gastrulation in amphibians is glycogen. It has been discovered that the amount of glycogen becomes considerably diminished in the invaginating cells of the dorsal lip of the blastopore. This was first discovered by histochemical methods, by using a specific stain for glycogen on sections of gastrulating embryos (Woerdeman, 1933). Later, by methods of chemical analysis, the exact amounts of glycogen consumed were determined; it was found that in the dorsal lip of the blastopore 31 per cent of the glycogen is lost during gastrulation, whereas in other parts of the embryo only from 1 per cent to 9 per cent is lost in the same time (see Brachet, 1950b).

Rapid breakdown of glycogen in the dorsal lip suggests a particularly active respiration in this area. Direct measurements of respiration, however, showed that the dorsal lip region is by no means the part of the gastrula which respires at the highest rate. To make measurements of respiration, frog gastrulae were cut into several regions, as indicated in Fig. 156. Two big pieces were made of the vegetal hemisphere (a dorsal and a ventral one) and four pieces of the marginal zone and the animal hemisphere (pieces 1 to 4), starting with the dorsal lip of the blastopore. The oxygen consumption was determined for each piece as well as the dry weight, total nitrogen and extractable nitrogen—the latter, as the reader will remember (see Chapter 5) is equivalent to the nitrogen of the active cytoplasm (total nitrogen less the nitrogen contained in the yolk).

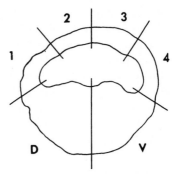

Figure 156. Diagram showing the pieces into which frog gastrulae were cut to study respiration of the different parts. The dorsal side, with the blastopore, is on the left. (After Sze, from Barth and Barth, 1954.)

When the oxygen consumption is related to dry weight of the fragments, it is seen that there is a great difference in the oxygen consumption of various parts of the embryo (see Table 9).

The highest oxygen consumption, if referred to dry weight or to total nitrogen — that is, to the whole mass of the embryonic tissue — is found at the animal pole of the gastrula, and the lowest oxygen consumption is at the vegetal pole. The dorsal side, including the dorsal lip, has a distinctly higher oxygen consumption than the ventral side. This would account for the difference in the breakdown of glycogen as between the dorsal and the ventral lip (see preceding paragraphs). We must realize, however, that not all parts of the cells of a frog gastrula respire; the yolk presumably does not respire at all, whereas it contributes to the dry weight and to the total nitrogen of parts of the embryo.

It would be desirable to eliminate the yolk from calculations of embryonic respiration, and this was done by calculating the oxygen consumption per unit of extractable nitrogen (= nitrogen of active cytoplasm). The data are given in the last line of Table 9, and they show that equal amounts of active cytoplasm have practically the same respiration rate in all parts of the gastrula. In other words, the differences in oxygen consumption observed are due to different amounts of active cytoplasm in relation to yolk; that is, to the gradient of yolk distribution (dealt with in section 4–2), and not to a local specifically higher rate.

The second peculiarity of the metabolism during the gastrulation period is a sharp increase in protein turnover, and particularly in protein synthesis.

In a newt embryo (*Triturus*), the rate of synthesis of protein, as measured

TABLE 9. OXYGEN CONSUMPTION IN DIFFERENT PARTS OF THE FROG GASTRULA IN MICROLITERS OF OXYGEN CONSUMED PER HOUR PER UNIT OF REFERENCE (FROM BARTH AND BARTH, 1953)

Per Unit of	Vegetal dorsal	Dorsal lip piece 1	Animal pole piece 2	Animal pole piece 3	Ventral lip piece 4	Vegetal ventral
Dry weight	1.2	3.7	4.4	3.9	2.7	0.9
Total nitrogen	12.0	37.0	53.0	46.0	30.0	8.2
Extractable nitrogen (nitrogen of active cytoplasm	11.0	12.0	13.0	13.0	13.0	11.0

by the uptake of radioactive precursors, increases fivefold between the stage of the beginning of gastrulation to the late tailbud stage when gastrulation is completed and most of the organ rudiments are formed (Tiedemann and Tiedemann, 1954). In the same way, the rate of radioactive precursor intake into proteins in the sea urchin embryo increases roughly threefold between the earliest gastrula, with primary mesenchyme migrating into the blastocoele, and the middle gastrula (Monroy and Vittorelli, 1962).

The source of materials for the protein synthesis is mainly the protein yolk, contained in the eggs of most animals. The breakdown of yolk granules has been investigated in amphibian embryos both electron microscopically and chemically. With the electron microscope, it can be seen that in amphibian embryos the first change in the yolk platelets consists in the disappearance of the amorphous or granular peripheral layer which contains, besides protein, considerable quantities of ribonucleic acid. The disappearing material goes into solution in the cytoplasm and becomes available for synthetic processes. The solubilization of the peripheral layer occurs in the invaginating chordo-mesoderm during gastrulation, in the neural plate during late gastrulation and early neurulation and still later in the epidermis (Karasaki, 1963b). The solubilization of the crystalline core ("main body") of the yolk platelets occurs considerably later, and, in endoderm, it is delayed till just preceding the stage when the larvae start feeding.

Chemically, the solubilization of the yolk platelets can be recorded either spectrophotometrically by the decrease of light absorption of the yolk platelets in a microscopic preparation (Vahs, 1962) or by separating the yolk platelets from homogenates of embryos and measuring their protein content (Rounds and Flickinger, 1958). By both methods it was shown that there is a rapid decrease of yolk platelet protein in the invaginating chordo-mesoderm starting from the beginning of gastrulation, and a slower decrease in the ectoderm in neurulation stages.

The protein turnover after the beginning of gastrulation seems, in addition, to be essentially different from what had been going on during cleavage. There is no doubt that during gastrulation cytoplasmic proteins are being synthesized at the expense of the yolk. The new proteins are qualitatively different from those of the yolk, and this manifests itself among other ways in a changing proportion of amino acids. In a careful study of the amino acid composition of the sea urchin egg, it has been found (Gustafson and Hjelte, 1951) that the relative amounts of the various amino acids (18 of these could be traced) remain practically unchanged during the first ten hours of development up to the stage of the mesenchyme blastula. With the beginning of gastrulation, although the total nitrogen of the embryo remains at the same level, some of the amino acids decrease in amount, others increase, and these changes continue throughout the period of development up to the pluteus stage (no observations were made on later stages). The changes in the constitution of the proteins have their counterpart in the changes in the quantities of some enzymes, which is perhaps another way of saying the same thing, as enzymes are proteins. The enzymes investigated fall into two groups (Gustafson and Hasselberg, 1951). Some remain unchanged in activity throughout the development up to the pluteus stage. Others, in particular the enzymes apyrase, succino-dehydrogenase, malic dehydrogenase and glutaminase, while remaining at the same level up to late blastula stage, show a clear increase beginning with the early gastrula stage.

The appearance at the gastrula stage of proteins which are qualitatively different from those present in the egg has been proved in sea urchins and in amphibians by applying the extremely sensitive methods of immunology (see also section 16–4). It has been found that the gastrula contains antigens, capable of causing the formation of antibodies, which were not present before, besides containing antigens already present in the egg at the beginning of development (Perlman and Gustafson, 1948; Clayton, 1951).

Protein synthesis, as we have reason to assume, can only proceed when sufficient quantities of messenger RNA are released into the cytoplasm from the nucleus. This is especially important if new kinds of proteins are to be synthesized. The appearance of new kinds of proteins is an almost direct evidence that new molecules of messenger RNA have arrived in the cytoplasm, new molecules that are different in their information content from the ones that might have been in the cytoplasm before. It is to be expected, then, that during gastrulation considerable amounts of new RNA should be synthesized in the nuclei of the cells. This can actually be shown by supplying to the cell radioactive precursors. In one experiment radioactive carbon (C^{14}) was supplied to *Triturus* embryos in different stages in the form of bicarbonate, and the radioactivity was then measured in different fractions of RNA. Table 10 gives the results of the experiment (Tiedemann, 1962). The

TABLE 10. UPTAKE OF RADIOACTIVE CARBON INTO VARIOUS FRACTIONS OF RNA DURING THE DEVELOPMENT OF A *Triturus* EMBRYO (FROM TIEDEMANN, 1962)

Stages	Nuclear RNA	Specific Activity Ribosomal (cytoplasmic) RNA	Soluble (transfer) RNA
Early gastrula	3600	1600	8500
Late neurula	18000	1800	10100
Embryo in early organo-genesis (tailbud stage)	22000	1950	13100

figures show specific activity which is the amount of radioactivity per weight unit; this amount is an indicator of the rate of uptake of precursor into the newly formed molecules of RNA, and thus of the rate of synthesis of RNA.

The data show that the specific activity of nuclear RNA, which includes messenger RNA, increases most rapidly (fivefold during gastrulation and neurulation stages), while the specific activity of the ribosomal and transfer RNA increases only slightly. This is in good agreement with the assumption that during gastrulation and the stages immediately following it the production of messenger RNA on the DNA templates proceeds at a rapid tempo.

9–4 ACTIVITY OF GENES DURING GASTRULATION

Apart from the foregoing data, which characterize the activity of the nuclear DNA in general terms, there are many indirect indications that nuclear genetic factors (the genes), after having been dormant throughout the period of cleavage, begin to manifest themselves during gastrulation, and in ever-increasing measure control the processes of development from this stage onward. This does not mean that the processes taking place during cleavage are not affected by genes, but the effect of the genes is then indirect: it is an action through the medium of the initial structure of the egg as shown in the case of dextral and sinistral cleavage (section 7–9). The structure of the egg cannot, of course, be under the influence of the paternal genes, which enter the egg only during fertilization.

In this section we are concerned with direct interference of the genes in the processes of development, an interference in which the paternal genes as well as the maternal genes can take part.

The evidence in this field is from two sources – from the observation of cleavage without participation of nuclei and from hybridization experiments.

Fragments of sea urchin eggs not containing the nucleus may be treated with agents which cause parthenogenetic activation of the egg (viz., hypertonic sea water). It has been found (Harvey, 1936) that the nonnucleated fragments begin to cleave and may reach the morula stage. The embryos, however, do not form a regular bastula and cannot gastrulate, which shows that the presence of nuclei is necessary for development to go beyond cleavage.

Hybridization experiments must be considered here in some greater detail. If the egg of one species is fertilized by a spermatozoon of another species, the nuclei of the two gametes may fuse and together participate in cleavage and development. Each cleavage cell would then consist of maternal cytoplasm (because the contribution of the spermatozoon to the cytoplasm of the fertilized egg is negligible), the maternal nuclear half and the paternal nuclear half. Embryos of this composition are **true hybrids**. The eggs may be treated just after fertilization, before the nuclei of the egg and the sperm have time to fuse, so as to remove the egg nucleus. This can be achieved, for instance, by puncturing the egg and allowing a small quantity of cytoplasm together with the egg nucleus to flow out of the egg. If the egg is fertilized with sperm of another species, an embryo will develop in which the cytoplasm is maternal, but the nucleus is paternal (see Baltzer, 1940). Such embryos will be referred to as **hybrid andromerogones** (the term **merogony** is applicable to the fertilization of a part or fragment of the egg; **androgenesis** is the development of an embryo having only paternal nuclei). **Andromerogones** are embryos in which an enucleated egg or egg fragment is fertilized by sperm of the same species. As a rule, the andromerogones are haploid.

The results of hybridization depend primarily on the relationship between the two parents. The penetration of the egg by foreign sperm is much more easily achieved than the subsequent cooperation with the maternal cytoplasm. Cases are known in which eggs were "fertilized" by sperm belonging to animals of a different class and even of a different phylum: fertilization of the sea urchin *Sphaerechinus* with sperm of the sea lily *Antedon;* fertilization of the sea urchin *Strongylocentrotus* with sperm of the mollusc *Mytilus.*

In these cases, the sperm penetrates into the egg and activates it but does not play any part in the subsequent development. This is tantamount to a parthenogenetic development of the egg, caused by the penetration of foreign sperm (see Morgan, 1927). If the animals are more closely related, as for instance in the case of a toad's eggs being fertilized by frog's sperm (*Bufo vulgaris* × *Rana temporaria*), the sperm nucleus fuses with the nucleus of the egg. The development (cleavage) begins, but the embryos die before the beginning of gastrulation owing to incompatibility between the sperm nucleus and the egg nucleus and cytoplasm. If the animals are still more closely related, such as species of the same genus, then the hybrids may be fully viable throughout the whole of development.

It is in the cases of rather closely related species, producing viable hybrids, that the influence of the nucleus can best be analyzed. Much of the work has been done on sea urchin development.

If two species of sea urchin, differing in the rate of cleavage, are crossed, the cleavage of the hybrid is always the same as the cleavage of the maternal species. In the sea urchin *Dendraster eccentricus*, the egg cleaves at the rate of 29 to 30 minutes between successive divisions. In *Strongylocentrotus franciscanus*, the interval between successive cleavages is 47 minutes. The hybrid has the maternal rate of cleavage. Also, if fragments of the egg devoid of a nucleus are fertilized, the resulting hybrid andromerogones cleave with a rhythm that is the same as in the maternal species (A. R. Moore, 1933).

The rate of cleavage cannot be influenced by the sperm nucleus. On the other hand, the characters of the larva – the pluteus – are clearly intermediate between the two parents; at the larval stage the sperm nucleus has been able to exert its influence. In a special case, the influence of the sperm nucleus has been discovered as early as the beginning of gastrulation. In the sea urchin *Lytechinus*, the mesenchyme cells produced from the micromeres (section 7–8) migrate into the blastocoele slightly earlier than the beginning of invagination of the archenteron. In the sea urchin *Cidaris*, the mesenchyme cells do not separate from the epithelium until after the archenteron begins to invaginate; they are consequently given off from the inner end of the archenteron. Further, the cleavage of *Lytechinus* proceeds at a much greater pace than in *Cidaris;* the blastula stage is reached after 5.5 hours in the *Lytechinus* embryos, but only after 16 hours in *Cidaris* embryos. The beginning of gastrulation is correspondingly delayed in the second species. When the *Cidaris* eggs were fertilized by *Lytechinus* sperm, the early stages of development up to the gastrula stage were performed exactly as in the maternal species, *Cidaris*. The rate of cleavage corresponded to that typical for *Cidaris*. As the gastrulation approached, the mesenchyme cells began to be separated from the blastoderm just as the invagination of the archenteron first became visible. The stage at which the mesenchyme cells migrated into the blastocoele was therefore intermediate between the two species, and this proved that at the beginning of gastrulation the paternal nucleus was already able to manifest itself (Tennent, 1914).

In hybridization experiments performed on amphibians, it is a rule without exceptions that the cleavage rate is strictly maternal. This also holds good in cases of hybrid andromerogones. It is thus shown that the cytoplasm alone determines the rate of cleavage. The pigmentation of the egg and early developmental stages is of course always maternal, because the egg pigment is synthesized before maturation. Differences in the pigmentation of the larvae become evident only much later when the melanophores, derived from the neural crest, become differentiated.

During the subsequent development the pigmentation depends on the nuclear factors. A hybrid andromerogone was produced by using eggs of the black race of the axolotl *(Ambystoma mexicanum)* and sperm of the white race. In the embryo, the cytoplasm was derived therefore from the black race and the nucleus from the white race. The animals were all white, thus showing that the nucleus dominated over the cytoplasm (Baltzer, 1941).

No crosses are known in amphibians in which morphological differences between the two parent species could be discovered in the early stages — the gastrulation or the neurulation stages. It is found, however, that the end of cleavage and the beginning of gastrulation is the stage when the incompatibility of the sperm nucleus and the egg nucleus and cytoplasm first manifests itself. In many hybrid combinations the hybrid goes through the early stages of cleavage more or less normally, but the development stops in the blastula or early gastrula stage *(Rana esculenta × Bufo vulgaris; R. esculenta × R. temporaria; B. vulgaris × R. temporaria; Triturus palmatus × Salamandra maculosa; R. pipiens × R. sylvatica; R. pipiens × R. clamitans* and others) (Morgan, 1927; J. A. Moore, 1946; A. B. C. Moore, 1950). If the true hybrid between two species is viable, the hybrid andromerogone may not be. The andromerogone embryos, even without hybridization, are always weaker than normal embryos due to the haploid state of their nuclei. However, the hybrid andromerogones are much inferior in their capacity for development. The hybrid combination *R. pipiens × R. capito* is fully viable up to adult stage when the chromosomes of both parental species are present. The andromerogone of *R. pipiens* fertilized with sperm of the same species develops into a tadpole. The hybrid andromerogone *(R. pipiens × R. capito)* develops normally through cleavage and gastrulation stages, but dies in the early neurula stage (Ting, 1951). The paternal chromosomes, in the presence of maternal chromosomes, may function normally and transmit the paternal characters to the diploid hybrid, but left alone with the foreign cytoplasm they prove to be inadequate for supporting development. Further cases are known in which the andromerogonic hybrid dies during gastrulation or shortly after *(R. pipiens × R. palustris; Triturus alpestris × T. palmatus; T. palmatus × T. cristatus)* (Hadorn, 1932; de Roche, 1937; A. B. C. Moore, 1950).

There is some direct evidence that in hybrids the paternal chromosomes cause the synthesis of proteins of their own species about the time of the beginning of gastrulation. The evidence was obtained by immunological methods in the following experiment. Eggs of the sea urchin *Paracentrotus lividus* were fertilized with sperm of *Psammechinus microtuberculatus*. Using the blood plasm of animals immunized against proteins of *Psammechinus microtuberculatus*, it was found that the fertilized eggs showed no trace of these specific antigens. Twenty-four hours after fertilization, however, when the hybrid embryos were in the mesenchyme blastula stage, antigens of the paternal species, *Psammechinus microtuberculatus*, could be clearly detected. As the paternal antigens could not be discovered earlier, it is evident that these antigens (predominantly proteins) had been built up in the cytoplasm, which is derived mainly from the egg, under the influence of the sperm chromosomes (Harding, Harding and Perelman, 1954). The death of nonviable hybrids and hybrid andromerogones is preceded by an arrest of at least some of the physiological processes which characterize the onset of gastrulation, such as the increase in oxygen consumption, glycolysis, and the increase in the amount of ribonucleic acid (Brachet, 1950a); the latter is especially suggestive, as this involves a synthetic process. We have seen that besides the synthesis of ribonucleic acids the embryo during gastrulation begins synthesizing new proteins, manifested as new antigens when investigated by serological methods. It is highly probable that in cases of incompatibility between the foreign paternal nuclei and the maternal cytoplasm these synthetic processes cannot go on, or cannot go on satisfactorily, hence the arrest of development and death.

If, on the other hand, the nuclei and the cytoplasm are compatible, the synthesis of new proteins and nucleic acids (and probably also other cytoplasmic substances) goes on progressively. Since some of the newly synthesized substances are different from the ones present before, rapid changes in the constitution of the embryo are inaugurated, changes that involve not only the position and the arrangement of cells, as in the gastrulation movements, but also their inherent physiological properties. This leads to the next period of development, in which the various parts become progressively differentiated from each other: the period of **organogenesis**.

Determination of the Primary Organ Rudiments*

The experiments of local vital staining and similar methods, allowing the experimenter to reconstruct fate maps, do not give any information as to whether or not the cells in the various areas actually have different potentialities for development. The only information that these experiments give is about the eventual destination of each part of the early embryo in normal development. Certain distinctions between cells belonging to the various areas are apparent, such as differences in yolk content, pigmentation and so on. There is, however, no *a priori* reason to believe that such differences are actually linked together with the future development of each part. In the previous pages it has been indicated that, even if isolated from its normal environment, each area of the blastula tends to perform morphogenetic movements that roughly correspond to the part which it would play in normal gastrulation. This again does not prove in itself that the type of differentiation which is to be expected from each presumptive area is already fixed in an early stage.

To find out whether the presumptive areas of a blastula are actually preformed for a specific part in the future development, methods other than observing normal development are necessary.

One of the methods used is the method of **transplantation**, already mentioned in another connection (section 9–1). Small pieces may be cut out of embryos in various stages of development and inserted into suitably prepared wounds of the same or another embryo. In the case of transplantation of a

---

*A review of this subject has been published by Saxén and Toivonen (1962).

piece of the same embryo to another place, the transplantation is said to be **autoplastic**. If the transplantation is from one individual to another of the same species, the transplantation is **homoplastic**. If the transplantation is to an individual of another species belonging to the same genus, the transplantation is **heteroplastic**. A transplantation to an individual more distantly related than species of one genus is called **xenoplastic**. The animal (embryo) from which a part is taken is referred to as the **donor**; the animal to which the part is transplanted is called the **host**.

In adult animals, especially highly organized animals such as vertebrates, transplantation is not easy, only autoplastic and homoplastic transplantations usually being successful. In embryos, however, and in lower invertebrates (such as the coelenterates), the grafts may heal successfully even after xenoplastic transplantations. Successful transplantations have been carried out between embryos of frogs and salamanders, and mammals and birds.

It is usually important to know later which tissues and cells are derived from the graft and which from the host. The distinction is easy if donor and host are sufficiently different from each other. The cells may be told apart by their size, staining properties, and other factors. Sometimes differences may be found even between cells belonging to closely related animals. Differences in pigmentation may be very useful. The eggs of *Triturus (Triton) cristatus*, for instance, are entirely devoid of pigment, whereas eggs of other species of *Triturus (T. taeniatus, T. alpestris)* have fine granules of black pigment in their cytoplasm. These pigment granules are distributed to all the cells during cleavage. If tissues of *T. taeniatus* and *T. cristatus* are joined in transplantation, the cells of *T. taeniatus* can be distinguished both macroscopically and in sections by the presence of pigment granules. If no natural differences can be discovered between the two animals (embryos) used for transplantation, artificial differences may be introduced by staining one of the embryos with vital dyes. The presence or absence of the dye will indicate the position of the graft. In some cases the vital staining may be preserved in sections of the operated embryo by special methods.

10—1 DETERMINATION OF THE NEURAL PLATE

Heteroplastic transplantation between *Triturus cristatus* and *Triturus taeniatus* embryos has been used to investigate the determination of the presumptive ectodermal areas—the epidermis area and the neural system area (Spemann, 1921). A small piece of the epidermis area of an early gastrula was transplanted into the neural system area of another embryo in the same stage of development (Fig. 157). The result was that the grafted material developed in conformity with its new surroundings and became first a part of the neural plate of the host (Fig. 157, c) and later a part of the neural tube (Fig. 158). There was every reason to conclude that it was differentiating as nervous tissue. In the case of a reverse transplantation, presumptive neural material differentiates into skin epidermis in conformity with its new surrounding (Fig. 157, d). Presumptive ectoderm (either from the epidermis area or from the neural system area) was transplanted also into the marginal zone of an early gastrula. In this case, the graft was drawn into the blastopore

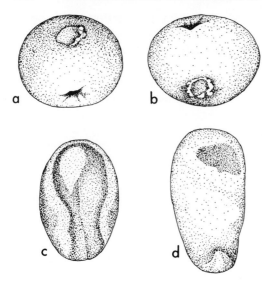

Figure 157. Exchange of presumptive epidermis and presumptive neural plate in the early gastrula stage of two *Triturus taeniatus* embryos differing slightly in density of pigmentation. *a, b,* Embryos immediately after the operation. *c, d,* The same embryos in the neural plate stage. In *c* the graft forms part of the neural plate. In *d* the graft forms part of the anteroventral epidermis. (From Spemann, 1938.)

in the course of gastrulation and was later found in different places in the interior of the host. In every case, the graft differentiated in conformity with its surroundings and took part in the development of various organs of the host: the notochord, the somites, lateral plate mesoderm, kidney tubules, wall of the gut (Mangold, 1923).

Figure 158. Section through anterior head region of a *Triturus taeniatus* embryo in which part of the brain (shown by asterisks) is developed from grafted *Triturus cristatus* presumptive epidermis. (From Spemann, 1938.)

It is thus evident that the fate of presumptive nervous system and presumptive epidermis is not fixed at the time of the stages used for the above
experiments. Besides having a definite normal fate—called the **prospective
significance**—the parts tested possess abilities to develop in various other
ways, under experimental conditions. This ability of the parts of an early
embryo to develop in more than one way is called the **prospective potency**
of these parts.

The prospective potency of the neural area is therefore shown to include
not only epidermis but also mesodermal and endodermal tissues. The prospective potency of the epidermis area includes nervous system and mesodermal and endodermal tissues as well. The two prospective potencies are
practically identical, in spite of the different prospective significance.

The potencies of the marginal zone and the vegetal region could not be
tested as easily as those of the presumptive ectoderm, because they both
tended to invaginate into the interior from every position in which they were
placed. However, in exceptional cases parts of the transplanted marginal
zone may remain on the surface at the end of gastrulation, and then they also
conform to their surroundings in their development and differentiate as
epidermis or neural system.

An entirely different result is observed if the transplantation of pieces of
ectoderm is performed at the end of the period of gastrulation. A transplanted
piece of presumptive neural system area will differentiate as brain or spinal
cord in whatever part of the embryo it has been placed. Usually in this case
the transplanted tissue sinks from the surface of the embryo—this would
correspond to neurulation in normal development—and develops into a
vesicle with thickened walls. Sometimes definite parts of the neural system
can be recognized, such as one or other of the brain vesicles or an eye (Spemann, 1919). The presumptive epidermis of a completed gastrula has likewise lost the ability to differentiate as nervous system. If it is transplanted
into the nervous system area it does not conform to its surroundings and may
interfere with the closing of the neural tube, but even if it does get enclosed
inside the neural tube it differentiates into epidermis and not into nervous
tissue.

Obviously some change has occurred between the early gastrula and the
completion of gastrulation. The prospective potencies of presumptive neural
tissue and epidermis have been narrowed down and are now the same as
their prospective significance, so far as these experiments go. This narrowing down of the prospective potency, which is equivalent to the fixing of the
fate of a part of the embryo, is known as **determination**. After the process of
determination has taken place the respective parts are said to be **determined**.
The experiments described so far show that the neural system as a whole is
determined by the end of gastrulation. They do not show, however, whether
every part of the neural system is determined at the same time. The determination of parts inside the primary organ rudiments will be dealt with
later (Chapters 13, 14 and 15).

The experiments described above also show that the determination of
parts of the ectoderm does not take place from causes inherent in the ectoderm itself. The differentiation of parts of the ectoderm is dependent on the

surroundings in which the ectodermal cells find themselves. Further experiments proved that the condition which is decisive in determining the development of the neural plate is contact of the ectoderm with the roof of the archenteron—i.e., with the sheet of cells representing mainly the presumptive notochord and somites—which shifts forward underneath the ectoderm during gastrulation. Parts of ectoderm in contact with the archenteron roof differentiate into neural plate and nervous tissue.

One of the most spectacular experiments showing the role of the archenteron roof was performed by Spemann's pupil, Hilde Mangold (Spemann and H. Mangold, 1924). Hilde Mangold transplanted heteroplastically (from *Triturus cristatus* to *Triturus taeniatus*) a piece of the dorsal lip of the blastopore of an early gastrula. The graft was placed near the lateral lip of the blastopore of the host embryo (also an early gastrula), and subsequently most of the graft invaginated into the interior, leaving, however, a narrow strip of tissue on the surface. When the host embryo developed further, it was found that an additional whole system of organs appeared on the side where the graft had been placed. The additional organs together comprised an almost complete secondary embryo. This secondary embryo lacked the anterior part of the head. The posterior part of the head was present, however, as indicated by a pair of ear rudiments. There was a neural tube flanked by somites and a tailbud at the posterior end (Fig. 159, top). A microscopic examination revealed the presence of a notochord, kidney tubules and an additional lumen in the endoderm representing the gut of the secondary embryo. All the parts of the secondary embryo were found to lie at about the same level as corresponding parts of the host. Since heteroplastic transplantation was used in this experiment, it was possible to determine what parts of the secondary embryo were developed from the graft, and which were developed from the cells of the host (Fig. 159, bottom). It was found that the notochord of the secondary embryo consisted exclusively of graft cells; the somites consisted partly of graft and partly of host cells. A small number of graft cells were present in the neural tube; these were certainly the cells that had not invaginated. The bulk of the neural tube, part of the somites, the kidney tubules and the ear rudiments of the secondary embryo consisted of host cells. The additional lumen in the endoderm was also surrounded by host cells. All these latter parts would not have developed if the graft had not been present. It follows that their development was due to some influence of the graft. This influence, causing the development of certain organs of the embryo, is called **embryonic induction**. The part which is the source of the influence is called the **inductor**.

From the experiment just described, it may be concluded that the induction of the neural system is due to the activity of the underlying tissues, the presumptive notochord and the presumptive somites in particular. The issue is somewhat complicated by the participation of both graft and host cells in some of the organs of the secondary embryo. This was later shown not to be essential: in other experiments the whole of the induced neural tube was developed exclusively from host tissue. It was further found that anterior parts of the brain could also be induced by the roof of the archenteron, so that the induced nervous system might be complete.

In special experiments it could be ascertained which parts of the gastrula

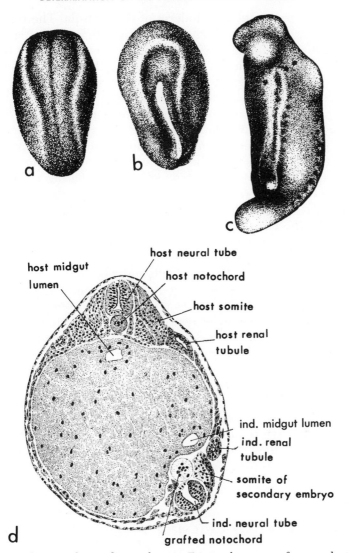

Figure 159. Induction of secondary embryo in *Triturus* by means of a transplanted piece of blastopore lip. *a* and *b*, Operated embryo in the neurula stage; *a*, dorsal view with host neural plate; *b*, lateral view with induced neural plate. *c*, Same embryo in the tailbud stage with an induced secondary embryo on the side. *d*, Same embryo, transverse section. (After Spemann and H. Mangold, from Spemann, 1938.)

are capable of inducing the neural system. Pieces were taken from all parts of the early gastrula and each slipped into the blastocoele of an embryo in the early gastrula stage. Only grafts taken from the dorsal lip of the blastopore and the adjoining parts of the marginal zone were found to be able to induce. The area capable of induction coincided, in fact, almost exactly with the presumptive areas of notochord, somites and prechordal plate (Bautzmann, 1926).

Likewise it has been ascertained what embryonic tissues are able to react to the induction by developing as nervous system. The tissue in question is the ectoderm or presumptive ectoderm of the gastrula. The reactive ability is highest in the early gastrula stage, it is still high in the midgastrula stage, begins to decline in the late gastrula and fades away with the beginning of neurulation. This can be shown by transplanting the inductor underneath the ectoderm in successive stages, and the result may be expressed as a percentage of successful inductions (Machemer, 1932).

In later stages, not only does the percentage of inductions diminish but the volume and degree of differentiation is also reduced. Complete neural systems or large brain vesicles may be induced by transplantation of inductors in the early gastrula stage, but in the early neurula inductions are very weak; they may consist of only a few cells differentiating as nervous tissue. The presumptive ectoderm of the blastula is not able to react to the inductive stimulus; if the inductor is transplanted in the blastula stage, the ectoderm reacts by the formation of a neural plate only after the gastrulation is completed. In all cases, the induced neural system develops simultaneously with the neural system of the host.

All this shows that the reacting cells must be in a particular state to be able to differentiate into nervous system under the influence of the inductor. This particular state of reactivity is referred to as **competence**. The competence for neural induction is restricted to the ectoderm and is present during a short period only. If during this period the presumptive ectoderm is not stimulated to differentiate to neural tissue, it differentiates as epidermis. No special stimulation (induction) is necessary to cause the latter differentiation, though it has been found that certain conditions must be satisfied if the epidermis is to develop progressively and produce normal skin epithelium. The condition is the presence of underlying connective tissue. Without underlying connective tissue, epidermis very quickly degenerates: the cells lose their polarity, they do not remain arranged as an epithelial layer but form a spongy mass consisting of irregular strands of cells, and eventually they perish.

10–2 SPEMANN'S PRIMARY ORGANIZER

Hilde Mangold's experiment brought out the fact that the transplanted dorsal lip of the blastopore exercises its influence not only on the ectoderm, by inducing the neural plate, but also on the mesoderm and endoderm. This has also been corroborated by further experiments. Extensive inductions can be produced in the mesoderm by transplanting pieces of the dorsal lip of the blastopore. The organs developed from the graft are usually supplemented by parts produced from the host tissue as a result of the induction, so that a more or less complete whole is developed. Together with the parts developed from ectoderm, a secondary embryo of various degrees of completeness arises. All the parts of the secondary embryo may be in harmonious relationship to each other, both in size and position.

It is the ability of the dorsal lip of the blastopore to cause, when transplanted, the development of a complete whole that led to the dorsal lip of the blastopore being called **organizer,** or **primary organizer** (Spemann, 1938). The organizer of the gastrula is that region of the egg that can be distinguished in the stages before the beginning of cleavage, as the **gray crescent**. Experimental evidence is now available that already at this early stage the gray crescent possesses the special properties of the organizer; furthermore it has been shown that the properties of the organizer are inherent in the cortex of the egg.

A. S. G. Curtis has succeeded in performing the remarkable experiment of transplanting parts of the cortex in the fertilized egg of the clawed toad *Xenopus laevis* at the beginning of cleavage. The gray crescent cortex was excised and transplanted into a ventral position on another embryo. The graft healed in its new position, cleavage occurred fairly normally, but after gastrulation a secondary embryo with neural tube and notochord was found to have developed at the site of the operation. In another experiment the cortex in the gray crescent area was removed; the result: failure of the embryo to develop any embryonic organ rudiments (Curtis, 1960, 1963).

We can thus link up the phenomena occurring during gastrulation with factors present at the beginning of development; i.e., we can trace the dorsal lip of the blastopore with its peculiarities to a specific part of the cytoplasm of the fertilized egg. The gastrulation movements and the determination of parts of the embryo during and after the gastrulation are thus foreshadowed by the organization of the egg before cleavage.

The inductions produced by a transplanted organizer or its part may vary in degree of complexity. When the induction is weak and the quantity of induced neural tissue is small, it is sometimes impossible to compare the induced tissue with any part of the normal nervous system. If, however, the inductor used is powerful, and the reaction of the competent tissue good, large organs or groups of organs are developed. In this case, the induced parts can be recognized as respresenting certain organs of the normal embryo: specific parts of the brain, such as forebrain, midbrain and medulla, the spinal cord, eyes, nose rudiments, ear vesicles, somites, pronephric tubules and tailbuds. The various parts are always in a more less harmonious relationship, so that parts belonging to the head are not mixed at random with parts belonging to the posterior trunk and tail region. In other words, the inductions are regionally specific.

The regional specificity may be imposed on the induced organs by the inductor. The anterior part of the archenteric roof induces head organs, and may be called a **head inductor** the posterior part of the archenteric roof induces trunk organs and tailbuds and may be called the **trunk** or **spino-caudal inductor**. The head inductor may be further differentiated into the **archencephalic** inductor, inducing forebrain, eyes and nose rudiments, and the **deuterencephalic** inductor, inducing hindbrain and ear vesicles (Lehmann, 1945).

During gastrulation, the anterior part of the archenteric roof invaginates over the dorsal lip of the blastopore earlier than the posterior part of the archenteric roof. The dorsal blastopore lip of the early gastrula therefore contains the archencephalic and deuterencephalic organizer (inductor), and the dorsal blastopore lip of the late gastrula contains the spinocaudal organizer (inductor). The inductions produced by the dorsal lip of the blastopore taken from the early and the late gastrula differ in accordance with expectation: the first tends to produce head organs, and the second tends to produce trunk and tail organs (Spemann, 1931).

In the case illustrated in Figure 159 the induction could be classified as

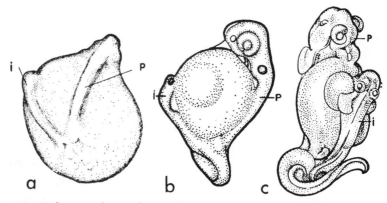

Figure 160.   Induction of a secondary embryo *(i)* by means of a grafted primary organizer in a frog. (After Spemann and Schotté, 1932.)

combined deuterencephalic and spinocaudal, but lacking archencephalic parts.

Although the "primary organizer" was first discovered in urodele amphibians, it was soon found that the dorsal lip of the blastopore and the roof of the archenteron of other vertebrates has the same function in development. In particular it was found that the chordo-mesoderm in all vertebrates induces the nervous system and the sense organs.

In frogs, the induction of a secondary embryo can be performed by the dorsal lip of the blastopore transplanted into the blastocoele of a young gastrula, in very much the same way as in newts and salamanders (see Fig. 160; Schotté, 1930). The same applies to the cyclostomes, in particular to the lampreys, whose cleavage is holoblastic and whose blastula and gastrula resemble those of amphibians (see Fig. 161, *a*; Bytinski-Saltz, 1937; Yamada, 1938). In bony fishes, inductions of secondary well-developed embryos were produced by transplanting the posterior edge of the blastodisc, which corresponds to the dorsal lip of the blastopore, into the blastocoele of another embryo (Fig. 161, *b*, *c*; Oppenheimer, 1936, in *Fundulus* and *Perca*), or by transplanting the invaginated chordo-mesoderm and endoderm (Luther, 1935, in *Salmo*). Neural inductions were also obtained by transplanting the

Figure 161.   Induction of secondary embryos by grafting of the primary organizer in the lamprey *(a)* and the perch *(b, c). p*, Primary embryo; *i*, induced secondary embryo. (*a*, From Yamada, 1938; *b, c*, from Oppenheimer, 1936.)

dorsal lip of the blastopore in the sturgeon (Ginsburg and Dettlaff, 1944). (See also Oppenheimer, 1947.)

In the birds, the existence of the primary organizer was established by experiments by Waddington and his collaborators. The inducing part was found to be the anterior half of the primitive streak, which for other reasons we have recognized as corresponding to the lips of the blastopore in amphibians. To test the inducing ability of the primitive streak, whole blastoderms were removed from the egg in early gastrulation or pregastrulation stages and cultivated *in vitro* on a blood plasma clot. Parts of the primitive streak from another embryo were then inserted between the epiblast and hypoblast. Very good inductions of secondary embryos were obtained in this way (Fig. 162; Waddington, 1933; Waddington and Schmidt, 1933; see also Waddington, 1952). Hensen's node does not differ in inducing ability from the part of the primitive streak immediately following, but the posterior third of the primitive streak cannot induce neural differentiation. We have seen that cells migrating through the posterior part of the primitive streak give rise to lateral plate mesoderm (p. 209). This part of the streak corresponds therefore to the lateroventral lips of the blastopore of an amphibian gastrula, so the lack of inducing ability of this part is not surprising. In later stages, neural induction may be caused by transplantation of the head process—the notochord rudiment.

Much light on the relation of the hypoblast to the epiblast of the avian blastoderm has been thrown by experiments performed by Waddington and his collaborators (Waddington, 1933, 1952). After excision of the whole blastoderm it is possible to separate the hypoblast from the epiblast, to join them together so that the anteroposterior (longitudinal) axis of the epiblast is placed at an angle of 90 to 180 degrees to the anteroposterior axis of the

Figure 162. Induction of a secondary embryo by means of a grafted primitive streak in a bird. *a*, Surface view; the secondary embryo is on the right. *b*, Section through the same embryo, showing the host axial system (right) and the induced neural tube lying above the neural tube and mesoderm developed from the graft (left). (After Waddington and Schmidt, from Waddington, 1952.)

a

b

hypoblast. The preparation is then cultivated *in vitro* on a blood plasma clot. It was found that, as a result of the discrepancy in the orientation of the epiblast and hypoblast, the primitive streak developing in the epiblast became curved, so as to coincide in part with the orientation of the hypoblast. When the rotation of the epiblast was 180 degrees, a completely new primitive streak appeared in some cases, with its anteroposterior axis orientated in accord with the position of the hypoblast, and thus pointing in the opposite direction to the one in which it should have been pointing normally. The hypoblast is thus capable of imparting its polarity to the epiblast and causing the complicated system of movements in the epiblast already described (section 8–7).

The primitive streak in birds is thus dependent on the underlying hypoblast for its formation. This process of induction is something for which no analogue has been found so far in other vertebrates.

No experiments on the primary organizer have been done in reptiles, but one would expect that the archenteron has the same inducing activity in this class as in other vertebrates.

Because of technical difficulties, only very inadequate information is available on the primary organizer and neural induction in mammals. A successful neural induction has been performed in a rabbit embryo by cultivating the early blastodisc on a plasma clot and implanting the primitive streak of the chick as an inductor (Fig. 163; Waddington, 1934). The experiment proves that the tissues of a mammalian gastrula have the competence for neural induction. It is practically certain that the primitive streak and the cells migrating from the streak (chordo-mesoderm) are the source of the inducing stimuli. This suggestion may be supported by the fact that the anterior end of a somewhat later rabbit embryo (with two pairs of somites) induced a neural plate in a chick embryo when placed under a chick blastoderm (Waddington, 1936).

More recently, it has been proved that the primary organizer and neural induction exist also in the lower chordates, and in particular in *Amphioxus*. Tung, Wu and Tung (1962b) transplanted pieces of tissue from the inner surface of the dorsal blastopore lip of an early gastrula of *Amphioxus* into the blastocoele of another embryo in the same stage (Fig. 164, *A*) and observed that a secondary embryo developed in the ventral region of the host with a notochord and mesoderm produced by the graft and a neural tube induced from host tissue (Fig. 164, *B*).

In ascidians, the development of the brain is dependent on the notochordal rudiment and also on the anterior endoderm, but the relation between

Figure 163. Induction of a neural plate in a rabbit embryo by means of a grafted piece of primitive streak of the chick. The induced neural plate *(I.n.p.)* is joined to the host neural plate *(H.n.p.)*. G, Cyst developed from the graft. (From Waddington, 1934.)

Figure 164. Neural induction in *Amphioxus* (Branchiostoma) *belcheri. A,* Diagram of operation: cells lying inside doral lip of the blastopore transplanted into the blastocoel of an embryo in the same stage of development. *B,* Transverse section of the host embryo with a secondary neural tube (nt) induced by the grafted notochord material (gn); hn, host notochord; hnt, host neural tube. Sec. emb-secondary embryo. (From Tung, Wu and Tung, 1962b.)

these parts is of a somewhat different nature: the ability to react to the induction is present only in the cells of the presumptive brain area. Other cells, such as cells of presumptive epidermis, cannot be converted to nerve cells by the action of the notochordal rudiment. In this way the "organizing" action of the notochordal rudiment is much more restricted than in amphibians and other chordates (Reverberi, Ortolani and Farinella-Ferruzza, 1960).

We will now consider the nature of the inducing stimuli. Most of the work has been done with amphibian material as the reacting system.

10–3   ANALYSIS OF THE NATURE OF INDUCTION

The induction of the neural plate by the underlying chordo-mesoderm suggests the problem of analyzing the nature of the influence exerted by the inductor on the reacting ectoderm. Spemann gave the active region the name of organizer, meaning that this was the part which organizes the process of development. He wanted to suggest that the term "organizer" was not merely a metaphor, and to say that the action of the organizer "is not a common chemical reaction, but that these processes of development, like all vital processes, are comparable, in the way they are connected, to nothing we know so much as to those vital processes of which we have the most intimate knowledge, viz., the psychical ones" (Spemann, 1938, p. 372).

This opinion of Spemann's has not, however, been borne out by subsequent experiments, or at least it has not been supported in its original form. It has been found that the nature of the inducing agent can be analyzed by physicochemical methods.

In the study of the nature of induction, the first question that had to be answered was whether some vital activity of the organizer is essential for neural plate induction; that is, whether the organizer can exercise its action only in the living state. To answer this question, attempts were made to test whether the organizer could retain its inducing power after its vital activities had been stopped. The organizer—the dorsal lip of the blastopore—was killed by various means—by boiling, by treating it with alcohol or petrol ether, by freezing or by desiccation—and was then implanted into a living embryo in an appropriate stage of development (the early gastrula stage). It was found that a killed organizer can still induce (Bautzmann, Holtfreter, Spemann and Mangold, 1932). The vital activity of the organizer is therefore not essential for induction. These experiments made it very likely that the roof of the archenteron produces its effect by liberating some chemical substance which is the immediate cause of induction. It is plausible that such a substance could be liberated even from dead tissue.

If chemical substances liberated by the inductor were responsible for its effect on the reacting cells, it should be possible to observe induction under conditions which would exclude the immediate contact between inductor and reacting tissue which occurs in normal development. For many years, all attempts to prevent immediate contact between the neural inductor and reacting presumptive ectoderm led either to an absence of induction or produced very dubious results. Eventually, however, very clear-cut neural induction was obtained by the interposing, in vitro, of a 20 μ-thick Millipore filter between a piece of organizer material (dorsal blastopore lip) and a piece of presumptive early gastrula ectoderm of Triturus (Saxén, 1961). The presumptive ectoderm exposed to the treatment later became rounded up, forming a vesicle with very distinct brain parts, including an eye with lens in one case. The average pore size of the filter was 0.8 μ, which of course allows very large molecules, including protein molecules, to pass through.

Experiments with Abnormal Inductors and Induction by Substances of Known Chemical Composition. After the first indications were obtained that the action of the inductor is mediated by chemical means, the obvious thing to do was to find out what kind of substance or substances were involved. This task turned out to be quite a difficult one, largely because of the small size of the embryo and the very minute quantities of the substances operating in the induction. The problem was therefore approached in an indirect way, first by trying to find sources of the "inducing substance" other than the roof of the archenteron, and second by trying out various chemicals for their ability to replace the natural induction.

A large series of experiments, carried out by many research workers, investigated whether the inducing substances can emanate only from the roof of the archenteron, or whether perhaps other tissues can also produce similar substances. It was shown experimentally that the second alternative is the correct one. First of all, it was found that the neural plate, once it has begun to differentiate, may be a source of an inductive stimulus for neural differentiation (Mangold and Spemann, 1927). The inductive ability is not restricted to the early stages of neural development, but is also present in the tissues which are derived from the neural plate; i.e., in the tissues of the brain and spinal cord in the larva and in the adult animal. If the roof of the archenteron is the normal inductor of the neural plate, the nervous tissue may be called an abnormal inductor of the same. The notochord and the dorsal mesoderm (the muscles derived from the somites) also preserve their ability to induce long after the time when the neural plate induction takes place in the normal embryo. It has been found, furthermore, that almost any tissue of the adult animal can induce a neural plate, and other organ rudiments besides, if it is placed under the presumptive ectoderm of an embryo in the early gastrula stage. Liver, kidney and muscles have been found to be very good inductors, but gut, skin and various other tissues have also been found to be effective (Holtfreter, 1934b).

In earlier experiments on organizer action, the inductor (the dorsal lip of the blastopore) was transplanted into a wound made in the blastoderm of the host embryo. The graft healed in and, at first, became part of the blastoderm. It later invaginated, owing to its inherent ability for that kind of morphogenetic movement, and so it came to lie underneath the reacting presumptive ectoderm. This method obviously could not be used with "abnormal inductors," which do not have the ability to invaginate. Instead, a different method was used: the piece of tissue to be tested, or a piece of coagulated extract, was pushed into the blastocoele of a late blastula or early gastrula through a cut made in the animal hemisphere of the host embryo (Fig. 165). The cut heals very quickly and later, when the gastrulation proceeds, the graft becomes wedged in between the invaginating endo-mesoderm and the ectoderm, usually somewhere in the liver region. The graft is pressed against the ectoderm and is thus in a good position to exercise its ability to induce.

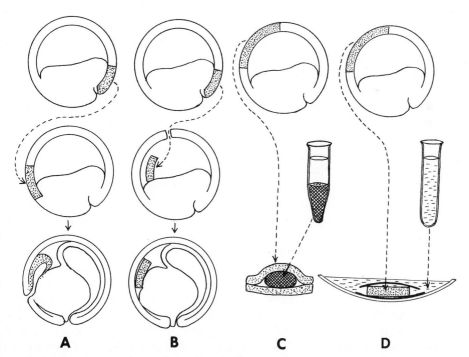

Figure 165. Four methods of exposing gastrula ectoderm to induction (diagrammatic). *A,* Transplantation of part of dorsal lip (stippled) into the ventral marginal zone, where it invaginates and forms a secondary archenteron. *B,* Transplantation of part of dorsal lip (stippled) into the blastocoele through a slit at the animal pole. Graft is eventually pressed against the ventral ectoderm. *C,* "Sandwich experiment": inductor (such as a centrifuged tissue homogenate) placed between two pieces of presumptive gastrula ventral ectoderm. *D,* Cultivation of a piece of presumptive ventral ectoderm of a gastrula in a watch glass filled with fluid containing inducing substance in solution. The reacting ectoderm is held between two layers of supporting material (silk) to prevent it from curling.

Further methods were devised to eliminate the possible interaction of the graft with the primary organizer of the host embryo. The "sandwich method" consists in cutting out pieces of presumptive ectoderm from the animal hemisphere of a blastula or beginning gastrula and then placing the inductor between two flaps of ectoderm. The edges of the pieces of ectoderm soon grow together, and the inductor is thus enclosed in a vesicle consisting of reacting material. A further problem is posed when it is intended to test fluid extracts for their possible inducing ability: in this case it is undesirable for the presumptive ectoderm to curl up and form vesicles because the distal surface of ectoderm, which covers such ectodermal vesicles from outside, is apparently less permeable than the inner surface, which comes into contact with the inductor in normal development. To prevent them from curling, the pieces of ectoderm are kept flat by holding them between two layers of nylon (Yamada and Takata, 1961) or by pressing them to the surface of a coverslip by a piece of silk or filter paper (Tiedemann, 1962). The four main methods of testing inductors are represented diagrammatically in Figure 165.

It is of special interest that inductions can be performed not only by tissues of the same or closely related species but also by tissues of various animals, even of animals belonging to different phyla of the animal kingdom. Using the newt as the host, the tissues of the following animals were found to be effective as inductors: *Hydra*, insects, fishes, reptiles, birds, mammals (mouse, guinea pig, man). This lack of specificity applied to both normal and abnormal inductors. The conclusion from these experiments must be either that the inductive substance is very widely distributed in animal tissues or that various substances may act as inducing agents.

As the normal inductor can act after being killed, so the abnormal inductors can induce after being killed by boiling or by immersion in alcohol or ether. A rather remarkable discovery made in this connection is that some tissues can induce better when they have been killed than if they are used in the fresh state. Some tissues that do not induce in the living state may induce when dead. This is the case with parts of the amphibian gastrula and blastula other than the dorsal blastopore lip region. Presumptive ectoderm and endoderm if killed by boiling or in other ways and implanted into the blastocoele will induce neural plates (Holtfreter, 1934a). Whether the inducing agent in this case is the same as the one emerging from the archenteron roof cannot be affirmed without further proof.

The next stage was obviously to try to isolate the active substance from the inducing tissues. Waddington, Needham and collaborators (1934) succeeded in preparing ether extracts from inducing tissues (amphibian embryos, adult newts, mammalian liver) which were capable of inducing a neural plate. The solubility of the inducing substance in ether suggests that it is of a fatty or lipoid nature. Further purification of the extract showed that the unsaponifiable fraction retained the inductive ability. Thus the inductive substance should be identified as belonging to the steroid group. Forthwith, inductions were attempted by introducing into the embryo various pure substances of the steroid group. The substance to be tested was, for this purpose, emulsified in egg albumen, the albumen was then coagulated, and a piece of the coagulum implanted in the blastocoele of a young gastrula. Some weak inductions were obtained in this way.

Waddington, Needham and collaborators concluded from this that the natural inducing substance is a steroid. It was soon found, however, that the steroids are not the only substances that can cause neural induction; neither are fat solvents the only means of extracting the active substance from inducing tissues. One of Spemann's collaborators, Wehmeier (1934), prepared an active extract by prolonged boiling of muscle in water. The extract was made into a jelly by adding agar, and pieces of the jelly were implanted into the blastocoele. Very large and well-developed neural plates were induced in this way (Fig. 166).

The latter extraction experiments were further corroborated by the implantation of various chemically defined substances beside the substances of the steroid group. Fischer, Wehmeier and collaborators (1935) found that a number of weak organic acids are good inductors — as, for instance, muscle adenylic acid, thymonucleic acid, dihydroxystearic acid, linolenic acid and stearic acid.

The quest after the "normal" inductor of the neural plate suffered a serious setback when it was accidentally discovered (Waddington, Needham and Brachet, 1936) that isolated gastrula ectoderm may be stimulated to produce neural tissue (in the form of neural tubes) by keeping it in a weak solution of the dye methylene blue, which obviously has nothing to do with the development of the normal embryo. Lastly it was found (Holtfreter, 1947c) that isolated presumptive ectoderm may be caused to develop into nervous tissue by a short exposure to a saline solution of a compostion which is not

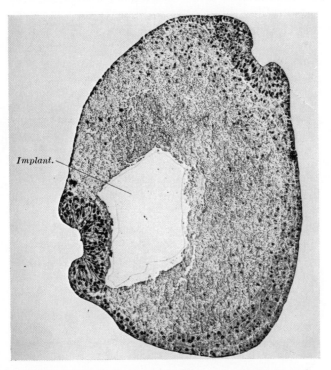

Figure 166. Induction of a secondary neural plate in an axolotl embryo by means of an implanted piece of agar containing substances extracted from muscle by boiling the muscle in water. (From Wehmeier, 1934.)

quite favorable to the cells. This is the case if the standard solution is more acidic or more alkaline than it should normally be—if the pH is lower than 5.0 or higher than 9.2.

Continued development in strongly acid or alkaline solutions is of course impossible; embryonic tissue exposed to these solutions very soon shows signs of damage. First of all the connections between the cells are broken; embryonic epithelia fall apart. The cytoplasm of the cells treated with acids or alkalis shows signs of liquefaction, noticeable because of an increased brownian movement in the interior of the cells, and the amount of the hyaline cytoplasm at the periphery of the cells increases. If the acid or alkaline treatment is continued, cytolysis sets in, the cell membrane breaks down and the cells disintegrate. (See Fig. 167.) If the duration of the treatment is short, and the cells are soon transferred to a normal solution, the disintegration of the cells is checked. For a time they may show very active ameboid movement, but later the cells tend to clump together—reaggregate—and may resume normal development except that the end result of this development is changed: neural differentiation is observed in a great proportion of the aggregates. Complete dispersal of the tissues into individual cells is not necessary for the change in their differentiation. The main effect appears to be a sublethal damage (cytolysis) to the cells from which they can recover. Some agents such as urea, causing damage to the cells without changing the pH of the medium, may have the same effect as acids and alkalis (Karasaki, 1957).

The neural induction by cytolyzing agents is obviously a completely different way of controlling differentiation from the normal processes of induction by the roof of the archenteron. The action of the roof of the archenteron

Figure 167. Treatment of amphibian embryonic cells with ammonia, with and without return of the cells to a normal medium. (From Karasaki, 1957.)

does not cause a sharp swing of the pH to the acid or the alkaline side; neither does it cause cytolysis in the overlying ectoderm. Even if it could be assumed that some specific inducing substances pass from the roof of the archenteron (or from pieces of adult tissues) into the ectoderm and thus change it qualitatively, no similar mechanism can be at work when solutions of ammonia or hydrochloric acid are used in cytolysis experiments. It has been suggested that the cytolysis "unmasks" some substance present in the ectodermal cells themselves, and that this substance, once released or activated, changes the presumptive epidermal cells into neural cells. Whether this interpretation is correct or not, it makes us regard with extreme caution any experiment in which neural differentiation is caused by treatment with various chemical substances. These substances may have nothing to do with normal induction but cause neural differentiation through their toxic action, which causes sublethal cytolysis of cells.

Emission of Inducing Substances by the Natural Inductors. We have seen that extracts of inducing substances made by chemical methods cannot be entirely relied on, since a variety of substances may produce inductions, partly through the channel of sublethal cytolysis. It was therefore a great advance when it was discovered, by Niu and Twitty, that tissues capable of induction themselves release inducing substances into the surrounding medium. It was only necessary to find a means of accumulating these substances in sufficient concentrations and to discover the best way to apply them to cells competent to react to the induction. The first part of the problem was solved by cultivating inductor tissues, such as the dorsal lip of the amphibian blastopore, parts of the neural plate, rudiments of the notochord and somites, in small quantities of saline by the hanging drop method (a drop of culture medium with the tissue to be cultivated is placed on a coverslip, and this is inverted over a hollow on a slide; the preparation is then sealed to prevent desiccation). The saline solution used was a specially modified one, now known as the "Niu and Twitty solution" (see Niu and Twitty, 1953). The inducing substances accumulate in the medium gradually; the active concentration is reached only after a week to ten days. The fragment of early gastrula ectoderm is then placed in the same drop of medium and cultivated for a further one to three weeks. It was found important for the success of the experiment that the fragment of ectoderm be very small, containing something like 15 to 20 cells. If the fragment is large, it rounds off and becomes covered with the surface coat (see section 9-1) which prevents substances from without from penetrating into the cells. With a very small fragment this does not occur, and there is a sufficient surface of unprotected cytoplasm into which the inducing substances may be taken.

In successful cases, and these may be up to 90 per cent in some experimental series, the cells of the ectodermal explant behave as if they were a part of a normal neural plate. Many of the cells scatter in the medium and become transformed into typical melanophores. Others remain in a clump and differentiate as nerve cells. The latter may produce nerve processes, which radiate into the surrounding medium (Fig. 168). The presence of the inductor tissues is no longer necessary for the success of the induction once the medium has been "conditioned" – i.e., has accumulated the necessary amount of inducing substances. Pieces of ectoderm cultivated in drops

Figure 168.   Neural tissue with radiating nerve fibers and melanophores developed from a piece of young *Triturus rivularis* ectoderm cultivated in conditioned medium. (From Niu, 1956.)

withdrawn from the original cultures and containing no inductor cells differentiate into nerve cells and melanophores just as readily as those which are kept in a drop with a piece of inductor (Niu, 1956).

The action of "conditioned" saline must be essentially different from the shock treatment by media with very high or very low pH which was referred to above. It was found by direct measurement that the saline after cultivation in it of inductor tissues is still very nearly neutral (it has a pH of 7.8). Neither was any trace of sublethal injury or cytolysis apparent. The action was obviously due to the presence of a specific substance or substances in the medium, and there appears to be no reason why these substances may not be the "natural" inducing substances; that is, the substances through the mediation of which the neural plate and other organs are induced in normal development.

For a further insight into the chemical nature of the inducing substances, Niu and Twitty's experiments have the same drawbacks as the experiments with the normal embryos: the quantities of substances produced are too minute for an elaborate chemical analysis. It could be ascertained that the condidtioned medium contains a macromolecular substance or substances of the nature of nucleoproteins. The nucleic acid component is mainly ribonucleic acid, though small amounts of deoxyribonucleic acid have also been found. So far it has not been possible to determine with certainty whether the inducing action is due to the nucleic acid component or the protein component. In some experiments (Niu, 1956), addition of ribonuclease to the "conditioned" medium reduced its inducing activity but did not abolish it, whereas addition of trypsin or chymotrypsin prevented induction completely —a result suggesting that the inducing substances are proteins. For further chemical analyses, embryologists still have to rely on "abnormal inductors" as a source of such substances.

It is of interest that the substances released by the inductors into the surrounding medium appear to change with the age of the inductor or with the duration of its sojourn in the medium. The reaction consisting of nerve cell and melanophore differentiation is observed when the inductor had been cultivated in the medium for seven to ten days. If the inductor itself differentiates into muscle cells, which happens especially if somites are used, or in some cases of explantation of parts of the neural plate (*cf.* data on the fate of parts of the neural plate in section 13–1), and if the cultivation is extended to 12 to 16 days, the reaction of the ectoderm becomes different: up to 73 per cent of the inductions lead to differentiation of myoblasts in the cultivated ectoderm. In this way a "mesodermal induction" (see section 10–5) could be reproduced *in vitro*. The presence of substances inducing muscle may have been a direct result of the particular type of differentiation going on in the inductor, the induction tending here to assimilate the reacting material to the inductor itself.

A further point that emerges from Twitty and Niu's work is that the ectoderm cells need not be in their typical association to be able to react to the inductor. Even in the standard experiment in which very small clumps of cells (15 to 20 cells, as indicated) were used, the arrangement of cells as in a normal blastoderm was lost. It was found possible, however, to expose individual, single, cells to the inducing stimulus. For this purpose single ectodermal cells were sucked into capillary tubes filled with "conditioned" saline. The cells seemed to thrive well, underwent several divisions and showed signs of transformation into promelanophores (Fig. 169; Niu, 1956). From this it follows that the reaction to an inducing substance consists in the change of properties of individual cells in the first instance, in the creation of *new kinds of cells.* Once the properties of the cells are changed their

Figure 169. Single ectodermal cell cultivated in a glass capillary tube filled with conditioned medium. Four photographs of the tube were taken on the 2nd (*a*), 4th (*b*), 5th (*c*) and 7th (*d*) days after explantation. *a,* The single cell which has been placed in the capillary tube. *b,* Three cells have been produced. *c,* Four cells have been produced. *d,* Eight cells have been produced by division of the original single cell. (From Niu, 1956.)

behavior is changed, and the formation of the multicellular organ rudiment, such as the neural plate, is the outcome of the new properties of all the cells comprising the rudiment. In the case of the neural plate the new properties of the cells cause them to form a thicker layer than the layer of epidermis, to make the edges of the layer curve upward, and so on. These processes will be dealt with in Chapter 12 and more specifically in section 12–3.

Chemical Analyses of Inducing Substances.   As has already been indicated, it is not very difficult to obtain extracts from tissues showing inductive action when brought into contact with competent embryonic cells, and such extracts may be prepared in a variety of ways. The simplest way is perhaps to homogenize the tissue and sediment the larger particles by centrifugation. However, chemical extraction by a variety of solvents has also been tried out. Adult tissues, as a source of inducing substances, enable the investigator to make use of a number of methods of purification which are normally applied in biochemical investigations since one may start with sufficiently large quantities of material.

Two schools have been especially successful in purifying extracts from tissues capable of imitating the action of the natural "primary organizer": namely, the school of Yamada in Japan and the school of Tiedemann in Germany. Yamada and his collaborators used guinea pig liver and guinea pig bone marrow as their main sources of inducing substance. The tissues in their experiments were homogenized and separation of fractions was achieved by ultracentrifugation, by sedimentation of nucleoproteins with streptomycin sulphate and of proteins with acidified solutions and with ammonium sulphate, and eventually by chromatographic separation on a diethylaminoethyl cellulose chromatographic column (Yamada and Takata, 1961; Hayashi, 1956; Yamada, 1958).

Tiedemann and collaborators used nine-day-old chicken embryos as starting material. The homogenates were either extracted with phenol, to obtain an active protein fraction, or by deoxycholic acid followed by sedimentation with ammonium sulphate, which separates a nucleoprotein fraction in the sediment and a protein fraction in the supernatant, both of which were found to possess inducing ability. The last stage of the purification was also carried out on a diethylaminoethyl cellulose chromatographic column (Tiedemann, 1961; Tiedemann, Becker and Tiedemann, 1961; Tiedemann, 1962).

The extracts prepared by workers of both schools contain fairly pure macromolecular substances (with a molecular weight between 43,000 and 100,000 – Tiedemann, 1962). Some of the inducing substances prepared in this way show all the chemical and spectrophotometric reactions of proteins; others are ribonucleoproteins. The inducing power of the preparation is no weaker than the inducing power of the natural organizer. Quantities of the order of 1 to 2 γ $\left(\gamma = \dfrac{1}{1000} \text{ mg.}\right)$ are sufficient to cause an induction when introduced into the blastocoele of a *Triturus* embryo (Tiedemann, 1962). Fractions containing only deoxyribonucleoproteins were completely inactive (Tiedemann, 1961).

It seems somewhat disconcerting that inducing activity should be present in two different groups of chemical compounds such as proteins on the one hand and ribonucleoproteins on the other. Furthermore, seeing that synthetic processes in cells are controlled by different kinds of ribonucleic acids (see section 2–3), it would be of great importance to know whether the participation of ribonucleoproteins in induction may mean that the ribonucleic acids involved are instrumental in bringing some kind of "information" from the inductor cells to the reacting cells.

Fortunately, some further experiments give a very clear and satsifactory answer to these problems. It has been convincingly shown by various investigators that the degradation of ribonucleic acid in inducing preparations by ribonuclease does not reduce the inducing ability of such preparations. In one experiment, for instance, a very active preparation was obtained from a liver homogenate by ultracentrifugation. The microsome fraction was used, which contains most of the cytoplasmic ribonucleic acid. The experimental lot of this preparation was incubated for 3.5 hours with ribonuclease. After ribonuclease treatment the substance was precipitated, and its inducing ability (as well as that of untreated controls) was tested by placing pieces of precipitate between two layers of gastrula presumptive ectoderm. The preparations were cultivated as explants in a saline solution. Table 11 gives the results of the experiment.

TABLE 11.   INDUCING EFFECT OF LIVER RIBONUCLEOPROTEIN TREATED WITH RIBONUCLEASE (AFTER HAYASHI FROM YAMADA, 1958)

	Control	*Experimental*
Ribonucleic acid content in mg. of RNA phosphorus per mg. protein nitrogen	148.6	0.84
Number of explants	49	52
Total neural induction	100%	100%
Archencephalic inductions	14%	15%
Deuterencephalic inductions	82%	77%
Atypical inductions	18%	17%

From Table 11 it is seen that although the ribonucleic acid content of the inductor was reduced to less than 1 per cent of the original quantity, the inducing power of the preparation was the same as in controls, not only in respect of the total number of inductions but also in respect of the type of induction observed. This result is supported by many similar experiments, and it appears therefore that ribonucleic acid cannot be the essential part in the chemical composition of an inductor.

In contrast to the action of ribonuclease, the treatment of tissues or tissue extracts with proteolytic enzymes — pepsin, trypsin or chymotrypsin — destroys their ability to induce.

Figure 170 shows in diagrammatic form the results of treating a liver extract with trypsin for varying times (Hayashi, 1958). It was found that the preparation completely lost its ability to induce neural structures after treatment for 120 minutes and only caused weak atypical inductions. Figure 171, *a* and *b*, shows the induction in the control compared with the lack of neural induction after treatment of the liver extract with trypsin (120 minutes).

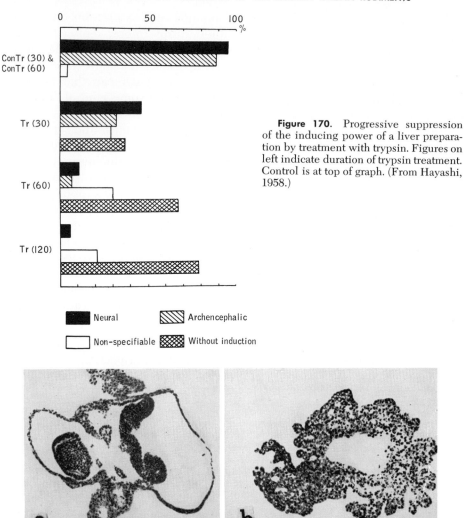

Figure 170. Progressive suppression of the inducing power of a liver preparation by treatment with trypsin. Figures on left indicate duration of trypsin treatment. Control is at top of graph. (From Hayashi, 1958.)

Figure 171. Results of implanting into a vesicle of *Triturus pyrrhogaster* early gastrula blastoderm of a pentose-nucleoprotein liver preparation without enzyme treatment *(a)* and after treatment with trypsin for 120 minutes *(b)*. There is archencephalic induction in *a*, lack of neural induction in *b*. (From Hayashi, 1958.)

There seems to be no doubt that the integrity of the proteins is essential for inductions by tissues and tissue extracts. Exactly similar results have been obtained by workers of the Tiedemann school.

The general conclusion from the above experiments is that the inducing principle in abnormal inductors is of protein nature. The protein may or may not be coupled with ribonucleic acid, but the inducing action is due to protein alone.

Similarly, as in the conditioned medium in the experiments of Twitty and Niu (p. 248), the protein and ribonucleoprotein preparations do not cause any visible damage to cells of the reacting tissue. Their inducing ability is therefore not mediated through sublethal cytolysis, as in experiments described on p. 246.

There is thus hardly reason to believe that the treatment acts in some roundabout way of "unmasking" an inducing substance present in reacting cells. Rather, one feels that the proteins contained in the tissue of advanced embryos (nine-day chicken embryos) and adults have some common properties with the natural inducing agents liberated from the roof of the archenteron, if they are not actually identical with these agents. As a further corroboration of this view, one may mention that an extract obtained from gastrulae and neurulae of *Triturus,* and presumably containing the "natural" inducing substance, is inactivated by trypsin treatment, similarly to the inactivation of inducing extracts dealt with in the foregoing pages (Tiedemann, Becker and Tiedemann, 1961).

10−4 MECHANISM OF ACTION OF THE INDUCING SUBSTANCES

The last question which may be considered in connection with the physicochemical nature of the processes of induction is about the way in which the inducing substances control the differentiation of cells. In principle it may be assumed that the inducing substances penetrate into the cells and, by interfering in the metabolic mechanisms in the interior of the cells, change their physicochemical composition. Although this mechanism of action seems to be fairly plausible, it is not self-evident.

The amount of ribonucleic acid in the region around the dorsal lip of the blastopore and in the dorsal lip itself is higher than in the lateroventral parts of the blastula and in the vegetal region. As the cells of the dorsal lip of the blastopore invaginate and become the roof of the archenteron, the amount of ribonucleic acid in these cells diminishes. Simultaneously the amount of ribonucleic acid increases in the cells of the presumptive neural plate. The ribonucleic acid content in the neural plate and neural tube is higher than in the epidermis. These changes in the distribution of ribonucleic acid have been interpreted to mean that ribonucleic acid passes from the roof of the blastopore into the presumptive neural plate cells, and that it is the actual inducing substance (Brachet, 1947). There are, however, other ways of interpreting these results, and more direct evidence would be needed to prove that the rubonucleic acid appearing in the neural plate is derived from the chordo-mesodermal cells.

Radioactive tracers have been used to learn whether, in the process of embryonic induction, substances pass from the inducing tissue into the reacting tissue. The general plan of such an experiment is as follows. Parts of one embryo are cultivated for some time in a solution containing substances which carry a "marked" atom—a radioactive isotope of carbon or sulfur. Labeled amino acids, methionine S^{35} and glycine C^{14}, and a nucleic acid precursor, orotic acid C^{14}, were used in some experiments (Ficq, 1954; Sirlin, Brahma and Waddington, 1956; Waddington and Mulherkar, 1957). These compounds are taken up into the tissues of the embryo. Next, inducing parts—roof of the archenteron or parts of brain rudiments—are excised from the embryo containing radioactive substances and transplanted into a normal embryo where the graft may induce neural plates or other structures from the host tissue. The embryo is then fixed and cut into sections, and the sections are coated with a photographic emulsion. The electrons emitted by radio-active atoms cause a darkening of the emulsion, and it is thus possible to discover where the radioactive atoms were situated at the time of fixation.

It has been found that the radioactive atoms do not remain restricted to the cells of the grafts, but that they become fairly widely dispersed in the host embryo. A high radioactivity is shown by induced neural plates, which may be the result of the passage of inducing substances from the graft into the host tissue. However, the host neural plates and tubes are also strongly radio-active, and radioactivity can be also discovered in the mesodermal and endo-dermal tissues of the host. These results are consistent with the assumption that the radioactive atoms are carried around in the host tissue by simple diffusion.

Furthermore, it cannot be claimed with certainty that the diffusing sub-stance was actually the macromolecular material which can reasonably be assumed to be the inducing agent. It could well be that the radioactive atoms were carried around as components of small molecules (single amino acids, mononucleotides and even smaller organic and inorganic molecules).

The last criticism does not apply to a further set of experiments in which use was made of immunological methods to trace the passage of substances from the inductor into the reacting tissue. Antibodies were prepared against malignant tumor tissue used in one experiment (Vainio, Saxén, Toivonen and Rapola, 1962), and against a purified protein preparation isolated from guinea pig bone marrow in another experiment (Yamada, 1962). The antibodies in the antiserum were later coupled to a fluorescent dye, rhodamine B.200. *Triturus* ectoderm was exposed to the action of the inductor (tumor tissue in one case, protein preparation in the other) for a few hours, then fixed and cut into sections. The sections were now treated with the antiserum coupled with the fluorescent dye. Owing to binding of antigen-antibody, the antibody molecules with the attached dye became localized in the section in positions which indicated the distribution of the antigen molecules (the molecules of the inductor). The fluorescent dye made these locations easily discernible. Distinct fluorescence was found in the reacting tissue, thus showing that antigen molecules had actually penetrated into it. Since the specificity of the antibody-antigen reaction would have disappeared if the antigen molecules were degraded to any great extent, it is therefore evident that the macro-molecues of the inductor substance penetrated into the reacting cells without being split up into small components.

The location of the macromolecules of the inductor in the reacting cells is of particular interest; most of them remained in the cytoplasm, very little of the transmitted material having penetrated into the nucleus. This can hardly be interpreted as proving that the nucleus is not involved in the changes of development brought about by induction. We know that new pro-teins are synthesized in the cells of the embryo at the time and after gastru-lation, and that large amounts of messenger RNA are produced in the nucleus during gastrulation and later. According to our present concepts of protein synthesis, inducing substances, being proteins themselves, cannot influence the synthesis of new proteins in the reacting tissue *directly*. It is much more likely that the proteins supplied by the inductor interfere in some way with the activities of the chromosomal DNA and thus in a roundabout way change the nature of the synthetic processes in the reacting cells. That the transmitted inducing material is initially localized in the cytoplasm suggests that between the molecules of the inductor and the nuclear DNA there are intercalated some further mechanisms about which only conjectures can be made at present. What these conjectures may be will be outlined in section 16–2, p. 505.

Yamada and his collaborators (1962) claim that the fluorescent antibody in their experiments was concentrated on the yolk platelets, and that the yolk platelets are the first cell inclusions which show changes at the beginning of differentiation. A partial solubilization of the yolk platelets, starting from their surface, is the first sign of impending differentiation of cells in the amphibian embryo (Karasaki, 1963b). The yolk platelets might thus be one of the links between the inducing substance and the nucleus of the reacting cell. Even if this were true, the same mechanism could not play a part in neural inductions in bony fishes, birds and mammals whose embryonic cells are devoid of yolk. As it is very unlikely that such a fundamental process as primary organizer action could be different in different classes of vertebrates, the conclusion seems inevitable that there must exist another path of action of the inducing substances in addition to their influence on the yolk platelets.

10–5 GRADIENTS IN THE DETERMINATION OF THE PRIMARY ORGAN RUDIMENTS IN VERTEBRATES

The Dorsoventral and Anteroposterior Gradients. The phenomenon of regional specificity raises the question whether the gray crescent does not contain after all two or even more different specific substances, responsible for the development of the head and the trunk regions (or the archencephalic, deuterencephalic and spinocaudal regions), with their separate inductors or organizers. Certain results achieved with abnormal inductors have been adduced in favor of this supposition.

When different tissues of various adult animals are tested as inductors, it is found that they do not all act exactly alike: some of them act preponderantly as head inductors, others as trunk inductors. Some induce only ectodermal parts (neural structures, sense organs); others also induce mesodermal organs and tissues (see Toivonen, 1949, 1950, 1953). For instance, the liver of the guinea pig, treated with alcohol, acts as an archencephalic inductor: that is, it induces large brain vesicles, bearing a resemblance to the telencephalon, diencephalon and mesencephalon (see p. 342, sometimes with eyes; it also induces noses and balancers (see p. 394). The kidney of the adder is a rare case of a predominantly deuterencephalic inductor; it induces brain parts resembling the hindbrain and also ear vesicles. The kidney of the guinea pig treated with alcohol is a spinocaudal inductor; it induces mainly spinal cord, notochord, bands of muscle segments arranged as they are normally in the trunk region of the embryo and often also complete tails with fin folds around their edges. Lastly, alcohol-treated bone marrow of the guinea pig induces almost exclusively mesodermal parts of the trunk and tail: notochord, rows of somites, nephric tubules and limb-buds.

The inducing properties of tissues may change depending on the type

Figure 172. A purely mesodermal induction (notochord, somites, pronephros) in isolated ectoderm caused by the non-nucleoprotein fraction of bone marrow. (From Yamada, 1958.)

of treatment. In particular it was found that heating (or boiling) the tissues reduces their ability to induce mesodermal and spinocaudal structures, whereas archencephalic inductions are still easily obtained. This and similar results have led to the conclusion that the regional nature of inductions produced by adult tissues is the result of the interaction of two factors contained in various proportions in the different tissues (Yamada, 1950; Nieuwkoop and others, 1952; Toivonen and Saxén, 1955; Toivonen, 1958). One factor is the "neuralizing agent" of Toivonen and Saxén, called "dorsalizing agent" by Yamada and "activating agent" by Nieuwkoop and others. When it is present alone it causes archencephalic inductions. It is the active principle of the alcohol-treated liver. The second principle is Toivonen and Saxén's "mesodermalizing agent" which is the same as the "caudalizing agent" of Yamada and the "transforming agent" of Nieuwkoop and others. If present alone, this second factor induces only mesodermal parts: notochord, muscle, kidney and limb-bud (see Fig. 172). This is the active principle of the alcohol-treated guinea pig bone marrow. A deuterencephalic induction is the result of the presence of a small amount of the mesodermalizing factor in addition to the neuralizing factor. A large amount of the mesodermalizing factor added to the neuralizing factor produces a spinocaudal induction.

That deuterencephalic structures are a result of a certain balance between neuralizing and mesodermalizing inducing substances has been shown by the following elegant experiment (Toivonen and Saxén, 1955). Two pellets, one

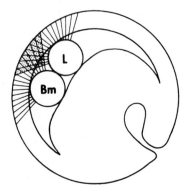

Figure 173. Simultaneous implantation of an archencephalic (liver—L) and a mesodermalizing (bone marrow—Bm) inductor into a newt's gastrula. (From Toivonen and Saxen, 1955.)

prepared from guinea pig liver and another prepared from guinea pig bone marrow, were implanted simultaneously into the blastocoele of a young gastrula (Fig. 173). The liver preparation alone would have induced exclusively archencephalic structures; the bone marrow alone induces trunk mesoderm. Together, however, they induced organs belonging to all levels, including deuterencephalic and spinocaudal structures: medulla, ear vesicles and spinal cord.

The two factors are actually substances with different chemical properties. The neuralizing substance is thermostable and soluble in organic solvents. The mesodermalizing substance is insoluble in organic solvents and highly thermolabile. The result of this latter property is that spinocaudal and deuterencephalic inductors on heat treatment induce archencephalic structures; in the fresh state they contain both substances but the mesodermalizing substance is destroyed by heat, whereas the neuralizing substance remains unchanged (at least after a short heat treatment—prolonged heat treatment inactivates the neuralizing substance as well). By graded heat treatment of a tissue its inducing properties may be changed gradually, as the ratio between the mesodermalizing and the neuralizing substances changes in favor of the latter (see Fig. 174).

It has been a matter of controversy for some time whether the neuralizing agent and the mesodermalizing agent are two distinct chemical substances, or whether they might be, after all, two aspects of the action of one and the same substance, or two states of one substance, a more labile state (the mesodermalizing agent) and a more stable state (the neuralizing agent). Experiments have now resolved this problem. It has been found that the neuralizing substance of the guinea pig liver can be isolated in the form of a ribonucleoprotein (Hayashi, 1956), either by sedimentation with streptomycin sulfate or by ultracentrifugation, as a result of which the microsomal fraction, containing the cytoplasmic nucleoprotein, shows the strongest archencephalic inductive action. The mesodermalizing substance of guinea

Figure 174. Change in the percentage of different types of inductions as a result of treating the inductor (slices of bone marrow) with heat for varying times (seconds) indicated below the lines on the diagram. (From Yamada, 1958.)

pig bone marrow, on the other hand, is not sedimented by streptomycin sulfate and is not contained in the microsome fraction after ultracentrifugation (Yamada, 1958).

The mesodermalizing substance is therefore a protein which does not tend to be coupled with nucleic acid. The two agents are thus distinctly different and separate substances, one possibly bound to the microsomes, the other not. There is no contradiction between the statement that the neuralizing substance can be obtained in the form of a ribonucleoprotein, and our previous finding that the active principle of the inducing substance is a protein and not a nucleic acid: if the active nucleoprotein prepared from liver is treated with ribonuclease, the inducing action is retained; if it is treated with proteolytic enzymes, the preparation loses its inducing ability (Hayashi, 1955, 1958).

The results obtained with abnormal inductors have been used to interpret normal development. It has been assumed (Toivonen and Saxén, 1955) that the same two substances are active as inducing substances of the archenteron roof, and that the regional differentiations in the normal embryo are controlled by a balance between the two substances distributed in the form of gradients. The gradient of the neuralizing substance is highest mid-dorsally and declines toward the lateral and ventral parts of the embryo. The mesodermalizing substance is most highly concentrated at the posterior dorsal end of the embryo and forms a declining gradient both in the anterior direction and in a lateral direction. This distribution of substances as originally contained in the archenteron roof is transmitted to the overlying ectoderm.

The anterior part of the archenteron roof (including prechordal plate) emits only the neuralizing substance and induces the archencephalon. No notochord and no somites are developed at this level. At a slightly posterior level, the notochord and somites are already present. There is some admixture of the mesodermalizing substance to the neuralizing substance, and as a result deuterencephalic structures (medulla and ear vesicles) are induced in the ectoderm. Still farther back, large amounts of the mesodermalizing substance are available, mesoderm develops into notochord and large masses of muscle, and the neural structure induced is a spinal cord (see Fig. 175). It will be seen that each level of the embryo will have a different concentration of the neuralizing and mesodermalizing agents.

The concept of two mutually permeating gradients reminds us at once of the animal and vegetal gradients of the sea urchin egg, though the relationships of the gradients to the main axes of the embryo (and egg) are different.

To give further confirmation to the theory of the interaction of the neuralizing and mesodermalizing gradients, it would be necessary to show that the neuralizing and mesodermalizing agents are acutally present in the normal embryo. In support of this it is indicated that the "trunk organizer" (p. 237, and see Spemann, 1931), the noninvaginated part of the dorsal lip of the blastopore of a middle and late gastrula, if treated with a heat shock (one hour at 30 to 38° C.) becomes an archencephalic inductor—"head organizer" (Takaya, 1955). We will remember also that in experiments of "conditioning" of the medium in which tissues of the archenteron roof had been cultivated (p. 248, Niu, 1956), a neuralizing substance becomes accumulated at first

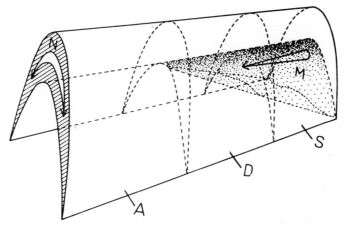

Figure 175.   Diagram of the neuralizing gradient *(N)* and the mesodermalizing gradient *(M)*. A, Archencephalic level; *D*, deuterencephalic level; *S*, spinocaudal level. (From Toivonen and Saxén, 1955.)

(inducing nerve cells and mesectodermal melanophores), and this is later superseded by a mesodermalizing substance which induces the differentiation of myoblasts.

Gradients, in the form of grading or fading out of certain properties, are very obvious in the early development of amphibia and other vertebrates. The dorsoventral gradient (the gradient of the neuralizing agent) can be traced both in the ectodermal and in the mesodermal layer. In the ectoderm the highest level of the gradient is associated with the development of the neural plate and neural tube. The next highest level of the gradient causes the differentiation of the neural crest. There is ample evidence that the development of the neural crest is the result of a weak induction of the same nature as the induction of neural tissue. When neural plates are induced, the cells on the periphery of the region exposed to the inductor, where the inductive stimulus is fading away, develop as neural crest. Sometimes, if the inductor is too weak to induce a neural plate, neural crest cells can still be induced. It is usually easy to notice the presence of neural crest cells on the site of induction, because some of them differentiate as pigment cells. Possibly a still lower level of the gradient is responsible for the differentiation of the various placodes, including nose and ear rudiments, the rudiments of cranial ganglia and of the lateral line sense organ system (see section 13–1).

Where the gradient of the neuralizing agent fades away, ectoderm differentiates as skin epidermis. In the chordo-mesodermal mantle, the dorsoventral gradient may be held to be responsible for the segregation of the notochord and the mesoderm in the gastrula of an amphibian. Those parts of the marginal zone in which the specific cytoplasmic substance is most highly concentrated become notochord, and those parts in which the concentration of the substance is lower become mesoderm (the somites). Those parts, lastly, in which the concentration of the cytoplasmic substances is minimal become unsegmented lateral-plate mesoderm (Yamada, 1937, also Dalcq and Pasteels, 1937). The gradient concept does not contradict our previous statement that the action of the primary organizer may include the

induction of somites and other mesodermal parts. This may be due to the presumptive notochord, as the highest level in the gradient system, establishing
a new gradient in the surroundings into which it has been transplanted. This
may involve a diffusion of the specific substance from higher levels of concentration into the surroundings where the concentration is lower.

Besides the gradient which has its highest level in the dorsomedian strip
of tissues diminishing toward both sides there is a second gradient, with a
center of highest concentration at the anterior end of the embryo, lessening
in a posterior direction. This anteroposterior gradient may be considered
to be another manifestation of the caudo-cranial mesodermalizing gradient;
its reverse side, as it were. This gradient is responsible for the differentiation
of parts of the nervous system, the most anterior part of the head being the
part where the gradient is at its highest.

Control of Development by Influencing the Gradient System.   The gradient
unites the parts of a developing embryo into one whole, into one morphogenetic system. Any factor that affects the gradient will therefore affect the
whole morphogenetic system, no matter how simple or even elementary the
factor itself may be. It is possible, for instance, to affect a morphogenetic system by depressing the level of the gradient at its highest point. One way of
achieving this is to expose the embryo to certain chemical substances such as
magnesium chloride or lithium chloride. Another way of depressing the high
level of the gradient is to remove part of the archenteron roof underlying the
anterior end of the nervous system. The result in both cases is about the
same: the most anterior parts of the nervous system fail to develop normally.
The defects can best be traced in the structure of the eyes. The injured
embryos develop a defect known as **cyclopia**: that is, the appearance of one
median eye instead of two lateral ones (Fig. 176). The median eye is really
the result of fusion in the midline of the two eye-forming areas, and every
intermediate state may be found in embryos in which the injury has not been
very severe. If very large parts of the underlying chordo-mesoderm have
been removed, or if the action of the chemical agent has been very strong,
the defects in the structure of the eyes are still greater—the single eye being

Figure 176.   Cyclopia in fish larvae, caused by
magnesium chloride treatment. Top left, normal
control. (After Stockard, from Huxley and de Beer,
1934.)

Figure 177.   Increasing degrees of cyclopic deficiencies in newt larvae (diagrammatic.) Upper left, normal larva.

reduced in size and failing to develop altogether in the extreme cases. The eyes are not the only organs affected in cyclopic embryos; other parts of the head are changed and reduced more or less in correspondence with the defects of the eyes (see Adelmann, 1936). The parts which may be involved are the brain, the nose, the ear, the mouth, the gill clefts. The defects spread from the front end backward as the injury is more and more pronounced. The nose rudiments and the forebrain are the first to be affected, so that the olfactory sacs become unpaired and finally disappear. Then follow the eyes and the mouth, the mouth becoming narrower and also disappearing. After the eye and mouth follow the posterior parts of the brain, the gill clefts and the ear vesicles. The gill clefts fuse in the midventral line, before disappearing one by one. In extreme cases practically the whole head is lacking (Fig. 177).

It must be understood that the complete presumptive ectoderm remains in place during the experiments just described; none of it is removed, neither do any of its parts become necrotic. All cells are there, but their development is changed as a result of an interference with the gradient system. The experiment with the lithium chloride or magnesium chloride brings out a further important phenomenon: although the whole embryo may be exposed to the chemical substance, it is only the topmost levels of the gradient system that are affected. This is a very common result: namely, that the highest point of a gradient is more easily damaged than the other parts. In fact a gradient can often be discovered by exposing the embryo to any mild injurious factor, such as weak poisons, abnormal temperature or ultraviolet radiation. The effect will be observed first, and sometimes only, at the highest point of the gradient if the intensity of the injurious factor has been chosen correctly. In vertebrates in stages following gastrulation, such a sensitive region is invariably the anterior part of the head.

Lithium can also affect the gradient in the chordo-mesodermal system. Treatment of the embryo during gastrulation with a weak solution of lithium chloride suppresses the development of the notochord, which has been postulated as representing the center of highest activity of the mesodermal gradient. If the development of the notochord is suppressed, the presumptive notochord cells differentiate according to the next highest level of the gradient and develop into somite tissue (Fig. 178). The right and left rows of somites are then continuous with each other across the midline, underneath the neural tube (Lehmann, 1937, 1945).

It has been reported that the opposite effect may be produced by treating frog embryos in the blastula stage with a solution of sodium thiocyanate (NaSCN). The result is the development of embryos in which the notochord is much larger and thicker than in control animals (Fig. 179). This means that a greater than normal area has shown a differentiation characteristic of the highest level of the gradient. This may be called raising the level of the gradient (Ranzi and Tamini, 1939).

Raising the dorsoventral gradient in the ectoderm should lead to an increase in the size of the neural system. In fact, embryos with excessively broad and massive brains have been observed after sodium thiocyanate treatment in fishes (see Huxley and de Beer, 1934) and frogs (Ranzi, 1957; Fig. 180). It should be mentioned, however, that the above results have been contradicted. It was suggested that the number of cells in the noto-

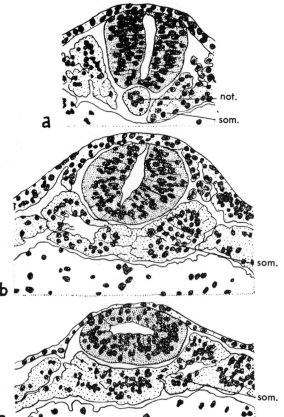

Figure 178. Transformation of presumptive notochord into somite mesoderm by means of the action of lithium in *Triturus. a,* Untreated control; *b, c,* lithium—treated embryos. *not.,* Notochord; *som.,* somites. (From Lehmann, 1945.)

Figure 179. Raising the dorsoventral gradient in a frog embryo with thiocyanate. *a*, Normal embryo; *b*, embryo with increased notochord after thiocyanate treatment. (After Ranzi and Tamini, from Lehmann, 1945.)

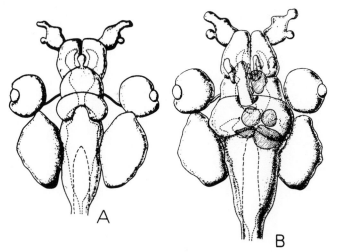

Figure 180. Reconstruction of the brain and sensory organs in a normal frog tadpole *(A)* and in a tadpole after treatment with thiocyanate *(B)*. (From Ranzi, 1957.)

chord is not increased by thiocyanate treatment, and that the embryos thus treated are stunted, which naturally leads to an increase of the notochord in cross section. The same applies obviously to the thickening of the neural system. Furthermore, it was claimed that in the above experiments not sufficient attention was given to the variability of the amphibian embryos (Ogi, 1957). The last word in this field has not yet been said.

Cyclopia is occasionally observed in natural conditions both in man and in domestic animals (see Adelmann, 1936). It is therefore very significant that the same effect can be produced experimentally. In this way we get an inkling of what goes on behind the scenes when a cyclopic monster is born. There must have been some injury to the gradient system concerned with the formation of the head in the embryo. The injurious effect may be produced by both hereditary and environmental factors. The cyclopia or similar defects may be the result of some toxicosis of the mother occurring at an early stage of pregnancy. This is known to be the case if a woman contracts the illness known as German measles (rubella) during the early weeks of pregnancy. The illness is not a serious one for the mother, but the toxin poisons the embryo, producing defects of the anterior part of the head (see Glatthaar and Töndury, 1950).

On the other hand, a gene has been found in guinea pigs (Wright and Wagner, 1934) which produces, in varying degrees, defects of a cyclopic nature, from the underdevelopment of the nose and mouth to almost complete absence of the head.

CHAPTER

11

Embryonic Adaptations

In this connection we will consider special organs or parts of the embryo which are not precursors of any of the organs of the adult or the larva but serve to satisfy the requirements of the embryo in respect to food or oxygen supply or to its protection.

The yolk in the egg cannot be considered as part of the embryo in this sense, although it fulfills the purpose of supplying nourishment for the embryo. However, in animals in which the amount of yolk is very large, special organs may be evolved to store the yolk and utilize it.

In the meroblastic eggs of fishes, the yolk is originally covered only by a thin membrane of cytoplasm which is continuous with the cytoplasmic cap at the animal pole at the beginning of cleavage. During gastrulation (section 8–6), the edge of the blastodisc, now becoming the rim of the blastopore, spreads over the surface of the yolk and eventually encloses the yolk altogether. The cell layers spreading over the yolk are the ectoderm, the mesoderm and the periblast—the syncytial layer formed on the surface of the yolk underneath the blastoderm. The endoderm in the bony fishes does not follow the movements of the blastopore rim, so that the yolk is not enclosed by the endodermal layer.

In the meantime the organs of the embryo are developed, and the body of the embryo raises itself away from the surface of the mass of yolk. Thus is introduced a partial separation between the body of the embryo proper and the **yolk sac** enclosing the mass of yolk. The broad connection between the body of the embryo and the yolk sac becomes constricted later, so that the yolk sac remains connected to the embryo proper by the stalk of the yolk sac (Fig. 181). A system of blood vessels is developed in the walls of the yolk sac, entering the heart by means of a pair of vitelline veins (also known as the omphalomesenteric veins). The yolk is broken down mainly due to the activity of the periblast, and so it becomes transportable through the blood stream to the embryo. As the yolk is used up, the yolk sac diminishes in size,

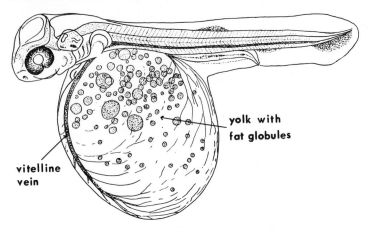

yolk with
fat globules

vitelline
vein

Figure 181.   Trout embryo with large yolk sac.

while the embryo grows. Hatching takes place in the meantime, the embryo becoming a free-swimming larva. The yolk sac is eventually retracted into the ventral body wall of the larva.

11—1   THE EXTRAEMBRYONIC STRUCTURES IN REPTILES AND BIRDS

In reptiles and birds, as in fishes, the yolk is eventually enclosed into a yolk sac, but the way this is done differs from that found in fishes. In reptiles and birds, the gastrulation movements do not take place on the edge of the blastodisc but inside it. The yolk is covered by the spreading of the edge of the blastodisc, and this process is not connected, therefore, in any way with gastrulation. The periphery of the blastodisc in reptiles and birds is differentiated as the area opaca, and it is the external edge of this that spreads over the surface of the yolk and eventually covers it. The cells of which the area opaca consists, beginning with the part nearest the embryo and progressing outward, split into three layers which are continuous with germinal layers developed in the area pellucida: the ectoderm, the mesoderm and the endoderm, the latter adhering to the surface of the yolk.

During the second and third days of incubation in the case of the chick, a network of blood vessels is developed in the inner part of the area opaca, which from this time onward becomes the **area vasculosa**. The outer part of the area opaca becomes the **area vitellina**. The development of the blood vessels in the area vasculosa is intimately connected with the differentiation of the first blood cells. This happens in the following way. First of all, groups of densely packed mesodermal cells appear in the area opaca all around the sides and the posterior edge of the area pellucida. These groups of cells are known as the **blood islands** (Fig. 182).

Next, the cells of the blood islands become differentiated into two kinds: the cells on the periphery join up to form a thin epithelial layer, the endothelium of the future blood vessels; the central cells, on the contrary, become separated from each other and are differentiated as blood corpuscles. Thus from the beginning the blood corpuscles are lying inside the blood vessels.

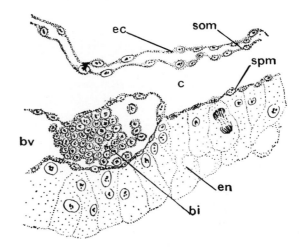

Figure 182. Section through area vasculosa of a chick embryo, showing a blood island. *ec,* Extra-embryonic epidermis; *som,* parietal layer of mesoderm; *spm,* visceral layer of mesoderm; *en,* endoderm; *bi,* blood island; *bv,* blood vessel. (From Wieman, 1949.)

Meanwhile, the adjacent blood vessels establish communications among themselves and the whole is transformed into a very irregular network. All the vessels of the area vasculosa are joined together on the periphery by the terminal sinus, which is the boundary line between the area vasculosa and the area vitellina (Fig. 183). The network of the area vasculosa becomes prolonged into the area pellucida and eventually establishes connection with the embryo proper. A connection with the blood system of the embryo is formed at two points: with the venous system, by means of right and left vitelline veins, joining in an unpaired ductus venosus which enters the sinus venosus of the heart, and with the arterial system by means of right and left vitelline arteries, which branch off from the dorsal aorta (see Figs. 184 and 253).

Before the middle of the second day of incubation the heart of the embryo begins to beat, and between the thirty-eighth and fortieth hours of incubation the blood starts circulating through the network of the yolk sac. The wall of the yolk sac develops outgrowths on its inner surface; i.e., on the surface facing the yolk. The outgrowths, supplied by blood vessels from the area vasculosa network, penetrate deep into the yolk and thus facilitate its absorption. The yolk, however, is not completely absorbed during embryonic life. Shortly before hatching, the yolk sac is retracted into the abdominal cavity of the embryo, and the walls of the abdominal cavity close behind it.

As in the fishes, the body of the embryo in birds and reptiles becomes separated from the yolk sac. This is achieved by the formation of folds which appear all around the body of the embryo. The folds involve all three germ layers and are directed downward and inward, undercutting the body of the embryo proper. These folds are known as the **body folds**.

Although the body folds eventually surround the whole embryo, the various sections of the fold do not appear simultaneously. The first to appear is the part of the fold just in front of the head. This section, which may be referred to as the **head fold**, undercuts the head and anterior part of the trunk of the embryo, so that these parts project freely over the surface of the yolk sac. The lateral and the posterior parts of the body fold develop soon after, the latter undercutting the tail end and the posterior part of the trunk, which now also project freely over the surface of the yolk sac, though this posterior part of the embryo is initially much shorter than the anterior part,

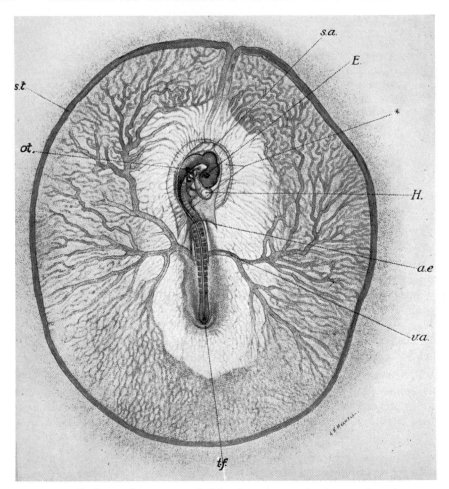

Figure 183. Chicken embryo surrounded by the area vasculosa. *a.e.*, Edge of amnion; *E.*, eye; *H.*, heart; *ot.*, ear vesicle; *s.a.*, suture along the line of fusion of amniotic folds; *s.t.*, terminal sinus; *t.f.*, tail fold; *v.a.*, vitelline artery. The asterisk indicates a depression in which lies the head of the embryo. (From Kerr, 1919.)

separated from the yolk by the head fold. The body folds gradually contract underneath the embryo, and eventually only a rather narrow stalk, the **umbilical cord,** connects the embryo with the yolk sac and other extraembryonic parts. The cord includes all the germ layers: an outer ectodermal lining, a double sheath of mesoderm and an endodermal canal connecting the cavity of the gut with the cavity of the yolk sac. In addition it contains the blood vessels going out to the yolk sac and other structures which will be referred to later.

Besides the yolk sac, the reptiles and birds develop three other extraembryonic organs, known as the **embryonic membranes.** These are the **amnion,** the **chorion** and the **allantois.**

The amnion and the chorion are developed together as upwardly projecting folds, the **amniotic folds,** appearing on the area pellucida just outside the body folds and eventually closing over the dorsal surface of the embryo (Fig. 185). The rudiment of the amnion and chorion first appears as a trans-

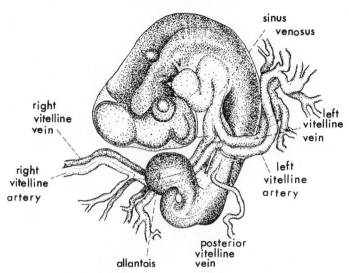

sinus
venosus

right
vitelline
vein

left
vitelline
vein

right
vitelline
artery

left
vitelline
artery

posterior
vitelline
vein

allantois

Figure 184. Three-day-old chick embryo viewed from the ventral side to show the origin of the vitelline vessels and the allantoic vesicle.

verse fold anterior to the head of the embryo. The fold bends backward over the anterior end of the head and covers it as with a hood. Subsequently, the lateral ends of the fold are prolonged backward along both sides of the embryo. The lateral folds approximate each other over the body of the embryo and fuse from the front end backward, so that more and more of the embryo becomes covered by the folds. Eventually a fold also develops behind the embryo, and the free edges of the folds fuse, thus completely enclosing the body of the embryo in a cavity—the **amniotic cavity**. The amniotic cavity is at first a very narrow slit between the embryo and the inner wall of the amniotic fold, but soon a fluid is secreted into the cavity, which distends it, so that the embryo floats freely in the cavity, connected to the extraembryonic parts only by the umbilical cord.

When the amniotic fold is first formed in front of the head of the embryo, it consists only of a part of the extraembryonic ectodermal layer. The lateral folds, however, from the start consist of the ectoderm and the somatic layer of the extraembryonic mesoderm. Mesoderm also penetrates secondarily into the anterior part of the fold, the composition of the fold therefore becoming uniform throughout.

The amniotic fold has two surfaces running out into an acute edge—the inner surface, facing the body of the embryo, and the outer surface, facing away from the embryo. The fusion of the amniotic folds of opposite sides occurs at the expense of their acute edges. The surface of the fold facing the embryo now lines the amniotic cavity and becomes the **amnion**. The surface of the fold facing away from the embryo, after the fusion of the folds, becomes continuous over the dorsal surface of the embryo (and over the amniotic cavity) and is now called the **chorion**. Some embryologists prefer to call this membrane, as found in birds and reptiles, the **serosa**, reserving the term **chorion** for the outer embryonic membrane of mammals.

From what has been said of the composition of the amniotic folds, it is

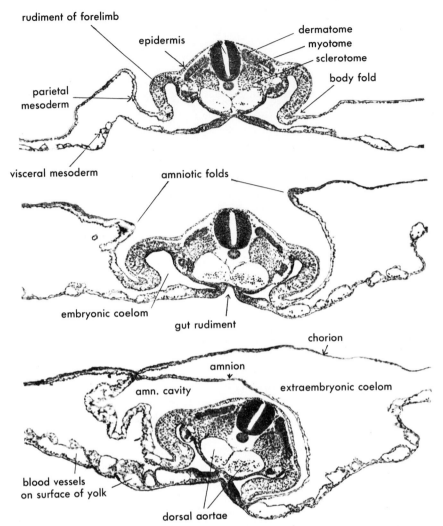

Figure 185. Three stages in the development of the amniotic cavity in the chick (transverse sections).

clear that the amnion consists of a layer of extraembryonic ectoderm on the inside (facing the amniotic cavity) and a layer of extraembryonic somatic mesoderm on the outside. The chorion consists of a layer of extraembryonic ectoderm on the outside and a layer of extraembryonic mesoderm on the inside, which are, of course, in continuity with the ectoderm and somatic mesoderm covering the yolk sac. In between the amnion and the chorion is the extraembryonic coelomic cavity, which is continuous with the coelomic cavity in the embryo proper.

The advantages that the embryo obtains from the development of amnion, chorion and the amniotic cavity are clear enough: the embryo becomes immersed in a container filled with fluid and thus can accomplish its development in a fluid medium, although the egg is "on dry land." It would appear therefore that the primary function of the amnion is to protect the embryo from the danger of desiccation. Besides this, the fluid of the amniotic cavity is an efficient shock absorber and protects the embryo from possible concussions. Lastly, it isolates the embryo from the shell of the egg, and thus protects it from adhesion to the shell or from friction against it. At the same time, the formation of the amniotic cavity has a slightly negative effect: it removes the embryo from the surface of the egg and thus from the source whence it could obtain oxygen.

The third embryonic membrane, the **allantois**, is very different in nature from the first two membranes. Originally the allantois is none other than a urinary bladder. A cleidoic egg, as that of a bird or reptile, has no means of disposing of the waste products of protein breakdown by removing them from the egg. A solution was found to the problem of waste disposal by excreting the protein breakdown products in the form of uric acid, which is deposited as water-insoluble crystals and stored inside the egg up to the time of hatching. The storage place is the urinary bladder. As the storage has to go on throughout the time of incubation, the urinary bladder has to increase to enormous proportions.

The allantois appears as a ventral outgrowth of the endodermal hindgut. It thus corresponds exactly in nature to the urinary bladder of the amphibia. The outgrowth consists of endoderm with a layer of visceral mesoderm covering it from the outside (Fig. 186). The allantois, however, grows very rapidly and soon penetrates into the extraembryonic coelom, into the space between the yolk sac, the amnion and the chorion. The distal part of the allantois expands and remains connected with the hindgut of the embryo by means of a narrow neck. When the body folds contract, separating the embryo from the extraembryonic parts, the neck of the allantois is enclosed together with the stalk of the yolk sac in the umbilical cord. The distal part of the

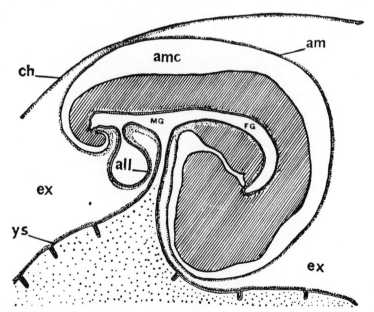

Figure 186. Early stage of development of the allantois in a four-day-old chick embryo. *all,* Allantois; *am,* amnion; *amc,* amniotic cavity; *ch,* chorion; *ex,* extraembryonic coelom; FG, foregut; MG, midgut; *ys,* yolk sac. (From Wieman, 1949.)

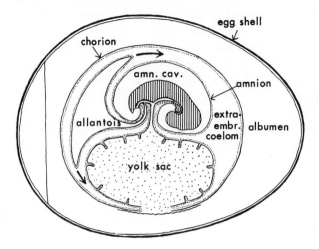

Figure 187. Later stage of development of the allantois in a chick embryo (diagrammatic), showing expansion of the allantois (indicated by arrows) in the extraembryonic coelom.

allantois becomes flattened and penetrates between the amnion and the yolk sac on one side and the chorion on the other side (Fig. 187). By the middle of the incubation period, the allantois spreads over the complete surface of the egg underneath the chorion. Thus the allantois comes into a position where it can take up a second function in addition to that of serving as a reservoir for storing uric acid.

The new function of the allantois is to supply the embryo with oxygen. A network of blood vessels develops on the external surface of the allantois, and this network is in communication with the embryo proper by means of blood vessels running along the stalk of the allantois and through the umbilical cord. The blood flows to the allantois from the dorsal aorta through a right and a left umbilical artery. These arteries leave the dorsal aorta at a point which is much more caudal than the starting point of the vitelline arteries. The returning blood flows to the heart through a pair of umbilical veins. These veins originally enter the right and left ducts of Cuvier respectively. Soon, however, this arrangement of blood vessels is changed. The right umbilical artery and the right umbilical vein disappear, and the left umbilical vein acquires a new central connection; it joins up with the left hepatic vein, whereupon the channel to the duct of Cuvier is closed, and the whole blood flow from the allantois passes into the left hepatic vein.

The allantoic circulation continues until the chick breaks the eggshell and begins to breathe the surrounding air. Then the umbilical vessels close, the circulation ceases, and the allantois dries up and becomes separated from the body of the embryo.

11−2 THE EARLY DEVELOPMENT OF MAMMALS*

The development of the mammals is greatly modified as compared with that of other vertebrates, and this is due to adaptations found in this class. There is good evidence that the mammals are derived from ancestors which

---

*A review of this subject was published by Austin in 1961.

were very closely related to the early reptiles or which can actually be classified as reptiles. As such, they must have had large yolk-laden eggs, and
their ontogenesis must have been very like that of reptiles. At some stage
in their evolution some of the mammals became viviparous, the embryo
receiving an adequate supply of nutrition from the mother while it was
retained in the uterus, and the yolk supply of the egg became superfluous.
The yolk supply consequently became progressively reduced and eventually
disappeared altogether. In this respect, however, there is a distinct gradation
in the three subdivisions of the class.

In the subclass Prototheria the eggs are laid and they develop outside the
maternal body (*Ornithorhynchus*), or, though developing in the maternal
body, they are not supplied with nourishment *(Echidna)*, this adaptation not
going further than the state of ovoviviparity (Chapter 5). The eggs therefore have a large amount of yolk, they are meroblastic, and the subsequent
development follows essentially a reptilian pattern (Flynn and Hill, 1939).

In the subclass Metatheria (the marsupials) the developing embryos
receive nourishment from the mother in the uterus, although the adaptations for this have not been pushed as far forward as in the next group, and
the young are born poorly developed. The yolk here has already become
superfluous, and its quantity in the egg is insignificant. Even so, the yolk is
not used by the embryo as in the reptiles and birds, but the mass of yolk
is ejected at the beginning of cleavage as the egg becomes divided into the
first two blastomeres (Hill, 1918).

In the most advanced subclass of the mammals, the Eutheria (placental
mammals), the egg is devoid of yolk right from the start.

Cleavage, Blastocyst and Development of Germinal Layers. With the disappearance of the yolk, the mammalian eggs have reverted to complete cleavage,
but the subsequent development bears ample evidence of the former presence of yolk, and in many respects the morphogenetic processes resemble
the processes found in meroblastic eggs with a discoidal type of cleavage.

The eggs of mammals are fertilized in the region of the funnels of the
oviducts or in the uppermost part of the oviduct. Through the action of the
ciliated epithelium of the duct, the fertilized eggs travel slowly down the
oviduct, and the cleavage of the egg, or at least the first stages of cleavage,
take place during the sojourn of the eggs in the oviduct. Although the cleavage is complete, it is by no means as regular as in the oligolecithal eggs of the
invertebrates and lower chordates. The synchronization of mitoses in the
blastomeres is lost very early. Even the first two blastomeres cleave at
different rates; consequently a three-cell stage is found and, subsequently,
stages with five, six, seven blastomeres, and so forth (Fig. 188).

The course of the cleavage process varies quite considerably in different
mammals. In the marsupials and a few insectivores, as for instance, *Hemicentetes*, the blastomeres become arranged in the form of a hollow sphere.
In the African elephant shrew *(Elephantulus)*, at the four-cell stage the
blastomeres already surround and enclose a cleavage cavity (blastocoele).
In the majority of mammals, however, the result of cleavage is a solid mass
of cells, a **morula**, in which some cells are superficial and others lie inside,
completely cut off from the surface by the enveloping cells (Fig. 189, A). The
sorting out of the superficial and the internal cells of the morula has been

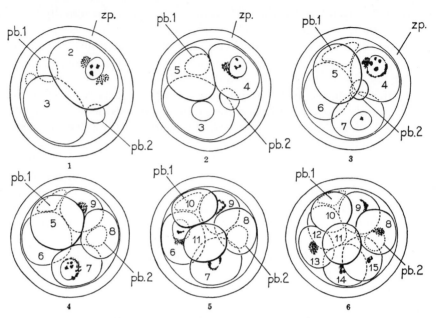

Figure 188.   Cleavage of the egg of a monkey *Macacus rhesus. pb.1* and *pb.2,* First and second polar bodies, *zp,* zona pellucida. (From Lewis and Hartmann, 1933.)

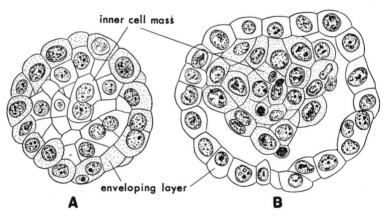

Figure 189.   Morula *(A)* and early blastocyst *(B)* of a bat, showing differentiation into an inner cell mass and the enveloping layer. (After van Benden, from A. Brachet, 1935.)

shown, at least in some mammals, to have some relation to the arrangement of the cytoplasmic substances in the egg.

The cleavage of the rat egg may be taken as an example. In this animal, as also in some others (see section 4–3), the subcortical cytoplasm on one side of the egg is basophilic, owing to the presence of numerous granules containing ribonucleic acid. The subcortical cytoplasm of the opposite hemisphere of the egg is vacuolated. The axis indicated by these two kinds of cytoplasm is approximately at right angles to the animal-vegetal axis of the egg (see p. 79). The cleavage planes bear no definite relationship to the cytoplasmic areas of the egg, and the two kinds of cortical cytoplasm are segregated into the blastomeres at random (Fig. 190). In the eight-cell stage,

Figure 190. Random distribution of different kinds of cytoplasm at the first division of the egg of the rat. Stippled area represents basophilic cytoplasm. (From Jones-Seaton, 1950.)

the blastomeres are all arranged in one plane (Fig. 191). By this time the basophilic and the vacuolated cytoplasms are distributed to different blastomeres. Now an important displacement of the blastomeres takes place: the blastomeres containing vacuolated cytoplasm spread out around the blastomeres with basophilic cytoplasm. The latter sink inward and are eventually completely surrounded by the former (Jones-Seaton, 1950).

In the rhesus monkey, the embryo early becomes subdivided into a mass of cells lying in the interior and an enveloping layer of cells. The origin of the two kinds of cells has not been traced in the primates. A subdivision into a layer of superficial cells and into a group of cells lying in the interior also takes place later in those mammals, in which the cleavage cells are at first arranged as a hollow sphere.

The internal and enveloping cells of early mammalian embryos diverge further and further in their physiological properties and later have a very different function and fate. The cells lying in the interior, known as the **inner cell mass**, have a more basophilic cytoplasm to start with; the basophilia greatly increases during the subsequent stages, indicating a rapid synthesis of ribonucleic acid in the cytoplasm. The inner cell mass is the main source of material for the body of the embryo proper. By contrast, the cells of the **enveloping layer** appear pale if they are stained with basic dyes, in particular with dyes which reveal the presence of ribonucleic acid (pyronine, toluidine blue). The enveloping layer gives rise mainly to extraembryonic parts (the embryonic membranes). The cells of the inner cell mass also give a positve reaction for alkaline phosphatase, whereas the reaction for alkaline

Figure 191. Cleavage of the rat's egg: eight-cell stage. (From Jones-Seaton, 1950.)

2nd polar body   zona pellucida   damaged cell

A   B   C

Figure 192.   The killing of one of the first two blastomeres in the rabbit. *A,* Normal two-cell stage in the cleavage of the rabbit egg. *B,* One of the two cells (on right) killed by pricking with a glass needle; the zona pellucida shows the perforation. The dead cell is slightly deformed. *C,* Operated embryo at a later stage: the surviving blastomere (on left) has divided in two. (Courtesy of Dr. F. Seidel, 1960.)

phosphatase in the enveloping layer remains negative (Dalcq, 1954).

The presence of different kinds of cytoplasm in mammals does not prevent a large degree of regulation taking place in the embryo when part of the egg cytoplasm is removed experimentally. Seidel has succeeded in killing off individual blastomeres in fertilized eggs of the rabbit and allowing the remaining blastomeres to develop (1960). Cleaving eggs were taken out of oviducts of females; one or several blastomeres were killed by pricking them with a fine glass needle. The intact blastomeres, which continued to cleave (Fig. 192) were then introduced into the uterus of another female. A number of completely normal embryos developed from one of the first two blastomeres after the other one was killed. Some of the embryos developed to term and remained alive till adulthood (Fig. 193). Even at the four-cell stage, one of four blastomeres can give rise to a normal animal after the other three of the blastomeres are killed.

The method used did not allow of separating the two or four first blastomeres, and it is not known, therefore, whether both of the blastomeres are capable of complete development. It has been stated before (p. 274) that the first cleavage furrows divide the egg cytoplasm of a mammal at random, and it is therefore quite likely that normal embryos develop from blastomeres which receive a sufficient amount of the basophilic cytoplasm which gives rise

Figure 193.   Rabbit developed from one of the first two blastomeres (on right) 2 months after birth together with its foster mother (the female, into the uterus of which the operated embryo was implanted). (Courtesy of Dr. F. Seidel, 1960.)

to the inner cell mass type of cells. This is confirmed by the fact that in some cases the surviving blastomere produced an embryo consisting of embryonic membranes only or of embryonic membranes and extraembryonic endoderm. Such a blastomere probably did not possess any basophilic cytoplasm or had an insufficient quantity of the same.

On the other hand, it is known that sometimes a single egg of a mammal may produce two or more embryos. This happens occasionally in humans, and then "identical twins" are born—identical because, being derived from the same fertilized egg, they possess an exactly similar hereditary endowment. It is not known, however, at what stage the doubling occurs in identical twins. In fact, it is likely that the splitting of the embryo occurs at the primitive streak stage and involves the separation of formative cells into two lots. Twinning in this form does not therefore shed any light on the organization of the egg and the potentialities of its parts.

Sooner or later a cavity appears inside the compact mass of cells of the morula (if it was not already present in the cleavage stage). The cavity is formed of crevices which appear between the inner cell mass and the cells of the enveloping layer. Fluid is imbibed into this cavity, so that it increases, the whole embryo becoming bloated to the same degree. The enveloping layer becomes lifted off the inner cell mass on most of its inner surface, remaining attached on one side only. This side corresponds later to the dorsal side of the embryo (Figs. 189, B, and 194).

A mammalian embryo in this stage is called a **blastocyst**. The cavity of the blastocyst may be compared to the blastocoele, but the embryo as a whole differs essentially from a blastula since its cells are already differentiated into two types: the inner cell mass and the cells of the enveloping layer.

A further step in the progressive differentiation in the mammalian blastocyst is the appearance of a layer of very flat cells on the interior surface of the inner cell mass: that is, on the surface facing the cavity. This layer of flat cells corresponds to the lower layer of cells of the chick blastoderm—the **hypoblast** (Fig. 194). The cells represent the presumptive endoderm, or at least a part of it.

The origin of the hypoblast (endoderm) cells is a subject of some controversy. The more generally accepted view is that the endoderm cells are split off from the inner cell mass. There are indications, however, that the endoderm cells in some mammals such as elephant shrew (van der Horst, 1942) or even in all mammals (Dalcq, 1954) are derived from the enveloping layer of cells. Some of these, near the edge of the inner cell mass, migrate inward along the internal surface of the inner cell mass and arrange themselves in a continuous layer, as stated above (Fig. 195). Unfortunately, the methods of local vital staining or marking of cells could not as yet be applied to the study of the migration of cells which give rise to the hypoblast in mammals. Failing this, the conclusion has to be reached on the grounds of differences in the staining reactions of the various cells. It is important to note, therefore, that the early endoderm cells in their lack of cytoplasmic basophilia and in their negative reaction for alkaline phosphatase differ from the cells of the inner cell mass and resemble the cells of the enveloping layer (Dalcq, 1954), thus making their origin from the latter fairly plausible.

If we recognize the layer of flat cells (endoderm of some authors) as the

Figure 194. Advanced blastocyst of monkey. *A*, General view (section); *B*, dorsal part of same under higher magnification. (From Heuser and Streeter, 1941.)

hypoblast, the remaining inner cell mass is seen to be equivalent to the epiblast of the chick blastoderm. As to the enveloping layer, it does not directly contribute any longer to the formation of the embryo proper. The function of the enveloping layer of cells is to establish a connection with the maternal body and to mediate between it and the embryo in supplying the latter with nourishment. This layer of cells is forthwith known as the **trophoblast**. The term trophoblast is often applied to the enveloping layer of cells from the very earliest stages of its formation. This would be a somewhat loose use of the term in view of the possibility that the endoderm (hypoblast) cells may be given off from the enveloping layer. The word *trophe* means nourishment; therefore it seems better to use the Greek term trophoblast or "nourishing" layer only from the stage where it no longer contains cells which become part of the body of the embryo. The cells at the expense of which the embryo proper will be developed—i.e., the inner cell mass and hypoblast—may be referred to as the **formative cells**.

The trophoblast corresponds in position to the chorion of the later embryos of the reptiles and birds, but there is the difference that the chorion,

Figure 195. Origin of hypoblast (endoderm) in a rat blastocyst. (After Dalcq, 1954.)

in its typical form, develops in conjunction with the amnion after all the germinal layers have been segregated, whereas the trophoblast precedes the germinal layers in its development. Obviously this is so because in mammalian development the connection with the maternal body must be established at an early stage. The hypoblast cells are at first found in the region of the inner cell mass only, but later they spread along the inner surface of the trophoblast and surround the internal cavity of the blastocyst, much as the endodermal cells in reptiles and birds surround the mass of uncleaved yolk. The inner cavity of the blastocyst thus acquires a resemblance to the yolk sac of the lower amniota, except that instead of being filled with yolk it is filled with fluid. In spite of this difference, the cavity within the enveloping endodermal layer is referred to as the yolk sac. As the hypoblast spreads out to enclose the cavity of the yolk sac, the inner cell mass also spreads out and becomes arranged into a plate, resembling the epiblast of the blastodisc of reptiles and birds. The arrangement of the formative cells in the mammalian blastocyst is now very similar to that in the avian blastodisc prior to the appearance of the primitive streak. Again there is the difference that the blastodisc of a bird lies on the surface of the sphere of uncleaved yolk, whereas under the blastodisc of a mammal there is only the fluid filling the yolk sac. The situation in mammals, that after a cleavage which is not discoidal the formative cells should be arranged in a disc, can only mean that the ancestors of the mammals had large yolky eggs with meroblastic discoidal cleavage.

In eutherian mammals, the blastodisc is primarily formed underneath the layer of trophoblast cells. In those whose development may be considered to be more primitive—as, for instance, in the rabbit, the ungulates, most insectivores and lemurs—the layer of trophoblast over the blastodisc (**Rauber's layer**) disappears, so that the epiblast becomes temporarily superficial (see Fig. 201, A). In the higher mammals, however, Rauber's layer does not disappear in the embryonic area; the formative cells are therefore never exposed to the exterior (see Figs. 196 and 201, B).

The blastodisc, consisting of an epiblast and a hypoblast, becomes quite sharply delimited from the remainder of the embryo (Fig. 196). The epiblast consists of a thick plate of columnar cells, clearly distinguished from the flatter and more irregularly arranged cells of the trophoblast. The hypoblast cells on the underside of the blastodisc may become cuboidal or even columnar, and in this they differ from the cells of extraembryonic endoderm lining the internal surface of the trophoblast. The hypoblast becomes especially thick, with the cells becoming high and columnar near one edge of the blastodisc. The thickening is the prechordal plate (see p. 193), and it denotes what will be the anterior end of the embryo.

The embryo now enters the phase of gastrulation. The gastrulation and formation of germinal layers in mammals resemble what is found in birds and in reptiles. A primitive streak is formed, and a Hensen's node is seen at the anterior end of the primitive streak. The primitive streak is, however, much shorter than in birds and, when fully developed, does not surpass half the length of the blastodisc, being confined to its posterior part. The cells of the primitive streak migrate downward and sideways between the epiblast and the hypoblast (Fig. 198). Some of the migrating cells appear to join the

Figure 196. Monkey embryo. Formation of the amniotic cavity by cavitation. (From Heuser and Streeter, 1941.)

Figure 197. Monkey embryo. Development of secondary yolk sac. (From Heuser and Streeter, 1941.)

hypoblast and so contribute to the formation of the endoderm (Heuser and Streeter, 1941). The loose cells migrating sideways give rise to the layer of mesoderm.

The cells migrating forward from Hensen's node remain packed more closely and give rise to the "head process" – the notochordal rudiment. The

Figure 198.   Monkey embryo in the primitive streak stage. Transverse section. (From Heuser and Streeter, 1941.)

notochordal rudiment in some mammals (including man) is perforated by a canal starting from Hensen's node. This is the archenteric canal which is also found in some birds, as mentioned before (p. 209), and which corresponds to the archenteron of lower vertebrates. In other mammals, either there is no archenteric canal or the canal, though present in the notochordal rudiment, does not open to the surface at Hensen's node. Where an archenteric canal is present (Fig. 199), its ventral wall fuses later with the hypoblast and is then

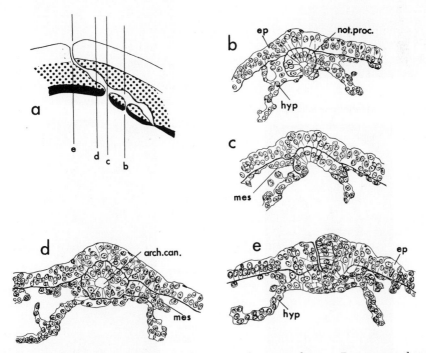

Figure 199.   The archenteric canal *(arch.can.)* in a human embryo. *a*, Reconstructed medial section, showing the relation of the canal to epiblast (white), hypoblast (black) and mesoderm (dots). Vertical lines show the levels of sections *b* through *e*. *ep*, Epiblast; *hyp*, hypoblast; *mes*, mesoderm; *not.proc.*, notochordal process. (From Grosser, 1945.)

perforated so that the archenteric cavity opens into the yolk sac cavity (this also occurs in the reptiles). Subsequently the notochord separates itself from the endoderm, and the endoderm closes underneath the notochord, forming again a continuous layer.

The primitive streak in mammals, as in birds, is a transient structure. Having given rise to the mesodermal layer and the notochord rudiment, the primitive streak starts shrinking, its anterior end with Hensen's node receding farther and farther back, while in the anterior parts of the blastodisc the germinal layers enter the next phase of development, the formation of the primary organ rudiments. The first of these to become visible is, of course, the neural plate, followed by the somites (Fig. 200). The subsequent development of the neural tube, notochord, mesodermal segments and so on will be treated together with the development of these parts in other vertebrates.

Figure 200. *See legend on opposite page.*

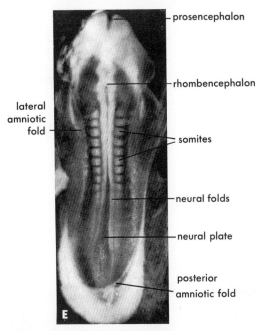

Figure 200. Rabbit embryos in gastrulation and early organogenesis stages. *A*, Embryo with fully developed primitive streak, age 7¼ days. *B*, Embryo with neural plate anteriorly but with primitive streak in posterior half, age 8⅔ days. *C*, Embryo with three pairs of somites, age 8¾ days. *D*, Embryo with four pairs of somites and well developed neural plate, which shows the main subdivisions of the future neural tube. *E*, Embryo with nine pairs of somites; neural plate closing to form the neural tube. (Courtesy of Dr. F. Seidel, 1960.)

We must now turn to the fate of those parts of the blastocyst which do not participate in the formation of the embryo: to the extraembryonic parts.

Extraembryonic Parts.   Toward the end of the period of cleavage, the embryo usually passes from the oviduct into the uterus. As a rule, the embryo is then in the blastocyst stage. In the uterus, the next important step in the development of the mammalian egg has to take place: the embryo becomes attached to the wall of the uterus, where it is to perform its subsequent development. This attachment of the blastocyst to the uterine wall is known as **implantation**. The attachment to the uterine wall is carried out by the cells of the trophoblast. Two basically different types of attachment are to be found. In most mammals, the blastocyst becomes attached to the surface of the uterine epithelium and therefore lies in the cavity of the uterus. In a smaller number of mammals—in man, but also in some of the rodents—the blastocyst penetrates deep into the uterine wall, and the development of the embryo takes place *inside* the uterine wall. The epithelium lining the cavity of the uterus at the site of implantation becomes destroyed. The destruction of the uterine epithelium is due to the activity of the trophoblast cells. The embryo is capable of imbibing the fluid filling the uterus and deriving from it nutrient substances, just as is the case in ovoviviparous dogfish, but this source of nutrition is insignificant as compared with the food supply that the embryo gets by diffusion from the maternal blood vessels, once the connection between the embryo and the uterine wall is established. The formation of this connection is called **placentation**, and it will be dealt with in the following section.

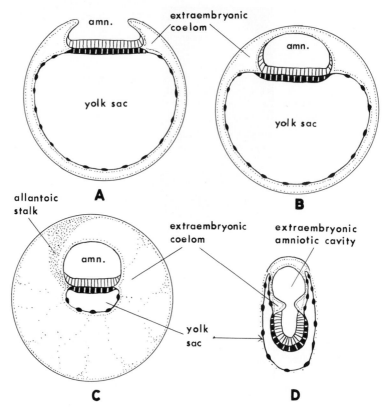

Figure 201. Diagrammatic comparison of the relation of the embryonic and extraembryonic parts (amnion, yolk sac) in a shrew *(A)*, a bat *(B)*, a human *(C)* and a mouse *(D)*.

At the time of implantation the embryo is still in the blastocyst stage, and the processes of gastrulation take place only after implantation. Into roughly the same period also falls the development of the embryonic membranes. This differs to a most amazing degree (see Mossman, 1937, and Goetz, 1938) in various groups of mammals, so that only the more general features of this process can be indicated here (see Fig. 201). If the blastodisc is exposed to the exterior by the disappearance of Rauber's layer in the embryonic area, the amniotic folds may develop around the embryo proper in much the same way as in reptiles and birds. After the fusion of the amniotic folds, the body of the embryo becomes enclosed in the amniotic cavity. A body fold later separates the embryo from the yolk sac, with which the embryo remains connected by means of the umbilical cord. The outer wall of the amniotic fold becomes the chorion. On the periphery, in the extraembryonic area, the ectoderm of the chorion is continuous with the remaining parts of the trophoblast. The trophoblast thus becomes a part of the chorion; it actually forms the epithelial layer of the chorion over most of the extraembryonic surface of the blastocyst. The mesoderm spreading from the embryonic area may supply this part of the chorion with a connective tissue layer (Fig. 201, A).

The development of the amniotic cavity in the way described above occurs relatively later, after gastrulation and the formation of primary organ rudiments. We find this method of amnion formation in the marsupials, ungulates (pigs), most insectivores and lemurs. In other mammals a tendency may be observed for the cells giving rise to the embryo proper to sink deeper into the blastocyst, so that the formative cells do not appear on the surface. Under these conditions the amniotic cavity can no longer be formed by the convergence of amniotic folds. Instead, the amniotic cavity is then formed by a crevice appearing between cells in the future blastodisc area. This mode of formation of the amniotic cavity is known as **cavitation**.

The split may occur either between the trophoblastic layer and the inner cell mass, or inside the inner cell mass. In the first case (Fig. 196), the amniotic cavity is only covered by the trophoblast, and an epithelial lining representing the amnion proper must be developed later, either at the expense of the edges of the blastodisc (in the bats) or at the expense of cells derived from the internal surface of the trophoblast (in higher primates, according to Heuser and Streeter, 1941). The amniotic cavity appears relatively earlier; its formation precedes gastrulation, instead of following it, as in the mammals having a more primitive type of development. In some rodents, such as the mice and rats, the tendency for the formative cells to sink deeper into the blastocyst goes even further and they become separated from the surface of the blastocyst not only by the Rauber's layer but, in addition, by a mass of cells which later become extraembryonic ectoderm. In this case, the amniotic cavity is formed (by cavitation) deep in the interior of the inner cell mass and is from the start separated from the trophoblast by cells of extraembryonic ectoderm (Fig. 201, D and Fig. 205, A). Further variations of amnion development have been described; references to these descriptions may be found in the papers by Mossman, 1937, and Goetz, 1938.

The development of the allantois also varies a great deal inside the class Mammalia. With the acquisition of viviparity, the original function of the allantois as a urinary bladder becomes altogether lost. As the maternal organism supplies the embryo with all the necessary nutrition, so also it takes over the removal of the waste products of metabolism from the embryo. Not only does the carbon dioxide produced by the embryo diffuse into the maternal blood, but the end products of the protein metabolism also find their way into the maternal blood and are excreted by the kidneys of the pregnant mother. This, of course, will be possible only if the end products of metabolism are readily soluble. Uric acid, owing to its insolubility in water, was the most suitable end product of protein metabolism in the case of the cleidoic eggs of reptiles and birds, but in the mammals we find that the end product of protein metabolism is urea which, owing to its solubility, can be passed from the embryo to the mother and can thus be disposed of. As a result, the storage of these waste products in the allantoic cavity is no longer necessary.

On the other hand, the function which was secondary in the case of birds and reptiles retains its importance for the mammalian embryo. The mammalian embryo, enclosed in the amniotic cavity and surrounded by the amnion and the chorion (trophoblast), is still in need of a pathway by which oxygen from outside (from the maternal organism) may be transported to its tissues. This pathway, in the higher mammals, is still supplied by the blood vessels of the allantois. Moreover, besides supplying the embryo with oxygen, the allantoic circulation now supplies the embryo with nutrient substances as well, as these can no longer be drawn from the yolk sac.

The result is that the endodermal part of the allantois (the epithelial lining of the allantoic vesicle) becomes gradually reduced in the higher mammals, while the mesodermal part, giving rise to the blood vessel system of the allantois, develops progressively. The endoderm of the allantoic stalk still fulfills a useful function, as it forms a bridge growing out from the embryonic body and reaching the chorion, along which the mesoderm spreads outward and establishes a connection with the trophoblastic epithelium. The expansion of the endodermal vesicle at the outer end is, on the other hand, wholly superfluous. The development of the allantoic mesoderm, however, may proceed even in the total absence of the endodermal component (in the guinea pig).

Two special cases will be mentioned here.

In the monkeys and in man, a typical blastocyst is formed with a cavity which becomes lined by hypoblast (endoderm cells). The blastocyst becomes attached to the wall of the uterus by its dorsal side: that is, by the side bearing the internal cell mass (Fig. 202).

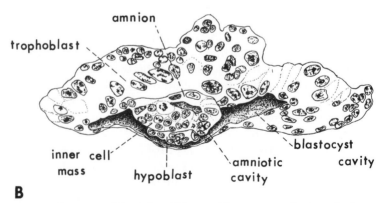

Figure 202.   Implantation of the 7-day-old human blastocyst. *A*, Photograph of section. (From Hertig and Rock, 1945.) *B*, Only the embryonic parts are shown, drawn as if the embryo were dissected in the plane passing through its main axis.

In man, the blastocyst sinks into the uterine wall, as a result of the destruction of the maternal tissues by the trophoblast, and the opening through which the blastocyst enters is closed by a clot of coagulated blood plasm and later covered up by a sheet of regenerated uterine epithelium. In the monkey, the blastocyst does not enter the uterine epithelium but, instead, becomes attached by its ventral side to the opposite uterine wall.

The amniotic cavity is formed by cavitation as described on p. 285. The epithelium surrounding the amniotic cavity is of very unequal thickness throughout. The roof of the amniotic cavity is formed by a fairly thin layer of epithelium; this is the amniotic ectoderm. The floor of the amniotic cavity consists of a very thick plate of cells arranged in a columnar epithelium. This plate, with the underlying layer of hypoblast (endoderm) which is also thickened, constitutes the bilaminar blastodisc, inside which the primitive streak will later appear and from which the body of the embryo proper will later develop (Fig. 203).

It is common to both monkeys and man that, at an early stage of development, even before the primitive streak is formed, numbers of loose mesenchymelike cells appear between the formative parts and the trophoblast. These cells, which may be compared to extraembryonic mesenchyme, are supposed to be derived from the trophoblast (Heuser and Streeter, 1941), whereas in most mammals extraembryonic mesoderm spreads out from the blastodisc and has the same origin as the embryonic mesoderm (that is, it is derived from the primitive streak). The delay in the development of the primitive streak in the higher primates, in conjunction with the need for accelerating the development of the extraembryonic parts which are required

Figure 203. Implanted 11-day-old human embryo prior to primitive streak formation, with amniotic cavity (*amn.*), secondary yolk sac cavity (*y. sac*) and extraembryonic mesenchyme (*e. mes.*). The embryo is surrounded by the trophoblast. (From Hertig and Rock, 1941.)

to supply the embryo with food and oxygen, must have made it necessary to provide for a second, unusual, source of extraembryonic mesoderm.

The extraembryonic mesoderm rapidly increases in quantity and gradually fills the cavity of the blastocyst, which was recognized as the yolk sac. A secondary, smaller yolk sac is then formed by the hypoblast cells connected to the blastodisc (see Fig. 197). The cavity of this secondary yolk sac is for some time much smaller than the amniotic cavity, but it catches up with the amniotic cavity later (at the time when the primitive streak appears). In the meantime, the mass of extraembryonic mesenchyme separates to form a cavity of its own, which is, of course, the extraembryonic coelom; the mesenchyme cells arrange themselves into a mesothelium lining this coelom. The extraembryonic coelom now becomes the greatest cavity in the blastocyst and takes up most of the space inside the trophoblast. In the area adjoining the posterior end of the embryo, the extraembryonic mesenchyme becomes concentrated and forms a strand leading from the blastodisc to the area of trophoblast, which enters into the formation of the placenta. The strand of mesoderm known as the **connecting stalk** or **allantoic stalk** represents the mesodermal component of the allantois, and through this strand of mesoderm the allantoic circulation is established later (Fig. 204). Here again it can be noted that the necessity for an early provision of the embryo with food and oxygen supplies has brought about a short-cut in the established pattern of the developmental processes. The endodermal part of the allantois —the allantoic vesicle (or allantoic diverticulum)—becomes superfluous and remains rudimentary, never reaching the placenta in monkeys and man.

The second type of modified mammalian development is that found in mice, rats and related rodents. The initial stages of cleavage and blastocyst formation in these animals do not differ essentially from that in other mammals. The implantation is interstitial but is achieved in an essentially different way from the implantation of a human embryo. The blastocysts entering the uterus from the fallopian tube, in which the earlier stages of development are passed, find their way into crypts along the ventral side of the uterus, which in these animals is almost completely subdivided into two long "horns." Thereupon the uterine epithelium adjoining the blastocyst degenerates, and the embryo comes into direct contact with the connective tissue of the uterine wall. The connective tissue then starts proliferating and completely encloses the blastocyst. The proliferation of the connective tissue is so abundant that the lumen of the uterine horn is completely occluded in the regions in which the blastocysts come to lie, and the passage along the uterus becomes opened up again only toward the end of pregnancy.

In the meantime, the blastocyst, instead of becoming bloated by accumulation of fluid in its cavity becomes elongated in a vertical direction (Fig. 205, A, B). The embryo in this stage is known as the "egg cylinder." Both the trophoblast and the inner cell mass covered by the hypoblast (endoderm) stretch, leaving very little space between them. In due time, the endoderm lines this cavity from the trophoblast side, converting it into the yolk sac. As the inner cell mass is attached to the trophoblast only at one end of the egg cylinder, the formative cells become almost completely surrounded by the yolk sac (Fig. 205, B). The amniotic cavity is now formed as a rather narrow

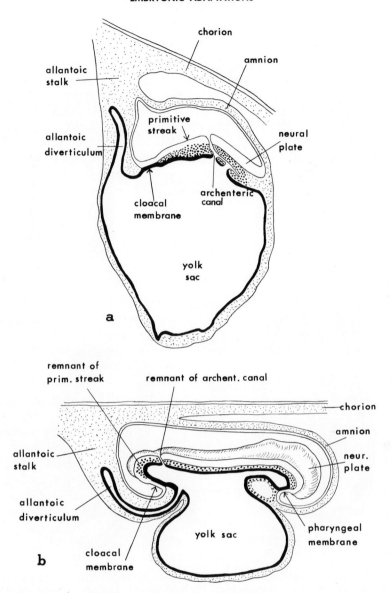

Figure 204. Semidiagrammatic median sections of the human embryo in the primitive streak stage (*a*) and the neural plate stage (*b*). The ectoderm is white, the endoderm black, the embryonic mesoderm coarsely stippled, the extraembryonic mesoderm finely stippled. (*a*, After Jones and Brewer, 1941, and Grosser, 1945; *b*, after Grosser, 1945.)

canal inside the inner cell mass. The cells of the inner cell mass form an epithelium surrounding the amniotic cavity; part of this epithelium represents the epiblast of the blastodisc. The formative cells make up about half the lining of the amniotic cavity, that half lying farther from the attachment of the egg cylinder. The other half of the egg cylinder contains only extraembryonic parts: extraembryonic ectoderm, extraembryonic endoderm and, at a later stage, also extraembryonic mesoderm.

Figure 205.   Four stages of development of a mouse embryo. *A.* Early egg cylinder stage; the inner cell mass has become subdivided into the rudiment of the embryo proper (epiblast) and extraembryonic ectoderm; the endodermal (hypoblast) layer has been formed. *B,* Later egg cylinder stage; the amniotic cavity has been formed by cavitation in both the embryo rudiment and the extraembryonic ectoderm. The latter has produced the ectoplacental cone, which is invading the maternal tissues; the endoderm has started spreading to cover the inner surface of the trophoblast (distal endoderm). *C,* Further development of the egg cylinder—the primitive streak stage. The cavity inside the egg cylinder has become subdivided into the amniotic cavity proper and the cavity of the ectoplacental cone, the extraembryonic coelom having developed between; the endoderm has lined the inner surface of the trophoblast, thus completely surrounding the yolk sac cavity. *D,* Embryo with open neural plate and seven pairs of somites; the embryo is curved around the amniotic cavity and is concave dorsally. The allantois is growing from the posterior end of the embryo into the extraembryonic coelom. (Modified from Snell, 1941.)

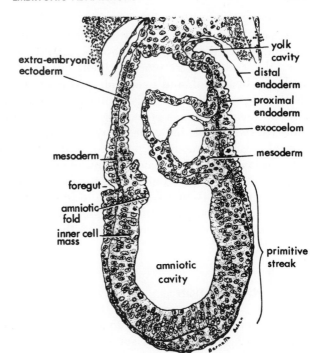

Figure 206. The primitive streak stage (section) in the development of the mouse. (Modified from Snell, 1941.)

At an early stage, the extraembryonic ectoderm lying at the upper end of the egg cylinder starts proliferating and forms a mass of cells called the **ectoplacental cone**. This mass of cells invades the maternal connective tissues and establishes close contacts with the maternal blood vessels. This is the beginning of the formation of the placenta. The amniotic cavity, originally stretching throughout the length of the egg cylinder (Fig. 206), later becomes constricted in the middle. One part of the cavity is now almost completely surrounded by formative cells (the cells of the epiblast), while only a very small part of the lining of this cavity can be recognized as being amniotic ectoderm.

The other part of the original amniotic cavity lies immediately underneath the ectoplacental cone and is therefore referred to as the ectoplacental cone cavity. When the ectoplacental cone cavity becomes separated from the amniotic cavity proper, a further cavity is formed between them which is entirely surrounded by mesoderm and represents the **extraembryonic coelom** or "**exocoelom**" (Figs. 205, C, 206). As the exocoelom increases, the ectoplacental cone cavity is squashed between the exocoelom and the ectoplacental cone, and eventually it diseappears. The structure of the embryo at this stage may be described as resulting from an invagination of the bilaminar blastodisc into the yolk sac. The dorsal surface of the blastodisc, instead of being flat as in most other mammals, is concave, and the ventral side (lined by the hypoblast) is convex and surrounded by the yolk sac cavity (Fig. 215, C).

In this abnormal position, the embryo proceeds to the formation of the primitive streak, which gives rise to the mesoderm of the embryo. The neural tube, the mesodermal somites, the heart and other parts of the embryonic body are developed in the usual way, but the body of the embryo, instead of being surrounded by the amniotic cavity, is curled round it with the dorsal side facing the cavity, while its convex ventral surface is surrounded by the yolk sac (Fig. 205, *D*). Only at a later stage, during the eighth day of intra-uterine life in the case of the mouse (total duration of pregnancy — 20 days), does the embryo start twisting itself out of this unusual position, starting with the head end, and eventually assumes the normal position in the amniotic cavity, with the body convex dorsally and concave ventrally. The amniotic wall becomes stretched so that the amniotic cavity surrounds the embryo. Before this happens, however, the allantois is formed as a proliferation of mesenchyme at the posterior end of the embryo. The allantois grows into the extraembryonic coelom and eventually establishes contact with the ectoplacental cone and enters into the formation of the placenta. The allantois in mice and rats is completely devoid of endodermal parts and consists only of connective tissue and blood vessels, which eventually serve to establish circulation between the embryo and the placenta. (For further details see Snell, 1941.)

11 – 3 PLACENTATION

The term **placenta** applies to any type of organ, built up of maternal and fetal tissues jointly, which serves for the transport of nutrient substances from the tissues of the mother into those of the embryo. Placentae are not found exclusively in mammals but appear also in animals belonging to various groups of the animal kingdom such as in *Peripatus* (Protracheata), *Salpa* (Tunicata), *Mustelus laevis* (Elasmobranchia) and certain lizards. The nature of the tissues entering into the formation of the placenta is not the same in all cases. A prerequisite for participation in the development of the placenta is, on the one hand, the superficial position of the part in question and, on the other, the possibility of the formation of a blood vessel network, which may undertake the transport of nutritive substances from the surface of contact with the maternal tissues to the developing embryo.

In mammals, there exist two essentially different main types of placentae. In the first type, the connection is established between the uterine wall and that part of the chorion which is lined by the yolk sac with its network of vitelline blood vessels. This type of placenta is called the **chorio-vitelline placenta**. It is found in some of the marsupials (*Didelphys, Macropus*). In the second type of placenta, the connection is established by the chorion lined by the allantois, with the allantoic blood vessel system taking over the transport of substances from the mother to the embryo. This type of placenta is called the **chorio-allantoic placenta**, and it is found in all the Eutheria as well as in some marsupials (*Parameles, Dasyurus*). Remnants of the chorio-vitelline placenta may be found either temporarily or even permanently in higher mammals, playing a subsidiary part in their placentation.

As the function of the placenta is to allow a passage of substances from the maternal to the fetal tissues, everything that accelerates this will increase the efficiency of this organ. A facilitation of the transport of substances through the **plancental barrier** (the surface separating the maternal from the fetal tissues) may be achieved in two ways:

(1) By increasing the surface of the contact, and

(2) by diminishing the thickness of the layer separating the maternal from the fetal blood.

The surface of contact between maternal and fetal tissues is increased by the development of outgrowths on the surface of the chorion, known as the **villi**. The villi are fingerlike or branched outgrowths of the chorion, containing connective tissue and blood vessels in their interior (Fig. 207). They fit into corresponding depressions in the uterine wall. The villi may be scattered all over the surface of the chorion, in the case of the pig, and this type of placenta is known as the **diffuse placenta**. In cattle, the villi are found in groups or patches, while the rest of the chorion surface is smooth. The patches of villi are called **cotyledons**, and the placenta of this type is known as the **cotyledon placenta**. In carnivores, the villi are developed in the form of a belt around the middle of their blastocyst which is more or less elliptical in shape. This is the **zonary placenta**. In man and the anthropoid apes, the chorion is at first all covered with villi, but the villi continue developing only on one side, the side turned away from the lumen of the uterus, while on other parts of the chorion the villi are reduced. The functional placenta therefore has the shape of a disc and is known as the **discoidal placenta**. A discoidal placenta has also been developed independently in the rodents (mouse, rat, rabbit and others). In the monkeys, the placenta consists of two discs—a **bidiscoidal placenta**.

The thickness of the partition between the maternal and fetal blood may be diminished by the removal of some of the intervening layers of tissue.

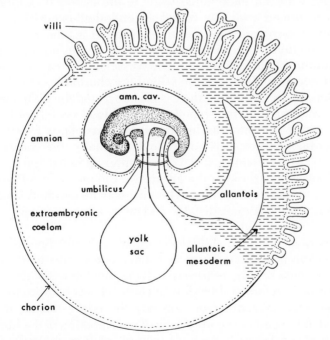

Figure 207.   Embryo of placental mammal, surrounded by embryonic membranes (diagrammatic).

Depending on which layers have disappeared, several types of placentae may be distinguished. The names given to the various types indicate the two tissues — one maternal, the other fetal — which are in immediate contact.

In the more primitive cases, the layers of tissue participating in the diffusion of substances from the mother to the embryo are the following:

1. The blood of the mother,
2. The endothelial wall of the maternal blood vessels,
3. The connective tissue around the maternal blood vessels,
4. The uterine epithelium,
5. The epithelium of the chorion,
6. Connective tissue of the chorion,
7. The endothelial wall of the blood vessels in the chorion,
8. The blood of the embryo.

If all these tissues are present in the placenta, the chorionic epithelium is in contact with the uterine epithelium, and the placenta is designated as an **epithelio-chorial placenta**. This type of placenta is found in all marsupials and in the ungulates (horses, pigs, cattle). In the case of an epithelio-chorial placenta the villi, in their growth, push in the wall of the uterus and later lie in pocketlike depressions of the uterine wall.

When the blastocyst is implanted and, subsequently, when the villi begin to grow, the superficial tissues of the uterine wall may be destroyed to a greater or lesser extent. If the destruction involves the uterine epithelium and the underlying connective tissue, the epithelium of the chorion may come into direct contact with the endothelial walls of the maternal capillaries. A placenta is then formed which is called an **endothelio-chorial placenta**. It is found mainly in carnivores but also in a few other mammals.

The destruction of the maternal tissues of the uterine wall may involve the endothelium of the maternal blood vessels. The cavities of the blood vessels are then opened up, and the villi of the chorion become bathed in the maternal blood, thus facilitating the gas exchange and the diffusion of nutrient substances from the maternal blood into the blood vessels of the chorionic villi. This type of placenta, the **hemo-chorial placenta**, is found in primates and in many insectivores, bats and rodents. Actually, the chorionic villi are surrounded by spaces (sinuses) devoid of an endothelial lining, into which maternal blood enters through the arteries of the uterus and from which the blood flows into the uterine veins. The villi may be ramified dendritic structures, or they may coalesce distally and form a more or less complicated network.

In the case of epithelio-chorial placentae, at parturition the villi can be pulled out of the pockets in which they have been embedded, and the fetal part of the placenta may be removed, leaving the surface of the uterine wall intact. There is therefore no bleeding at birth. This is not the case with other types of placentae. At parturition not only the fetal component of the placenta is shed, but a part of the uterine wall participating in the function of the placenta is torn away as well. An open wound is left on the wall of the uterus, and hemorrhage inevitably occurs. In the latter case the placenta is said to be **deciduous**, whereas in the first case the placenta is **nondeciduous**.

The hemorrhage at parturition is normally stopped by the same mechanism as serves for the expulsion of the newborn: the contraction of the muscular wall of the uterus constricts the blood vessels and thus slows down the flow of blood, until clotting of the blood stops the hemorrhage altogether.

PART V

ORGANOGENESIS

The germinal layers formed as a result of the process of gastrulation are the source of material for the development of all the organ rudiments of the embryo. The germinal layers become progressively subdivided into groups of cells which have been called **primary organ rudiments**, because some of them are composite in their nature and undergo a further subdivision until all the various parts are segregated from each other in the form of **secondary organ rudiments.**

The formation of the primary organ rudiments has been described in connection with the process of gastrulation.

12

Morphogenetic Processes Involved in Organogenesis

The way in which sheets of epithelial cells give rise to the various organ rudiments is largely the same as that by which gastrulation is achieved: that is, by means of morphogenetic movements—by changes in the position and arrangement of cells. The movements can be studied by the same methods as those involved in gastrulation—by the application of local vital staining, for instance.

The movements are different in nature, depending on whether they are performed by epithelial cells or by cells of the mesenchyme. By epithelial cells we mean cells in close formation, adhering to one another, independent of whether they are spreading in a sheet or forming a compact mass. The following classification of morphogentic processes is a modification of the one given by Davenport (1895).

12-1 MORPHOGENETIC PROCESSES IN EPITHELIA

The changes observed in epithelial cells leading to the formation of organs are mainly of the following types:

Local Thickenings of the Epithelial Layer. This is a very common method of organ formation. We have seen before that the formation of a neural plate takes place in this way. The thickening is brought about by the epithelial layer flowing, as it were, toward the region in which the organ rudiment is to appear, in this case the mid-dorsal region of the embryo. As the thickening becomes discernible, the epithelial cells may become elongated in the direction perpendicular to the surface of the epithelial layer.

This elongation of cells is very distinct in the neural plate. The cells become columnar, and in the case of the urodele amphibians, at least, single cells stretch right through from the external to the internal surface of the neural plate, in spite of its increased thickness. This means that the formation of the neural plate involves a rearrangement of the cells of the epithelial layer, because the ectoderm of the late gastrula in amphibians consists of at least two layers of cells, and this two-layered state is retained by the presumptive epidermis, whereas in the neural plate a single layer of columnar cells is found. It has been suggested that the elongation of individual cells of the epithelium is the mechanism by which the thickening of the layer is brought about (Holtfreter, 1947b). This is, however, not always the case; sometimes the increase in thickness of an epithelial layer is brought about, at least in part, by a local increase in the number of cell layers.

In the case of multiple organs, more than one thickening may develop simultaneously in the same sheet of epithelium. A very clear-cut example of this may be seen in the development of the hair follicles of mammals. Before the appearance of the rudiments of the hair follicles, the epidermis is a two-layered sheet of epithelium, with cells more or less flattened and of uniform thickness. Then, rather suddenly, numerous concentrations become visible, scattered at more or less regular intervals throughout the epithelial layer (Fig. 208). In each concentration the cells lie closer together, and the individual cells, especially in the lower layer of epithelium, are less flat than before, approaching the cuboidal or even the columnar shape. At a slightly later stage the number of cell layers is also increased. This concentration of cells is brought about by the cells flowing toward the respective centers, since no increase of cellular reproduction (mitoses) could be discovered in the early hair follicle rudiments (Balinsky, 1950).

Separation of Epithelial Layers. Epithelial layers or masses of cells may be subdivided into parts by the appearance of crevices between groups of cells, the cells on the opposite sides of a crevice losing connection with one another. The crevices may appear at any spot, but perhaps the most common occurrence is for the crevices to be either parallel to the surface of the epithelium or perpendicular to it. In the first case, the epithelial layer is split

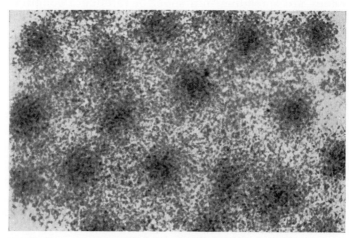

Figure 208.   Rudiments of hair follicles in the skin of a mouse embryo (surface view).

into two layers lying on top of one another. The original crevice may be increased by the secretion of fluid into it and may become a more or less spacious cavity. This is the case with the formation of the parietal and visceral layers of the lateral plate mesoderm and the coelomic cavity between them. An instance of crevices appearing perpendicular to the surface of the epithelium is found in the development of the mesodermal somites. The upper edge of the mesodermal mantle becomes subdivided into segments by crevices running between cells perpendicular to the surface of the epithelium and at the same time perpendicular to the main axis of the body (see Fig. 135). The masses of cells thus formed (the somites) are of approximately the same size. This suggests that each somite is formed around a center of attraction whose force is limited, so that only a certain number of cells can be kept together, the cells losing connection with each other where the attraction of the center is too weak. A rhythmic pattern of differentiation is thus produced.

A splitting of epithelial masses often follows the formation of local thickenings. Thus the neural tube eventually loses its connection with the epidermis.

Folding of the Epithelial Layer.   The folding of epithelial layers can occur either in the form of linear folds, resulting in the formation of grooves, or as approximately round depressions, forming pockets. The direction of folding is as a rule toward the originally proximal surface of the epithelial layer. In the ectoderm, and later in the epidermis, the folding is therefore directed inward. In the invaginated parts of the embryo, as in the whole of the endoderm, the folding is directed outward—that is, away from the lumen of the alimentary canal.

The folding is usually foreshadowed and accompanied by a thickening of the epithelial layer. This is the case in the neural tube formation: at first the neural plate appears as a thickening of the ectoderm; next this thickened plate starts to fold inward, thus forming a neural groove and eventually rolling into a tube. This is followed by the fusion of the edges of the neural tube and its separation from the remaining epidermis (see Fig. 137). If a linear fold becomes closed in and separated from the original epithelial layer, the resulting structure is a hollow tube. If a pocketlike depression becomes closed in and separated from the original epithelial layer, the result is a hollow vesicle. An example of the first formation is the neural tube and of the second formation the rudiment of the inner ear—the ear vesicle (see Fig. 297). Most of the glands are developed as pocketlike invaginations of the epithelium, and this shows how common this type of morphogenetic process is. Of course, the invagination of the archenteron, as found in a sea urchin or *Amphioxus,* is also an example of pocketlike infolding of an epithelial layer. What has been said about the mechanism of the invagination and the change in the shape of cells as a possible cause of the infolding applies to all infoldings in general.

Thickenings Followed by Their Excavation to Form Tubes or Vesicles.   By no means always are tubes or vesicles produced by infolding of the epithelial layer. Quite often the initial stage is a solid thickening of the epithelium (as discussed previously). Such a solid thickening may acquire an internal cavity secondarily by the separation of cells in the middle. This cavity may or may not be connected with the external surface of the epithelium. It is very remarkable that one and the same organ in different animals may develop in different ways: as an infolding in some and as a solid thickening becoming excavated later in others. This is the case with the development of the neural tube in various vertebrates; it is formed by infolding in the elasmobranchs, in the urodele amphibians and in the amniotes. It develops as a longitudinal thickening that later separates itself from the epidermis and acquires a central cavity in the Myxinoidea and in the bony fishes. In the Anura a sort of intermediate state is found, the groove being very shallow and the neural tube being in part solid at the beginning. Other organs such as the eye, the ear and the lens may develop either as hollow pocketlike invaginations or as solid masses of cells. The underlying mechanism of both formations must therefore be similar in nature.

If the thickening of an epithelial layer is directed outward, it takes the form of an "outgrowth." The formation of an outgrowth is probably never caused by a local increase of growth rate; that is, increased multiplication or increase in size of the cells. Much as in all other cases of organ formation, the outgrowths are caused by the concentration of cells and their rearrangement. Such outgrowths are formed on the surface of the chorion in mammals (the chorionic villi—see section 11–3), or on the gills in amphibians and fishes (the gill filaments). The outgrowths may be simple and fingerlike or may develop secondary outgrowths when the whole becomes dendritic or plumose. The tips of the outgrowths may be solid, but once they have appeared, the solid outgrowths of epithelium become hollowed out, so that connective tissue and blood vessels may penetrate into the outgrowth. Blood capillaries develop in a similar way: first as solid strands of endothelial cells, pushing forward from existing blood vessels, and being hollowed out later. The cavity in this case is the lumen of the capillary. The speed with which the solid outgrowths are hollowed out differs from case to case, and no strict boundary can be drawn between these and outwardly directed folds or outpushings which are hollow right from the start.

Fusions of Previously Separated Cell Masses. These may play a certain part in morphogenesis. For example, the edges of the neural plate fuse along the midline dorsally after the neural plate has rolled itself into a tube. Also, blood capillaries growing out from the arteries and from the veins fuse their ends to establish an open pathway for the blood circulation.

Breaking Up of Epithelial layers to Produce Mesenchyme. This is a very important morphogenetic process, even if it does not lead directly to the formation or organ rudiments, because it furnishes the material from which further organ rudiments may develop. An epithelial layer or a portion of it may sometimes break up into mesenchyme altogether, so that the epithelium as such disappears or a gap is left in the previously continuous layer. An example of this process is found in the development of the neural crest; a part of the ectodermal epithelium forming the edge of the neural folds splits up into disconnected cells, leaving a gap between the neural tube and the epidermis. (Sometimes, however, the neural crest cells are given off from the dorsal wall of the neural tube after its separation from the epidermis.) The other possibility is for individual cells to slip out from an epithelial layer, so that the latter remains intact though depleted of part of its cells. This process is a very common occurrence; thus the visceral layer of the lateral plate mesoderm gives off cells which, as mesenchyme, surround the alimentary canal and are later differentiated into the smooth muscle and connective tissue of the intestine.

The breaking up of epithelial layers and the migration of individual cells out of such layers are the result of a change in the physiological properties of the cells, most especially of their surface layers. The cells do not adhere to one another on contact, as do epithelial cells, but glide freely, and thus they move about each independently of the other. This can be observed if such cells are cultivated *in vitro* (Holtfreter, 1947a,b).

12−2 MORPHOGENETIC PROCESSES IN MESENCHYME

The morphogenetic processes in mesenchyme naturally are somewhat different from those occurring in the epithelial cell masses. The most typical of those are reviewed here.

Aggregation of Mesenchyme into a Mass.   Such aggregations may be formed in the mesenchyme independently of epithelial parts of the embryo. Mesenchyme cells are drawn together to form densely packed masses without, however, joining up into an epithelium. Each cell retains its ability to migrate freely, thus showing that the specific properties of the surface cytoplasm have not been changed. Such mesenchyme aggregations later differentiate as cartilage, bone or muscle tissue.

Attachment of Mesenchyme to Another Body.   In normal embryonic development, it is often observed that mesenchyme cells become concentrated near the surface of an epithelium or around some epithelial structure such as a vesicle or tube. The aggregated mesenchyme may later develop into cartilage or bone and thus produce a skeletal capsule around or near the epithelial structure. Such skeletal capsules develop around the nasal sac and the inner ear of vertebrates. The brain case as a whole is developed in a similar way. In other cases the mesenchyme does not differentiate as skeletal tissue, but it may develop into a fibrous capsule, which is found around many internal organs (kidneys, liver, spleen).

Acquistion of Epithelial Connections by Mesenchyme Cells.   Mesenchyme cells are sometimes secondarily rearranged into an epithelium and become typical epithelial cells in so far as their relationships to each other are concerned. Such a transformation takes place in the mesoderm produced from the primitive streak in birds and other Amniota. The cells migrating from the streak are ameboid, but later the sheet of these migrating cells fuses into a regular epithelium—the mesodermal mantle (later subdivided into somites, lateral plates, etc.). Another case of the same kind is found in the development of blood vessels. The endothelium of blood vessels consists of cells which had been mesenchyme cells before, but which have joined together to form an epithelial layer. It is true that the epithelia developed from mesenchyme differ from those which had never lost their epithelial properties. Thus the endothelia possess the capacity for phagocytosis in common with many connective tissue cells, a property which is not found in the ectodermal and endodermal epithelia of vertebrates.

Degeneration.   Parts of the embryo that have become redundant may be removed by degeneration of the cells of which such a part consisted. Actual necrotization of cells has been recorded (Saunders, Gasseling and Saunders, 1962). By means of necrotization of mesenchyme cells in the part of the rudiment originally connected by a broad base to the body, a limb-bud becomes constricted proximally so that in later stages the part of the limb attached to the body is narrower than its distal portions (see Fig. 316).

12−3 FACTORS DIRECTING THE MOVEMENT OF CELLS DURING ORGAN RUDIMENT FORMATION

Some factors concerned in directing the morphogenetic movements of cells have already been mentioned. The most important factor of this kind is the one responsible for the epithelial or mesenchymal arrangement of cells, and this factor operates through a change in the properties of the cell surface.

Isolated embryonic cells, kept in a suitable medium, quite generally possess the ability for movement. In the case of epithelial cells, if two or more cells come in contact, they adhere to one another, and at the same time their motility is greatly reduced if it does not disappear altogether. In the case of cells of mesenchymal nature, the contacts between cells do not lead to their adhering together and do not decrease their motility. Differentiation of the cells tends to immobilize them, and differentiated connective tissue cells, such as fibroblasts, do not move about if the tissue is in the normal state. Between free motility and complete immobilization there may exist an intermediary state, in which the cell constantly sends out pseudopods, but these are soon withdrawn, and other pseudopods are sent out in different directions, so that the cell sometimes remains in the same place in spite of very active motility (de Bruyn, 1945).

Although in epithelial masses the motility of individual cells is reduced, the sheet of epithelium can move as a whole. This movement is best observed in tissue cultures. It may be seen that the edge of an epithelial sheet becomes pushed outward, sometimes in a broad line, sometimes forming more or less narrow tongues, forcing themselves ahead of the main mass. Epithelial sheets can spread only over a solid substrate, and the same is true, with a reservation, for the mesenchyme cells. The reservation is that mesenchyme cells may travel along (and through) a network of fibers, whereas such a substrate could not support the movement of an intact epithelial layer.

From what has been said it is clear that the migration of embryonic cells can be taken for granted, and that it is the directing of this migration along definite channels and to definite destinations, so that an organized whole is gradually built up, that has to be accounted for. The properties of the substratum along which the cells migrate are among the major factors affecting the direction of migration. As has been already indicated, the cells cannot move through space filled only with fluid. In the parts of the embryo occupied by mesenchyme, however, the intercellular spaces are filled with a colloidal solution which is in part gelated, so that fibers of molecules are stretched through the space in various directions. These fibers serve as a substratum for the migration of mesenchyme cells. If the fibers of the intercellular substratum do not show any orientation, the migration of mesenchyme cells is disorganized, and the cells become scattered equally in space. If the fibers of the intercellular substratum become oriented in any direction, the mesenchyme cells migrate along the oriented bundles of fibers. This can be proved experimentally with cells in tissue cultures. The fibers of the plasma clot on which the cells are cultivated may be caused to be stretched in a certain direction by various means, as for instance by allowing the clot to set under mechanical tension. The cells will then follow the direction of the plasma clot fibers in their migration (Fig. 209 — Weiss, 1929; Doljanski and Roulet, 1934).

If the mesenchyme cells aggregate around an epithelial vesicle, this aggregation may be the result of the orienting influence of the epithelium on the fibers of the intercellular substrate. If these fibers are strecthed perpendicularly to the surface of the epithelial vesicle, the migrating mesenchyme cells will converge toward the vesicle. Once having reached the surface of the epithelium, the cells of the mesenchyme may be held there by intercellular bonds whose nature is not well understood but whose existence can hardly be doubted (Weiss, 1947).

The influences of adjoining parts on the movements of migrating cells is not the only form of interaction of parts playing an important role in the development of organ rudiments. Influences of a nature similar to the induction of the neural plate by the roof of the archenteron have been discovered in the development of organ rudiments. Such influences may modify the movements of cells, but not directly. The direct result is a modification of the properties of cells, and as a consequence of this the movements of cells are also altered. This can be illustrated by the development of the neural crest; the neural crest differentiates together with the neural plate as a result of an induction from the roof of the archenteron. Once induced, the neural crest cells acquire new properties, they become mesenchyme cells and start migrating away from their source of origin, while both the cells of the epidermis and the cells of the neural tube remain relatively stationary.

Figure 209.   Cells growing in tissue culture. Left—micelles in substrate are oriented by allowing the blood plasma to clot under stress. Right—no orientation of micelles in substrate. (After Weiss, from Kühn, 1955.)

12—4 DEVELOPMENT OF GENERAL BODY FORM; "STAGES" OF DEVELOPMENT

Changes in Body Shape.   While the various organs are being formed, the shape of the embryo as a whole undergoes far-reaching changes. During the period of organogenesis, in the case of the vertebrate embryo the main changes are:

1. Elongation of the body
2. Formation of the tail
3. Subdivision of the body into head and trunk
4. Development of appendages
5. Separation of the embryo proper from the extraembryonic parts (the latter process has already been dealt with in sections 11–1 and 11–2).

Some of the processes enumerated above also occur in invertebrates; in particular, the elongation of the body occurs in annelids and arthropods. The subdivision of the body into sections, such as head, thorax and abdomen, is typical for insects and, with modifications, for some other arthropods. The development of appendages is an essential feature of arthropod development. Other processes concerning the body as a whole may occur in invertebrates but have no counterpart in vertebrate development. For instance, in insects the body of the embryo undergoes a peculiar shifting from the surface of the egg into the interior of the yolk, whence it emerges again at a later stage.

In holoblastic vertebrates, of which the amphibians may serve as an example, the embryo retains a spherical shape (i.e., the shape possessed by the unfertilized egg) up to the end of gastrulation and the beginning of neurulation. In the neurula stage the embryo becomes slightly elongated in an anteroposterior direction, but only after the completion of neurulation does the elongation of the embryo become really prominent. A tail rudiment, the **tailbud**, appears at the posterior end of the body and rapidly develops into an elongated appendage, but the rest of the body also stretches out, becoming at the same time flattened laterally and, to a certain extent, lower in a dorsoventral direction (Fig. 210).

Although most of the organ rudiments of the embryo are involved in this elongation, there is experimental evidence that not all are equally active. If the notochord rudiment of an amphibian embryo in the neurula stage is excised, the embryo remains stunted and does not stretch as usual (Fig. 211— Hörstadius, 1944; Kitchin, 1949). On the other hand, the notochordal rudiment will stretch and form an elongated rod even if it is cultivated *in vitro* and is not accompanied by other parts (Fig. 212—Holtfreter, 1929b). Isolated parts of the neural system or induced brain vesicles, when no other tissues accompany them, fail to elongate. From this it appears that the notochord changes its shape actively, while the nervous system is being pulled in length by the adjacent notochord. In amniotes the elongation starts in the primitive streak stage, so that the body of the embryo is already long and narrow by the time the main axial organs (neural tube, notochord, dorsal mesoderm giving rise to the somites) are laid down.

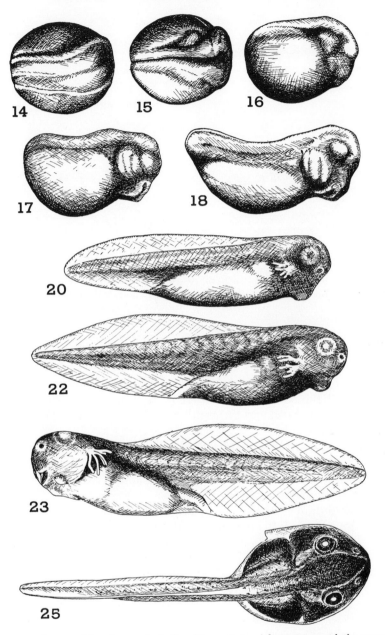

Figure 210.   Stages of development of a frog *(Rana pipiens)*, beginning with the neurula stage. The numbers indicate stages of development after Pollister and Moore, 1937. (Redrawn after Rugh, 1948.)

The formation of the tail rudiment will be dealt with in section 13–1.

The subdivision of the body in terrestrial vertebrates into head and trunk is largely dependent on the reduction of the branchial apparatus. As will be described in section 15–3, the system of visceral clefts and arches is fully developed in embryos of all vertebrates. In fishes and the larvae of amphibians, the visceral clefts and arches persist and take up the area on the

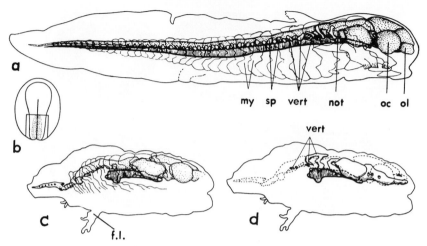

Figure 211. Results of excision of the notochord of an amphibian (*Ambystoma punctatum*) embryo. *a*, Normal larva. *b*, Diagram of operation; stippled area of the archenteron roof removed. *C*, Operated larva; drawing shows notochord (vertical lines), neural system (stippled) and contours of muscle segments. *d*, Same larva, showing notochord and cartilaginous skeleton. *f.l.*, Forelimbs; *my*, muscle segments; *not*, notochord; *oc*, eye; *ol*, nose; *sp*, spinal ganglia; *vert*, vertebrae. (From Hörstadius, 1944.)

ventral side and posterior to the head. In terrestrial vertebrates, the branchial apparatus loses its respiratory function and becomes reduced. As a result of this, in later embryonic stages the area of the body posterior to the head fails to grow at the same rate as other parts, thus producing a constricted section between the head and the trunk (see Figs. 213, 214). The constriction is accentuated further by:

(a) a certain amount of longitudinal stretching of the neck region, as the result of which the cervical vertebrae are as a rule somewhat longer than thoracic vertebrae (this is not true in some mammals with shortened necks such as man or the whales), and

(b) the withdrawal of the heart, originally situated in the neck region, next to the branchial clefts, into the trunk (thorax). (See Figs. 213, 214.)

The development of appendages, particularly the paired limbs, will be described in section 14–3.

Normal Stages of Development. The changing appearance of the embryos, especially during organogenesis, invites the distinguishing of certain stages

Figure 212. Explantation of the dorsal blastopore lip of an axolotl gastrula. The notochord has developed in the form of an elongated rod in the middle of the explant. Lateral parts are mesoderm. At the anterior end is a piece of ectoderm (pigmented). (From Holtfreter, 1939b.)

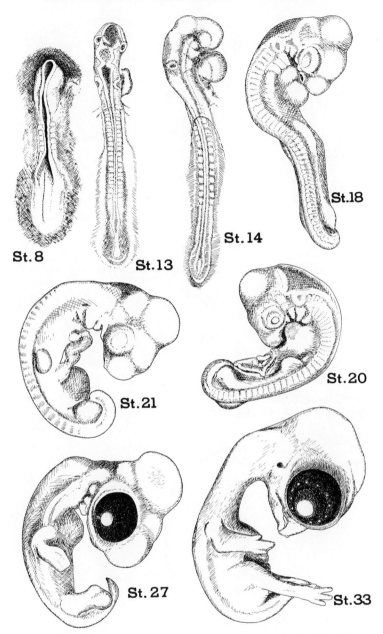

Figure 213. Stages of development of a chick. (Stages 18 and 20 after Keibel and Abraham, from Keibel in Hertwig, 1906; stages 13, 14, 21, 27, 33 from Hamburger and Hamilton, 1951; stage 8 from Patten, 1957.)

which can be referred to when it is desired to indicate how far an embryo has progressed in its development. Tables of "normal stages" have been worked out for a number of species of animals, especially those that are most often used for research.

In the latter half of the nineteenth century, an ambitious work on establishing series of normal stages for a large number of animals was undertaken by Keibel and his collaborators. This work was an essential contribution to

Figure 214. Stages of development of the human embryo. Figures show approximate age in days. (22-day-old embryo, after Arey: Developmental Anatomy; 37-day-old embryo redrawn from Hamilton, Boyd and Mossman, 1947; the rest after Streeter, 1942–1951.)

the science of comparative embryology (see p. 8) but went into oblivion later, when the interest of the great majority of embryologists shifted from a descriptive to an experimental approach to the development of animals. However, it soon became evident that tables of normal stages were quite as important for experimental work, as it was often necessary to indicate precisely at what stage an operation or other experiment was carried out.

The table of normal stages of *Ambystoma* (= *Amblystoma*) *punctatum*, prepared by Harrison, was the first made expressly with experimental investigations in view. Harrison's table has never been published but has been made accessible privately to many workers in the field and has been widely used. Harrison's stages were later redrawn and included in Rugh's book *Experimental Embryology* (1948). Other tables of normal stages followed; the most widely used ones are probably the stages of *Rana pipiens* by Pollister and Moore (1937) and the stages of the chick by Hamburger and Hamilton (1951). There is still no up-to-date table of normal stages of the development of the human embryo. (See, however, the series of papers by Streeter, 1942–1951.)

In compiling a series of normal stages the embryologist is confronted with the task of deciding what characteristics should be selected for distinguishing one stage from another. The characteristics that are often used are:

1. Age of the embryo
2. Size of the embryo
3. Morphological peculiarities of the embryo

In human embryology in particular, the first two critera are often used. It is customary for an author to refer to embryos by age (five-week embryo, two-month-old embryo) or by size (an embryo or fetus of so many mm. crown-rump length). Both these critera are, however, not very convenient; the age of an embryo is often not known, and, in animals other than mammals, the rate of development is dependent on the temperature of the environment to such an extent that a statement about the age of the embryo is meaningless unless the temperature at which the development has proceeded is likewise indicated. The size of the embryo is no true indication of its degree of development, as the dimensions of the embryo vary to a great extent. It may be noted here that some variability in the size of embryos may be ironed out later in the course of development, which adds to the difficulty of using size as a criterion for the definition of stages.

What remains is to base the normal stages on morphological properties of the embryo, and especially on properties that can be easily ascertained by external examination of the embryo, without its fixation or dissection—that is, largely on external features. In the initial stages of development (cleavage stages), the number and size of the blastomeres may conveniently be used. During gastrulation, the shape of the blastopore or its equivalent (primitive streak) may be used. Just after gastrulation, the neural plate offers easily recognizable features. During early organogenesis, the number of pairs of somites has often been used to define the stage of development of the embryo. The somites, though not strictly speaking "external features," can be seen on external inspection, especially in the amniotes. In still later stages, the development of the appendages presents very easily distinguishable and convenient characters for the definition of normal stages.

Although morphological characters appear to be the best criteria for establishing the stage of development of an embryo, there are certain limitations even in this approach. It has been found that the development of different parts (organs) of the embryo is not always strictly coordinated in time;

sometimes certain ones develop more rapidly, sometimes others. So if two embryos have certain organs (for instance the forelimbs) in exactly the same condition, they may at the same time differ in the degree of development of other organs (the nervous system or the liver, for instance). This phenomenon of **heterochrony**, or unequal rate of development of parts, must be always borne in mind when any tables of normal stages are being used or referred to.

The Anatomy of Representative Stages of Development of the Frog and the Chick Embryos.   A few stages of the frog and chick embryos will now be considered in greater detail. The stages chosen will serve as landmarks which, it is hoped, will help the student to sort out the information concerning the development of the separate organ systems of the embryo, as dealt with in the subsequent three chapters (Chapters 13–15). In those chapters the student will find extensive information on the various organs and organ systems of the body, some of which will be mentioned briefly for the first time in this section.

Frog embryo after completion of neurulation, stage 17 (Fig. 215).   The neural system is in the form of a closed tube, broadened anteriorly where the brain will develop. The parts of the brain are beginning to be indicated by thickenings and constrictions of the neural tube, and the eye rudiments are bulging laterally from the forebrain. The notochord stretches underneath the neural tube from the midbrain level to the posterior end of the body where it fuses with other tissues which are as yet in an undifferentiated state. Under the notochord in the posterior part of the body there lies a strand of endodermal cells: the **subchorda**, a structure which exists for a short time and soon disappears. Laterally to the notochord the mesoderm is subdivided into segments: the somites. The endoderm surrounds the gut cavity, which is broad anteriorly and narrow in the posterior part of the body. In the anterior part of the gut, lateral outpushings represent the branchial pouches. At the posterior end an anal opening has been formed, but the mouth is not perforated, although the endoderm and ectoderm are in contact at the site of the future mouth. Above the place where the mouth will be, an ingrowth of the ectodermal layer represents the rudiment of the hypophysis. Lateral to the foregut, masses of mesectoderm can be seen; these give rise to the visceral skeleton. Underneath the foregut, groups of mesodermal cells represent the rudiment of the heart. The posterior end of the body above the anus is elongating in the form of a tailbud, still in an early stage of development; hence this stage may be referred to as an early tailbud stage.

4 mm. frog embryo, stage 19 (Figs. 216–223).   The tailbud has elongated and has developed into a clearly recognizable tail with an axis consisting of neural tube, notochord and segmented mesoderm, and a fin fold all around its edge. The neural system has developed further; the eye vesicles have been constricted at the base and thus subdivided from the brain. The parts of the brain are more distinctly indicated. Ear vesicles have been formed to the right and left of the hindbrain. The nose rudiments are in the form of placodes— thickenings of the epidermis. The pharyngeal membrane separating stomodeum from the endodermal foregut has become thin and will soon be perforated. Ventral to the mouth, the adhesive organs have become well developed. The foregut has become subdivided into an anterior part, the pharynx, and the posterior part which will give rise to the gastric and duodenal section of the alimentary canal. The pharynx has produced gill pouches laterally.

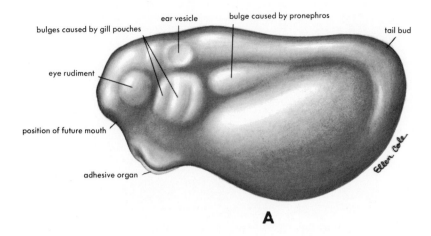

bulges caused by gill pouches

ear vesicle

bulge caused by pronephros

tail bud

eye rudiment

position of future mouth

adhesive organ

Ellen Cole

A

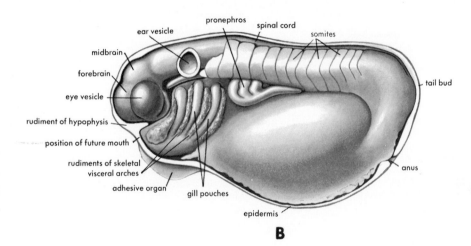

ear vesicle

pronephros

spinal cord

somites

midbrain

forebrain

eye vesicle

rudiment of hypophysis

position of future mouth

rudiments of skeletal
visceral arches

adhesive organ

gill pouches

epidermis

tail bud

anus

B

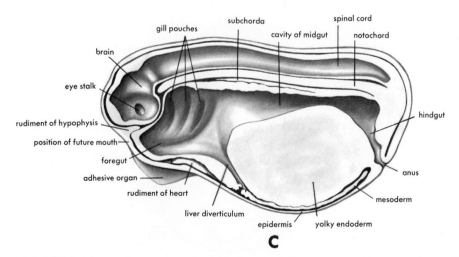

gill pouches

subchorda

cavity of midgut

spinal cord

notochord

brain

eye stalk

rudiment of hypophysis

position of future mouth

foregut

adhesive organ

rudiment of heart

liver diverticulum

epidermis

yolky endoderm

hindgut

anus

mesoderm

C

Figure 215.   A frog embryo in an early tail bud stage. *A*, External view; *B*, same embryo with
the skin of the left side removed; *C*, same embryo cut in the median plane.

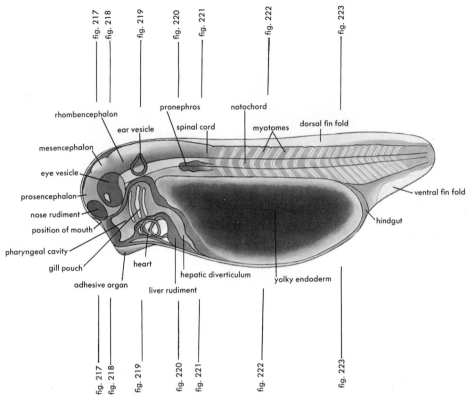

Figure 216. 4 mm. frog embryo (drawing made from a specimen cleared and mounted in Clarite). The vertical lines indicate the levels represented by photographs of transverse sections (Figs. 217 to 223). The sections used for the photographs are from different embryos; this accounts for some slight discrepancies between the drawing and the photographs.

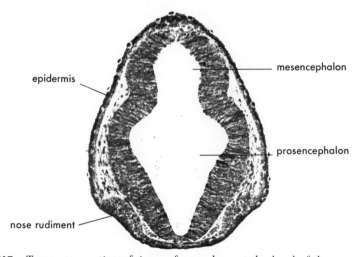

Figure 217. Transverse section of 4 mm. frog embryo at the level of the prosencephalon and nose rudiments. This and the following photographs correspond to the embryo illustrated in Figure 216 in which the levels of the sections are also shown.

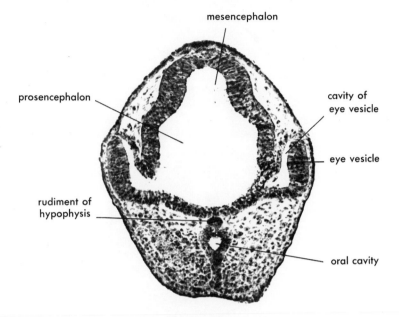

Figure 218. Transverse section of 4 mm. frog embryo at the level of the eye rudiments.

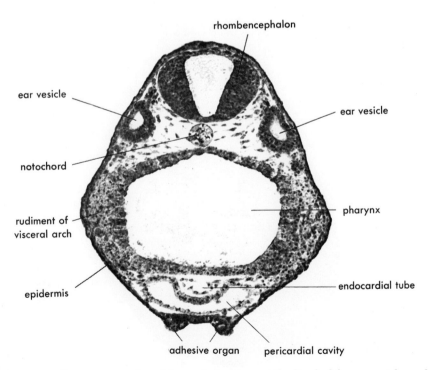

Figure 219. Transverse section of 4 mm. frog embryo at the level of the ear vesicles and the heart.

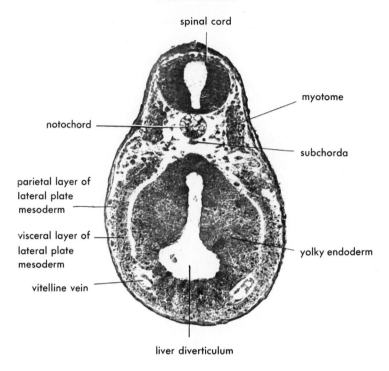

Figure 220.   Transverse section of 4 mm. frog embryo at the level of the liver diverticulum.

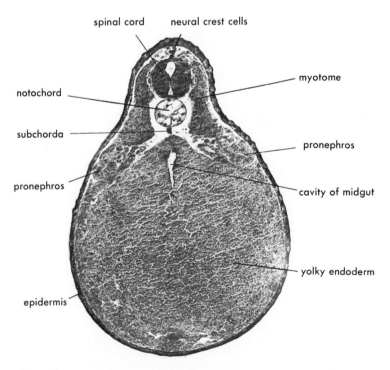

Figure 221.   Transverse section of 4 mm. frog embryo at the level of the pronephros.

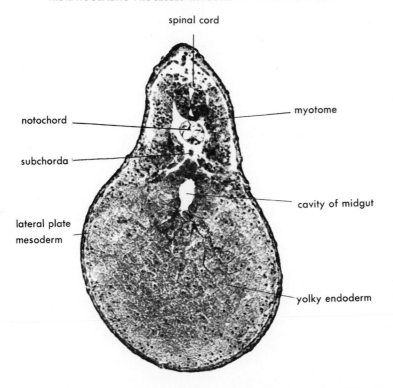

Figure 222.   Transverse section of 4 mm. frog embryo at the mid trunk level.

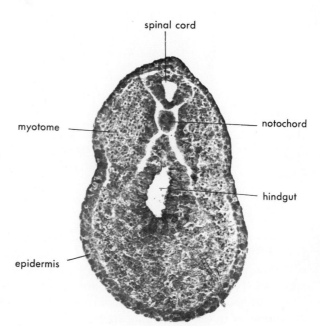

Figure 223.   Transverse section of 4 mm. frog embryo at the posterior trunk level.

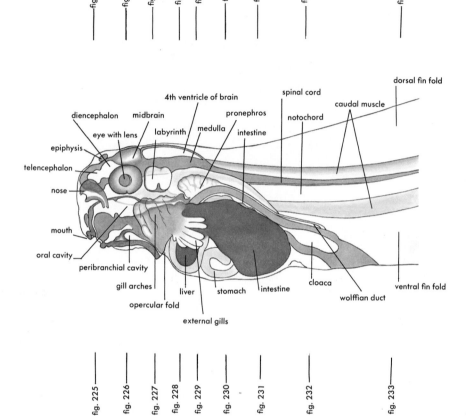

Figure 224. 10 mm. frog embryo (drawing made from a specimen cleared and mounted in Clarite). The vertical lines indicate the levels represented by photographs of transverse sections (Figs. 225 to 233). The sections used for the photographs are from different embryos; this accounts for some slight discrepancies between the drawing and the photographs.

Underneath the pharynx the heart rudiment is developing; in cross section (Fig. 219) one can see the thin walled endocardial tube and the thicker parts of lateral plate mesoderm which will give rise to the myocardium and pericardium. The pronephric tubules are in the process of formation (Fig. 221). The posterior part of the endodermal gut is still very much in the same condition as in the preceding stages.

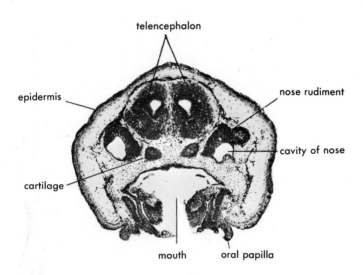

telencephalon

epidermis

nose rudiment

cavity of nose

cartilage

mouth   oral papilla

Figure 225. Transverse section of 10 mm. frog embryo at the level of the nose and mouth. This and the following photographs correspond to the embryo illustrated in Figure 224, which also shows the levels of the sections.

10 mm. frog embryo, stage 23 (Figs. 224–233). The embryo has changed its shape and has become a tadpole. The head and trunk are bloated and form together a more or less egg-shaped body; the tail has elongated and has become a powerful swimming organ, with segmented muscle laterally and broad fin folds dorsally and ventrally (Fig. 233). The brain is rapidly differentiating; the forebrain has produced the two hemispheres of the telencephalon (Fig. 225). The roof of the medulla has become membranous. The nose rudiments have invaginated and are in the form of sacs connected to the exterior by nares. The eyecup is clearly differentiated into a neural retina and pigment layer. A lens has been formed (Fig. 226). The ear vesicles are on the way to produce the labyrinths; endolymphatic ducts can be seen on the dorsomedial aspect of each labyrinth (Fig. 227). The pronephros consists of several (three) convoluted tubules which form thickenings on the sides of the body anteriorly, and the wolffian ducts have been developed. The mouth is open and is surrounded by horny jaws and teeth and soft circumoral papillae. The gill clefts are perforated, and fingerlike external gills project from the sides of the head in the branchial region. The endodermal gut is differentiated into its various parts. In sections one can distinguish pharynx, esophagus, lung rudiments, stomach, liver, gallbladder, pancreas and intestine. The intestine has already become coiled spirally and largely contributes to the bloating of the body of the tadpole.

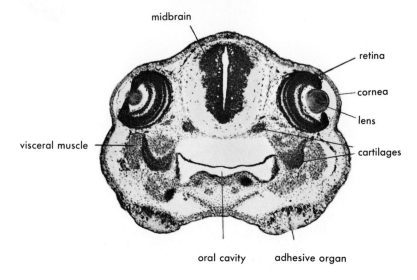

Figure 226. Transverse section of 10 mm. frog embryo at the eye level.

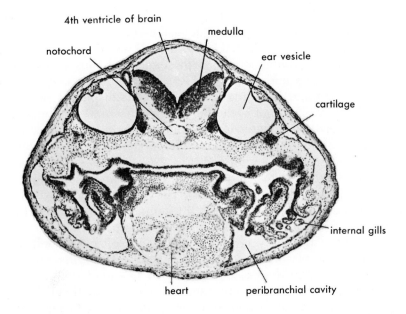

Figure 227. Transverse section of 10 mm. frog embryo at the ear level.

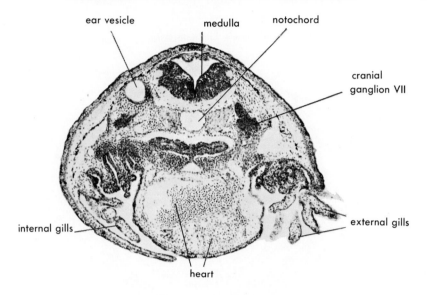

Figure 228.   Transverse section of 10 mm. frog embryo at the level of the external gills.

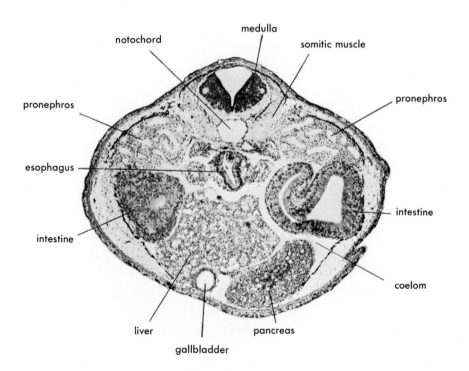

Figure 229.   Transverse section of 10 mm. frog embryo at the level of the pronephros.

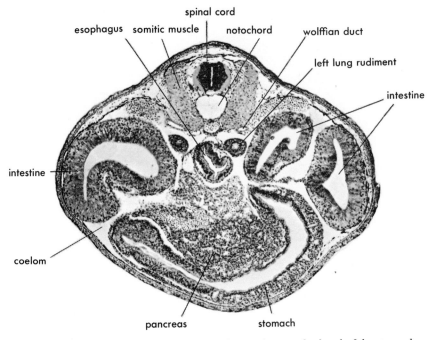

Figure 230.   Transverse section of 10 mm. frog embryo at the level of the stomach.

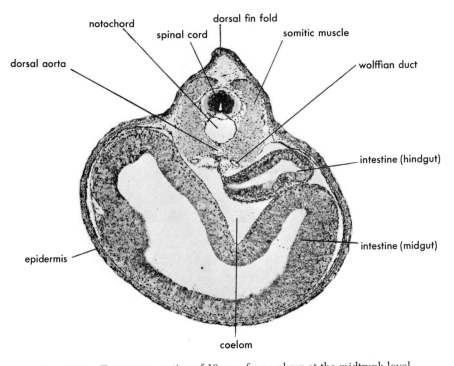

Figure 231.   Transverse section of 10 mm. frog embryo at the midtrunk level.

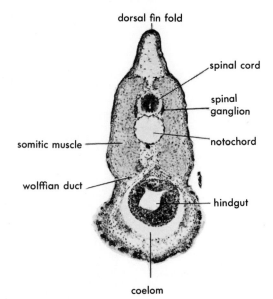

Figure 232. Transverse section of 10 mm. frog embryo at the level of the hindgut.

dorsal fin fold

spinal cord

spinal ganglion

somitic muscle

notochord

wolffian duct

hindgut

coelom

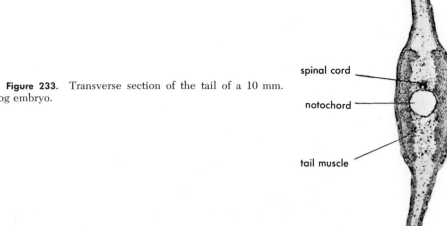

Figure 233. Transverse section of the tail of a 10 mm. frog embryo.

dorsal fin fold

spinal cord

notochord

tail muscle

ventral fin fold

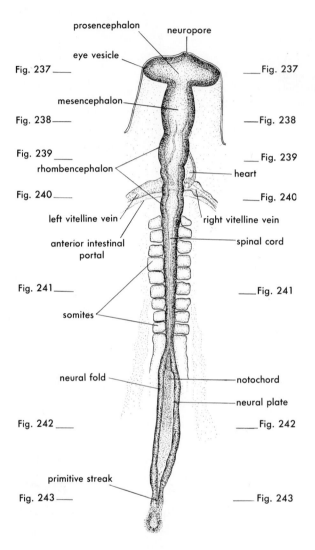

prosencephalon   neuropore

eye vesicle

Fig. 237 ____   ____Fig. 237

mesencephalon

Fig. 238 ____   ____Fig. 238

Fig. 239 ____   ____ Fig. 239
rhombencephalon   ____ heart

Fig. 240 ____   ____Fig. 240

left vitelline vein   right vitelline vein

anterior intestinal   spinal cord
portal

Fig. 241 ____   ____Fig. 241

somites

neural fold   notochord
                           neural plate

Fig. 242 ____   ____Fig. 242

primitive streak

Fig. 243 ____   ____ Fig. 243

Figure 234. Chick embryo stage 10 (age 29 to 30 hours). Drawing made from a specimen cleared and mounted in Clarite. The lines indicate the levels represented by transverse sections shown in Figures 237 to 243.

Chick embryo, stage 10 (29 to 30 hours) (Figs. 234–243). The most conspicious parts of the chick embryo in this stage are the brain and spinal cord rudiments and the somites, of which there are 9 to 10 pairs. The brain shows a subdivision into primary brain vesicles, and eye vesicles are already prominent. Nevertheless, the closing of the neural tube is not quite completed: anteriorly the cavity of the neural tube is still open to the exterior by the neuropore, and at the posterior end the neural folds have not come together and there is still an open neural plate present. Still farther back, the remnants of the primitive streak have not yet disappeared. Underneath the

Figure 235. Chick embryo, stage 10 (age 29 to 30 hours). Lateral view reconstructed from a series of sagittal sections showing nervous system, blood vessels, somites, pronephros and gut rudiment. Lines refer to photographs of transverse sections.

neural tube lies the notochord which at its posterior end is continuous with the primitive streak material. Posteriorly to the somites lies the still unsegmented mesoderm. The body folds have undercut the anterior end of the embryo, so that the foremost part of the head is lifted above the surface of the yolk, but farther back the separation of the body from the yolk sac has not yet begun. The anterior part of the gut is already closed and separated from the yolk sac, but from the anterior trunk region on the gut is open ventrally. Pronephroi have started developing. The blood vessel system is represented by separate vessels on the right and left sides of the body, only in the heart the rudiments of the right and the left side are fusing together (Fig. 239). There is one pair of aortic arches (the first) at the anterior end of the body. The embryo as a whole is symmetrical.

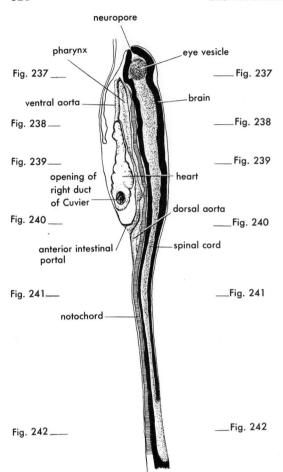

neuropore

pharynx

Fig. 237 ___

eye vesicle

___ Fig. 237

ventral aorta

brain

Fig. 238 —

___ Fig. 238

Fig. 239 ___

___ Fig. 239

opening of
right duct
of Cuvier

heart

Fig. 240 ___

dorsal aorta

___ Fig. 240

anterior intestinal
portal

spinal cord

Fig. 241 —

___ Fig. 241

notochord

Fig. 242 ___

___ Fig. 242

Figure 236. Chick embryo, stage 10 (age 29 to 30 hours). View of embryo cut in the medial plane, reconstructed from a series of sagittal sections showing nervous system, notochord, rudiment of gut and the blood vessel system. Lines refer to photographs of transverse sections.

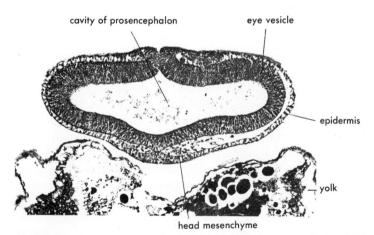

cavity of prosencephalon

eye vesicle

epidermis

yolk

head mesenchyme

Figure 237. Chick embryo, stage 10. Transverse section at eye vesicle level. This and the following photographs correspond to the embryos illustrated in Figures 234, 235 and 236, and the levels of the sections are shown in these figures.

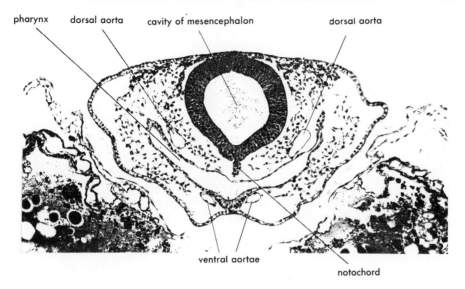

Figure 238. Chick embryo, stage 10. Transverse section at midbrain level, showing the gut enclosed completely on the ventral side, and the paired dorsal and ventral aortae.

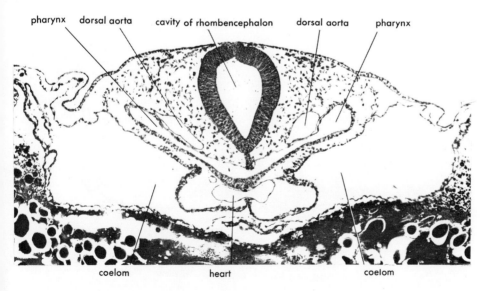

Figure 239. Chick embryo, stage 10. Transverse section at level of rhombencephalon. The heart is single at this level although its origin from two halves is clearly shown. The gut is completely enclosed on the ventral side.

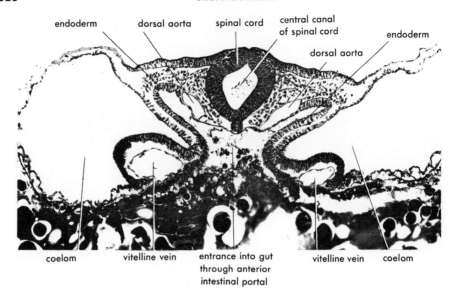

Figure 240. Chick embryo, stage 10. Transverse section at level of the anterior intestinal portal, showing also the proximal parts of the vitelline veins.

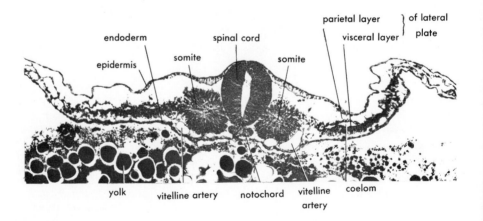

Figure 241.   Chick embryo, stage 10. Transverse section in trunk region with closed neural tube and somites.

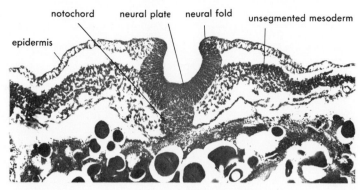

Figure 242. Chick embryo, stage 10. Transverse section, showing open neural plate and undifferentiated mesoderm.

Figure 243. Chick embryo, stage 10. Transverse section at posterior end, showing primitive streak.

Chick embryo, stage 15 (50 to 55 hours) (Figs. 244–251). The anterior end of the embryo is twisted to the right, so that in this part the left side of the embryo lies flat on the surface of the yolk, largely because the brain of the embryo has become bent at an angle at the midbrain level. The parts of the brain are clearly recognizable. The eye is already in the eyecup stage with a lens lying in the pupil. The lens is, however, not yet separated from the epidermis and is in the form of a sac with an opening to the exterior. The ear rudiments are also in the form of pockets open to the exterior. The nose rudiment is still only a thickening of the epidermis. Masses of cells lateral to the brain represent the rudiments of the large cranial ganglia. The number of pairs of somites has greatly increased, but at the posterior end of the body there is still some unsegmented mesoderm present. The neural tube is not completely closed at the posterior end, and even a remnant of the primitive streak is to be found, though the immigration of cells from the streak has ceased. The first three pairs of gill pouches have been formed. The blood vessel system of the embryo has undergone a marked development. The heart is a large and conspicuous organ just underneath the head. A paired ventral aorta conveys blood into the first pair of aortic arches, which are still the only ones to carry blood. The dorsal aortae are paired anteriorly and posteriorly but are fusing in the median region. Anterior cardinal veins are well developed, but the posterior cardinal veins are very small. The yolk sac circulation is carried on by means of large vitelline veins joining the sinus venosus and the vitelline arteries, which at this stage appear to be direct continuations of the dorsal aortae.

Figure 244. Chick embryo, stage 15 (age 50 to 55 hours). Reconstruction from a series of horizontal sections showing nervous system, somites, kidney rudiments and alimentary canal with gill clefts. The lines on the sides indicate the levels represented by sections shown in Figures 246 to 251. The sections used for the photographs are from a different embryo, and this accounts for some slight discrepancies between the drawing and the photographs.

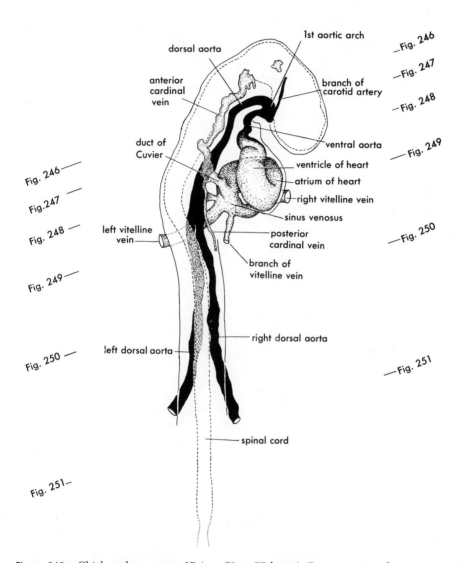

Figure 245. Chick embryo, stage 15 (age 50 to 55 hours). Reconstruction from a series of horizontal sections showing the blood vessel system. Lines on the side indicate levels of photographs in Figures 246 to 251.

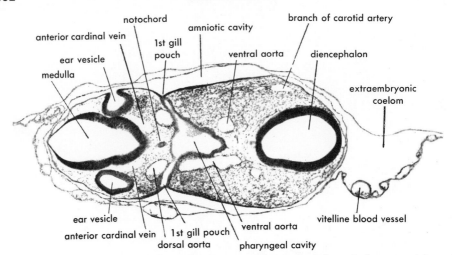

Figure 246. Chick embryo, stage 15. Section at a level passing through the ear vesicles, still connected to epidermis, and the first gill pouch. This and the following photographs correspond to the embryo illustrated in Figures 244 and 245.

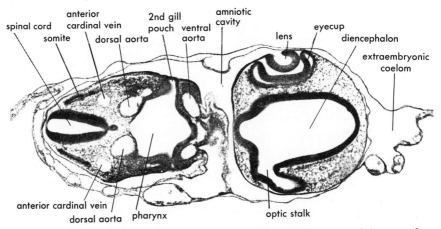

Figure 247. Chick embryo, stage 15. Section passing through the eyes and the second pair of gill pouches.

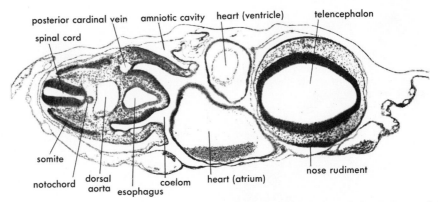

Figure 248. Chick embryo, stage 15. Section passing through the telencephalon and the heart.

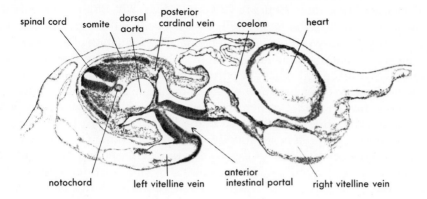

Figure 249. Chick embryo, stage 15. Section at the level of the anterior intestinal portal and the proximal parts of the vitelline veins.

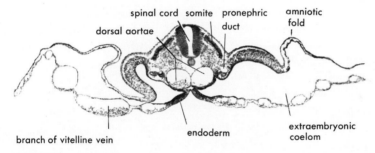

Figure 250. Chick embryo, stage 15. Section through the anterior trunk region at level of forelimb rudiments.

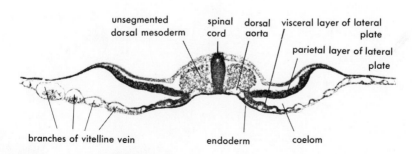

Figure 251. Chick embryo, stage 15. Section through posterior trunk region. Somites and notochord not yet differentiated at this level.

Chick embryo, stage 19 (68 to 72 hours) (Figs. 252–262). The curvature of the anterior part of the head and body has become even greater, and more of the embryo's body is lying on the left side. The formation of the neural tube and the segmentation of the mesoderm have been completed: posteriorly the body ends with the tail which is curved downwards. Limb-buds — the rudiments of the fore- and hindlimbs — are conspicuous. The brain vesicles are developing further and the hemispheres of the telencephalon are clearly discernible. The nose rudiments are in the form of pockets, the lens and the ear vesicles are completely separated from the epidermis. The cranial ganglia and some of the cranial nerves can be clearly seen. The mouth is open, and there are four pairs of gill pouches present; the anterior three pouches open to the exterior as gill clefts. The rudiments of the posterior part of the hypophysis, of the epiphysis and the thyroid gland can be found (the latter could not be shown in the figures). The alimentary canal shows subdivision into

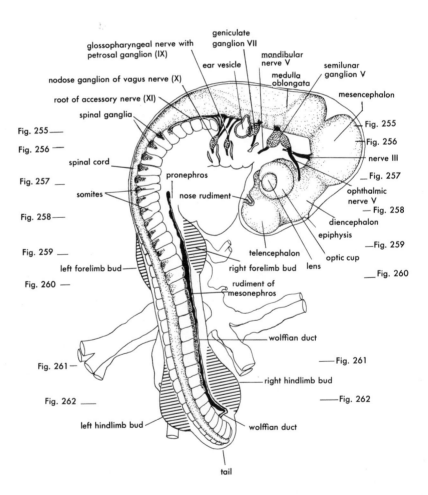

Figure 252. Chick embryo, stage 19 (age 68 to 72 hours). Reconstruction of the nervous system and mesodermal organs (except blood vessels). The lines on the sides indicate the levels of Figures 255 to 262.

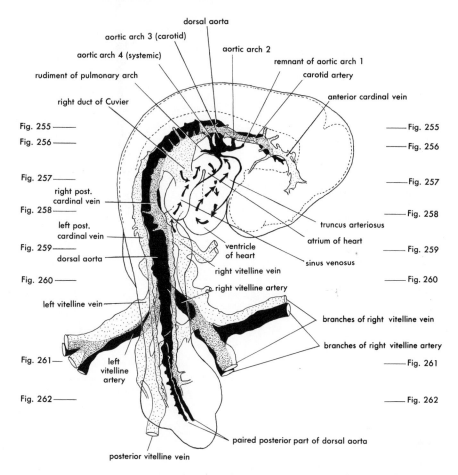

Figure 253. Chick embryo, stage 19 (age 68 to 72 hours). Reconstruction of the circulatory system of embryo shown in Figure 252. The lines on the sides indicate the levels of Figures 255 to 262.

several parts: the pharynx with gill pouches, the esophagus with the lung rudiments and the gastroduodenal part with the liver rudiment. The middle part of the gut is open ventrally, but the hindgut is separated from the yolk sac and the rudiment of the allantois has been formed as a ventral outgrowth from the hindgut. Three pairs of aortic arches are present—they are the second, third and fourth pairs, the first pair having been reduced by this stage. The internal carotid arteries are well developed. The dorsal aorta, unpaired along most of its length, is a very large vessel. The vitelline arteries are now seen as lateral branches of the aorta. Posteriorly, the dorsal aorta is still paired. Both anterior and posterior cardinal veins are present, the latter in close association with the metanephric kidneys, the rudiments of which can be traced along most of the trunk region of the body. The wolffian ducts reach the cloaca and open into it. The vitelline veins, as well as the vitelline arteries, are very conspicuous. The main branches of the veins and arteries follow the same course, the veins lying more superficially than the arteries.

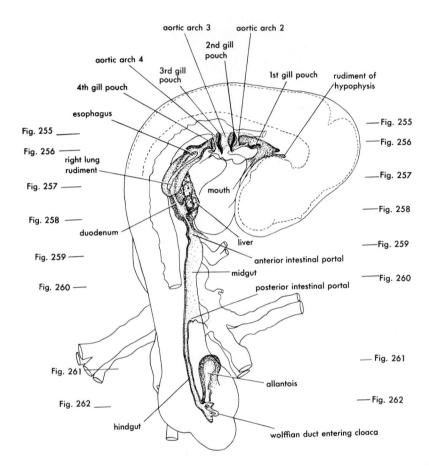

Figure 254. Chick embryo, stage 19 (age 68 to 72 hours). Reconstruction of the alimentary canal and associated structures of the embryo shown in Figures 252 and 253. The lines on the sides indicates the levels of Figures 255 to 262.

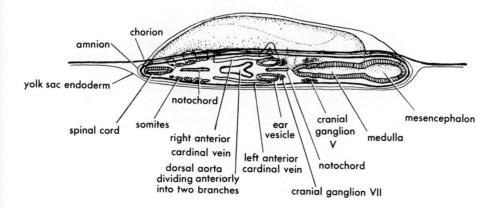

Figure 255.   Chick embryo, stage 19, dissected at the level of the ear vesicles.

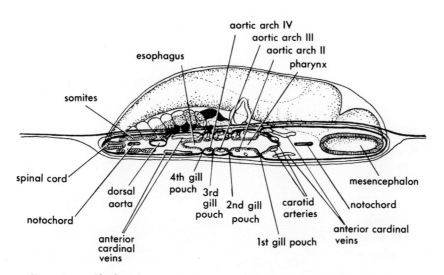

Figure 256.   Chick embryo, stage 19, dissected at the level of the gill pouches.

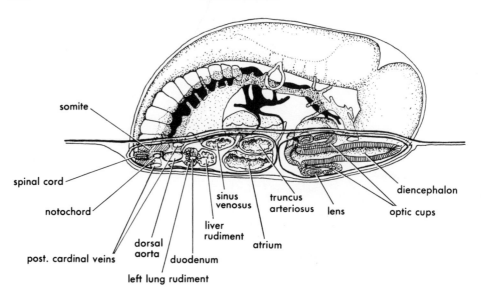

Figure 257. Chick embryo, stage 19, dissected at the level of eyes and heart.

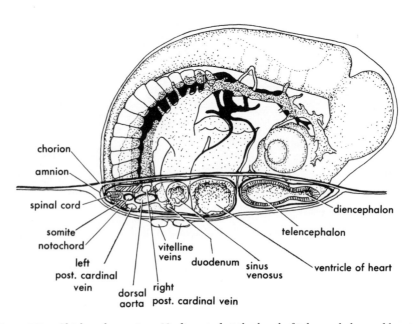

Figure 258. Chick embryo, stage 19, dissected at the level of telencephalon and heart.

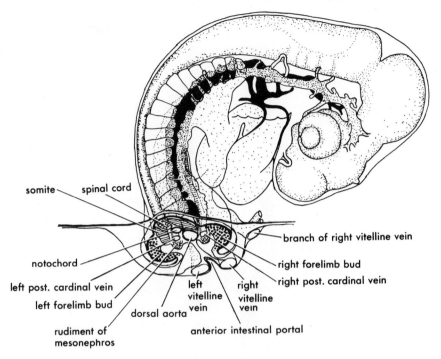

Figure 259.   Chick embryo, stage 19, dissected at the level of the fore-limb buds.

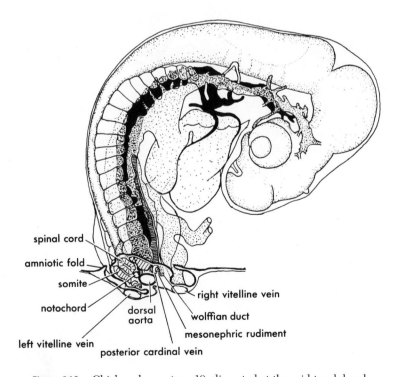

Figure 260.   Chick embryo, stage 19, dissected at the mid-trunk level.

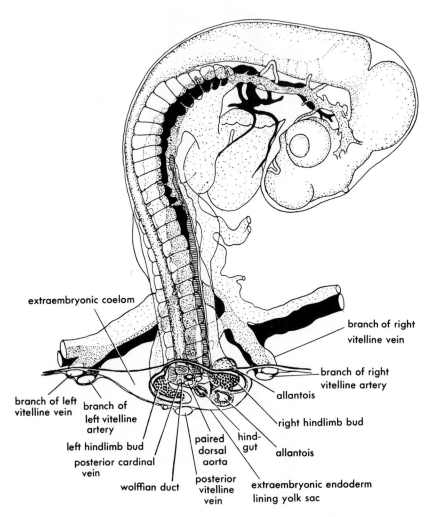

Figure 261. Chick embryo, stage 19, dissected at the level of the hind gut and allantois.

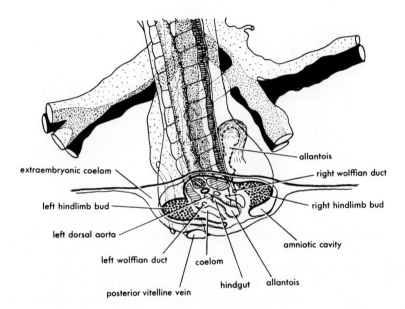

Figure 262. Posterior part of chick embryo, state 19, dissected at the level of the cloaca.

Development of the Ectodermal Organs in Vertebrates*

*A more detailed description of organogenesis in vertebrates may be found in the books by Nelsen, 1953, Witschi, 1956, and Patten, 1958.

13—1 DEVELOPMENT OF THE CENTRAL NERVOUS SYSTEM

The central nervous system of vertebrates develops from the primary rudiment—the neural tube. The origin of the neural tube has been described earlier (section 8–5). The tube when formed is of unequal diameter throughout; its anterior end is expanded, the cavity is broader and the walls are thicker than in the posterior part of the tube. This foreshadows the development of the brain from the anterior part of the neural tube and the development of the spinal cord from the posterior part.

The various parts of the brain (forebrain, midbrain, etc.) are first indicated as thickenings of the wall of the neural tube, followed up, especially in the case of the cerebral hemispheres, by the development of pocketlike evaginations of the brain wall. Shallow constrictions develop early all around the neural tube, thus permitting the distinguishing of several "brain vesicles." Three such brain vesicles appear at the beginning. The most anterior brain vesicle, the **prosencephalon**, later gives rise to the **telencephalon** and the **diencephalon**. The second brain vesicle, the **mesencephalon**, is not subdivided further and develops into the midbrain. The third brain vesicle, the **rhombencephalon**, gives rise to the **metencephalon** (cerebellum) and the **myelencephalon** (medulla oblongata) (Fig. 263). The medulla oblongata becomes constricted by shallow furrows into a number of segments, **neuro-**

Figure 263. Primary brain vesicles and eye rudiments of a 33-hour-old chick embryo. *pros,* Prosencephalon; *mes,* mesencephalon; *rhomb,* rhombencephalon; *opt,* eye vesicles.

meres. This segmentation, which is especially clear in fish embryos, is, however, only temporary and does not leave any trace in the organization of the adult brain. It is not correlated with the metameric arrangements of the cranial nerves.

Even before the prosencephalon is clearly subdivided into the telencephalon and the diencephalon, a pair of saclike protrusions appear on its lateral walls. These protrusions are the rudiments of the eyes which are thus, basically, specially differentiated parts of the brain. In this stage, they are called optic vesicles. The optic vesicles become constricted from the remainder of the prosencephalon, and the connecting **optic stalk** later forms the basis for the development of the optic nerve. The optic stalk (and the optic nerve) join that part of the brain vesicle which becomes the diencephalon. By the method of local vital staining, as well as by observation of peculiarities of pigmentation, it has been possible to trace back the cells of the optic vesicle to the open neural plate. In the neural plate the presumptive material of the optic vesicles lies far forward, close behind the transverse neural fold and rather near to the midline (Fig. 264). In the course of development, the eye rudiments are drawn out away from one another and into a more lateral position than they occupied initially. The subsequent development of the optic vesicles will be dealt with in a special section.

Figure 264. Position of the presumptive eye rudiments in the neural plate of an amphibian. Shadowed areas show the position of the eyes in the very early neurula. The dashed contour shows their positions in the early neurula. (From Manchot, 1929.)

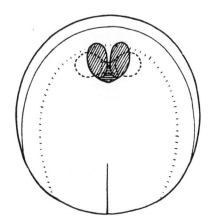

After it has been closed, the neural tube undergoes very considerable stretching, together with the stretching of the embryo as a whole, especially in its posterior half. As this stretching is at the expense of the thickness of the tube, it tends to enhance the difference in bulk between the brain and the spinal cord.

A most peculiar transformation occurs in the posterior part of the neural plate and tube. The neural plate here reaches right to the blastopore. When the posterior part of the neural tube elongates, it does so to a greater extent than the ventral part of the embryo. The posterior end of the neural tube is therefore carried beyond the blastopore. As its hindmost tip is attached to the blastopore, the neural tube becomes bent on itself some distance from the blastopore. The apex of the bend now becomes the tip of the tail rudiment (Fig. 265). The major part of the neural tube, from its cranial end to the apex of the bend, differentiates as central nervous system (brain and spinal cord). The inflected part of the tube, however, the part lying between the apex of the tail rudiment and the blastopore, differentiates as muscle of the tail region. It loses its central canal and becomes split along the midline into two lateral masses or strips of cells which forthwith shift upward, so as to lie on both sides of the notochord and spinal cord. Cranially these cell masses join up with the dorsal part of the mesodermal mantle. Together with the latter, the presumptive muscle of the tail region is subdivided into muscle seg-ments—the somites. No stalks of somites and no lateral plate are developed in the tail region, and in this respect the segmentation of the presumptive muscle derived from the neural plate differs from the segmentation of the trunk mesoderm. By local vital staining it is possible to determine exactly what part of the neural plate differentiates as caudal muscle, and what part differentiates as neural. tissue. The boundary between the two parts runs straight across the neural plate at about one-sixth the distance to its posterior end (Bijtel, 1931, 1936).

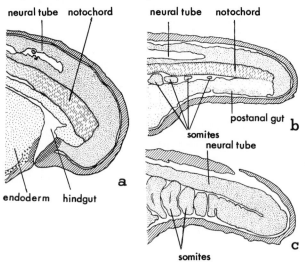

Figure 265. Transformation of the posterior end of the neural tube into the caudal somites in an amphibian embryo. *a*, Early tailbud stage; *b*, late tailbud stage, median section; *c*, same, paramedian section. (From Bijtel, 1931.)

It has been shown previously (in the section on gradients in amphibian development, 10–5) that the roof of the archenteron is responsible for the differentiation of the various parts of the neural plate and neural tube. The anterior part of the archenteron roof—namely, the prechordal plate—induces predominantly the forebrain and eyes (archencephalic inductor), a more posterior part of the archenteron roof induces the hindbrain and associated structures (deuterencephalic inductor), and the most posterior part of the archenteron roof induces spinal cord and muscle (spino-caudal inductor). The induction of muscle by the spino-caudal inductor becomes comprehensible from what has just been stated about the fate of the posterior end of the neural plate.

A corollary to the experiments on the regional specificity of inductors is provided by the following experiments designed to test the determination of parts of the neural plate. It was desired to test whether in the neural plate, after it has already made its appearance but before it starts to differentiate into its subordinate organ rudiments, the various parts are interchangeable, or whether they are already determined for their respective destinations. For this purpose, pieces of the young neural plate were cut out and reimplanted into the same or another embryo. The transplanted parts were placed in abnormal orientations, as for instance with reversed anterior and posterior ends, or they were placed in an altogether different region of the neural plate. The result was found to be different depending on whether the pieces of the neural plate were taken with or without the underlying archenteron roof. If the graft consisted of neural plate cells only, the graft differentiated in agreement with its surroundings and the original polarity of the graft or its place of origin did not manifest itself. Rotated grafts gave rise to parts of the brain which were in complete harmony with their surroundings (Alderman, 1935). Pieces of neural plate taken from its posterior region and transplanted into the anterior region differentiated as brain parts instead of differentiating as spinal cord or muscle. In short, the development of the neural system went on as if nothing had happened (Umanski, 1935). The various parts of the neural plate were found not to be determined, or else their determination was not final and could be overridden by the influence of the surrounding tissues.

If, however, the neural plate material was taken together with the underlying archenteron roof, the graft differentiated in accord with its original prospective significance. Inverted sections of the brain developed if the graft was inverted (Spemann, 1912b); the normal location and differentiation of the eyes was disarranged if the rotation of a piece involved the eye region of the neural plate. That this result is due to the rotation of the archenteron roof together with a portion of the neural plate is clearly proved by experiments in which only a piece of archenteron roof was rotated, while the neural plate remained in its normal position. This experiment caused a derangement in the development of the eyes (Alderman, 1938). The removal of a part of the archenteron roof underlying the eye region of the neural plate causes defects in the development of the brain and eyes; parts of the forebrain are found to be missing, and the eyes are fused into one cyclopic eye (Adelmann, 1937; see also section 10–5).

What has been said in respect to determination of the structure of parts developing from the neural plate (of which the eyes are the most easily recognizable) may be extended to the determination of the functional mechanism developing in the brain. As will be shown later (p. 354) the normal movements of the forelimb in salamander larvae depend on a central mechanism ("action system" of Weiss, 1955) which is located in the spinal cord, at the level of the three pairs of spinal nerves III, IV and V) which supply the forelimbs. If the area of the neural plate giving rise to this segment of the spinal cord is excised and replaced by a more posterior part of the neural plate, the graft will fit into its new position and acquire the functional properties necessary for controlling the movements of the forelimbs. If a similar transplantation is carried out later, in the tailbud stage, replacing the spinal cord at the forelimb level by a more posterior section of the cord, the graft can no longer fully take over the function of the more anterior section, and the movements of the forelimbs supplied by nerves from the graft are abnormal (Detwiler, 1936). At the same stage (tailbud), however, the section of the neural tube which develops into the medulla (the rhombencephalon) may be cut out and replaced, with inversion of its anteroposterior axis, and not only does the graft develop into a morphologically perfect medulla, tapering from anterior end backward, but it acquires a functional polarization in harmony with the rest of the central nervous system; all the nervous responses, in particular the control of the swimming movements, of the operated larvae may be perfectly normal (Detwiler, 1949).

These experiments proved that the detailed structure of the central nervous system, on which its functional properties depend, is not determined at the time when the rudiment of the nervous system is first formed, but the peculiarities of the various parts of the brain and spinal cord are elaborated gradually throughout an extended period.

The further development of the brain and spinal cord is more or less complicated, depending on the degree of perfection that the central nervous system attains in any group of animals. Whereas in the lower vertebrates such as elasmobranch fishes and amphibians, for instance, the adult conditions do not depart greatly, in so far as the shape of the brain is concerned, from the conditions in the embryo, in higher vertebrates (and especially in mammals) the brain, which in the early embryo does not differ very much from the brain of an amphibian or fish embryo, changes later in a most striking way as a result of progressive development of certain parts.

Later Development of the Spinal Cord.   The spinal cord in later embryonic stages is a tube with the lumen—the central canal—in the form of a vertical slit (as seen in cross section). The lumen is lined by a layer of epithelial cells, the **ependyma**. At the top and at the bottom of the slitlike central canal, the ependyma forms a roof plate and a floor plate. Laterally the ependyma participates in the proliferation of cells of the spinal cord which give rise to the mass of nerve cells and neuroglia cells of the cord (Fig. 266).

The walls of the spinal cord are thickened laterally, and, as the proliferation of cells continues in the sides of the cord, the growth of the lateral parts soon outstrips the growth of the dorsal and ventral walls. Ventrally the tissue of the cord grows downward, leaving in the middle a narrow slit, the **ventral median fissure**. Dorsally the central canal becomes compressed; the ependy-

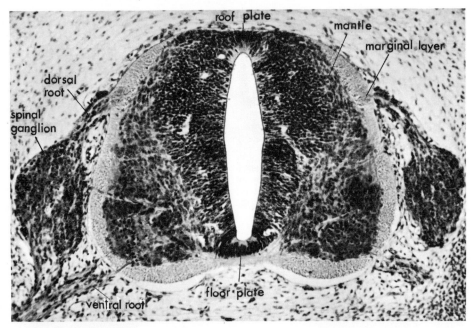

Figure 266.   Transverse section of the spinal cord of a young pig embryo (7 mm.), showing spinal ganglia and roots of the spinal nerves.

mal layers of the right and left side fuse and form a membranelike structure, the **dorsal median septum**, which separates the masses of nervous tissue above the central canal just as the ventral median fissure separates the nervous tissue beneath the central canal.

Even before the dorsal part of the central canal becomes obliterated, owing to the fusion of the ependymal layers of both sides, a longitudinal, outwardly directed groove appears on the sides of the canal. The groove bears the name of **sulcus limitans**, and it serves as a margin dividing each lateral wall of the spinal cord into two parts: the upper part is the alar plate, and the lower part is the basal plate (Fig. 267). When the nervous centers of the spinal cord become differentiated, the sensory centers develop in the alar plate while the motor centers develop in the basal plate. In this way, the sulcus limitans indicates the subdivision of the spinal cord into a sensory and a motor region.

After the obliteration of its dorsal part, the central canal becomes approximately rounded or oval in cross section (Fig. 267).

While the gross changes in the shape of the spinal cord and its central canal are going on, the cells in the walls of the cord undergo a number of transformations leading eventually to the development of the spinal cord as a functioning part of the nervous system (see Fig. 268). The several processes that are involved follow.

Proliferation.   The cell divisions in the central nervous system are restricted to the stratum immediately adjoining the lumen of the neural tube. The amount of proliferation, which can be roughly judged from the number of the mitoses in any region, differs from one part of the neural tube to another, and it has been claimed that the formation of outgrowths or swellings on the

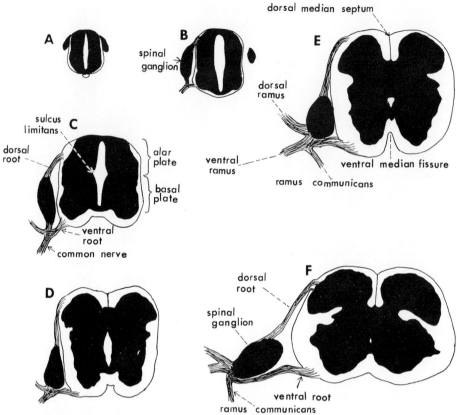

Figure 267. Changes in the gross morphology of the spinal cord during embryonic development of a mammal (the elephant shrew, *Elephantulus myurus*). Camera lucida drawings of cross sections made to the same scale. *A*, An embryo with 30 somites; *F*, fetus close to parturition. The gray matter of the cord and the ganglia are shown in black; the marginal ayer and the white matter in later stages are shown in white. The nerves and spinal ganglia have been drawn only on the left side (except for first two stages).

Figure 268. Stages in development of neurons in the central nervous system (diagrammatic).

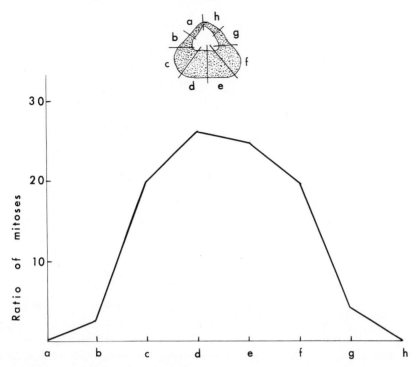

Figure 269. Correlation between the thickness of the wall and the proportion of mitoses in the brain of a newt *Triturus pyrrhogaster*. The ratio of mitoses in the different sectors of the brain circumference is given in pro mille to the total number of ependymal cells. (Redrawn from Takaya and Watanabe, 1961.)

surface of the neural tube, which have been dealt with on page 342, is always preceded by an increase in the number of dividing cells near the lumen in the area where the swelling is to appear (Frank, 1925).

The uneven thickening of the neural tube is a direct result of a differential rate of proliferation of the cells lying next to the cavity of the tube. When the percentage of cells in mitosis is estimated in different parts of the neural tube, it is seen that the percentage is highest in the parts where the wall of the tube becomes thickened and lower where the wall of the tube remains thin (Takaya and Watanabe, 1961 – Figs. 269, 270).

Migration. Some of the dividing cells remain near the lumen of the neural tube and so preserve the continuity of the center of proliferation (*cf.* section 17–2), while others migrate outward and settle down on the outer border of the mass of cells and there start differentiating into the functional neurons. In this way a layer of young neurons is formed just underneath what will become the white matter of the spinal cord (see Fig. 268). This layer is often referred to as the **mantle**. In addition to this primary migration, nerve cells may carry out more complicated migrations up or down the length of the neural tube, forming concentrations of nerve cells known to anatomists as the various nuclei of the brain and spinal cord.

Cell differentiation. The cells constituting the early neural tube appear to be all alike. Later, however, some of the cells become neurons of various types, while others become neuroglia cells and never acquire nervous functions. Lastly, quite a considerable number of cells in the various parts of

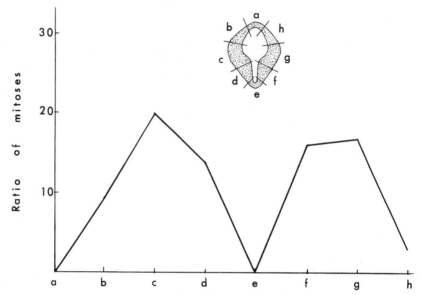

Figure 270. Same as in Figure 269 but with a section of neural tube of a different shape. (Redrawn from Takaya and Watanabe, 1961.)

the central nervous system degenerate during the embryonic period (during the fifth to sixth day of incubation in the chick, after Hamburger and Levi-Montalcini, 1949), thus enhancing the differences in cell numbers in the various areas. At present there is no means of finding out in advance what will be the fate of any given cell, but the experiments referred to above show that the fates of individual cells are probably not firmly fixed in early stages.

The part of the spinal cord from the central canal to the outer boundary of the mantle contains numerous cells (neurons and neuroglia cells) and is the "gray matter" of the cord. Outside the mantle lies the **marginal layer** of the cord (Fig. 266). This layer is made up of the processes of the ependymal and neuroglia cells to which are later added in increasing numbers the axons of the neurons. When these become myelinated, the marginal layer acquires a whitish appearance in the fresh state. Hence this part of the spinal cord is known as the **white matter**.

The gray matter in a transverse section of a fully differentiated spinal cord has a shape somewhat similar to a butterfly with spread wings (Fig. 267, *E*, *F*). The "body" of the butterfly lies in the region of the central canal. The fore wings spread into the area of the alar plates and are known as the **dorsal columns** of the spinal cord. The neurons located in this region are connected to the afferent sensory axons coming in from the dorsal roots of the spinal nerves (see further on p. 351). The hind wings of the butterflylike figure spread into the area of the basal plates and are called the **ventral columns** of the spinal cord. The most important groups of neurons located here are the motor neurons, sending out their processes by way of the ventral roots of the spinal nerves to the somatic muscles of the body. On the sides, between the dorsal and the ventral columns, a slight expansion of the gray matter represents the **lateral columns** of the spinal cord. These contain the cell bodies of the motor neurons sending their axons to the smooth muscles in the internal organs. These are the "visceral" muscles, and accordingly the neurons supplying them are the visceral motor neurons.

The axons located in the white matter of the spinal cord are assembled in bundles, or tracts, each tract consisting predominantly of nerve fibers with a similar function. The three main bundles of nerve fibers in the spinal cord are: the **dorsal funiculus**, situated between the dorsal median septum and the dorsal roots of the spinal nerves; the **lateral funiculus**, taking up the space between the dorsal and the ventral roots; and the **ventral funiculus**, situated between the ventral roots of the spinal nerves and the ventral median fissure.

Development of Spinal Nerves and Spinal Ganglia.   The spinal cord becomes connected with the organs of the body, the limbs and the tail by means of **spinal nerves**. In the development of the spinal nerves a very important part is played by the **spinal ganglia**. These do not form from parts of the neural tube but from cells of the neural crest, the origin of which has been described on p. 198. The cells of the neural crest migrate from their site of origin above the neural tube to the sides of the spinal cord and aggregate as small compact masses of cells segmentally arranged along the whole length of the spinal cord. The groups of cells become the rudiments of the spinal ganglia.

The main part of the cells in the spinal ganglia differentiate as nerve cells, and long processes grow out from these cells, connecting them to the peripheral organs and to the spinal cord. The longer processes growing outward mainly to the skin are afferent and sensory and serve to bring nerve impulses to the spinal ganglia and through them to the central nervous system. The shorter processes growing out toward the spinal cord enter the latter as the main part of the **dorsal roots** of the spinal nerves and make connections with the cells in the dorsal columns of the spinal cord. The ventral roots of the spinal nerves are formed by outgrowths of the motor neurons situated in the ventral columns of the spinal cord and are efferent in nature, serving to supply nerve impulses to the somatic muscles of the body. The fibers of the motor nerves are actually the first to be formed.

When the sensory nerves start developing, the outward-growing fibers emerging from the spinal ganglia meet the nerve fibers leaving the spinal cord by way of the ventral roots, and together they form mixed sensory-motor nerves (Figs. 266, 267). The nerves branch again to supply different areas of the body. A dorsal ramus supplies the dorsal integument and muscles of the back. A ventral ramus supplies the side of the body and the ventral surface and also gives off a connecting branch — the **ramus communicans** — to the ganglia of the autonomic nervous system (Fig. 267, *E, F*). (See further p. 371.)

The limbs of vertebrates are supplied by the spinal nerves belonging to several segments in the case of both fore- and hindlimbs. Before entering the limbs, the nerves become interconnected forming plexuses: the **brachial plexus** for the forelimb and the **lumbar plexus** for the hindlimb.

Dependence in Development of Nerves and Nerve Centers on Peripheral Organs.   It is common knowledge that the nerves and nerve centers show a certain correspondence in the degree of their development with the organs they supply. Thus the spinal nerves supplying the limbs in terrestrial animals are stronger than the other spinal nerves, the corresponding ganglia are larger, and the spinal cord itself has swellings in the cervical and the lumbar region, from which the fore- and hindlimbs are innervated.

It can be shown experimentally that, at least in part, this correspondence in the degree of development of the nervous system and the peripheral organ is due to a direct correlation between the two.

If the forelimb rudiment of a salamander embryo is removed and the limb fails to develop, the nerves of the brachial plexus remain smaller (thinner) than they would have been if the limb was there. Also the spinal ganglia III to V are smaller. The number of cells in each ganglion may be reduced to 50 per cent as compared with the normal or the unoperated side of the same animal. If an additional limb rudiment is transplanted, the local spinal nerves supply the nerves to the transplanted limbs, and then these nerves increase in thickness and the corresponding ganglia increase in size. The increase in the number of cells may be up to 40 per cent (Detwiler, 1926a). In similar experiments performed on the chick embryo, it could be shown that the sensory and motor parts of the spinal cord are similarly reduced in the absence of a limb and increased in cases of peripheral overloading (transplantation of an additional limb-bud). (See Hamburger, 1934, and Bueker, 1947.) Reduction occurs both in the gray matter (the cells) and the white matter (the fibers) of the spinal cord.

The mechanism by which the size of the nerve center (a spinal ganglion or a part of the brain or spinal cord) is changed by a change of the periphery is fairly complicated. When the periphery connected to a nerve center is increased, the increase of nerve cells in the center may be brought about by:

(1) Increased proliferation—this has been found in some cases, but seems to be of minor importance
(2) Increase in the number of cells which differentiate as neurons
(3) Decrease in the number of degenerating cells

All three of these factors may act simultaneously or become prominent in changing proportions in various cases. The effect of a decrease in the periphery seems to be mainly to cause a degeneration of large numbers of nerve cells, sometimes as much as 90 per cent in restricted areas having no other peripheral connections. One of the most remarkable facts in this dependence of the nerve centers on the periphery is that cells may apparently be affected although they have no direct connections with peripheral organs. Nerve cells may degenerate even though the organs to which they should have been related are removed before nervous connection between the central nervous system and the periphery is established. In the case of overloading, cells which do not normally send their processes into the area concerned are drawn into supplying the additional periphery. (See further Piatt, 1948; Weiss, 1955; Hamburger, 1956.)

Not only the volume (thickness) of the nerves is dependent on the organs which they supply but the paths which the nerves take, and thus the whole configuration of the peripheral nervous system is determined by the periphery.

The mode of development of the nerves was a subject of controversy as long as embryology relied on purely descriptive methods. The conflicting theories were those of His and Hensen. According to His, the nerves consist of processes growing out from the nerve cells and eventually reaching their organs of destination or making contacts with the processes of other nerve cells in the central nervous system. According to Hensen, the nerve fibers develop from intercellular bridges connecting all the cells of the multicellular animal from the earliest stages of development. The controversy was solved by Harrison (1908), when he tried cultivating in a plasma clot pieces of neural tube taken from frog embryos. He could observe directly the formation of outgrowths from the nerve cells and could see the free ends of the processes push forward through the medium. Harrison's findings were corroborated by numerous investigators, and it was also shown that the processes of nerve cells can establish new connections *in vitro*, if nervous tissue is cultivated together with a different type of tissue (muscle tissue, for example).

The problem now arises as to what directs the nerve fibers in their outgrowth from the central nervous system or from the cranial and spinal ganglia to the peripheral organ. The answer is given by the results of embryonic transplantations. If the forelimb rudiment of an amphibian embryo, prior to the outgrowth of the nerves, is cut out and transplanted to a position very near the original one, the brachial nerves will deviate from their normal paths and will be deflected in the direction of the transplanted limb. If the distance of the transplanted limb from the original position is not too great, the brachial nerves will penetrate into the limb and ramify in it just as if the limb was in its normal position. The limb in this case becomes fully functional and moves in coordination with the other limb.

The same may happen if an additional limb is transplanted into the immediate vicinity of the host limb (Fig. 271). The brachial nerves will develop branches running out to the additional limb and will supply it (Detwiler, 1930, 1926b). If the normal path of the nerves is blocked by some obstacle,

Figure 271. Nerve supply to a transplanted limb. Only the nerves supplying the limbs are drawn. The numbers indicate the spinal ganglia. (After Detwiler, from Mangold, 1928.)

Figure 272. *a,* A mica plate *(M)* inserted in the path of outgrowth of the spinal nerves to the hindlimbs in a frog embryo. *b,* The nerves have grown around the obstacle and have reached the hindlimbs. (From Hamburger, 1929.)

the outgrowing nerves may avoid the obstacle, go around it and still reach their normal destination. This has been observed when a piece of mica was inserted into a frog embryo between the spinal cord and the region where the hindlimb rudiments were to develop. The nerves formed loops around the mica plate and still reached the hindlimb rudiments (Fig. 272 – Hamburger, 1929). However, if the limb rudiment is placed farther away from the normal limb site, or if the obstacle between the spinal cord and the limb rudiment is too great, the nerves fail to be attracted to the limb. If the limb rudiment is placed on the side of the embryo, too far for the normal forelimb or hindlimb nerves to reach it, it still will attract the local spinal nerves. These nerves will grow into the limb but they cannot provide for the normal functioning of the limb: the limb cannot move.

It appears that only the areas of the spinal cord from which the nerves of the brachial and lumbar plexuses originate possess the properties necessary for controlling the function of limbs. These properties, as we have seen previously (p. 346), are established at some time between the neurula and the tailbud stage. The centers controlling the movements of the fore- and hindlimbs are interchangeable, however: when forelimb buds were transplanted in place of hindlimb rudiments, they acquired normal mobility. Limbs transplanted to the head may be supplied by fibers of the cranial nerves and then they can be seen to move synchronously with the respiratory movements of the jaws and gills. The movements of the limb are, however, rather of the nature of twitchings and differ from the coordinated movements of normal limbs (Detwiler, 1930).

The last experiment has already shown that the attraction of the nerves by the peripheral organs may be unspecific to a certain extent, the nerves growing out to organs other than the ones they normally supply. This is further borne out by the following experiment. An eye was transplanted into the side of a salamander embryo after the forelimb rudiment was removed. The brachial nerves were deflected from their normal path and grew out toward the transplanted eye. Having approached the eye, however, the brachial nerves failed to penetrate into the eye and establish an actual connection with it but stopped with free ends in the tissue surrounding the eye (Detwiler and van Dyke, 1934). Two aspects of the nerve supply to organs must thus be recognized: one aspect is the outgrowth of nerves toward the organ, and the other aspect is the actual establishment of a connection between the nerve and the organ. The attraction of the outgrowing nerves to peripheral organs seems to be unspecific to a very high degree; possibly any growing mass of tissue will attract a nerve that is sufficiently near to it. The connections between the nerve and the end organ can be made only if the two correspond to each other, at least in a general way.

The nature of the attraction of nerves to peripheral organs has been investigated in special experiments. It was shown that the nerves are not directed by any chemical substances diffusing from the peripheral organs; neither can their outgrowth be controlled by electrical currents or magnetic fields. It is thus not a case of chemotaxis or galvanotaxis. What actually directs the outgrowing nerve fiber is the ultramicroscopic structure of the colloidal intercellular matrix, through which the tip of the nerve fiber is moving. It is thus the same factor as that which directs the movements of mesenchyme cells. The nerve follows pathways consisting of bundles of oriented molecules or colloidal micellae (Fig. 273). The peripheral organs can influence the direction of nerve outgrowth by altering the submicroscopic structure of the intercellular matrix surrounding them. This they do probably by withdrawing water from their surroundings and causing a shrinkage which orients the particles of the matrix along lines radiating from the intensively growing organ. This radial arrangement of particles of the matrix naturally causes the nerves to converge toward the center around which the matrix is so polarized (Weiss, 1934).

Figure 273. Outgrowth of nerve fibers in fibrous media with a different degree of ultrastructural organization (random arrangement in center turning into prevailing horizontal orientation on left and strict vertical orientation on right). (From Weiss, in Willier, Weiss and Hamburger, 1955.)

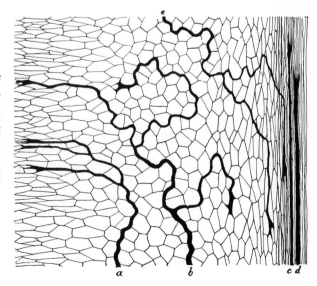

A counterpart to the dependence of the nervous system on the peripheral organs is the influence which the nerves exercise on the organs which they supply. This influence does not concern the initial stages in the development of organs but sometimes is very important for their subsequent differentiation. The muscles are originally formed before the nerves are developed, and the differentiation of muscle tissue may proceed for some time in the complete absence of nerve supply, as for instance when the whole of the neural plate is removed in an early stage of development. The histological differentiation may proceed so far that the muscles become functional — that is, they may show contractions, spontaneously or as reactions to direct stimulation. If the innervation of the muscle does not occur, however, the muscle fibers undergo a fatty degeneration and are eventually resorbed (Hamburger, 1929). Thus some sort of **trophic** influence of the nerves is necessary for the persistence of muscle tissue.

Some sense organs depend for their persistence on a continued influence of the nerve endings supplying them. The gustatory organs in fishes and in man degenerate if the nerve which supplies them (the glossopharyngeal nerve) is interrupted. If a regeneration of the nerves takes place, the regenerating fibers on reaching the epithelium cause the epithelial cells to differentiate as gustatory buds in place of the ones that had previously degenerated (Detwiler, 1926b).

The Development of the Brain. We will first trace the features manifest in the development of the brain in all vertebrates and then point out some of the peculiarities found in higher vertebrates, especially in mammals and in man.

As has been indicated earlier, the anterior brain vesicle, the prosencephalon, gives rise at its anterior end to the telencephalon. The latter produces in an early stage two bulges directed anterolaterally which become the cerebral hemispheres (Figs. 274, 275). Each bulge of the telencephalon contains a pocketlike cavity, which is an extension of the original cavity of the anterior brain vesicle (prosencephalon). The two cavities are known as the **first** and **second ventricles** of the brain. Originally they are in broad communication with the rest of the cavity of the prosencephalon, but later the channels leading into the first and second brain ventricles may become constricted. These channels are called the **foramina of Monro** (also known as the interventricular foramina).

The cerebral hemispheres grow out forward beyond the original anterior end of the prosencephalon. The median strip of the anterior wall of the prosencephalon persists in a relatively unchanged state as the **lamina terminalis**.

The telencephalon in lower vertebrates is the primary center of the olfactory sense and is intimately connected with the olfactory organs which develop immediately anterior and lateral to it. The nerve fibers growing out from the sensory cells in the olfactory organs penetrate into the telencephalon near its anterior end, in a part which differentiates as the olfactory lobe.

Being in the first place a center for the olfactory sense, the telencephalon shows the same kind of dependence on the olfactory organ as the spinal nerves and the spinal cord show in respect of the peripheral organs to which they are connected. This has been shown by removing the olfactory rudiments

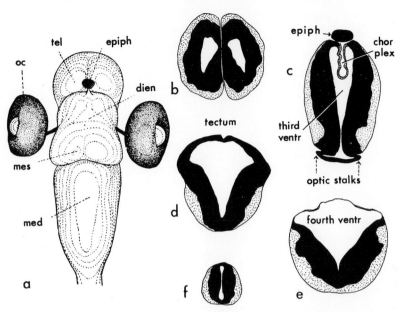

Figure 274. Reconstruction of the brain and eyes in a young frog tadpole *(a).* (After Spemann, from Huxley and de Beer, 1934.) Transverse sections of *(b)* telencephalon, *(c)* diencephalon, *(d)* mesencephalon, *(e)* medulla, *(f)* spinal cord. *epiph,* Epiphysis; *dien,* diencephalon; *med,* medulla; *mes,* mesencephalon; *oc,* eye; *tel,* telencephalon. In the sections, masses of cells (gray matter) are shown in black, and fibers (white matter) are indicated by stippling.

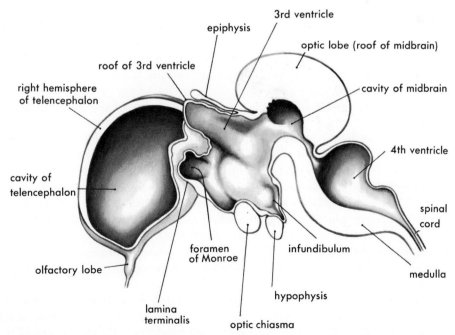

Figure 275. The brain of an 8-day chick embryo, dissected in the median plane. The right telencephalon hemisphere, however, has been dissected in a paramedian plane to show the cavity of the brain. (Redrawn from Lillie, 1919.)

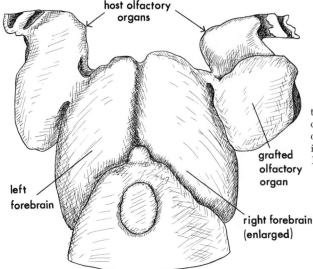

host olfactory organs

Figure 276. Hyperplasia of the right lobe of the telencephalon due to transplantation of an additional olfactory organ in *Ambystoma*. (From Burr, 1930.)

grafted olfactory organ

left forebrain

right forebrain (enlarged)

and by transplanting additional ones. In the absence of an olfactory organ, the corresponding lobe of the forebrain remains underdeveloped (Burr, 1916). If an additional olfactory organ is transplanted into the region beside the normal one, the fibers of the olfactory nerve grow from the transplanted organ into the adjoining lobe of the forebrain, and this causes an increase in the size of the latter (Fig. 276 – Burr, 1930).

In the lower groups of vertebrates, the walls of the cerebral hemispheres are only moderately thickened, and the nerve cells remain accumulated on the inner surface of the walls; that is, on the surface facing the internal cavity.

In the higher vertebrates, starting with the reptiles, the outward migration of nerve cells is not restricted to the mantle surrounding the cavity of the brain, but the migrating cells penetrate beyond the layer of nerve fibers which make up the white matter originally surrounding the gray matter and accumulate near the surface giving rise to the **cortex** of the cerebral hemispheres.

The diencephalon in all vertebrates is remarkable in that it produces a great variety of structures with different functions, in addition to the two eye vesicles that are referred to later. The brain cavity in the region of the diencephalon remains fairly large and is known as the **third ventricle** of the brain. The cells in the brain wall become concentrated mainly in the sides of the diencephalon; they become thickened and are known as the **optic thalamus**. The thickening is continued here until the inner surfaces of both sides meet in the middle, forming what is called the **commissura mollis**. The optic thalamus is primarily an association center, which increases in importance in higher vertebrates.

The greater part of the dorsal wall, or we may call it rather the roof of the diencephalon, becomes membranous and later does not contain any nerve cells at all. Instead it is richly supplied with blood vessels and becomes the **choroid plexus**, which later bulges down into the cavity of the third ventricle. The choroid plexus is the pathway by which nutrition and oxygen are brought into the ventricles of the brain. Processes of the choroid plexus may penetrate from the third ventricle into the first and second ventricles by way of the foramina of Monro.

Only the posterior section of the roof of the diencephalon retains the nervous character, but parts of it form dorsally directed outgrowths, of which the most important are the parietal organ and the pineal organ or epiphysis. Both are formed as rather long, fingerlike outgrowths of the brain roof, the end sections of which become transformed into more or less rounded masses of cells while the stalks become constricted and may even be interrupted later. In lower vertebrates, either the epiphysis (in some frog tadpoles—see Eakin, 1961) or the parietal organ (in reptiles), or both (in cyclostomes) become eyelike organs, but in higher vertebrates they differentiate as glandular structures. The homologies and the function of these structures have been the subject of many investigations (see Stebbins and Eakin, 1958), but in neither respect has a clear answer as yet been given. Both organs develop mid-dorsally, that is, at the site where the neural folds had fused at an earlier stage. This raises the question whether the presumptive material of each organ is contained in one of the neural folds or in both. It has been found that at least in the case of the epiphysis there are originally two rudiments, one on each edge of the neural plate, and that after neurulation these two rudiments fuse into one single unpaired organ (van de Kamer, 1949).

The floor of the diencephalon produces in all vertebrates a funnellike depression, the **infundibulum**. Part of the wall of the latter becomes segregated from the brain wall and fuses with an outgrowth from the stomodeal invagination (see section 15–2), the two together forming the **hypophysis** or **pituitary gland**, the most important endocrine gland in vertebrates. The walls of the diencephalon on the sides and posterior to the infundibulum differentiate as another important nerve center, the **hypothalamus**, which is the center controlling, through the autonomic system, the vegetative functions of the body.

The midbrain remains a fairly simply organized part of the brain. The walls of the midbrain become thickened mainly ventrally, but the lateral walls and the roof are also fairly thick, and the latter gives rise to an important nerve center, the **tectum**. The cavity of the midbrain becomes narrow and is known as the **aqueduct of Sylvius**. In the lower vertebrates, fishes and amphibians, the tectum serves as the primary center of the visual organ, and the nerve fibers entering the brain from the eyes end here. Beginning with the anuran amphibians, however, the posterior part of the tectum acquires connections with nerve fibers coming in from the ear, and in the amniotes the tectum develops four thickenings, the **corpora quadrigemina**, of which the two anterior thickenings are concerned with the sense of vision while the two posterior ones are related to the sense of hearing.

As the hemispheres of the telencephalon are related to the olfactory organ, so also the tectum of the midbrain, in lower vertebrates, is related to the eyes and is dependent in its differentiation on the nerve fibers entering the midbrain from the eyes. In amphibians and fishes, the optic tectum fails to develop normally and remains thinner than usual if the eye rudiment is removed or reduced in size in an early stage (Dürken, 1913; Harrison, 1929; White, 1948).

The ventrolateral parts of the midbrain show some resemblance to the basal plates of the spinal cord, inasmuch as they contain groups of motor cells which send out processes forming two pairs of motor nerves. These are the third (oculomotor) and fourth (trochlear) cranial nerves (see p. 364).

In mammals, the lateroventral parts of the mesencephalon are very enlarged, owing to the number of nerve fibers passing through this part of the mesencephalon on the way from the cerebral hemispheres to the medulla and the spinal cord. These thickened parts are known as the **cerebral peduncles**.

The neural tube may be fairly straight or only slightly curved at the time of its formation, but in later stages it becomes bent at an angle at one or more levels. These bends are known as **flexures**. The most important flexure, and the one found consistently in all vertebrates, is that at the level of the mid-brain, known as the **cephalic flexure**. Here the foremost part of the brain (the telencephalon and the diencephalon) are bent downward in front of the anterior tip of the notochord.

The rhombencephalon gives rise to the metencephalon and the medulla oblongata. The cavity of the rhombencephalon expands especially anteriorly, just behind the midbrain, and becomes the **fourth ventricle**. The roof of the medulla thins out and is converted into a second choroid plexus – the **posterior choroid plexus**, similar to the one developed from the roof of the dien-cephalon. The future nerve cells are concentrated lateroventrally in the floor of the medulla but separated into two masses by a median groove. This arrangement of nervous tissue gives the medulla a very characteristic appearance in cross section (Fig. 274, *e*).

In spite of differences in gross configuration, the rhombencephalon in its internal organization shows an unmistakable similarity to the spinal cord. A ventral floor plate is continued along the whole length of the rhomben-cephalon, forming a median groove – the **median sulcus**. On the sides of the rhombencephalon there is clearly indicated a lateral groove – the sulcus limitans – subdividing the mass of tissue on each side into a basal plate and

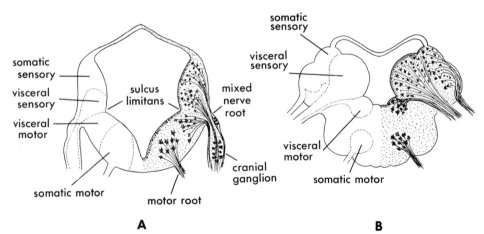

A   **B**

Figure 277. Comparison of the location of the functional components in the medulla ob-longata of a human embryo, 10.2 mm. *(A)*, and of an adult bony fish *(B)*. (Redrawn from Herrick, 1934.)

an alar plate. Owing to the expansion of the membranous roof of the rhombencephalon, the alar plate lies lateral rather than dorsal to the basal plate (see
Fig. 277). The rhombencephalon, as indicated before, gives rise to the metencephalon and the medulla oblongata.

The metencephalon in a younger embryo is no more than a slightly
thickened section at the anterior end of the medulla (which in higher vertebrates gives rise to the **pons varolli**) and a transverse bar in the roof of the
brain just behind the mesencephalon and anterior to the choroid plexus of the
fourth ventricle.

The ventral part of the metencephalon is largely taken up by longitudinal nerve fibers running up and down the brain (among them a continuation
of the fibers constituting the cerebral peduncles). In addition to these, however, the walls of the metencephalon contain the primary centers ("nuclei")
of several cranial nerves. Nearer the midline lie the groups of motor neurons
that give rise to the motor components of the trigeminal nerve (V), to the
abducent nerve (VI), and to the motor components of the facial nerve (VII).
Farther toward the sides of the metencephalon lie the primary centers, to
which are directed the sensory fibers of nerves V (trigeminal), VII (facial)
and VIII (auditory). These centers are, however, elongated and extend far
into the next section of the brain, the medulla (see Fig. 278).

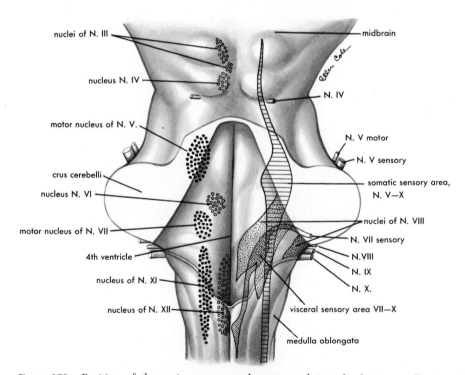

Figure 278. Position of the main sensory and motor nuclei in the human midbrain and
medulla oblongata. Dorsal view after removal of the cerebellum and the roof of the fourth ventricle. The nerve centers are shown as projected onto the surface. The motor nuclei are drawn on
the left side only; somatic motor nuclei are indicated by circles and visceral motor nuclei by black
dots. The sensory nuclei are drawn only on the right side; general somatic sensory nuclei are
indicated by horizontal lines, visceral sensory nuclei by oblique hatching, and auditory (special
somatic) nuclei by stippling. (Redrawn from Herrick, 1934.)

The dorsolateral part of the metencephalon, corresponding to the alar plate of the spinal cord, gives rise to the cerebellum. The cerebellum, although a mid-dorsal organ in its final form, develops from two swellings of the brain tissue to the right and left of the anterior end of the membranous roof of the fourth ventricle.

The development of the cerebellum starts rather late. In the human embryo, the growth of the cerebellar rudiments begins during the second month of pregnancy. At two months the swellings are very distinct, though still separate. Later the two swellings fuse, producing the **vermis** of the cerebellum in the midline, while the lateral parts become the hemispheres (Fig. 279).

As in the telencephalon, the nerve cells migrate in the cerebellum from their place of origin near the cavity of the brain toward the external surface, producing the cortex of the cerebellum.

In the medulla, the main mass of gray matter lies adjacent to the fourth ventricle. Here are situated the centers of the the cranial nerves entering and leaving the medulla. The arrangement of the centers is not segmental, but rather the nerve cells concerned with different functions performed by the posterior cranial nerves are arranged in columns, stretching along the length of the medulla and extending in part into the metencephalon anteriorly and into the spinal cord posteriorly (Fig. 278).

The somatic motor neurons (especially those of the hypoglossal nerve) take up a position on both sides of the median sulcus. Farther outward lie the visceral motor neurons, sending out their fibers as parts of cranial nerves

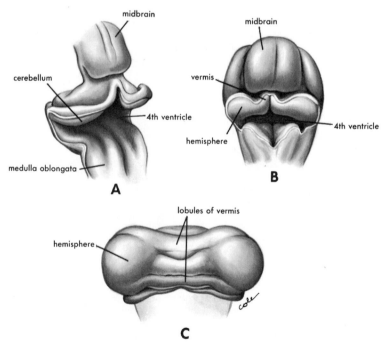

Figure 279. Development of the cerebellum in a human embryo: *A*, in a 6-week embryo; *B*, in a 2-month embryo; *C*, in a 4-month embryo. (After His and Prentiss from Arey: *Developmental Anatomy,* 1947.)

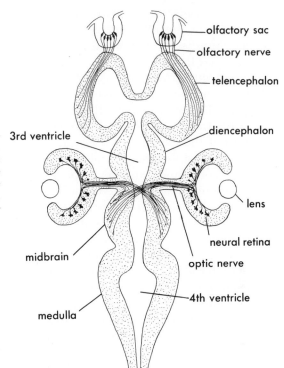

Figure 280. Diagrammatic horizontal section of the brain in a mammal. The diagram also shows the relations of the olfactory and optic nerves to the brain. The parts developing from the neural tube are shown by stippling; the parts developing from the epidermis are white.

Labels on figure: olfactory sac; olfactory nerve; telencephalon; 3rd ventricle; diencephalon; lens; neural retina; midbrain; optic nerve; 4th ventricle; medulla

IX and X (glossopharyngeal and vagus nerves). Still farther laterally, beyond the sulcus limitans, are situated the primary centers of visceral sensory components of cranial nerves VII (facial), IX (glossopharyngeal) and X (vagus). Right on the outer edge of the medulla lie the primary centers for the somatic sensory components of the posterior cranial nerves, including the primary center for the acoustic nerve (VIII).

Depending on the degree of development of the various components of the cranial nerves, the corresponding centers are increased in various degrees. The powerful development of visceral sensory nerve components in fishes, and also of the lateral line system, is accompanied by conspicuous longitudinal swellings in the inner surface of the medulla in these animals (Fig. 277, *B*).

At its posterior end, the medulla gradually merges into the spinal cord. The membranous part of the roof becomes narrower and eventually disappears, and the medioventral groove becomes deeper and is directly continued as the central canal of the spinal cord, while the alar plates converge and fuse dorsally over the canal.

Development of Cranial Nerves and Ganglia.   The cranial nerves of vertebrates, when compared with the spinal nerves, show a great diversity in configuration, distribution and function, and the same diversity can also be noted in their development in the embryo.

To start with the two most anterior nerve pairs, nerves I (olfactory) and II (optic) are completely different in nature and cannot be in any way compared with the spinal nerves (Fig. 280).[*]

---

[*]The unpaired and poorly developed *nervus terminalis* is not sufficiently well studied to be considered here.

Nerve I (olfactory) consists of fibers which are processes of the primary nerve cells of the olfactory organ. The fibers are not joined together in a compact bundle (or two bundles), so that one could speak of many olfactory nerves rather than of only a pair of nerves being present. The nerves are very short and enter the olfactory lobe of the telencephalon. The fibers of the olfactory nerves establish connections with nerve cells in the telencephalon.

Nerve II (optic) is not really a peripheral nerve at all but must be regarded as a nerve tract in the central nervous system. The sensory retina of the eye develops at the expense of a lateral outgrowth of the brain wall and is thus essentially a part of the central nervous system. The stalk of the eye vesicle becomes converted into the optic nerve. When the cells of the nervous retina differentiate (see section 13–2 on the development of the eye), the ganglion cells situated on the distal surface of the sensory retina produce axons which grow along the stalk and enter the brain. In the optic chiasma, the fibers cross to the opposite side and end in the contralateral half of the brain, but in mammals a smaller portion do not cross and end in the ipsilateral side. The termination of the optic nerve fibers is in the roof of the midbrain (the tectum opticum).

The following nerve pairs (III to X in fishes and amphibians and III to XII in amniotes) may be compared to a certain extent with spinal nerves, even though the comparison cannot be complete in any case (Figs. 281, 282).

The three nerves supplying the external eye muscles develop very much like the ventral (motor) roots of the spinal nerves: they are mainly constituted of axons growing out from groups of motor neurons located in the basal plates of the brain. As already mentioned, the centers of nerves III (oculomotor) and IV (trochlear) lie in the ventral part of the mesencephalon. The oculo-motor nerve leaves the brain on the ventral surface of the mesencephalon. The fibers of the trochlear nerve, on the other hand, take a most unusual course: from their point of origin they grow upward around the brain lumen, cross over on the posterior part of the mesencephalon roof, and emerge dorsally on the border between the mesencephalon and metencephalon. Each nerve then supplies the superior oblique muscle on the side opposite to that where lie its corresponding nerve cells (Fig. 283). The nerve cells producing the fibers of the abducent nerves lie in the basal plate of the meten-cephalon, and the nerves leave the brain through the floor of the medulla.

The mixed and sensory cranial nerves – V, VII, VIII, IX and X – possess ganglia, and in this respect they resemble the dorsal roots of the spinal nerves. The development of the cranial ganglia differs, however, from that of the spinal ganglia. It has been proved experimentally, and is generally recognized, that the spinal ganglia develop from cells of the neural crest. The cranial ganglia, on the other hand, derive their material from two sources: from the neural crest and from thickenings of the epidermis on the sides of the head known as the **placodes**. Two rows of such thickenings can be distinguished in the lower vertebrates (fishes and amphibians), an upper row of **dorsolateral placodes** and a lower row of **epibranchial placodes** (Fig. 284).

The dorsolateral placodes play a role in the development of the lateral line sense organs (see p. 386) and also of the ear, which may be said to develop from one of these placodes (see p. 388). The epibranchial placodes are located just above the gill slits. In amniotes the placodes are not as distinct as in

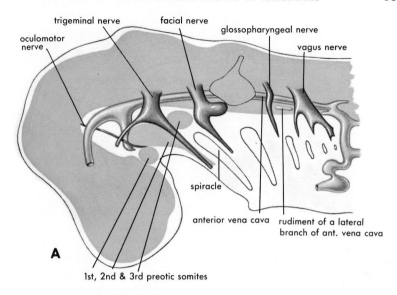

oculomotor nerve · trigeminal nerve · facial nerve · glossopharyngeal nerve · vagus nerve · spiracle · anterior vena cava · rudiment of a lateral branch of ant. vena cava · 1st, 2nd & 3rd preotic somites

A

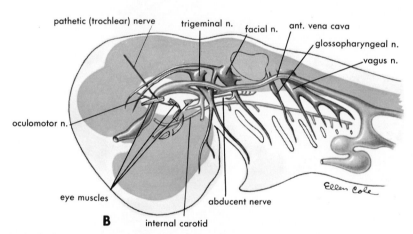

pathetic (trochlear) nerve · trigeminal n. · facial n. · ant. vena cava · glossopharyngeal n. · vagus n. · oculomotor n. · eye muscles · abducent nerve · internal carotid

B

Figure 281. Two stages in the development of cranial nerves in the dogfish, *Scyllium.* A, Earlier stage, with preotic head somites intact, not all cranial nerves present yet. B, Later stage with preotic somites differentiating into eye muscles and all cranial nerves present. (After de Beer, 1924.)

lower vertebrates, but nevertheless migration of cells from slightly thickened portions of the epidermis and their contribution to the formation of nerve ganglia has been definitely established (see Fig. 285).

Simple observation proved to be inadequate to establish the contribution of the two sources to individual ganglia, with the result that widely divergent views were held on the subject by different authors. In recent years, however, experimental methods have been applied, and the question of the origin of the various cranial ganglia has been solved in a satisfactory way.

The experimental approach consists in cutting out parts of the neural tube with the neural crest in early embryos and observing whether particular ganglia would be formed without the neural crest (Levi-Montalcini and Amprino, 1947, Hamburger, 1961; Hammond and Yntema, 1958). A counter-

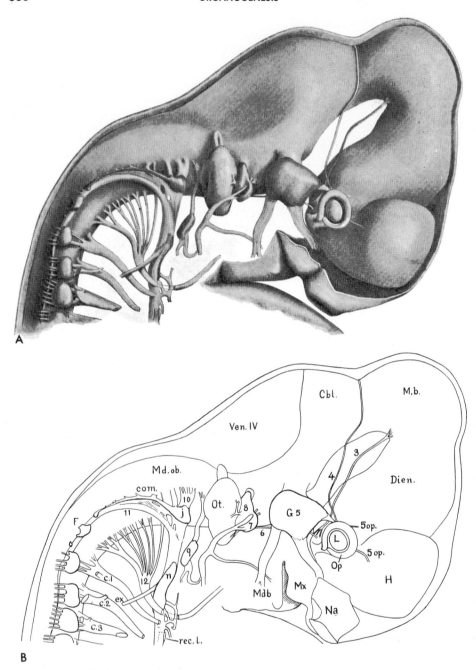

Figure 282. The brain and cranial nerves of a 12 mm. pig embryo. c.l, c.2, c.3, spinal (cervical) nerves 1-3; Cbl., cerebellum; com., commissure joining accessory ganglia of vagus nerve; Dien., diencephalon; ex, external branch of the spinal accessory nerve; F, "Froriep's ganglion," ganglion of a vestigial spinal nerve preceding the "first"; G, gasserian ganglion (V); H, cerebral hemisphere; j, jugular ganglion (X); L, lens; M.b., midbrain; Mdb, mandibular process (rudiment of lower jaw) with mandibular nerve (V); Md.ob., medulla oblongata; Mx, maxillary process (rudiment of upper jaw) with maxillary nerve (V); n, ganglion nodosum (X); Na, nasal pit; Op, optic cup; Ot., otocyst (ear vesicle); rec.l., recurrent laryngeal nerve (branch of X); Ven. IV, roof of fourth vesicle; 3, oculomotor nerve (III); 4, trochlear nerve (IV); 5 op., branches of ophthalmic division of trigeminal nerve (V); 6, abducent nerve (VI); 7, geniculate ganglion of facial nerve (VII); 8, vestibular ganglion (VIII); 9, petrosal ganglion (IX); 10, vagus nerve (X); 11, spinal accessory nerve (XI), partially fused with the vagus nerve; 12, hypoglossal nerve. (From Lewis, 1903.)

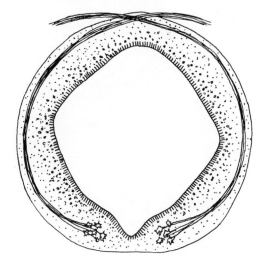

Figure 283. Diagrammatic transverse section through the midbrain of a human embryo (10 mm.) showing the course of the fibers of the trochlear nerve. (Redrawn from Arey, 1947.)

part of such an experiment is the removal of a strip of epidermis on the side of the head containing the presumptive material of the placodes (Hamburger, 1961). Cranial ganglia developing after operations of the first type must be derived from the placodes; parts which are found after operations of the second type can be presumed to be derived from the neural crest. Much of the work on the origin of cranial ganglia was done on chicken embryos.

Another possible approach to the problem is the transplantation of epidermis between amphibian embryos differing in the amount of pigment in cells. If epidermis of a darkly pigmented species is transplanted to a host having light pigmentation, the ganglia formed from the transplanted epidermis can be at once recognized by their dark pigment (Balinsky—unpublished experiments).

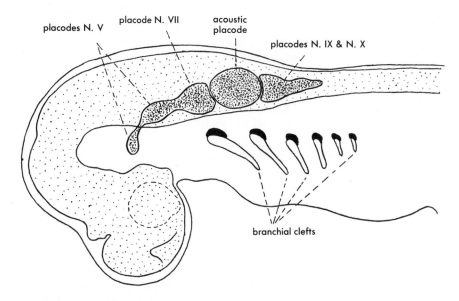

Figure 284. Diagram showing position of the dorsolateral placodes (close stippling) and epibranchial placodes (black) in a fish embryo. The brain and spinal cord are shown by sparse stippling. (Combined from Ihle, 1947 [after Froriep] and from Goodrich, 1958.)

Figure 285. Origin of the trigeminal ganglion in the chick embryo from neural crest and from a dorsolateral placode: m, medulla oblongata; nc, neural crest mesenchyme; pl, trigeminal epidermal placode; pm, mesenchyme derived from placode. (From Hamburger, 1962.)

By applying experimental methods, it has been established (see Hamburger, 1961) that the ganglion of the trigeminal nerve (V), the **ganglion semilunare**, is composed of both neural crest cells and cells from a placode (presumably a dorsolateral placode). The cells of placodal origin are mainly responsible for the outgrowth of the purely somatic sensory ophthalmic and maxillary nerves and for the somatic sensory fibers of the mandibular nerve. The visceral motor fibers of the mandibular nerve are derived from a center in the wall of the metencephalon. A very unusual peculiarity of the trigeminal nerve is that some sensory fibers of this nerve are processes of cells lying not in the ganglion but in the brain itself, in the lateral wall of the mesencephalon. These fibers join the mandibular nerve and terminate in masticating muscles of the jaws. The roots of the trigeminal nerve leave the brain laterally on the most anterior part of the medulla. The somatic sensory fibers establish connections with a very elongated column of cells lying in the upper part of the alar plate in the metencephalon and the medulla.

The facial nerve (VII) in aquatic vertebrates supplies innervation to the lateral line canals of the head and the muscles in the region of the hyoid arch. In the terrestrial vertebrates the lateral line sense organs disappear, and the muscles of the hyoid arch change their function, becoming the facial muscles in mammals and man. Accordingly the facial nerve becomes mainly a visceral motor nerve in higher vertebrates. In addition to this, it also contains visceral sensory fibers supplying taste buds and visceral efferent fibers to the salivary glands. The ganglion of the facial nerve in the higher vertebrates, the **geniculate ganglion**, is derived almost exclusively from an epibranchial placode, while in fishes it has a contribution from a dorsolateral placode forming a special upper section of the ganglion. This disappears with the disappearance of the lateral line sense organs. The roots of the facial nerve leave the brain on the side of the medulla immediately behind the roots of the trigeminal nerve. The nerve center of the motor component of the facial nerve lies in the floor of the metencephalon. The visceral sensory fibers terminate in the median part of the alar plate in the anterior part of the medulla, while the fibers connected to the lateral line system, where present, are connected to a column of nerve cells on the outer edge of the alar plate of the medulla.

The acoustic nerve (VIII) is a very special nerve and may be considered as a specially differentiated section of the facial nerve. The roots of the two nerves lie very close to one another in fishes and amphibians, though they are clearly separated in amniotes. The **acoustic ganglion** is derived from cells of the ear rudiment, the ear vesicle (Campenhout, 1935, and Batten, 1958). As the ear vesicle is formed from a thickening of the epidermis belonging to the dorsolateral placodal system, the acoustic ganglion may be said to be of placodal origin. The fibers from the acoustic ganglion to the brain terminate in special centers in the alar plate of the medulla.

The glossopharyngeal nerve and the vagus have much in common in their composition and development. In both, the cells of the ganglia are derived from two sources, the neural crest and the placodes, but contrary to what is seen in the semilunar ganglion of the trigeminal nerve, the cells from different sources do not join together in one ganglion but form separate ganglia. The glossopharyngeal nerve (IX) has an upper "**root**" ganglion, consisting of cells of neural crest origin, and a lower **petrosal ganglion**, derived from an epibranchial placode. The nerve is mainly sensory (supplying taste buds!) and visceral motor, and its primary centers lie in the medulla.

The vagus nerve (X) also has two main ganglia, the upper **ganglion jugulare** corresponding to the root ganglion of the glossopharyngeal nerve and consisting of cells derived from the neural crest, and a lower **ganglion nodosum**, derived from epibranchial placodes. In addition to these a number of **accessory ganglia** adjoin the jugular ganglion posteriorly. These ganglia are connected to the medulla by independent rootlets, but the fibers of the accessory ganglia connecting them with the periphery are joined to the fibers of the main vagus nerve. The vagus nerve supplies several visceral pouches, starting with the second branchial pouch, whereas the more anteriorly lying nerves each supply only one visceral pouch (the glossopharyngeal supplies the first branchial pouch, and the facial nerve supplies the spiracular pouch). The presence of several ganglia connected to the vagus is an additional proof of the polysegmental nature of this nerve. The accessory ganglia of the vagus represent a transition from the cranial to the spinal nerve system. The central connections of the vagus nerve are similar to those of the glossopharyngeal nerve but extend farther back, well into the spinal cord.

The visceral motor fibers belonging to the vagus supply the muscles of the branchial arches in fishes (except the first), but in amniotes these fibers become separated from the vagus as an independent nerve, the **spinal accessory nerve** (XI), supplying muscles of the pharynx and of the shoulder (m. trapezius and m. sternocleidomastoideus) which have been developed in the course of evolution from the branchial muscles.

In amniotes, the somatic motor neurons lying in the floor of the medulla, in direct continuation with the ventral (motor) columns of the spinal cord, produce fibers which leave the medulla by a number of separate roots on its ventral surface and then join to form the main trunk of nerve XII, the **hypoglossal nerve**, which is a somatic motor nerve supplying the muscles of the tongue. In cyclostomes, a similar nerve is formed by the joining together of ventral roots of several spinal nerves which are connected to dorsal nerve roots and spinal ganglia in a manner typical of spinal nerves. Traces of this condition are preserved even in some mammals where connections of strands of the hypoglossal nerve to ganglia, in particular to the accessory ganglia of of the vagus, have been observed in the embryos.

The Human Brain. The development of the brain in the higher vertebrates can best be illustrated by a brief description of the changes which the brain rudiment undergoes in the human embryo.

The brain of the human embryo toward the end of the first month after conception is not very different from the brain of an amphibian embryo, except that it is distinctly more elongated (Fig. 286, a). The eye rudiments are separated from the prosencephalon, the cephalic flexure is indicated, but there is as yet no trace of the progressive development of the hemispheres of the forebrain or of the cerebellum.

Soon after the beginning of the second month after conception, the telencephalon forms a conspicuous bulge dorsally in front of the eye rudiments. The bulge is slightly bilobed; this is the first indication of the future hemispheres of the brain. The **cephalic flexure** is increased to such an extent that the brain appears to be bent on itself (Fig. 286, b). In addition to the cephalic flexure, the brain now shows two more flexures. At the level of the anterior part of the rhombencephalon, the brain is bent with the convexity facing downward; this is the **pontine flexure**. The metencephalon with the pons varolii (after which the flexure is named) lies in front of the flexure, and most of the medulla remains posterior to the flexure. A third flexure, with the convexity facing dorsally (the same as the cephalic flexure), appears at the junction between the medulla and the spinal cord. This is the **cervical flexure.**

About the middle of the second month after conception, the flexures of the brain become much more distinct, expecially the pontine flexure. The development of the cerebellum does not make much progress, but the midbrain enlarges very considerably and attains its largest relative size. The main advance, however, is shown by the telencephalon; the two lobes indicated previously enlarge greatly and spread out forward, upward and backward, partially covering the laterodorsal surfaces of the diencephalon (Fig. 286, c).

By the beginning of the third month after conception, the hemispheres of the telencephalon constitute by far the greatest part of the brain (Fig. 286, d). They have expanded backward to such an extent that they almost completely cover the diencephalon. A broad shallow groove on the outer surface of each hemisphere (the future lateral fissure) indicates the separation of the temporal lobe of the brain. The mesencephalon is greatly expanded dorsally and forms a large mass posterior to the cerebral hemispheres.

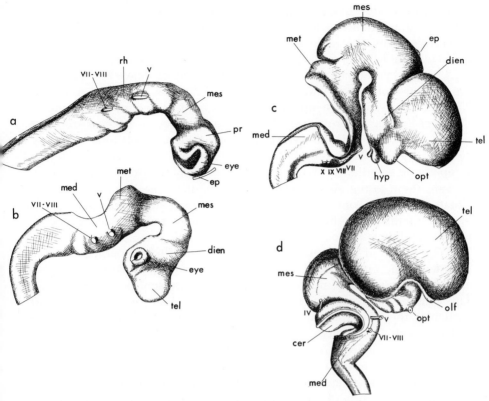

Figure 286. Four stages in the development of the brain in a human embryo. *cer*, Cerebellum; *ep*, epiphysis; *dien*, diencephalon; *hyp*, hypophysis; *med*, medulla; *mes*, mesencephalon; *met*, metencephalon; *olf*, olfactory bulb; *opt*, optic stalk (or nerve); *pr*, prosencephalon; *rh*, rhombencephalon; *tel*, telencephalon. Roots of the cranial nerves are indicated by means of Roman numerals. (After Hochstetter, from Grosser, 1945.)

The cerebellum is the last part of the brain to become conspicuous on inspection from the outside, since the rudiments of the cerebellum are formed originally as masses of brain tissue bulging into the fourth ventricle from the sides of the metencephalon. These masses increase and later fuse together above the cavity of the brain, and only after this does the rudiment of the cerebellum swell to the exterior in front of the fourth ventricle. This occurs toward the third month after conception.

At the age of four months after conception, the cerebral hemispheres have grown so large that they cover the midbrain from the sides and touch the cerebellar hemispheres, which by this time have become clearly discernible. Even at this time the surface of the cerebral hemisphere, apart from the lateral fissure, is quite smooth, but during the second half of the period of pregnancy the surface becomes wrinkled and folded, giving rise to the characteristic gyri of the human brain.

The Development of the Autonomic Nervous System. The autonomic nervous system consists exclusively of efferent neurons conveying nervous impulses to the cardiac and smooth muscles, to digestive and sweat glands, and to some endocrine glands.

The bodies of the neurons of the somatic motor nerves and visceral motor

nerves are located in the basal plates of the spinal cord and brain, and the
axons of these neurons lead directly to the effector muscles. In the sympathetic system, the pathway from the spinal cord to the effector organ is
made up of at least two neurons. The body of the first neuron lies in the spinal
cord, in the lateral part of the basal plate. The axons leave the spinal cord in
the ventral motor roots and then, by way of the rami communicantes (see p.
351), reach a system of sympathetic ganglia lying in two rows right and left of
the dorsal aorta, where these fibers terminate. Because the neurons whose
bodies are located in the central nervous system reach only as far as the
ganglia, they are known as **preganglionic neurons.** Nerve cells located in the
sympathetic ganglia, receiving the impulses from the preganglionic neurons,
forward them to the effector organs directly or by means of further neurons
situated in the secondary and even tertiary sympathetic ganglia—the latter
located in the immediate vicinity of the effector organs (on the gut, the
bladder and so forth).

The origin of the preganglionic neurons of the sympathetic system, as
well as of the cranial components of the parasympathetic system (visceral
efferent components of nerves VII, IX and X), present no special problems.
The origin of the ganglia of the autonomic system, on the other hand, in
particular the origin of the chain of sympathetic ganglia, has been a subject of much controversy. At least three possible sources of these nerve
cells have been considered, namely, an origin from the neural crest, from the
neural tube and from the local mesoderm.

After much inconclusive work in which descriptive methods were used,
a satisfactory solution of the problem has been reached by the use of experimental methods (see Yntema and Hammond, 1947). When parts of the neural
crest are removed in young embryos (of the chick), there is an immediate
effect on the development of the sympathetic ganglia, which are either
reduced or in some cases may be complately lacking (Hammond and Yntema,
1947; Nawar, 1956). The other two sources under consideration (the neural
tube and the local mesoderm) were not tampered with in these experiments,
so the defects are a clear indication that the sympathetic ganglia and the
neurons contained in them are of neural crest origin. Even the tertiary sympathetic ganglia in the walls of the gut are of neural crest origin and are absent
when access of the neural crest cells to the gut rudiment is precluded by
operation (Andrew, 1963). In a separate investigation with the same methods,
it was found that the ciliary ganglion (the parasympathetic ganglion connected to the oculomotor nerve) is also formed from cells of the neural crest
originating in the mesencephalon area of the neural tube (Hammond and
Yntema, 1958).

The actual formation of the sympathetic ganglia takes place in rather
early stages of the development of the embryo, before the spinal nerves
start growing out. When the neural crest cells migrate downward from their
site of origin, dorsal to the neural tube, groups of the migrating cells accumulate along the dorsal aorta. The cells first aggregate into paired ganglia, and
these become linked with one another lengthwise to form a longitudinal
nerve cord on each side of the dorsal aorta. The cord is secondarily extended
forward into the head region. When the spinal nerves start growing out, they
eventually establish connection with the sympathetic trunks by means of the
rami communicantes, as already stated.

13−2   DEVELOPMENT OF THE EYES

The Optic Cup.   The origin of the optic vesicles has already been described. The optic vesicles push outward until they reach the epidermis, displacing the intervening mesenchyme, so that they come into direct contact with the inner surface of the epidermis. After this the external surface of the optic vesicle flattens out and invaginates inward, so that the vesicle is

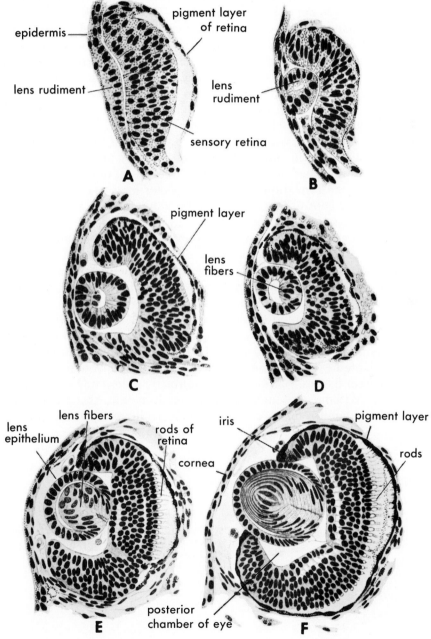

Figure 287.   Stages of the development of the eye in the axolotl. (After Rabl, from Spemann, 1938.)

transformed into a double-walled, cuplike structure—the **optic cup** (Fig. 287). The invaginated wall of the optic cup is much thicker than the remaining external wall. The first is to develop into the **sensory retina** of the eye, the second develops into the **pigment coat** of the retina (**tapetum nigrum**). The rim of the eye cup later becomes the edge of the pupil. The cavity of the optic cup is the future posterior chamber of the eye, filled by the vitreous body. The opening of the eye cup is very large at first, but later the rims of the cup bend inward and converge, so that the opening of the pupil is constricted and reduced to its final relative dimensions. The rim of the optic cup surrounding the pupil becomes the **iris**. The constriction of the pupil does not take place equally all around the circumference of the eye, but it remains open longer on the ventral edge of the eye cup. A groove, the **choroid fissure**, remains here, cutting through the otherwise approximately circular edge of the eye cup and reaching inward as far as the optic stalk (Fig. 288). This fissure serves for the entry into the posterior chamber of the eye of a blood vessel and of mesenchyme cells which are found later in the vitreous body. The fissure normally closes during embryonic life.

The size of the optic vesicles relative to the rest of the prosencephalon may vary considerably in different vertebrates. Even in one order among vertebrates as in the frogs, it was found by direct measurement that the mass of cells used for the formation of the eye vesicles may, in different species, range from 10 per cent to 50 per cent of the volume of the prosencephalon (Balinsky, 1958). As a general rule, the eye rudiments are large in bony fishes, reptiles and birds, smaller in amphibians and relatively very small in mammalian embryos. The determination of the optic cup is due to the action of the underlying roof of the archenteron on a part of the neural plate. In the late neural plate stage the determination appears to be irrevocable, and parts of the optic vesicle cannot differentiate in any other way than by developing into retina, iris or pigmented epithelium of the eye. The eye rudiment may be excised and transplanted into any region of the embryo, and its development will continue more or less normally, producing a heterotopic eye.

A transplanted eye rudiment, although no longer capable of being transformed into other tissues, cannot develop normally unless it is surrounded by mesenchyme. Without mesenchyme in its environment, the differentiation of the optic rudiment remains extremely poor (Holtfreter, 1939b; Lopashov, 1956).

Figure 288. Eye cup, showing the position of the choroid fissure in respect to the lens and the eye stalk. (After Froriep, from Korschelt, 1936.)

choroid fissure

The determination of the eye as a whole does not mean that all the parts of the eye rudiment are determined as well. The determination of the parts of the eye occurs much later. The eye rudiment in the neural plate stage and in the optic vesicle stage may be split into two, and each half develops into a complete eye. This can best be demonstrated if a part of the eye rudiment is transplanted. It is found then that the remaining and the transplanted part each develop into a small eye. Experiments have also been performed on the eye rudiment at the stage when the optic vesicle is being transformed into an optic cup, and the two parts of the cup, the future sensory retina and the future pigment coat, become morphologically distinguishable. A piece of the presumptive pigmented epithelium may be excised and transplanted into the vicinity of a normal eye of another embryo, and it develops into a complete eye, consisting both of a pigment coat and a sensory retina (Fig. 289 – Dragomirow, 1933). However, a prerequisite for this is that the piece be not too small; very small fragments of the eye rudiment usually develop into pigmented epithelium only.

The ability of a part of the organ rudiment to develop as a whole is reminiscent of a similar ability in the early stages of cleavage in some animals. The process observed in both cases is known as **self-regulation**. It is found in many organ rudiments and, in fact, can be considered as a common property of organ rudiments. The ability to self-regulate presupposes that the parts of the rudiment (or of the egg in the early cleavage stages) are not determined.

In the case of the eye cup, the absence of determination of parts can be demonstrated also in another way. If a suitable inductor is applied to the

Figure 289. A whole eye, developed from a transplanted piece of presumptive pigment coat. (From Dragomirow, 1933.)

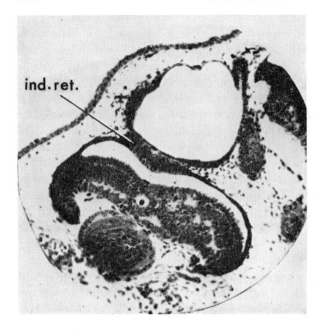

ind. ret.

Figure 290. Induction of an additional sensory retina (*ind. ret.*) in an eye by means of contact with an ear vesicle. (From Dragomirow, 1936.)

outer surface of the optic cup—that is, to the surface which normally differentiates into the pigmented epithelium—it may be induced to develop as sensory retina, so that the eye has two retinas, a normal one and an additional one. The latter is never as large as the normal one. A suitable inductor for this purpose is the sensory epithelium of an ear (Fig. 290). The experiment therefore consists in the transplantation of an optic vesicle into the immediate vicinity of the ear vesicle to ensure the close contact of the epithelia of the two organ rudiments (Dragomirow, 1936).

With advancing development it is apparent that the rim of the optic cup becomes increasingly different from the deeper-lying parts. The constriction of the pupil already referred to, takes place at the expense of a considerable thinning out of the wall of the rim of the optic cup. The thinned-out portion becomes the iris of the eye, while the remaining part, which stays considerably thicker, gives rise to the retina proper.

In the iris, large amounts of pigment are deposited in the outer epithelial layer (this layer is actually a part of the pigment coat of the eye cup). In addition to cells carrying pigment, this layer also gives rise to the smooth muscle fibers of the sphincter and dilator muscles of the iris. In the sensory retina, the cells start differentiating into the sensory and nerve (or ganglion) cells. The first trace of this differentiation is seen in the arrangement of the nuclei of the cells in several layers, of which the nuclei situated in the layer nearest to the pigment coat belong to the future rod and cone cells. The rudiments of the rods and cones appear as cytoplasmic processes on the inner ends of these cells. The remaining nuclei, arranged in two or more layers nearer to the cavity of the eye cup, give rise to the various types of intermediate and ganglion cells of the retina. Nerve processes, arising from the ganglion cells of the retina, grow out toward the brain, and the path which they take is along the stalk of the eye cup. In this way the stalk of the optic cup becomes transformed into the optic nerve. On reaching the floor of the diencephalon, in all vertebrates except mammals, the nerve fibers do not enter the same side of the brain but cross over to the opposite side and there penetrate into the wall of the diencephalon and the mesencephalon. Where the nerve fibers of the two eyes cross and bypass each other on their way to the contralateral parts of the brain arises the **optic chiasma**. In mammals, the crossing of the fibers of the optic nerve in the chiasma is not complete, a small proportion of the fibers entering the brain on the same side as the eye in which they originated.

The optic cup, even when fully differentiated, is not yet a complete eye. Certain accessory structures have to be added to it to make the eye fully functional. The most important of these structures is the **lens**, which serves for the refraction of the rays of light entering the eye. The lens is not developed from the optic cup, but from the epidermal epithelium with which the optic vesicle comes in contact, as mentioned before. As the outer wall of the optic vesicle begins to invaginate to become the retinal layer of the optic cup, a thickening appears in the epithelium which is in contact with the invaginating part of the optic cup (see Fig. 287, *a*). This thickening is the rudiment of the lens.

The Lens. The way in which the lens rudiment is separated from the remainder of the epidermis varies in different classes of vertebrates. In birds and mammals, the epidermal thickening folds in to produce a pocket which is for a short time open to the outside and later a vesicle lying in the opening of the iris (in the pupil). In amphibians and bony fishes, the thickening in the formation of which only the inner layer of epidermis takes a part is nipped off from the epidermis as a solid mass, but later the cells of this mass rearrange themselves into a vesicle. In both cases the vesicle must undergo further differentiation before the lens can function as a refracting body. This happens in such a way that the cells on the inner side of the lens vesicle elongate, become columnar at first and later are transformed into long fibers. During this transformation, the nuclei of the cells degenerate and the cytoplasm becomes hard and transparent. The fibers are arranged in the lens in a very orderly way, forming the spherical or ellipsoid refracting body of the lens. Part of the lens epithelium remains unchanged and covers the sphere of fibers distally. The junction between the unchanged lens epithelium and the mass of fibers is the growth point of the lens; here the epithelial cells are continuously transformed into fibers, so that the refracting body grows by apposition of new fibers.

Between the development of the optic cup and the development of the lens there exists, in most of the vertebrates studied experimentally, a direct causal relationship; the development of the lens is dependent on an induction from the optic vesicle. As the optic cup touches the epidermis, it gives off a stimulus of some kind, which causes the epidermis cells to develop into the lens rudiments (Lewis, 1904). Any epidermal cells are able to react to the induction of the optic vesicle, and without this induction the lens does not develop at all or at least the development is defective. The dependence of the lens development on the action of the optic cup can be shown by several types of experiments. One type of experiment is to remove (excise) the eye rudiment before it can reach the epidermis. Such an operation usually leads to the absence of the lens. The other experiment is to remove the epidermis which normally would have formed the lens and replace it with a piece of epidermis taken from another part of the body, from the head or even from the belly. In this experiment it was observed that the epidermis, if in contact with the optic vesicle, develops into a lens. A third type of experiment is to transplant the optic vesicle, without the epidermis normally covering it, under the epidermis in an abnormal position. In this case the local epidermis may be caused to develop a lens (see Mangold, 1931b).

For a long time it was believed that an intimate contact between the optic vesicle and the epidermis is indispensable for lens induction. A thin layer of cellophane inserted between the optic vesicle and the epidermis in a chick embryo completely stopped the inducing action of the optic vesicle (McKeehan, 1951). Insertion of a porous membrane, which presumably allowed for the passage of macromolecules, between the eye vesicle and the epidermis in a frog embryo also precluded lens induction (de Vincentiis, 1954). However, experiments have been reported (McKeehan, 1958) in which a partial screening of the epidermis from the eye vesicle in a chick embryo by a thin slice of agar did not prevent the complete development of the lens. The inducing agent could thus get either through or around the agar. This would suggest that the inducing agent is a chemical substance.

Apart from this, not much is known as to the nature of the stimulus responsible for the induction of the lens. It has not been possible to extract a lens-inducing substance from the optic vesicle. On the other hand, some of the "abnormal" inductors of neural plates are known to induce "free" lenses, that is, lenses without an eye. The thymus of the guinea pig seems to be especially suitable for this purpose (Toivonen, 1940, 1945). That the stimulus in this case is exactly the same as that exercised by the optic cup remains to be proved.

There is one peculiar similarity between the induction of the neural plate and the induction of the lens; it concerns the distribution of the cytoplasmic ribonucleic acid in the components participating in the process. The eye vesicle at the time when it comes into contact with the presumptive lens epidermis contains a large amount of ribonucleic acid. At the same time, the presumptive lens epidermis has little ribonucleic acid, and in this respect it is no different from the rest of the epidermis. After the contact is established, the ribonucleic acid in the cells of the eye vesicle is found to be concentrated near the outer margin of the cells, that is, where the cells touch the epidermis. Large amounts of ribonucleic acid now appear also in the presumptive lens cells, at first only at their proximal ends, where they are in contact with the eye vesicle, but later in the outer parts of the epidermal cells. In subsequent stages, the ribonucleic acid content in the retinal cells decreases, while it continues to increase in the cells of the lens rudiment (McKeehan, 1956). There is no proof, however, that the ribonucleic acid actually passes from the eye cup cells into the lens rudiment cells.

In another experiment, performed on *Xenopus* embryos (Sirlin and Brahma, 1959), the proteins of the eye cup cells were marked by supplying them with radioactively tagged phenylalanine (containing C^{14}). Subsequently radioactive material was found to have passed into lens rudiments induced by the marked eye cups which were transplanted into normal embryos. Although this experiment is open to the same criticisms as the experiments with readioactively marked inductors of the neural plate (see p. 253), the results are compatible with an assumption that a chemical substance passes from the eye cup into the reacting epidermis during lens induction, and that this substance is a protein. There would thus be a similarity in this respect between the mechanism of induction of the neural plate and the mechanism of lens induction.

The relation of the lens development and the optic cup development is complicated rather considerably by the fact that in a few amphibians — *Rana esculenta, Xenopus laevis, Rhacophorus schlegelii* and others to a lesser extent — (Spemann, 1912a; Balinsky, 1951; Tahara, 1962) the lens shows a certain degree of independent development ("self-differentiation") even in the absence of the optic cup, that is, when the optic cup has been previously removed. The degree of independent development varies from a tiny nodule of epidermal cells to a rather typical lens with fiber differentiation. The development is never completely normal, as lenses without eyes undergo a far-reaching degeneration once the initial stages of development have been passed. Nevertheless the independent development of lenses shows that the eye cup is not the only part which may be involved in lens development. The experiments in which free lenses have been induced by abnormal inductors (thymus) suggest that the "self-differentiation" of lenses, where it occurs, is due to some other influence on the differentiation of the epidermal cells, and that this influence is responsible, in some species, for "independent" lens development (that is, lens development which is independent of the eye cup).

What these influences might be may be concluded from some experiments in which belly ectoderm was not capable of developing a lens when transplanted just before the formation of the optic vesicle, but was able to react if transplanted in the neurula stage. It follows that to be able to react the epidermis must be in position some time before the contact with the optic vesicle is established. During this time, the head mesoderm lies immediately underneath the presumptive lens epidermis, and it was concluded that the influence of the head mesoderm is the factor which prepares the epidermis for the subsequent induction emanating from the optic vesicle (Liedke, 1951, 1955). Presumably, in some species, the "preparation" goes so far that the development of the lens may start even if the eye vesicle is not present.

Our conclusion may perhaps be framed in another way: we may say that the development of the lens is a result of induction emanating from two sources, from the head mesoderm and from the eye vesicle. Normally both are necessary for successful lens development. There is some evidence that the relative importance of the two inductors may be changed by environmental factors; keeping the developing embryos at a low temperature seems to favor the induction by the head mesoderm, so that the induction by the eye vesicle becomes unnecessary (Ten Cate, 1953; Jacobson, 1955).

The differentiation of the lens cells into lens fibers in normal development is caused by the same induction as the development of the lens as a whole. It has been proved that the contact with the presumptive retinal layer of the eye can induce lens fiber differentiation. The epithelial cells of the lens rudiment are all capable of fiber differentiation if they are exposed to a

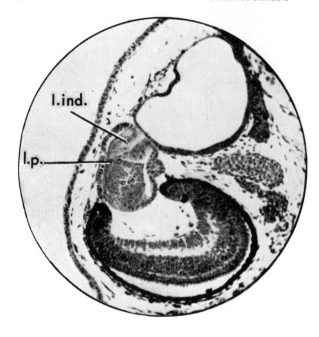

Figure 291. Induction of an additional mass of lens fibers (*l. ind.*) by means of contact with an ear vesicle. *l.p.*, Primary lens fibers. (From Dragomirow, 1929.)

suitable stimulus. The contact with retinal tissue or with the sensory epithelium of an ear vesicle (Fig. 291) (compare what has been said on the induction of the retina) may cause the formation of an additional mass of lens fibers, so that under experimental conditions lenses may develop having two independent masses of fibers (Dragomirow, 1929).

Accessory Structures. The other accessory structures of the eye which are present in all vertebrates having functional eyes are the **choroid coat**, the **sclera** and the **cornea**. The choroid coat and the sclera develop from mesenchyme accumulating around the eyeball, in the way mesenchyme cells accumulate around many organs giving rise to their connective tissue capsules (see section 12–2). In the case of the eye, the interior layer of mesenchyme cells gives rise to a network of blood vessels surrounding the pigment epithelium. The outer layer of mesenchyme forms a fibrous capsule around the eye, which serves for its protection and for the insertion of the eye muscles. The capsule may either remain fibrous or develop cartilage or even bone (in reptiles and birds).

The cornea originates in part from mesenchyme, but the epidermal epithelium also plays an essential role in its formation. The connective tissue part of the cornea is continuous with the sclera, while the corneal epithelium is continuous with the skin epidermis or with the epithelium of the eyelids where such are present. Both the epithelium and the connective tissue of the cornea become transparent, so that the rays of light may enter the eye. The development of the cornea can easily be traced in living amphibian embryos. Initially the epidermis covering the eye is pigmented, for the epidermal cells contain granules of pigment derived from the egg. In the cells of the presumptive cornea these pigment granules become dissolved, and later, when the chromatophores develop in the connective tissue of the skin, the cornea remains free of them.

The transformation of the skin into the cornea is caused by an induction, the source of which is the eyeball. This can be proved by transplanting the eyeball heterotopically or by replacing the normal cornea by skin from another part of the embryo. The stimulus can be given off by both the eye cup and the lens; if the lens alone is transplanted, the epidermis over it loses its pigment and differentiates as cornea. If the eye is removed, the cornea does not develop at all (Spemann, 1901; Fischel, 1919; Mangold, 1931b).

The induction of the cornea presents an interesting peculiarity as compared with the neural plate and the lens induction in amphibians. The competence to differentiate as cornea is found in the skin not only during a short period of embryonic development but for a long time, long after the normal differentiation of the cornea has taken place. Also the eyeball retains its inductive ability for a long time, probably permanently. What is more, the persistence of the cornea is dependent on the continuous presence and influence of the eyeball. If, in a late amphibian larva or an adult, the eye is removed, the cornea soon loses its transparency, it is invaded by chromatophores and becomes more or less normal skin. On the other hand, a fully differentiated piece of skin will lose its chromatophores and become transparent cornea if it is transplanted over the eye.

In the development of the eye induction takes place repeatedly and some parts, after having been induced, become themselves a source of inducing stimuli. A whole chain of inductors can thus be made out:

The roof of the archenteron induces the neural plate, and therefore also the eye cup rudiment which is part of the neural plate.

The eye cup rudiment, becoming the optic vesicle, induces the lens (acting together with head mesoderm).

The lens induces the cornea (acting together with the optic cup).

Parts developing as a result of induction, and inducing in their turn, may be called secondary, tertiary, etc., inductors, or organizers of the second grade, third grade, and so forth.

13–3   THE FATE OF THE NEURAL CREST CELLS

The neural crest at the time of its formation is represented by a mass of loose cells lying dorsally to the neural tube. Almost at once after the formation of the crest, the cells of which it consists start migrating in a lateral and ventral direction from the place of their origin (Fig. 292). As they move, the neural crest cells form into streams, bypassing as they go certain organs (viz., the eye, the gill pouches). These streams of neural crest cells are especially conspicuous in the head and neck region, while in the trunk region the neural crest cells are more scattered, right from the start (Stone, 1926, and Raven, 1931). The neural crest cells move mainly along the inner side of the epidermis, between it and the layer of mesoderm; they penetrate, however, into the interstices between the neural tube and the inner surface of the mesoderm as well. Sooner or later, the most advanced neural crest cells reach the midventral line of the body. Not all of them, however, travel as far as this; rather, they become spread all along the path, some of the cells even retaining their original position dorsal to the neural tube.

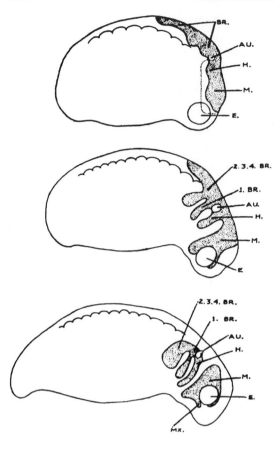

Figure 292. Three stages in the migration of neural crest cells in the salamander *Ambystoma punctatum.* *AU.,* Ear vesicle; *BR.,* branchial neural crest cells (numbers refer to particular branchial arches); *E.,* eye; *H.,* hyoid neural crest cells; *M.,* mandibular neural crest cells; *MX.,* maxillary neural crest cells. (From Stone, 1926.)

The migration of the neural crest cells is a complicated process, dependent on many factors. One of the factors seems to be a repulsion of the migrating cells from one another owing to the substances produced by the metabolism of the cells. If the neural crest cells are cultivated *in vitro,* the cells spread evenly in the medium available (Twitty and Niu, 1948). In the organism, however, the even distribution of neural crest cells is disturbed by the surrounding tissues and organ rudiments which lie in the path of the migrating cells (as has been mentioned) and are bypassed. Other rudiments seem to attract the neural crest cells, in some way, or keep them fixed once they have reached a certain position. So the neural crest cells are held along the upper edges of the somites and also along the upper edge of the lateral plate. Later, when part of the neural crest cells differentiate into chromatophores, these accumulations of neural crest cells become conspicuous as longitudinal strips of pigment (Fig. 293; Twitty, 1949).

The migration of neural crest cells can be observed in several different ways. The neural crest cells, being ectodermal cells, are, in amphibians, distinguishable from the mesoderm cells by their smaller content of yolk

Figure 293. Larva of the newt *Triturus cristatus,* with longitudinal stripes of pigment. (From Balinsky, 1925.)

granules and by a greater amount of pigment derived from the egg. Another way of tracing the neural crest cells is by means of local vital staining. If the staining is applied to the neural folds, the neural crest cells derived from these can readily be seen against the background of unstained ectoderm and mesoderm. A third method is based on the ability of the neural crest cells to differentiate into melanophores. By isolating parts of the embryo in sufficiently early stages and cultivating them in suitable surroundings, it is possible to prove that without the neural crest cells no pigmentation can develop in the skin or in other organs and tissues as well. If, however, a part of the embryo is isolated and transplanted after the migrating neural crest cells have reached this part, the pigment cells later differentiate in the graft. The actual differentiation of pigment cells occurs after the migration has been completed; while on the move the neural crest cells do not differ in their pigment content from other cells, and this of course makes it difficult to observe their migration directly. This last method of investigating the migrations of neural crest cells has been applied in mammals and birds in which the first two methods are not feasible (Rawles, 1948).

In the fishes and amphibians, the pigment cells are found predominantly in the connective tissue—in that of the skin, but also in the peritoneum, in the walls of blood vessels and elsewhere. In the birds and mammals, the pigment is found predominantly in the epithelial derivatives—the hairs and the feathers. Nevertheless, the production of the pigment is also due to the activity of the neural crest cells. The latter penetrate into the hair and feather follicles and deposit the pigment granules in the hairs and the feathers as they grow out of the follicles. If the access of the neural crest cells to the hair and feather follicles is precluded, the hairs and feathers may develop normally, but they are completely devoid of pigment (Rawles, 1947). For further information on the role of neural crest cells in the pigmentation of feathers in birds, see also Willier (1952).

Besides the pigment cells, other types of cells are also differentiated from the neural crest cells.

The visceral skeleton is almost completely developed from neural crest cells. The visceral arches occupy approximately the same position as the streams of neural crest cells in the early embryo. The mass of neural crest cells behind the eye, that is, between the eye and the first branchial pouch, becomes the mandibular arch, the upper part of which becomes differentiated as the **quadrate**, and the lower part gives rise to the **Meckel's cartilage** or mandible proper (Fig. 294). The mass of neural crest cells between the first and second branchial pouches becomes the hyoid arch, the next becomes the first branchial arch, and so forth. The mass of neural crest cells moving downward in front of the eye contributes to the formation of the anterior half of the trabeculae of the skull (Stone, 1926; Raven, 1931; Hörstadius and Sellman, 1946). The neural crest cells of the trunk region, on the other hand, do not participate in the development of skeletal tissues (Raven, 1936), both the axial skeleton (vertebral column) and the limb skeleton being derived from the mesoderm. Rather peculiarly, one element of the visceral skeleton in the amphibians, the second basibranchial, is also of mesodermal origin.

The papillae of the teeth in urodele amphibians have been shown to be derived from neural crest cells (de Beer, 1947). It is highly probable that the papillae of the teeth in all other vertebrates are of the same origin.

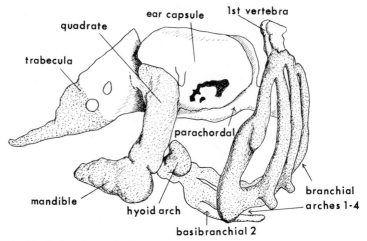

Figure 294. Skull of a salamander larva, indicating parts developing from neural crest material (stippled) and from mesoderm (white). (From Stone, 1926.)

The role played by the neural crest cells in the development of the peripheral nervous system has been a matter of controversy. At present it is accepted that the spinal ganglia and the ganglia of the autonomic nervous system are built up by the neural crest cells (see pp. 351–372), but that the ganglia of the cranial nerves (V, VII, IX, X) are developed only in part from neural crest, the other part being contributed by the dorsolateral or epi-branchial placodes (see pp. 365–368). In addition to the ganglion cells, the neural crest contributes to the development of the nervous system by supplying material for the sheaths of the nerves (Schwann cells) and the meninges (at least the pia mater and arachnoidea) (Piatt, 1951). Lastly, the neural crest cells are found to differentiate as subcutaneous connective tissue, although here they are joined by mesenchyme cells derived from the mesoderm.

As the neural crest cells may take such divergent paths of differentiation, the question arises whether the fate of individual crest cells is determined by environmental influences or whether these cells already differ at the time when they leave the neural folds. Apparently both the above alternatives are partially true. If different parts of the neural fold are explanted in a culture medium (Niu, 1947) or transplanted to the side of an embryo (Hörstadius and Sellman, 1946; see also Hörstadius, 1950), different results are obtained depending on the area from which the neural fold has been taken. Pieces of cranial neural folds under these conditions produce only small numbers of melanophores but they give rise to cells which may develop into cartilage. Neural folds of the trunk region, when explanted or transplanted, give rise to very numerous melanophores, but no pro-cartilage cells are given off. On the other hand, it has been shown that cartilages develop from neural crest cells only when they are induced to do so by adjoining tissues. Pieces of cranial neural crest were cultivated in an epithelial vesicle either alone or together with other tissues such as neural plate, notochord, foregut endoderm, midgut endoderm and lateral mesoderm. Under these conditions, cartilage developed from neural crest cells only when they were cultivated together with foregut endoderm. Trunk neural crest under the same condition produced only melanophores and mesenchyme and no cartilage (E. W. Okada, 1955). It follows that:

(1) Only cranial neural crest is competent to produce cartilage.
(2) It can do so only under the influence of foregut endoderm (see also section 15–3).

There is some evidence (Stevens, 1954) that among the pigment cells in amphibians the two types, that is, melanophores and guanophores, are already distinct while the cells are migrating from the site of their origin — the neural folds.

13–4 THE FATE OF THE EPIDERMIS AND THE STRUCTURES DERIVED THEREFROM

When the epidermis is first segregated from other parts of the ectoderm (neural plate, neural crest) during the process of neurulation, it is still a very complex rudiment. Most of it becomes the epidermis of the skin, but a number of other structures besides are derived from it. Some of these have been mentioned already: the lens, the cornea and the cranial ganglia.

The epidermis itself gives rise to quite a large number of special differentiations, such as various unicellular and multicellular skin glands, including the sweat glands and the sebaceous glands, the hairs, feathers and scales and various other special structures derived from the above. The development of some of these parts falls under histogenesis rather than organogenesis and will not be dealt with here.

In the early embryo the epidermis is a sheath of epithelium. In frogs the epithelium consists of two layers of cells: the outer **covering layer** or **periderm** and the inner so-called **sensory layer**. The latter name is given not because the layer as such has nervous functions but because some sensory organs are derived from parts of this layer. In birds and mammals, the epidermis of early embryos consists originally of one layer of cells, i.e., is one cell thick. Only at a later stage do an inner and outer layer of cells become differentiated, the inner layer becoming the **generative** (or **Malpighian**) **layer** of the epidermis. The skin is then composed of the epidermis and the layer of mesenchyme partly derived from the neural crest and partly from the dermatomes (see p. 396) which gives rise to the **dermis**.

The Placodes. Many structures derived from the epidermis make their first appearance in the form of plate-shaped thickenings of the epidermal epithelium. Such thickenings have been called **placodes**. That the ganglia of the cranial nerves are derived in part from placodes has been stated. When the lens rudiment first appears as a thickening of the epidermis, it bears a great similarity to the other placodes. A pair of placodes, appearing in front of the anterior end of the neural plate and probably deriving their material from the neural fold itself, develops into the olfactory sacs. A placode appearing against the side of the hindbrain invaginates and produces a vesicle which is eventually separated from the epidermis. This is the ear vesicle, the rudiment of the internal ear (the ear labyrinth). The placode from which the ear vesicle is developed is the **auditory placode**. Parts of the epidermis adjoining

Figure 295. Migration of cells of the lateral line rudiment, demonstrated by uniting the anterior half of an embryo of *Rana sylvatica* and the posterior half of an embryo of *Rana palustris*. (After Harrison, from Weiss, 1939.)

the auditory placode also become thickened, and from these placodes develop the **lateral line sense organs**. In the aquatic vertebrates (fishes, aquatic larvae of amphibians), the lateral line organs are distributed over the head (in several rows), and a row of the same organs stretches backward along the side of the entire body and tail. Wherever the lateral line organs are found, the cells of which they consist come from the placodes of the ear region.

In amphibians, the backward migration of the lateral line organ cells could be demonstrated in a grafting experiment. Two embryos belonging to different species of frogs were cut transversely in halves, and the anterior half of a darkly pigmented species (*Rana sylvatica*) was grafted on the posterior half of a lightly pigmented species (*Rana palustris*). It could be subsequently observed how the darkly pigmented cells of the lateral line rudiment of the anterior half migrated out into the posterior half and along the trunk and tail (Fig. 295; Harrison, 1904).

In the case of lateral line sense organs, the pathway of the migrating cells is dependent on the surroundings through which they migrate. If the anterior half of a frog embryo is transplanted onto another embryo whose own lateral line organ rudiment had been removed previously, the lateral line cells of the anterior half grow out into the second embryo, and once they have reached the path taken normally by the lateral line cells in their migration, they start moving along this path, even though their new direction is at an angle to the one they had been following before (Fig. 296). This shows that the path of migration is determined by a factor lying outside the migrating cells themselves (Harrison, 1904). It has been shown that the path of migration in this case is determined by the mesoderm.

Figure 296. Migration of cells of the lateral line rudiment in an experiment in which the anterior part of a *Rana palustris* embryo was grafted on to the back of a *Rana pipiens* embryo. (After Harrison, from Huxley and de Beer, 1934.)

The development of the placodes is probably always dependent on a stimulus from the tissues situated under the epidermis. This has been proved in some cases, as in the case of the lens of the eye. The ear is also dependent in its differentiation; this follows from the experiments in which the ear vesicles have been induced heterotopically as the result of the transplantation of various inductors. The ear vesicle is among the structures that are very often induced when the primary organizer is transplanted but also can be induced in experiments with transplantation of adult tissues and of parts of the neural plate and neural tube (Guareschi, 1935; Gorbunova, 1939; Kogan, 1939). The latter experiments suggest that in normal development the ear vesicle is induced by the medulla oblongata. This, however, cannot be the sole inductor, as the ear vesicles may develop in their normal position after the medulla oblongata is removed at an early stage, either alone or together with most of the central nervous system rudiment. It is concluded, therefore, that the development of the ear vesicle is dependent on multiple induction, that similar stimuli are emitted both from the medulla oblongata and from the mesoderm developing from the roof of the archenteron (Harrison, 1935; Albaum and Nestler, 1937).

It is probable that the induction of the ear vesicle proceeds in two stages: first the presumptive ear ectoderm is acted upon by the underlying mesodermal mantle in the late gastrula and early neurula stages, and later the determination is finally stabilized by the influence of the medulla which, as the result of the closure of neural folds, comes into close contact with the epidermis in the ear region (Yntema, 1950). We have seen a similar case in the "independent" development of the lens in some species of frogs (p. 379).

A similar duplication in the sources of induction has been postulated for the nose rudiment, namely, an earlier induction by mesoderm and a later induction by the forebrain. It has been claimed, for instance, that the anterior portion of the neural plate if transplanted under the epidermis on the flank may induce a nose rudiment locally. In more careful experiments it was found, however (Zwilling, 1940; Schmalhausen, 1950), that nose rudiments may develop in the absence of brain tissues, and so the alleged inductions must be due to the nose rudiment material being grafted together with the presumptive forebrain. The two rudiments are thus induced simultaneously by the underlying roof of the archenteron and initially lie very close to one another.

The Olfactory Organ.   Although the nose rudiments seem to be determined at a very early stage (late gastrula) they first become discernible morphologically after the closure of the neural tube, in the form of two thickenings of the epidermis, the **olfactory placodes**, just anterolaterally to the hemispheres of the telencephalon (Figs. 217, 248). The central part of each placode becomes invaginated, and the olfactory placode thus becomes converted into an olfactory sac which is open to the exterior by the external naris. Parts of the wall of the olfactory sac, especially the dorsal and lateral wall, are differentiated as olfactory epithelium. The primary sensory cells of the olfactory epithelium develop on their proximal ends nerve processes (axons) which converge to form the olfactory nerve. The olfactory nerve grows into the adjacent wall of the telencephalon, bridging the narrow gap between the olfactory organ and the brain.

In most fishes the olfactory organ retains essentially the same structure in the adult state, but in the group of Choanichthyes among the fishes and in the terrestrial vertebrates the structure of the olfactory organ is further complicated by the internal nares, and in the mammals also by the naso-lacrimal duct.

The internal nares or **choanae** arise by a perforation of the nose sac cavity into the oral cavity. The actual perforation is preceded by the formation from a part of the ventral wall of the nose sac of an elongated tube stretching backward and down toward the oral cavity. This tube is the nasal canal, in which the epithelium lining the canal becomes thin and is thus fairly sharply segregated from the thicker epithelium giving rise to the sensory parts (Fig. 225). With the elongation of the nasal canal the sensory part appears to be a dorsolateral growth of this canal, although the sensory part is actually the older portion of the olfactory organ. The internal (posterior) end of the nasal canal fuses eventually with the epithelium lining the oral cavity, and the intervening membrane becomes perforated as internal nares. The **Jacobson's organ**, where it is present, is another section of the olfactory sac retaining sensory function. It develops from a medioventral part of the sac.

The development of the naso-lacrimal duct will be discussed together with the development of the face (in section 15–2).

The Ear. The **auditory placode**, from which the internal ear is developed, initially shows considerable similarity to the olfactory placode, and is also converted by invagination into a saclike structure (Fig. 297), but in the early stages there already are important differences. Whereas in the amniotes

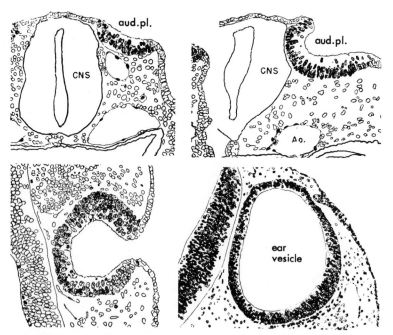

Figure 297. Four stages in the development of the inner ear from auditory placode—*aud. pl.*—to completed ear vesicle in a human embryo. *CNS*, Central nervous system; *Ao.*, dorsal aorta. (From Streeter, 1942, 1945.)

the whole epidermal layer is involved in the formation of the auditory placode, and it later invaginates to form a sac which is, at least temporarily, open to the exterior, in the frogs the auditory placode is formed by the thickening of the interior "sensory" layer of the epidermis, while the external, covering layer is not involved at all (Fig. 219). As a result, when the placode invaginates, there is no opening or pit on the surface of the skin. In both cases, however, the opening of the sac becomes constricted and closed, so that eventually the rudiment of the ear takes the form of a completely closed vesicle — the **ear vesicle**. In the bony fishes the auditory organ is formed not by invagination but as a solid mass of cells on the inner surface of the epidermis, and is hollowed out secondarily.

The ear vesicle is the rudiment of the most essential part of the internal ear — the **labyrinth**. When first formed, it is somewhat pear-shaped, the pointed end directed upward. This pointed end later gives rise to the endolymphatic duct. Soon the ear vesicle starts expanding, pushing away the surrounding loose mesenchyme. Parts of the wall of the vesicle become very thin; the epithelial cells become flat. These will be the membranous areas of the labyrinth. Other parts, in particular parts of the medioventral wall of the vesicle, remain thick or even become thicker; the cells in these areas become columnar and give rise to patches of sensory epithelium which form the maculae of the internal ear. Even before it is subdivided into membranous and sensory parts, the ear vesicle gives off on its median surface a group of cells which become the acoustic ganglion (ganglion of nerve VIII). (See Campenhout, 1935.)

The expansion of the ear vesicle is unequal so that the vesicle becomes constricted in some places and bulges out in others. As a result, the shape of the organ becomes increasingly complicated so that it eventually deserves its name — the labyrinth (Fig. 298). The sacculus is subdivided by a constriction from the utriculus. The utriculus becomes drawn into three mutually perpendicular folds, the rudiments of the semicircular canals. The sides of the folds eventually stick together and become perforated while parts of the original cavity along the edges of the folds remain open and become the semicircular canals, opening at both ends into the cavity of the utriculus. A hollow outgrowth of the sacculus forms the rudiment of the lagena in lower vertebrates, and in higher vertebrates this outgrowth becomes very elongated and coiled to give rise to the cochlea. As the ear vesicle changes its shape and produces the various parts of the labyrinth, the sensory areas become subdivided and further differentiated until each of the maculae have taken up their final position in the fully developed labyrinth.

As the ear vesicle expands to produce the labyrinth, it becomes surrounded by mesenchyme cells which later give rise to cartilage and produce the cartilaginous ear capsule which surrounds and protects the inner ear. There is a direct causal relationship between the ear vesicle and the development of the ear capsule: if the ear vesicle is removed, the ear capsule does not develop; if a foreign ear vesicle is transplanted in the tailbud stage, the local mesenchyme cells may aggregate around it and produce an additional cartilaginous capsule (Lewis, 1907). The mesenchyme that is used for the ear capsule is of mesodermal origin, derived from the sclerotomes (see section 14–1). Mesenchyme of neural crest origin, as well as subcutaneous

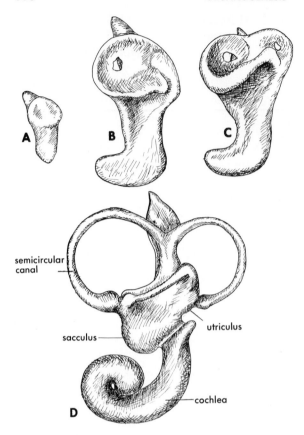

Figure 298. Development of the labyrinth from the ear vesicle in a human embryo. The drawings show lateral views of the left ear. (Modified from Streeter, 1906.)

mesenchyme, is apparently not capable of reacting to the induction by the ear vesicle. As a result, an ear vesicle transplanted heterotopically does not always cause a good capsule to be developed around it. The most complete capsules develop around ear vesicles transplanted to the immediate vicinity of the normal ear, between the ear and the eye, where the grafted vesicle can draw on the same supply of mesenchyme as the normal ear vesicle. However, the sclerotome mesenchyme of the trunk—that is, the mesenchyme giving rise to the cartilages of the vertebrate column and the ribs—reacts to the ear vesicle by forming large masses of cartilage, which may partially surround the grafted ear vesicle (Balinsky, 1925; Syngajewskaja, 1937).

The concentration of mesenchyme on the surface of the ear vesicle may be partly the result of its expansion, which would lead to the mesenchyme being compressed against its surface. However, there is no doubt that mesenchyme cells may travel considerable distances to reach the ear vesicle and to invest it with cartilage. In experiments of transplantation of the ear vesicle to the trunk region it can be seen that thick bars of cartilage grow out from the vertebral column to the ear vesicle, presumably indicating the pathway which had been followed by the mesenchyme. In the same experiments it can also be seen that the total amount of cartilage in the area is greatly increased, so that the ear vesicle must either stimulate the proliferation of skeletogenic mesenchyme or increase the proportion of mesenchyme cells which become chondroblasts. The reverse occurs in the case of the removal of the ear vesicle: not only does the ear capsule not develop, but there is no superfluous cartilage in the area; in the absence of the ear vesicle the proliferation of the pro-cartilage cells is short of the normal, or else the cells that should have become cartilage cells differentiate along other paths.

The development of the ear gives us another example of a chain of inductions. The primary inductor—the roof of the archenteron, consisting of presumptive chordo-mesoderm—causes the development of the hindbrain. This as a secondary inductor stimulates the development of the ear vesicle (in conjunction with the direct action of the mesoderm on the presumptive ear ectoderm). The ear vesicle, as a tertiary inductor, causes the formation of the cartilaginous capsule.

One might have expected that the development of the middle ear would be related to the development of the inner ear, but this is not the case. The middle ear, consisting of the eustachian tube, the ear ossicles (columella in the frog) in the cavity, and the tympanic membrane, develops normally after the removal of the ear vesicle. This may be because the middle ear is derived from the branchial apparatus, which is a very essential part of the vertebrate organization, deeply rooted in the basic mechanism of vertebrate development and thus not in need of stimulation from the inner ear. In this case the functional apparatus—the organ of hearing—is made up of two parts not causally connected in development but linked together only through the medium of their definitive functioning (see Yntema in Willier, Weiss and Hamburger, 1955).

Besides the organs developing from placodes, a number of structures are developed from the epidermis which in their early stages can be classed as "outgrowths" or, more correctly, as protrusions. These are: the unpaired fin fold, the external gills (in aquatic vertebrates), the "balancer" (in the larvae of salamanders) and the paired limbs.

The Fin Fold.   The unpaired fin fold is a structure found in all fishes and in the larvae of amphibians. It is a vertical fold of skin which starts in the posterior head region or the anterior trunk region and stretches backward all along the back and dorsal side of the tail, bends over to the ventral side of the tail and can be traced forward, along the ventral side of the tail and the belly to the middle of the trunk. The fold consists of epithelium and connective tissue. In fishes, parts of the fold are invaded later by skeletogenous tissue which produces fin rays, thus transforming these parts into the unpaired fins of the adult (Fig. 299). Parts of the larval fin fold in between the unpaired fins of the adult disappear. In amphibians which metamorphose into terrestrial

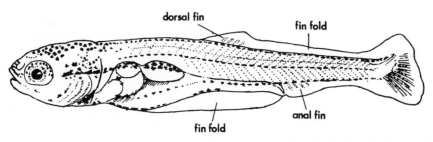

Figure 299.   Development of the unpaired fins from parts of the fin fold in a fish larva. (From Balinsky: Proc. Zool. Soc. London, *118*, 1948.)

adults (all Anura and some of the Urodela), the fin fold disappears at meta-morphosis, but it may persist in neotenic species or in some purely aquatic salamanders (*Cryptobranchus*).

The fin fold first appears as a longitudinal thickening of the epidermis, seen as a ridge on external inspection. The thickening increases by shifting upward and toward the midline of the adjacent strips of the epidermis. The cells moving in from the right and left flanks remain separated as two layers of epithelium, except at the crest of the ridge. There is, however, no hollow in between the two layers. The fold is hollowed out a bit later by the two epithelial layers separating in the middle, and then connective tissue cells of neural crest origin penetrate into the fold.

Although the neural crest cells enter into the formation of the fin fold in a later stage, they are actually responsible for the determination of the whole structure. If the neural crest cells are removed shortly after their formation, or the neural folds, from which they arise, are cut away, the fin fold is not developed in the region of the defect (Fig. 300, *A, B*). If a piece of the neural fold, or a mass of the neural crest cells, is transplanted under the epidermis in any part of the body, a fin fold develops at the site of the transplantation (Fig. 300, *C, D*) (Terni, 1934; Du Shane, 1935). The ability to induce the development of the fin fold is found in the trunk neural crest cells only. The neural crest cells of the head cannot induce a fin fold, although the epidermis of the head region is fully competent to react by developing a fin fold, if it is exposed to the action of the necessary inductor. The extent to which the fin fold reaches anteriorly is thus dependent on the extent to which the neural crest possesses the ability to induce the fold (Terentiev, 1941).

The External Gills.   The external gills are protrusions of epidermis, with connective tissue, blood vessels and muscle inside. They develop as outwardly directed pockets above the gill clefts and are found in some fishes (*Polypterus*, the lungfishes, *Misgurnus*) and in amphibian larvae. The original

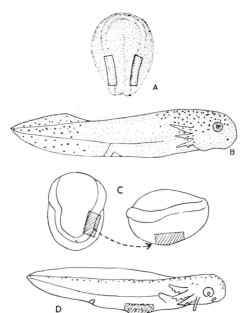

Figure 300. Experiments showing dependence of the fin fold on the neural crest in salamander embryos. *A*, The neural folds removed on both sides in the neurula stage; *B*, result: no fin fold and no melanophores in the region of the operation. *C*, Transplantation of the neural fold onto the side of another embryo in the neurula stage (graft shaded); *D*, result: fin fold developed on the side. (*A* and *B* from Du Shane, 1935.)

Figure 301. Development of the forelimbs, gills and balancer in *Ambystoma punctatum.* The stages are shown after Harrison's normal table. (After Harrison, from Mangold, 1929.)

outpushing forms the shaft of the external gill; on this shaft develop secondary branches, which are formed at first as solid, outwardly directed thickenings of the epidermis of the shaft and are subsequently hollowed out (Fig. 301). Sometimes the shaft is so short that the gill appears to be a bunch of filaments which may branch in their own turn.

The pattern manifested in the development of the gills has been found in the Urodela to be dependent not on the epidermis but on the inner layers of the embryo. The epidermis of the gill region may be lifted and replaced again after it has been rotated 90 or 180 degrees. If such an operation is carried out before the gill development begins, the external gills will appear in their normal position just as if nothing had happened (Harrison, 1921a). A piece of epidermis taken from the flank may be transplanted over the gill region to replace the local epidermis, and if the transplantation is carried out early enough (soon after the closure of the neural folds) the normal development of the external gills is not impeded. The mesoderm of the gill region (in the first type of experiment) may be included in the graft which is implanted in inverse orientation, and the gills will still develop in their normal position, although the development may not go as smoothly as when only the epidermis is involved. If, however, the endoderm of the gill region is rotated together with the other germ layers, the developing gills are dependent on the new orientation of the graft, even if it is disharmonious with the other parts of the embryo (Fig. 302). It is therefore the endoderm that determines the position of the developing external gills (Severinghaus, 1930).

The part played by the endoderm in the development of the external gills may also be tested by completely removing the endoderm of the gill region, leaving the two other layers intact. The result is that the external gills do not develop at all (Mangold, 1936).

The Balancers and Adhesive Organs.   The **balancers** are tentaclelike organs present in the larvae of many species of urodele amphibians (newts and salamanders). The organ is situated, one on each side, just behind the angle of the mouth underneath the eye. It is a slightly curved cylindrical process, consisting of epithelium and a connective tissue core. The connective tissue is especially dense just underneath the epithelium, where it forms a cylindrical supporting membrane. Proximally this membrane is attached to the quadrate. The epithelium on the tip of the balancer produces a mucous secretion and is therefore slightly adhesive. A newly hatched larva of a newt or salamander uses the balancers for support, when resting on the ground, and to prevent the body from falling on one side in the stages when the forelimbs are not yet developed (Fig. 301, *F, G*). When the forelimbs become functional they take over the support of the body, and the balancers gradually degenerate (Fig. 301, *H*; see Harrison, 1925a).

The balancers would not deserve our attention, if it were not that these simple organs lend themselves to some experiments of considerable interest. The epidermis of the balancer is normally derived from a part of the ectoderm lying just outside the neural fold in the vicinity of the eye rudiment. Other parts of the ectoderm, however, possess ability to develop into a balancer when stimulated by an inductor. Balancers have often been induced in experiments on the "primary organizer" and on the inducing ability of the archenteron roof. The development of balancers is an indication that the

Figure 302.   Transplantation of the gill rudiment in the salamander. *a*, Stage of operation and area which was excised for transplantation. *b, c*, Gills in abnormal positions developed from grafts rotated 180 degrees during operation. (From Severinghaus, 1930.)

inductor possesses the regional specificity of an archencephalic inductor (see section 10–5).

The part of the organizer actually responsible for the induction of the balancer in normal development is probably the archenteron roof, but the adjacent portion of the neural plate, once it has been determined, also possesses the ability to induce a balancer (Mangold, 1931a). Further experiments on the development of balancers are described in section 16–3.

The larvae of anurans do not possess balancers, but tadpoles of frogs and toads develop a different organ with somewhat similar biological functions. This is the **adhesive organ**, also known as the **oral sucker**. As a matter of fact, the adhesion which is effected by the organ is not due to a sucking action but to the secretion of a sticky slime. The adhesive organ is a glandular structure consisting of very elongated columnar cells which produce a copious secretion of mucoprotein (see Eakin, 1963). The swimming powers of a newly hatched tadpole are very limited, and after swimming for a few seconds the tadpoles tend to become attached either to some submerged objects (to the glass in an aquarium) or even to the surface film of the water. The sticky secretion of the adhesive organ keeps them suspended; otherwise they would be lying most of the time on the bottom, where the oxygen supply may be considerably depleted.

When fully developed, the adhesive organs vary from one species to another (see Figs. 215, 219). Most often they are in the form of a V-shaped furrow with thickened edges (especially in toad tadpoles), but in some species of frogs they have the shape of two conical projections or even have the form of one unpaired conical outgrowth (in *Xenopus*).

It is interesting to note that the adhesive organs are the first part of the body of a frog embryo to become functionally differentiated (see section 16–1). The differentiation of the organs begins in some toad species immediately after neurulation, and they start secreting before the tadpole can swim. This is advantageous for the animal because, after hatching, the tadpoles for some time remain hanging on the outer surface of their egg membranes. At this stage the tadpoles possess a limited power of locomotion owing to the ciliary action of their epidermis.

As the tadpole develops and its swimming ability improves, the adhesive organs cease secreting and degenerate.

The Paired Limbs.   The early rudiments of paired limbs are similar to the gill rudiments in so far as they are outpushings of the epidermis which are filled with a mass of mesenchyme cells. In the case of the limbs, however, it is the differentiation of the mesenchyme into parts of the skeleton and muscle of the limb that deserves the greatest attention; the limbs will therefore be dealt with in conjunction with the organs derived from the mesoderm.

There is still one more structure of great importance which is derived from the epidermis; it is the mouth invagination (the stomodeum). Its formation and further development can be most convieniently dealt with together with the other parts of the alimentary canal, which are derived from the endoderm.

14

Development of the Mesodermal Organs in Vertebrates

14—1 THE FATE OF THE SOMITES AND THE ORIGIN OF THE SOMATIC MUSCLES

The somites, when first formed, are masses of mesodermal cells with a small cavity in the middle. The cells are arranged radially around the central cavity. With further development, the shape of the somites changes; they become extended in the dorsoventral direction and flattened mediolaterally. In the vertebrates with discoidal cleavage, this leads to the elevation of the dorsal parts of the embryo above the general level of the blastodisc.

The flattening of the somite is accompanied by a change in the shape of its central cavity (the myocoele); instead of being spherical, the cavity becomes a narrow vertical slit. An inner wall and an outer wall become clearly distinguishable, corresponding to the parietal and visceral layers of the lateral plates. The inner wall of the somites becomes very much thicker than the outer wall.

The fate of the inner and the outer wall of the somites is completely different. The outer wall contributes to the formation of the connective tissue layer of the skin, and is therefore called the **dermatome**. The inner wall produces skeletogenous tissue and the voluntary striated muscles of the body. The skeletogenous tissue develops from the lower edge of the inner wall of the somite, and this part of the somite is therefore called the **sclerotome** (Fig. 303). The sclerotome breaks up into a mass of mesenchyme cells. The cells migrate into the spaces surrounding the notochord and the spinal cord, envelop these organs and later differentiate into cartilage, thus forming the

Figure 303. Differentiation of the somite in a chick embryo.

bodies and the neural arches of the vertebrae. The hemal arches in the tail region and the ribs are of the same origin.

The dorsal part of the inner wall of the somite is the source of somatic muscle in the vertebrate's body. It is therefore called the **myotome**. The cells of the myotome rearrange themselves so that they become elongated in a longitudinal direction. These longitudinally elongated cells differentiate subsequently into the striated muscle fibers. Originally each myotome becomes a muscle segment, separated from the one anterior and the one posterior to it by a connective tissue layer, the vertical myocomma. At one time in its development the whole somatic musculature of the vertebrate consists of such segments arranged in linear order.

In the lower vertebrates, the myotome is the largest part of the somite, the sclerotomes being small and rather inconspicuous. In the Amniota, however, the sclerotomes are much larger. Only the upper edge of the inner wall of the somite adjoining the dermatome becomes the myotome. The size of this part increases rapidly; the myotomes grow downward to assume the same position, lateral to the neural tube and the notochord, that they occupy in the amphibians right from the start.

Developing as they do from the somites, the myotomes are originally dorsal in position. In the course of the subsequent development, the muscle segments spread downward in the space between the skin on the outside and the somatic layer of the lateral plate on the inside, until the muscle segments on the right and the left side meet ventrally. It is in this stage, with minor alterations, that the somatic muscles persist in the fishes and in the aquatic larvae of amphibians. The segmentation of the lateral and ventral muscles, as well as of the dorsal muscles, is directly derived from the segmentation of the mesodermal mantle in somites.

In terrestrial vertebrates, the primitive segmentation of the somatic muscles is more or less obliterated in connection with a change of locomotion. The segmented lateral bands of muscle are adapted to locomotion by lateral inflections of the body and the tail. The locomotion by means of two pairs of legs requires a completely different organization of the muscle system; as a consequence, only traces of the original muscle segmentation can be discovered in the terrestrial vertebrates.

In *Amphioxus,* muscle segments continue anteriorly almost to the tip of the snout. With the development of the brain and the skull, in vertebrates, the head region is exempted from the process of propelling the body by lateral inflections. The somatic muscles become superfluous in the head region. Nevertheless, mesodermal somites are formed in the head region of the embryo. The muscle segments derived from the somites lying posterior to the ear (the postotic somites) may persist and be linked up with the muscle segments of the neck region. The somites lying anterior to the ear vesicle are always very transitory structures: A part of the cells of these somites, however, differentiates as somatic muscle. The muscles derived from this source do not serve for locomotion but are the six pairs of oculomotor muscles: the four rectus muscles and the two oblique muscles on each side (see Fig. 281, *a, b*).

14−2   THE AXIAL SKELETON: VERTEBRAL COLUMN AND SKULL

In most vertebrates, the axial skeleton passes through three phases in its development. In the first phase, the supporting system of the body is represented by the notochord. In the second phase, cartilage develops partly in direct connection with the notochord, partly independently of the latter. This condition is preserved in the adult state of contemporary cyclostomes and elasmobranch fishes (we are not concerned with the question of whether this condition is primitive or secondary). In the remainder of the fishes and in tetrapods, the cartilaginous skeleton is later replaced or supplemented by the bony skeleton. The bony skeleton and its relationship to the cartilaginous skeleton are amply dealt with in courses on comparative anatomy of vertebrates and may, therefore, be entirely left out of consideration. We will consider here only the following aspects in the development of the skeleton:

1. The origin of cells giving rise to the cartilaginous skeleton.
2. The arrangement of the parts of the early cartilaginous skeleton in relation to the other organ rudiments of the embryo.
3. The dependence of the formation of the skeletal parts on the adjoining structures.

The material for the cartilaginous axial skeleton in the body and tail of vertebrates is derived, as was mentioned on page 396, from the sclerotomes. The sclerotomes, being parts of the somites, are segmental in origin, but once they become transformed into mesenchyme the segmental arrangement is largely lost, and the mesenchyme spreads out as a continuous sheath along the notochord, enveloping the spinal cord above and the caudal artery and vein below the notochord in the caudal region. In this continuous mesenchymal sheath, nodules of cartilage, known as the **arcualia**, appear later in close apposition to the external surface of the notochord. Typically the arcualia appear in double pairs; one pair is formed dorsolaterally to the notochord and another pair ventrolaterally. The dorsolateral arcualia grow out dorsally alongside the spinal cord and unite above the spinal cord to form the **neural arch**. The ventrolateral cartilages in the caudal region grow downward and unite underneath the caudal vein to form the **hemal arch**. In the cervial and thoracic region they give rise to lateral outgrowths — the rudiments of the ribs. At the same time the proximal parts of all four cartilages spread out around the surface of the notochord, contributing in varying degrees to the formation of the body of the vertebra (Fig. 304).

The cartilaginous neural and hemal arches do not bear a simple relationship to the somites (or sclerotomes); in many groups of vertebrates there are two series of cartilages (two pairs of dorsal elements and two pairs of ventral elements) developed in each mesodermal segment (*cf.* in elasmobranchs, in part also in amniotes). In other cases, although there is only one set of cartilages formed, these are situated intersegmentally at the junction of two myotomes (the myotomes retain the original segmentation of the somites). The way in which the original cartilage rudiments cooperate in the formation of the definitive vertebrae will not concern us here.

The fact that the cartilaginous (and later bony) vertebral column replaces the notochord functionally suggests that the location and the arrangement of the vertebral cartilages should be dependent on the notochord. In the absence of the notochord, the cartilaginous axial skeleton is very irregular (see Fig. 211). Cartilage, however, is not completely absent in those sections of the body which do not have the notochord. The notochord is thus not indispensable for the formation of axial cartilages. The irregularity of the latter could be a secondary effect of the extirpation of the notochord, seeing that other systems, such as the spinal cord and segmented muscles, are greatly distorted as a result of the failure of the embryo to stretch normally.

In some experiments (Holtzer and Detwiler, 1953) in which the spinal cord instead of the notochord was removed from salamander embryos, it was found that the axial cartilages were either completely absent or reduced to insignificant vestiges. This could not be the result of damage to the sclerotomes, since in other experiments very extensive defects of the somites,

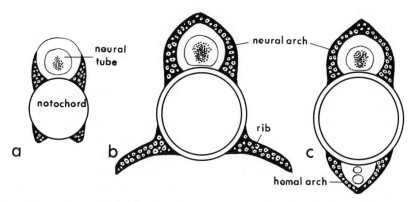

Figure 304. Diagram of the dorsal and ventral pairs of arcualia (*a*) giving rise to the neural arch and the ribs in the trunk (*b*) and to the neural arch and the hemal arch in the tail (*c*).

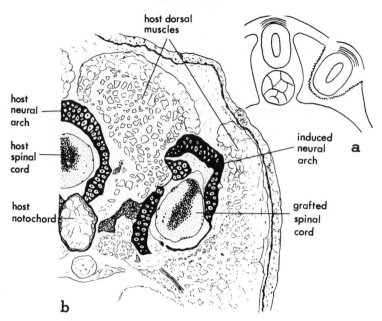

host dorsal
muscles

host
neural
arch

host
spinal
cord

host
notochord

induced
neural
arch

a

grafted
spinal
cord

b

Figure 305. Transplantation of a section of spinal cord into the dorsolateral mesoderm of a salamander embryo. *a*, Diagram of operation; *b*, result: the graft surrounded by an induced vertebra. (From Holtzer and Detwiler, 1953.)

including the sclerotomal region, were completely restored at the expense of the remaining fragments of the somites. The results of extirpation experiments were corroborated by the transplantation of pieces of spinal cord into an incision on the lateral surface of the somites of another embryo (Fig. 305, *a*). It was found that complete and well-developed neural arches were formed in association with the grafted spinal cord (Fig. 305, *b*).

The segmentation of the neural arches has not so far been considered. In normal development there is a definite relationship between the segmentation of the longitudinal dorsolateral muscles, the segmentation of the spinal nerves and ganglia, and the segmentation of the vertebral skeletal elements, in particular that of the neural arches. There is a pair of spinal nerves with spinal ganglia corresponding to each muscle segment, the ganglia being situated opposite the median surface of the muscle segment. The neural arches alternate with the spinal ganglia and are thus situated intersegmentally with respect to the myotomes, so that each neural arch (and subsequently each vertebra) is connected to two consecutive muscle segments. The blood vessels also bear a relationship to this common pattern: an intersegmental artery arising from the dorsal aorta along each myocomma, close to the vertebral column (Fig. 306).

Experimental evidence is available to show that this whole system of metamerically arranged parts is originally dependent on the segmentation of the muscle rudiments (Detwiler, 1934). In a salamander embryo at the tailbud stage, the anterior somites are somewhat broader than the posterior ones, so that if a block of several somites in the brachial region is removed and replaced by a block of somites from the posterior trunk region, more somites may be fitted into the wound than had been cut out. Thus somites

Figure 306. The relation between the muscle segments *(m)*, the spinal ganglia *(spg)*, the intersegmental arteries *(is)* and the vertebrae in a larva of *Ambystoma*. *bc*, Bony cylinder of centrum of vertebra; *da*, dorsal aorta; *nar*, neural arch; *nt*, notochord. (From Goodrich, 1930.)

7 to 12 could be substituted for somites 3 to 5 (Fig. 307). As a result, the number of muscle segments on the operated side was increased in comparison with the normal. It was found that the number of spinal nerves and spinal ganglia was increased also, but not necessarily in strict correspondence to the number of muscle segments, one nerve sometimes supplying more than one muscle segment. On the other hand, the number of neural arches was found to be strictly in accord with the number of spinal ganglia, a bar of cartilage always appearing between two adjacent ganglia (Fig. 308). Since the ganglia are formed earlier than the cartilages, there can be no doubt that the neural arches are dependent on the ganglia and not the other way around.

The whole chain of reactions would then appear to be as follows. The neural crest cells which are produced along the whole length of the neural tube become aggregated opposite the median surfaces of the somites (or myotomes), and these aggregations become the rudiments of the spinal ganglia. Next, the cells of the skeletogenic mesenchyme, produced by the sclerotomes, spread out over the notochord and neural tube, but they are apparently repulsed by the spinal ganglia and thus, instead of forming a continuous sheet of cartilage enclosing the spinal cord, they give rise to a series of disconnected elements (the dorsal arcualia) alternating in position with the spinal ganglia. This is obviously not the complete picture, as it does not account for the cases in which two pairs of cartilages appear between each consecutive pair of spinal ganglia. It is thus likely that some structures other than the spinal ganglia, the neural tube and the notochord take part in determining the position of early cartilaginous rudiments.

Figure 307. *Ambystoma punctatum* embryo with somites 7–12 (GR.S. 7–12) transplanted in place of somites 3–5. (After Detwiler, 1934.)

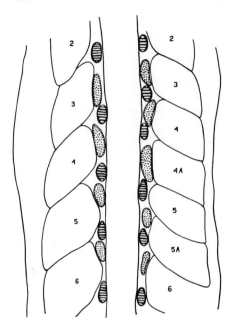

Figure 308. Result of increasing the number of somites (on right side). The number of spinal ganglia (shaded) and neural arches (stippled) increased, as compared with control side (left). (From Detwiler, 1934.)

The neural portion of the cranium in vertebrates in part bears the same relationship to the notochord and to the neural tube as does the axial skeleton in the posterior parts of the body. But there is little, if any, trace of a segmentation in the development of the cranium, and important parts of the cranium are quite peculiar in this respect.

In the lower vertebrates at the earliest stages of development, the cartilaginous cranium consists of several independent rudiments. These are: (1) The trabeculae; (2) the parachordals; (3) the capsules of the sense organs—the nose, the eye and the ear (Fig. 309).

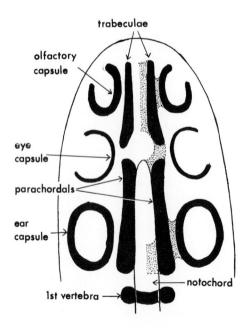

Figure 309. Diagram of the component elements of the vertebrate chondrocranium. Black areas represent cartilages in the initial stage. The fusions of the components are indicated by the stippling on the right side of the diagram.

The **trabeculae** (or **trabeculae cranii**) are a pair of elongated cartilages which appear in the most anterior part of the head, in front of the hypophysis. The trabeculae lie ventrally and ventrolaterally to the diencephalon and telencephalon, and their upper edges are wedged in between the brain on the inside and the rudiments of the nose and the eye on the outside. It has been established both by observation and experiment that the mesenchyme from which the trabeculae are developed comes from two different sources (*cf.* p. 383). The anterior part of the trabecula is formed of neural crest cells migrating forward and downward anterior to the eye cup. The posterior part of the trabecula is of mesodermal origin and is derived from the prechordal plate mesenchyme.

The **parachordals**, or parachordal cartilages, are derived from the mesenchyme produced by the sclerotomes of the somites in the head region. This mesenchyme spreads out on both sides of the notochord and eventually chondrifies in the form of two longitudinal rods, situated alongside the notochord and ending anteriorly at the same level as the notochord, that is, just posteriorly to the infundibulum and the rudiment of the hypophysis. The parachordals are very similar in origin and position to the rudiments of the cartilaginous vertebral column, but they lack the segmentation of the latter (possibly because the cranial ganglia, owing to the greater breadth of the neural tube in the head region, lie much farther laterally and away from the region in which development of the parachordals is taking place).

The cartilaginous **capsules of the sense organs** — the nose, the eye and the ear — develop from skeletogenic mesenchyme accumulating around the surface of the epithelial parts of these organs. The source of the mesenchyme may not be the same in all three cases. It is fairly certain that the ear capsule is formed by mesenchyme derived from the same sclerotomes as give rise to the parachordals. In fact, the ear capsules are formed in close proximity and even in continuity with the parachordals, and strands of mesenchyme have been observed leading from the rudiments of the parachordals to the site in which the cartilaginous ear capsules start to develop (Filatoff, 1916).

It has been claimed (O. Schmalhausen, 1939) that cartilage of the nose capsules is derived from the epithelial nose rudiment itself. It would seem that this statement needs further corroboration. On the other hand, we have seen that the nasal placodes develop in very close proximity to the anterior transverse neural fold. The neural fold being the source of neural crest cells, it would not be very astonishing if the neural folds could produce the nasal cartilages as well as the epithelial parts of the olfactory organ.

In most vertebrates, the eyeball is surrounded first by a connective tissue capsule, the sclera, which becomes cartilaginous in later stages. The source of the cells forming the sclera has not yet been established.

The capsules of all three sense organs are dependent in their development on the epithelial parts of the organs. This has been clearly shown in the case of the ear capsule (*cf.* section 13–4, The Ear) and is very probably true in the case of the olfactory capsule and the sclera of the eye, as these capsules fail to be formed if the epithelial parts of these organs are removed.

The parachordals, though spatially intimately associated with the notochord, show a high degree of independence from the latter organ. In experiments in which the notochord rudiment was removed (see p. 306), the development of the base of the skull does not seem to be affected to any extent. In particular, there is no foreshortening of the posterior part of the head, in sharp contrast to the shortening and stunting of the trunk and tail region in the absence of the notochord.

The further development of the cartilaginous skull (chondrocranium) is characterized by the enlargement and fusion of the initially formed cartilages. The right and left trabeculae fuse across the midline underneath the forebrain, and their posterior ends fuse with the tips of the parachordals. The parachordals envelop the notorchord, particularly its dorsal side, and so give rise to the **basal plate** of the skull. At the point where the infundibulum and the hypophysis are situated, the cartilages leave a ventral opening (the hypophyseal fenestra) which persists for a long time and is closed only much later by cartilage or bone on the ventral side. The posterior ends of the parachordals grow upward and eventually fuse above the medulla, thus enclosing the foramen magnum of the skull. The nose capsule and the otic (auditory) capsule become firmly joined to the trabeculae and the parachordals respectively, thus contributing to the formation of the lateral walls of the chrondrocranium. Gradually the lateral edges of the cartilaginous skull grow upward, and in the more primitive vertebrates (cyclostomes, many fishes and amphibians) form a roof over the dorsal surface of the brain. In teleost fishes and in all amniotes, however, the cartilaginous skull remains incomplete on the dorsal surface, and the cranial roof is formed by bone at a later stage. In higher vertebrates, mammals in particular, the initial stages in the development of the cartilaginous skull may be speeded up in such a way that the trabeculae and parachordals are fused right from the start—a condition which is achieved in lower vertebrates secondarily.

14—3 DEVELOPMENT OF THE PAIRED LIMBS

The paired limbs of vertebrates are very complex organs, built up of components derived from several different sources—from the lateral plate mesoderm, the epidermis and the somites, to name only the main components. Nerves and blood vessels are of course also indispensable components of differentiated limbs.

The first trace of the development of limbs may be found in the lateral plate mesoderm; the somatic layer of the lateral plate becomes thickened just underneath its upper edge. The cells of this thickening soon lose their epithelial connections and are transformed into a mass of mesenchyme without the somatic layer having lost its continuity. It is therefore a case of migration of mesenchyme cells from an epithelial layer, rather than that of the breaking up of epithelium into mesenchyme. The mesenchyme accumulates between the remaining lateral plate epithelium and the epidermis and soon becomes firmly attached to the inner surface of the epithelium (Fig. 310). The thickening of the lateral plate mesoderm and the subsequent formation of a mass of mesenchyme under the epithelium may coincide rather closely with the position of the two pairs of limbs, that is, they may appear in two disconnected regions—just behind the branchial region and just in front of the anus. This is the case in the amphibians. In other vertebrates,

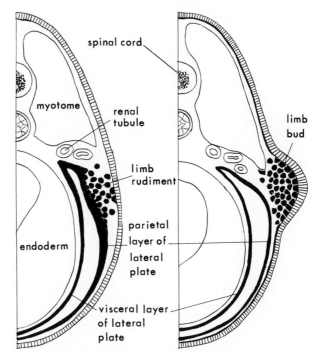

spinal cord

myotome

renal
tubule

limb
bud

Figure 310. Diagram of the
origin of limb mesoderm in an
amphibian embryo.

limb
rudiment

endoderm

parietal
layer of
lateral
plate

visceral layer
of lateral
plate

however, the thickening and the mesenchyme accumulation may spread far
beyond the actual region of limb development. In fishes the early limb rudiments are more elongated anteroposteriorly in the earlier stages than in the
later stages of development. In the amniotes the thickenings and the mesenchyme gatherings are continuous throughout the whole length of the body
in the form of horizontal ridges — the **wolffian ridges** (see Fig. 213, Stage 18).
However, the most anterior and the most posterior parts of the ridge are
thicker than the intermediate part, and it is only these anterior and posterior
parts that develop progressively, giving rise to the forelimbs and hindlimbs.
The intermediate part of the wolffian ridge later disappears.

The epidermis over the mesenchyme mass becomes slightly thickened
and bulges outward. This happens over the wolffian ridge as well, but in the
intermediate parts of the ridge the epithelial thickening disappears together
with the gathering of mesenchyme. In the regions where the fore- and hindlimbs are to develop, the protrusion, consisting of a thickened epithelial
covering and of an internal mass of densely packed mesenchyme, increases
and becomes the **limb-bud**.

Of the two components contributing to the formation of the limb-bud, the
mesoderm is determined as such at an early stage shortly after the closure of
the neural tube. Pieces of lateral plate may be cut out in this stage and transplanted under the epidermis on the flank or on the head. The local epidermis
will then become the epithelial component of the limb-bud, and a limb will
develop heterotopically. The presumptive epidermis of the limb in the same
stages, that is, before a limb-bud has been formed, does not possess any
special properties and, if transplanted alone, will not give rise to a new limb.
Epidermis from any part of the body is able to cooperate with the presumptive
limb mesoderm in forming a limb-bud. This can be shown by removing the

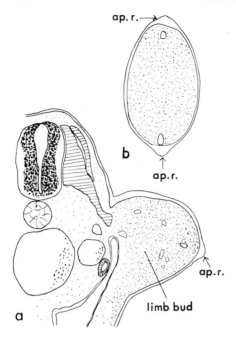

ap. r.→

b

ap.r.

ap.r.

limb bud

a

Figure 311. Advanced limb-bud with apical ridge *(ap.r.)*, in a chick embryo *(a)* (from Saunders, 1948) and cross-section of the forelimb-bud in a rat *(b)* (from Milaire, 1956).

epidermis in the limb region and then covering the wound with a flap of epidermis taken from any part of the body (Harrison, 1918; Balinsky, 1931).

The epidermis is, however, by no means a passive component in limb development. This is especially clearly shown by some peculiarities of limb development in higher vertebrates. In the amniotes, the limb-bud becomes slightly flattened at an early stage, and an epidermal thickening develops along the edge of the flattened bud. The thickening is in the form of a very sharply defined ridge and sometimes (in reptiles) even takes the form of a solid fold of the epidermis. In cross section the ridge looks like a nipple (Fig. 311). It is referred to as the ectodermal apical ridge.

The cells of the ridge differ from the ordinary epidermal cells not only in their arrangement but also in their physiological properties. It was found that they contain more ribonucleic acid and more glycogen, and they differ very conspicuously from surrounding epidermal cells in their high content of the enzyme alkaline phosphatase (Fig. 312—Milaire, 1956). All these biochemical properties may be taken as indications of active metabolism.

The apical ectodermal ridge is indispensable for the normal outgrowth of the limb rudiment. If the ectoderm of the apical ridge of a wingbud of a three-day chick embryo is removed without causing damage to the under-

marginal vein

apical ridge

Figure 312. Part of cross-section of the limb-bud in a rat stained for alkaline phosphatase. The apical ridge shows intense positive reaction. (From Milaire, 1956.)

Figure 313.   Apex of wingbud from which the epidermis with apical ridge has been removed (left), and control normal wingbud with apical ridge (right). (From Saunders, 1948.)

lying mesoderm (Fig. 313), the distal parts of the wing fail to be formed, although the proximal parts develop quite normally (Saunders, 1948). If the ectoderm covering the limb-bud in a chick embryo is removed and replaced by epidermis from another part of the body, the latter is found to be incapable of developing an apical ridge. The result is that the development of the whole of the distal part of the limb is suppressed. The girdle may, however, develop normally, and a short piece of cartilage representing the proximal part of the humerus or femur may be formed. This is in some contradiction to to the conditions found in amphibian embryos, where flank or head ectoderm, as was indicated, may participate in the development of a limb, but then there are no apical ridges on amphibian limb-buds.

The investigation of the role of the epidermal apical ridge in the development of limbs in birds was extended further after it had been discovered that the mesoderm and ectoderm of a limb-bud may be separated very neatly by chemical instead of mechanical means (Zwilling, 1955). Treating a limb-bud with a trypsin solution causes the epidermis to separate from the mesodermal core of the bud. The mesoderm after this treatment is not fully viable, but the epidermis is quite healthy and may be used to cover the mesodermal part from which the epidermis is removed by immersion in a solution of Versene (the latter treatment destroys the epidermis, which comes off in flakes, but leaves the mesoderm in a very good condition).

After the mesoderm of a limb-bud is covered by epidermis of a different origin, the two stick firmly together, and such a composite limb-bud may be implanted onto the flank of a third embryo and there allowed to grow into a limb (Fig. 314). In this way it was possible to combine the mesoderm of a legbud with the epidermis of a wingbud and vice versa. The structure of the

developing limb was in every case determined by the origin of the mesodermal component; it was a wing if the mesoderm was taken from a wingbud,
and a leg if the mesoderm was that of a posterior limb rudiment. The origin
of the ectoderm did not affect the nature of the developing limb. This experiment stresses the leading part played by the mesoderm in limb development.

The next experiment emphasizes the importance of the epidermis. In a
"wingless" mutation in fowls, the forelimb-bud appears approximately at
the same time as the normal limb-bud but fails to grow and produce a limb,
though parts of the limb girdle may be present. It was noticed that the epidermis covering the wingbud in the affected embryos does not have an apical
ridge. The experiment was therefore undertaken of combining the mesoderm
of a normal wingbud with the epidermis of an embryo of the wingless strain.
The result was as had been expected; in the absence of an apical ridge the
bud did not grow and no distal parts of the wing were formed (Zwilling, 1956).

The competence for limb development can be shown to be present all
along the flank of the embryo between the forelimb and hindlimb region
even if it does not manifest itself in normal development. In amphibians it
is possible to induce a supernumerary limb by introducing an inductor into
the region between the forelimb and the hindlimb rudiments (Fig. 315).
Originally the ear vesicle was used as a limb inductor (Balinsky, 1925), but
later it was found that other organ rudiments such as the hypophysis and the
olfactory sac can also induce a limb if transplanted into the side of a young
embryo. Under the influence of the induction, the local mesodermal cells
accumulate as a compact mass under the epidermis, the epidermis is also
made to react, and an additional limb develops. Depending on whether the
induced limb lies nearer to the normal forelimb or hindlimb region, it may
resemble a forelimb or a hindlimb in its structure (Balinsky, 1933).

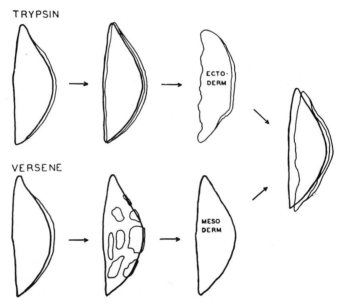

Figure 314. Separation and recombination of the limb-bud mesoderm and epidermis in the
chick embryo. (From Zwilling, 1956.)

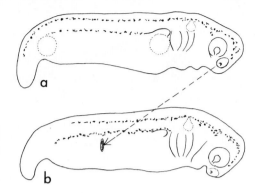

Figure 315. Induction of a supernumerary limb in *Triturus taeniatus* by means of a grafted nose rudiment. *a, b,* Diagrams of the operation. The position of the normal rudiments of the fore- and hindlimb shown in *a. c,* Larva with induced limb.

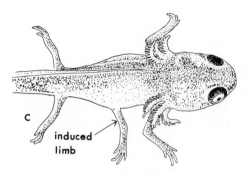

induced limb

Experiments on limb induction suggest that in normal development, as well, there must be some factor determining which part of the mesoderm competent for limb development actually produces a limb rudiment. Limb-buds are often induced together with other structures when "spino-caudal" inductors are introduced into embryos in the gastrula stage (p. 237). By transplanting the presumptive somite mesoderm together with the notochord into the lateral plate region of an embryo in the neurula stage, it is possible to induce the lateral plate mesoderm to develop into kidney (normally produced by the stalks of the somite). In these experiments it has often been observed that additional limb-buds developed together with the kidney tubules (Yamada, 1937). It follows that the determination of the limb mesoderm occurs in conjunction with the determination of other parts of the mesodermal mantle. The kidney in itself cannot, however, induce a limb.

Differentiation in the Limbs.   After the limb-bud has grown so far that its length exceeds its breadth, the differentiation of the subordinate parts of the limb sets in. We have already noted the slight flattening of the limb-bud. Now the distal portion of the bud becomes flattened even more, and at the same time it becomes distinctly broader than the proximal part of the limb rudiment. The flattened and broadened distal part is the hand (or foot) plate. The edge of the plate is initially circular, but soon it becomes pentagonal, the projecting points indicating the rudiments of the digits. While the tips of the digit rudiments keep growing out farther, the intervening sections are retarded in their growth, so that the digits become separated by distinct incisions. The five digits appear simultaneously in all amniotes with pentadactyl limbs, but in amphibians, especially in urodeles, the first two digits appear earlier and digits 3, 4 and 5 are formed one after another on the poste-

Figure 316. Rotation of the developing forelimb in the lizard. (After Braus, from Hertwig, 1906.)

rior edge of the limb. Where less than five digits are present in the adult limb, or more than five in cases of hyperdactyly, this condition is reflected in the structure of the hand (foot) plate.

In the early limb rudiments, the future flexor surface is ventral and the future extensor surface is dorsal, but as the limb elongates a rotation takes place so that the flexor surface is turned posteriorly, and eventually it may even face in a posterodorsal direction. The preaxial edge of the limb, which is originally anterior, is then turned downward (Fig. 316). With the elongation of the limb, it becomes bent at the elbow joint (or knee joint). A less pronounced flexion develops at the base of the carpus (or tarsus). The three main sections of the limbs thus become recognizable externally.

Concurrently with changes in the external appearance of the limbs, differentiation occurs in the interior of the limb rudiments. The mesenchyme cells which are closely packed in a young limb-bud become segregated into areas in which the mesenchyme is lying more loosely and into other areas in which the mesenchyme cells are crowded. The latter are the rudiments of the skeletal parts of the limb. The concentrated masses of mesenchyme in due course become converted into procartilage, and then, by further deposition of intercellular matrix, into cartilage. Whereas in the initial stage of mesenchyme concentration large sections of the limb skeleton are represented by a common mass of mesenchyme, in the procartilage stage individual elements of the skeleton are laid down as separate units; these may fuse together later.

The differentation of the limb skeleton generally proceeds in a proximodistal direction, though some deviations from this order are of fairly general occurrence. In amphibians, the first skeletal part to become recognizable is the **stylopodium** (humerus or femur). Parts of the **zeugopodium** (radius and ulna in the forelimb, tibia and fibula in the hindlimb) are laid down next, and the **autopodium** differentiates considerably later. The girdle rudiments appear after the stylopodium, but earlier than the autopodium. In higher vertebrates the girdle tends to be developed simultaneously with the proximal elements of the limb. In the autopodium, the proximodistal sequence is upset by the larger skeletal elements, the metacarpals and metatarsals differentiating more rapidly than the smaller elements, namely, the carpals and the tarsals. In the digits, however, the proximal phalanges are laid down earlier than the distal ones (see Sewertzoff, 1931).

The blood vessels appear in the limb-bud at an early stage, and, although the pattern of the arteries, veins and capillaries is too variable to deserve much attention here, one blood vessel may be mentioned. It is situated along

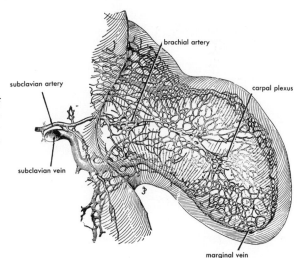

Figure 317. Reconstruction of the blood vessels in a limb rudiment of a pig embryo. (From Woollard: Carnegie Contrib. Embryol., 22.)

the edge of the hand (or foot) plate, just underneath the ectodermal apical ridge, and possibly it is responsible for supplying nutriment to this rapidly growing area of the limb (Fig. 317).

The pattern according to which the various constituent parts (bones, muscles, blood vessels, nerves) are arranged in each limb is asymmetrical —proximal and distal ends, dorsal and ventral surfaces, anterior and posterior sides of the limb being different from one another. The first indication of this asymmetrical pattern can be noted when the tip of the limb-bud grows out in a slanting posterior direction instead of growing straight out away from the side of the body (Fig. 301).

Special experiments have been carried out to find out how the asymmetry of the limb, and thus the basic pattern of its differentiation, is determined. Experiments were originally carried out on the embryos of the salamander *Ambystoma punctatum*. Forelimb rudiments were transplanted at different stages after the end of neurulation in such a way that either one limb rudiment axis or two or all three were inverted (disharmonious) with respect to the host's body (Harrison, 1921b). The inversion of the proximodistal axis could only be carried out with the mesodermal part of the limb rudiment, but this is not of importance, as it is the mesoderm that is the carrier of the limb determination (Harrison, 1925b; Swett, 1937). The transplantations were done either **orthotopically**, that is, in place of a normal limb rudiment, or **heterotopically**, on the flank. The experiments showed that the three axes of the limb rudiment were not determined simultaneously. In the earliest rudiments immediately after neurulation, the anteroposterior axis is already fixed; limb rudiments, transplanted disharmoniously, with this axis inverted, had the tip of the limb-bud growing forward instead of backward, and the limbs later had their postaxial (ulnar) side placed anteriorly (Fig. 318). At the same time, the inversion of the dorsoventral axis of the transplanted limb rudiment could still right itself; that is, the original upper part of the rudiment developed into the ventral (palmar) surface of the limb and the original lower part of the rudiment developed into the dorsal surface of the limb. This shows that the pattern of the limb differentiation was not yet fixed

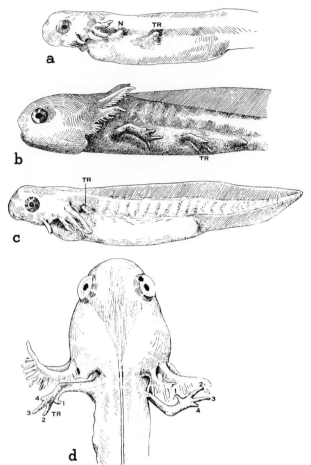

Figure 318.   Experiments
demonstrating the properties of
the forelimb rudiment of the
salamander *Ambystoma puncta-*
tum in the tailbud stage. *N*,
Normal limb; *TR*, transplanted
limb. *a*, Transplantation of a
right limb rudiment to the left
side, with inversion of the
dorsoventral axis. *b*, Same animal later. *c*, Left limb transplanted   orthotopically   with
inverted   anteroposterior   and
dorsoventral axes. *d*, Same animal later; a.p. axis determined
and retained in new position.
(From Harrison, 1921b.)

in respect to its dorsoventral axis and that this pattern could be imposed
upon the limb rudiment by the host, that is, by the parts which were in connection with the limb rudiment in its new postion. In a later stage of development when the tail rudiment begins to elongate, the dorsoventral axis of
the limb was also found to be determined; if the limbs were transplanted in an
inverted position, with the dorsoventral axis of the limb rudiment the inverse
of the dorsoventral axis of the host, the limb developed with an abnormal
orientation, its plantar surface facing upward. The surroundings could no
longer change the pattern of limb differentiation in respect to the dorsoventral axis, as well as in respect to the anteroposterior axis (Fig. 319).

Figure 319.   Heterotopic transplantation of the limb rudiment in
the late tailbud stage, with inverted
dorsoventral axis. The palmar surface   of   the   transplanted   limb
(partially reduplicated) facing upward. (From Swett, 1927.)

At the same time that the dorsoventral axis of the limb rudiment is determined, the proximodistal axis may still be inverted without impairing the normal development of the limb. Only in a later stage, when the limb-bud begins to be visible from the outside, does the proximodistal axis show signs of being determined, and if the limb mesoderm is transplanted with the axis inverted the limb shows abnormalities in its development. (A limb cannot actually grow inward into the body because it would then be no longer in contact with the epidermis, and this contact is indispensable for the differentiation of parts of the limb.)

In cases when the transplanted limb rudiment grows out in a disharmonious orientation to the host, it is often observed that a kind of regulation occurs by means of the formation of a second limb-bud, whose orientation and differentiation is harmonious with the host's body. The appearance of the second limb-bud is the result of a sort of splitting of the original rudiment and is due to an influence of the host on the graft. This influence is not strong enough to invert the axial structure of the transplanted rudiment as a whole, but is sufficiently strong to divert a part of the cells of the transplanted rudiment and to cause them to take on the axial structure of the host. If the original disharmonious limb were now to degenerate (as sometimes happens), the host would be in possession of a normal set of limbs.

The splitting of a limb rudiment (or any other organ rudiment) to produce two similar rudiments is known as **reduplication**. That reduplication is possible shows that the cells of the rudiment are not determined each to fulfill a definite part in the developing organ, even though the axial pattern of the rudiment as a whole is determined. From this it is further inferred that the determination of the axial pattern is not a matter of determining what each cell or group of cells has to do in the process of development of the organ, but it is a matter of polarity, of a heteropolar structure of the rudiment as a whole. This immediately recalls the polarity of the egg in the early stages of development, and some similarity between the rudiment of an organ and the early egg as a whole is indeed shown. Both possess the ability to develop a number of subordinate parts, each within its own scope of action (the whole animal in the case of the egg, one organ in the case of an organ rudiment), and without these subordinate parts being represented by discrete particles in the initial system.

Just as the egg can be split mechanically into parts and each part will develop into a miniature whole, so an organ rudiment, in a suitable stage of development, may be split mechanically into halves, and each half will develop into a complete organ. We have already mentioned similar results in the case of the eye rudiment. The same applies to the limb rudiment. The limb rudiment up to the stage of the limb-bud formation may be cut in two and each half transplanted separately, or the two halves left in place and kept apart by inserting a piece of extraneous tissue between them. Each will develop into a whole limb (Fig. 320 – Swett, 1926). The two limbs resulting from such a splitting may later grow to the normal size. Splitting of limbs may sometimes occur accidentally in young amphibian larvae developing in nature, or it may possibly be caused by the pressure of folds of the amnion in higher vertebrates, and abnormalities will be the result: limbs that are completely or partially reduplicated. If the splitting of the rudiment is due to a mechanical cause rather than being spontaneous, the two halves retain the same axial structure (polarity), thus being replicas of each other.

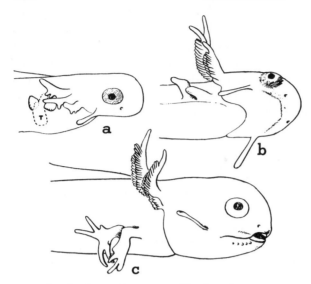

Figure 320. Splitting of the forelimb rudiment, with a strip of extraneous tissue (*T*) inserted across it (*a*) to produce two limbs (*b, c*). (From Swett, 1926.)

The limb girdles normally develop in intimate connection with the limbs themselves. The mesodermal material for the girdle is derived from the peripheral parts of the mesenchyme mass, the central part of which becomes the limb-bud. However, in their determination the girdles are partially independent of the limbs. The limb girdles may develop independently of the limbs, if the development of the limb itself is suppressed in some way or other, as by the removal of the limb-bud (Detwiler, 1918). In limb induction experiments, limb girdles sometimes are found where the limb itself fails to develop. The development of the girdle is in no way dependent on the existence of an interaction with the epidermis of the skin, as is that of the limb itself.

In birds, the limb girdle may also develop fairly well even if the distal part of the limb is absent as a result of a failing cooperation between mesoderm and ectoderm, as in cases where the epidermis over the limb-bud lacks an apical ridge.

If the girdle (shoulder girdle or pelvic girdle) develops in the absence of the limb, it may be normal in its peripheral parts, but the fossa for the articulation with the humerus or femur does not develop in the absence of at least the proximal part of the stylopodium (humerus or femur) (Balinsky, 1931). The thickening of the girdle in the region of the articulation is also lacking in the absence of a limb. In so far as these parts are concerned, the amphibian girdles are dependent on the limbs. In bony fishes, in which the cartilaginous part of the shoulder girdle is reduced to a small skeletal element in the region of articulation, the bony **cleithrum** can develop independently of the pectoral fin (Balinsky, unpublished).

The mesenchyme of the limb-bud does not contain all the mesodermal cells used for the development of a limb; after the limb-bud is formed it receives an additional supply of mesodermal cells from the lower edges of the myotomes. These cells produce the muscles of the limb or at least a part of these. In fishes it is possible to observe **muscle buds** being formed at the lower edges of the myotomes. These muscle buds are protrusions of the cell masses of the myotomes. The muscle buds push downward and outward until they enter the limb-buds. In the limb-bud itself, the muscle buds derived from different myotomes fuse into a common mass of cells (myoblasts) from which the muscles of the limb subsequently develop. In the higher vertebrates, beginning with amphibians, muscle buds are not found, although the migration of individual cells from the myotomes into the limb rudiments may take place.

In the fishes, if the lateral plate mesoderm of the limb region is transplanted to near the midventral line on the abdomen, it gives rise to fins which are devoid of muscles (Lopashov, 1950), thus proving that the lateral plate mesoderm is not capable of producing the limb muscles. Muscles are developed, however, if a part of the somite is included in the graft. In amphibians, on the other hand, when the rudiment of the limb, consisting of lateral plate mesoderm with or without epidermis, is transplanted heterotopically, it will develop into a complete limb with muscles. This, however, does not definitely exclude the participation of the myotome material, since under experimental conditions some regulation could have taken place, just as half the rudiment may produce a whole limb in cases or reduplication.

The nerve supply to the developing limbs has been dealt with in the section on the differentiation of the nervous system (13–1).

14 — 4 DEVELOPMENT OF THE URINARY SYSTEM

The excretory organs in vertebrates are essentially aggregates of uriniferous tubules, connected originally at their proximal ends with the coelomic cavity by ciliated funnels (the **nephrostomes**) and communicating to the exterior by a system of ducts which, in the lower vertebrates, open into the cloaca. Both the tubules and the ducts are of mesodermal origin, and they develop from the stalks of the somites (the **nephrotomes**). In the most primitive vertebrates, such as the cyclostomes, and also in the Gymnophiona, one uriniferous tubule develops from the nephrotome in each mesodermal segment.

The nephrotome, prior to the development of a uriniferous tubule, is a strand of cells connecting the somites to the lateral plate mesoderm. The cells become separated into the parietal and visceral layer, and the cavity, which we may call the **nephrocoele**, is for a while continuous with both the myocoele and the definitive coelom between the two sheets of the lateral plate mesoderm. The connection of the nephrocoele with the cavity of the somite is soon obliterated, but the connection with the cavity of the lateral plate persists in the more primitive type of vertebrate excretory organs and becomes the nephrostome. The dorsolateral wall of the nephrotome becomes drawn out into a hollow tube, the cavity of which is an extension of the nephrocoele. The tube, which is in open connection with the coelomic cavity, becomes the uriniferous or renal tubule. The distal (outward) ends of the most anterior tubules (that is, the tubules formed in the anterior part of the trunk) soon turn backward and then fuse with each other, thus giving rise to the common excretory duct, known as the **pronephric duct**.

It is an essential feature in vertebrates that the renal tubules are associated with bunches of fine blood vessels (the **glomeruli**), through the endothelial walls of which the blood plasma containing excretory products is filtered into the uriniferous tubules or into the coelom in the immediate vicinity of the nephrostomes, so that the nitrogenous waste products may be carried through the tubes and the excretory ducts and removed from the body. Either the mass of blood vessels is invaginated into the wall of the renal tubule, which enlarges to contain the glomerulus and becomes the **Bowman's capsule**, or else the blood vessels form a bulge on the wall of the coelom. In this case the structure is referred to as the **external glomerulus**, or, if glomeruli of several segments are joined together, as the **glomus**. It is believed that the segment of the coelomic cavity into which the glomus projects is itself derived from an expansion of the nephrocoele, or several nephrocoeles (Fig. 321).

The basic pattern of development of the excretory organs as described above becomes modified in various degrees. As with many other organ systems, in vertebrates the development of the excretory tubules progresses in a craniocaudal direction, the tubules differentiating earlier in anterior segments than in posterior ones. The tubules which develop and begin functioning earlier, i.e., those of the anterior part of the trunk, tend to show more primitive conditions in their organization, while those developing later are modified to a greater degree. In the most primitive vertebrates, the cyclostomes and some fishes, the differences between the anterior and posterior parts of the excretory system are only gradual, but in the higher vertebrates we may distinguish more or less clearly three sections of this system: the **pronephros**, the **mesonephros** and the **metanephros**.

The most anterior nephrotomes give rise to the pronephros, the mesonephros develops from those of the midtrunk region, and the metanephros is derived from the nephrotomes of the posterior part of the trunk. The resulting three types of kidneys can thus be distinguished as anterior, middle and posterior with respect to their place of origin. The pronephros is the first to develop, the mesonephros second, and the metanephros, if present, appears latest of all.

The three types of kidneys differ also in the way in which they are produced by the stalks of the somites, in the presence or absence of the nephrostomes, in the position of the glomerulus and in the origin and connections of the excretory ducts. In the pronephros, the nephrostomes are well devel-

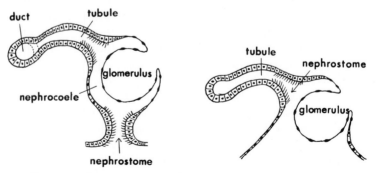

Figure 321.   Diagrams of two main types of an excretory unit, with internal glomerulus (left) and external glomerulus (right). (From Fraser, 1950.)

oped and the glomeruli tend to be replaced by a common glomus (see previous description), though in some primitive forms, such as the Gymnophiona, each tubule of the pronephros may be supplied with a separate glomerulus. In the mesonephros, a separate glomerulus is, as a rule, intercalated in the course of each uriniferous tubule. Nephrostomes are present at first but may disappear later. In the metanephros, the nephrostomes are not formed at all, and the uriniferous tubules begin with the Bowman's capsules.

Further differences in the development of the tubules and ducts can best be described separately in relation to each section of the excretory system. Since all three types of kidneys are nothing but local differentiations of one system stretching throughout the body of a vertebrate, morphological features do not necessarily change abruptly from one section to another, and transitional conditions may sometimes be found (see Fraser, 1950).

The Pronephros. The description of the origin of a uriniferous tubule given on page 415 follows the observations made on the embryos of Gymnophiona (Brauer, 1902) and may be taken as representing the typical development of the pronephric tubules in the most archaic groups of vertebrates. The strictly segmental origin of the tubules is an essential feature of this development. In amphibians, the pronephric tubules are formed from a common mesodermal thickening appearing beneath the third and fourth somites (in salamanders) or second, third and fourth somites (in frogs). Nevertheless, the number of the pronephric tubules corresponds to the number of segments participating in the development of the pronephros.

The rudiment of the pronephros can be traced back in amphibians to the neurula stage. By means of vital staining, the presumptive material of the pronephros was found to lie in the mesodermal mantle just outside of the edge of the neural plate, posterior to the middle of the embryo (Fig. 322 – Yamada, 1937; Muchmore, 1951). In the neurula stage, mesoderm of this region is capable of self-differentiation when transplanted heterotopically (Fales, 1935). At the same time, however, other parts of the mesodermal mantle also possess the ability to develop into renal tubules, as for instance when an inductor (the notochord) is transplanted into the lateral plate region of the embryo. The presumptive somites, when isolated from the notochord and cultivated *in vitro* (surrounded by a coat of skin epidermis for protection), may develop into renal tubules even though their normal destiny would be a different one (the development of muscle). After the end of neurulation (closure of the neural tube), the competence for the development of the

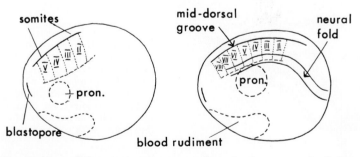

Figure 322. Position of the presumptive pronephros in the very early (left) and middle neurula (right). (After Yamada, 1937.)

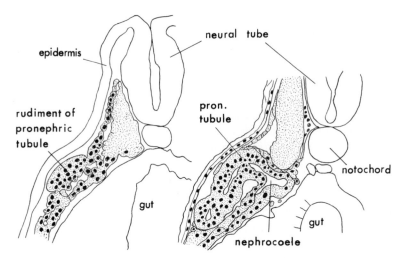

Figure 323. Early development of a pronephric tubule in the frog. (After Field, from Brachet, 1935.)

pronephric tubules is restricted to the presumptive material of the pronephros. From this stage onward the pronephric rudiment cannot be replaced, and the removal of the rudiment leads to the absence of the pronephros.

The sequence of events during the transformation of the nephrotomes into the pronephric tubules, in frogs, salamanders and higher tetrapods, is not so clear as in the lower vertebrates. It is carried out by means of a rearrangement of cells, that is, by morphogenetic movements. The end result is, however, the same: several pairs of pronephric tubules are formed; they open by means of the nephrostomes into the coelomic cavity (Fig. 323) and fuse distally to form the pronephric duct (Fig. 324).

The formation of the pronephric duct, by fusion of the distal ends of the pronephric tubules, is a very important phase in the development of the excretory system, as this duct not only serves the pronephros but is also instrumental in providing pathways for the outflow of urine from the mesonephros and metanephros and, in the males, for the passage of spermatozoa.

In the salamanders, it has been shown that the pronephric duct develops right from the start from a more caudal part of the mesoderm than the pronephric tubules; while the two pronephric canals develop from the mesoderm lying under the third and fourth somites, the rudiment of the pronephric

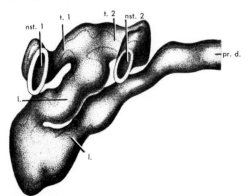

Figure 324. Reconstruction of the pronephric canals in a newt embryo (median view). *nst. 1, nst. 2,* First and second nephrostomes; *t. 1, t.2,* first and second pronephric tubules; *l,* loop formed by joint part of tubule; *pr. d.,* pronephric duct. (After Mangold, from Spemann, 1938.)

duct lies under the fifth, sixth and seventh somites. If the rudiments of the pronephric tubules are removed, or if the embryo is bisected transversely between the levels of the fourth and fifth somites, the pronephric duct can still develop, thus showing that the pronephric tubules and the pronephric duct are determined independently of each other (Holtfreter, 1943c).

Once they have been formed, both the pronephric tubules and the pronephric duct elongate very considerably. The pronephric tubules, as a result of their elongation, are thrown into numerous loops and eventually form a more or less spherical body, consisting of tangled and intertwined tubules. The pronephric duct, on the other hand, remains straight, and while it elongates, its posterior free end pushes itself backward along the lower ends of the somites. This backward movement of the tip of the pronephric duct ends when the duct reaches the cloaca and fuses with its wall, while the lumen of the duct opens into the cavity of the cloaca.

The backward elongation of the pronephric duct may be interrupted in various ways, as by making a deep incision across its path. If the wound remains gaping, the pronephric duct cannot spread beyond the wound, and the duct is not continued into the posterior part of the body (Waddington, 1938; Holtfreter, 1943c). If, however, the wound is too small or is covered to a sufficient extent, the tip of the elongating duct may find its way around the wound and penetrate into the posterior part of the body. Behind the wound, the duct returns to its level under the lower edges of the somites and eventually reaches the cloaca (Fig. 325, *a*, *b*). This experiment shows that the elongation of the pronephric duct is largely independent of the surrounding parts, although the latter do seem to direct the duct by furnishing a suitable path for its movement. The same is borne out with the utmost clarity by some further experiments (Holtfreter, 1943c), in which embryos in the closed neural tube stage were bisected transversely, one half reversed, and the two parts caused to heal together with opposite dorsoventral orientation (see Fig. 325, *c*, *d*). When the pronephric ducts reached the level of the operation in their backward elongation, the tip of the duct changed its direction and

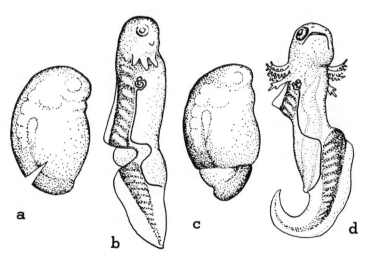

Figure 325. Pronephric duct reaching the cloaca by an abnormal path after transection of the embryo (*a*, *b*) and after rotation of the posterior part of the embryo through 180 degrees (*c*, *d*). (From Holtfreter, 1943c.)

struck a new path across the lateral body wall, until it reached the somites
of the inverted posterior part of the embryo. It then elongated along the edge
of the somites and reached the cloaca as usual.

The development of the pronephric duct shows a great similarity to the
development of the lateral line (section 13–4). In both cases the migration
of the posterior end of the organ rudiment along the length of the body is due
to intrinsic tendencies of the cells of the rudiment, but the organs and tissues
with which the rudiments come in contact influence the path taken by the
migrating cells (see also section 12–3).

The kidneys of the most primitive living vertebrates, the cyclostomes and
elasmobranch fishes, in their development and organization in the adult,
show features characteristic of the pronephros, although they may perhaps
be more correctly described as representing a stage in which the differentiation into pronephros and metanephros has not yet taken place. The
typical pronephros is a functional kidney of the larval stages of bony fishes
and amphibians. In frog tadpoles, the pronephric canals form a bulky convoluted mass on both sides in the anterior part of the trunk at the level of the
forelimbs, on the median aspect of the pectoral girdle (Fig. 229). In frog tadpoles approaching metamorphosis, the pronephros gradually degenerates; the
glomus shrinks, the neprhic tubules are resorbed and the anterior portions
of the pronephric ducts are also resorbed. The function of excretion is taken
over by the mesonephros.

In embryos of amniotes, the pronephros develops in the anterior trunk
region, but it is not functional at any stage. In the human embryo, about
seven pairs of rudimentary pronephric tubules are formed. These soon
degenerate, but not before they give rise to the pronephric ducts, which
remain after the pronephric tubules have disappeared.

The Mesonephros.   The mesonephric tubules are derived from the nephrotomes, as in the case of the pronephros, but their interrelation is by no means
so simple. Only in the more archaic groups of vertebrates (selachians, Gymnophiona, ganoids) are the renal tubules formed directly from the nephrotomes
(Fig. 326). In most amphibians and in all higher vertebrates, the mesodermal
cells of the nephrotomes dissolve into a mass of mesenchyme stretching on
each side of the body along the dorsal edge of the lateral plates from the level
where the pronephros ends to the pelvic region. This elongated mass of
mesenchyme is known as the **nephrogenic cord** or nephrogenic tissue (Figs.
244, 252). The mesonephric tubules are developed from the nephrogenic tissue by a secondary aggregation of the mesodermal cells.

The aggregating cells begin by forming epithelial vesicles which stretch
and elongate to become tubes. One end of such a tube becomes connected
to the pronephric duct, while the other end becomes invaginated to form the
Bowman's capsule; or, in rarer cases, it opens into the coelomic cavity by
a nephrostome while a Bowman's capsule is formed higher along the course of
the tubule. The Bowman's capsules become supplied by small branches from
the dorsal aorta. The number of the mesonephric tubules does not correspond
to the number of segments, several tubules being developed in the region
of each segment. Even if at first only one tube is formed in each segment,
it soon gives rise by budding to secondary and tertiary tubes, and so on. If
present at first, the nephrostomes may disappear later. In the frogs, the

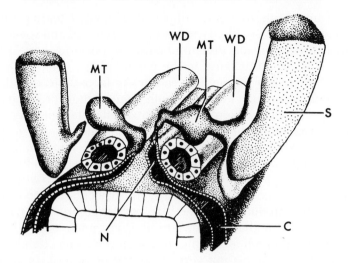

Figure 326. Relation of the mesonephric tubules to other mesodermal parts in the embryo of a sturgeon. The rudiment of the mesonephric tubule *(MT)* is shown as still connected to the somite *(S)* on one side, and just separated on the other. *C*, coelom; *N*, nephrostome; *WD*, wolffian duct. (After Maschkowzeff, from Fraser, 1950.)

nephrostomes lose their connection with the rest of the nephric tubule but open secondarily into the veins (connecting the veins to the coelom).

The nephrogenic tissue is not at once determined for differentiation as mesonephros. If the presumptive material of the mesonephros of a newt embryo in the neurula stage is transplanted into the pronephric area of a tailbud stage embryo, the grafted tissue gives rise to excretory tubules of the pronephric type. On the other hand, the same material taken from a tailbud stage embryo on grafting will produce mesonephric tubules even if it comes to lie at the site where a pronephros should have developed (Machemer, 1929).

The mesonephric tubules do not produce a duct of their own. As the tubules are formed, their distal, free ends join up with the pronephric duct, which thus becomes the duct of the mesonephros as well and is then called the **wolffian duct**. As the mesonephric tubules reach the wolffian duct, the walls of the latter bulge out, forming collecting ducts. The mesonephric tubules, especially the ones formed later, open into these collecting ducts rather than into the wolffian duct itself.

The development of the mesonephros has also been found to be dependent on the pronephric duct in another way. The nephrogenous tissue develops into the mesonephric tubules only if stimulated to this by the pronephric duct. In the preceding section, experiments have been mentioned in which the penetration of the pronephric duct into the posterior half of the body was prevented by placing an obstacle (in the form of a gaping wound) in its path. When the operation is successful—that is, if the duct does not reach the region where the mesonephros normally develops—the nephrogenous tissue fails to form the renal tubules or forms only poorly developed tubules (Waddington, 1938; O'Connor, 1939). Apparently some stimulus (induction) from the pronephric duct is necessary for the normal development of the mesonephric tubules from the nephrogenous tissue.

The most anterior mesonephric tubules degenerate later in many animals, so that the kidney becomes shortened at its anterior end and somewhat more compact. In many fishes and in amphibians, the posterior part of the mesonephros shows some traits found in the metanephros: complete absence of nephrostomes, joining of the nephric tubules to large collecting ducts — outgrowths of the wolffian duct. For this reason, some authors prefer to regard the kidney in these animals as a joint mesonephros and metanephros, giving it the special name of **opistonephros**. In fishes and amphibians, the mesonephric (or opistonephric) kidney is the excretory organ of the adult animal.

In reptiles and birds, on the other hand, the mesonephros functions only during the embryonic period of development and loses its excretory function at the time of hatching. In the mammals, the placenta takes on the task of removing excretory products from the blood of the embryo and passing them into the blood of the mother, from where they are removed by the maternal kidneys. In mammals such as the pig, in which the connection between the fetal and maternal tissues is not very close, the mesonephros is still active as an excretory organ, and a certain quantity of urine eventually reaches the cavity of the allantois and the amniotic cavity. In mammals having a very close connection between the fetal and maternal tissues (as in rodents with a hemochorial placenta), there is no sign of excretory activity in the mesonephros, which is thus a rudimentary organ like the pronephros.

The Metanephros.   The metanephros develops from the posterior part of the nephrogenic cord, the part adjacent to the cloaca. There is no trace of a relation of the tubules to the nephrotomes, although the nephrogenic tissue is primarily derived from the latter. As in the case of the mesonephros, the metanephros does not develop a duct of its own but uses the pronephric duct as a means of removing the urine that it excretes. However, the connection between metanephros and the pronephric duct is established not directly but by means of a special outgrowth or branch of the duct. Before the metanephros starts differentiating, a bud is formed on the pronephric duct a small distance in front of the point where the duct joins the cloaca. The bud elongates in the direction of the posterior part of the nephrogenic cord and eventually penetrates into the mass of nephrogenic tissue. The duct formed in this way becomes the **ureter** and the bud from which it develops is the **ureteric bud**. Having reached the nephrogenic tissue, the end of the ureter begins to branch, the branches later becoming the collecting tubules of the kidney (Fig. 327). The point at which the branching begins expands to form the renal pelvis. The nephrogenic mesenchyme accumulates around the tips of the collecting tubules and in due course differentiates into the renal tubules with their glomeruli. No trace of nephrostomes can be discovered in the metanephros at any stage.

As in the mesonephros, the conversion of the metanephrogenic tissue into a system of renal tubules is dependent on a stimulus from the excretory duct — in this case from the ureter and its branches, which develop from the ureteric bud. In experiments on chick embryos, in which the backward growth of the pronephric duct is prevented by destroying its growing tip, no wolffian duct develops in the posterior part of the body and naturally no ureteric bud is formed (Gruenwald, 1952). The result is that no metanephric kidney is formed on the operated side of the embryo.

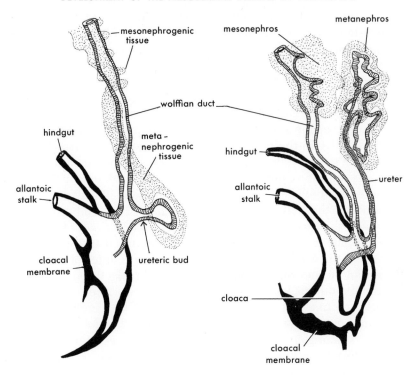

Figure 327. Development of the ureter and the metanephros in a rabbit embryo. (After Schreiner, from Brachet, 1935.)

A confirmation of results gained by operation may be found in certain defects caused by mutations (see p. 530).

The metanephros is the functional kidney in the postembryonic life of reptiles, birds and mammals. In lizards, the fully differentiated metanephros largely retains the position of the metanephrogenic part of the nephrogenic cord: the functional kidney lies at the level of the hindlimb and even projects into the base of the tail. In birds and mammals, however, at an early stage the metanephric kidneys become displaced in an anterior direction. The metanephros shifts past the posterior end of the mesonephros and eventually comes to lie at about the same level as the latter: in the lumbar region, in mammals, and filling the space underneath the synsacrum and the pelvic girdle in birds. Concurrently with the displacement of the kidneys, the ureters elongate to a very great extent as compared with their length at the time when the ureteric bud first contacts the metanephrogenic tissue (see Fig. 327).

The excretory ducts of the kidney in most vertebrates acquire close relations with the reproductive organs. These relations and the modifications of the excretory ducts in this connection will be dealt with together with the development of sexual organs.

14—5 DEVELOPMENT OF THE HEART

The heart in vertebrates develops from the mesoderm forming the ventral edges of the lateral plates in the pharyngeal region of the body. It will be most convenient to describe first the development of the heart in animals such as the amphibians and to consider later the development of the heart in higher vertebrates.

The Heart in Lower Vertebrates.   During gastrulation in the amphibians, the sheet of mesoderm advances forward from the blastopore, penetrating between the ectoderm and the endoderm. The rate of movement of the meso- derm is greatest in the dorsal region of the embryo, intermediate laterally and least ventrally. In the neurula stage, the dorsal and dorsolateral parts of the mesodermal mantle have reached the head region of the embryo; ventrally there remains an approximately triangular area in which there is no meso- derm intervening between ectoderm and endoderm. This triangle, roughly corresponding to the oral and pharyngeal region of the embryo, has its apex posteriorly and the broad base anteriorly. The posterior part of the area is the site of development of the heart, and it is later filled in by the mesoderm participating in the formation of the heart. The most anterior part of the area remains free of mesoderm, and here the mouth breaks through after a fusion between the endoderm and the ectoderm has taken place.

The presumptive material of the heart is found in the edges of the meso- dermal mantle bordering the mesoderm-free area on the right and on the left. By vital staining in the neurula stage, it has been shown that the pre- sumptive material for the heart is located in the edge of the mesodermal mantle, rather high on the flank on each side, where it adjoins the parts of the neural folds which become the hindbrain portion of the neural plate (Fig. 328).

If the mesoderm of this area is stained with nile blue sulphate or neutral red (by lifting a flap of ectoderm and mesoderm and applying a piece of cel- lophane soaked in stain to the *inner* surface of the mesodermal layer), it can be observed that the mesoderm shifts in later stages in a ventral direction and eventually comes to lie midventrally in the area where the heart can be seen to differentiate. The particles of vital stain remain in the cells long enough for it to be ascertained that the stained material on each side of the embryo gives rise to exactly one half of the heart rudiment (Fig. 328, *D*), the other half being derived from a similar area of mesoderm on the other side of the embryo.

Parts of the free edge of the mesodermal mantle may be excised in the neurula stage and cultivated in a saline solution (Goerttler, 1928; Bacon, 1945; Jacobson, 1960). To prevent the mesoderm from disintegrating, it is sometimes isolated together with a flap of ectoderm; the ectoderm then closes into a vesicle with the mesoderm inside. The mesodermal cells under these conditions differentiate into muscle tissue, and this begins to pulsate rhyth- mically—an unequivocal indication that the developed muscle tissue is cardiac muscle, as only this type of muscle is capable of autonomous rhyth- mical contraction. It has been claimed (Bacon, 1945) that in some experiments the heart rudiments explanted in neurula and even late gastrula stages can even produce pulsating tubes having an obvious resemblance to normal hearts.

It is rather remarkable that there is a definite discrepancy between experiments using the vital staining technique and explantation experiments. While vital staining indicates that the material going into the formation of the

Figure 328.   Origin of the heart mesoderm after experiments of vital staining in *Ambystoma punctatum*. *A*, Diagram showing the position of stained mesoderm (stippled) just outside the neural fold, in the hindbrain region of a neurula. *B*, Embryo in early tail bud stage with stained mesoderm in the ear region. *C*, Embryo in late tail bud stage with the heart mesoderm shifted to the ventral position, where the heart rudiment is actually formed. *D*, Cross section through the heart region of an embryo in which the heart mesoderm was stained on the right side in the neurula stage (as in *A*). The stained material (stippled) on the right half of the heart includes all layers: endocardium, myocardium and pericardium. (After Wilens, 1955.)

heart lies in the upper part of the mesodermal mantle, heart differentiation has been observed in explanted pieces taken from different parts of the free edge of the mesodermal mantle: from the upper part (Jacobson, 1960), from the middle part (Bacon, 1945) and from the ventral part (Goerttler, 1928; Fig. 329). It would seem that mesoderm in a wide region of the early embryo has a potentiality for heart development. From this wider area the potentiality for heart development is later restricted to the actual material participating in the formation of the heart in normal development.

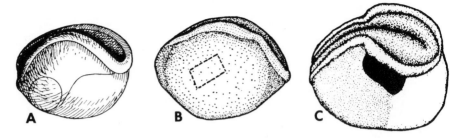

Figure 329.   Diagrams showing origin in the neurula stage of mesoderm that differentiated into cardiac muscle tissue in different experiments. *A*, Goerttler's experiments (Goerttler, 1928). *B*, Bacon's experiments (Bacon, 1945). *C*, Jacobson's experiments (Jacobson, 1960). Position of mesoderm differentiating as heart in explant is shown by circle in *A*, by quadrangle in *B* and in black in *C*. Only in the last case did the explant consist of material normally giving rise to heart according to Wilens. (Compare with Figure 328.)

In these early stages, the development of the heart is in some way dependent on the endoderm. By cutting through the ectoderm and the mesodermal mantle and removing the whole of the endoderm, it is possible to produce newt embryos which consist of ectoderm and mesoderm only (Mangold, 1936; Balinsky, 1939). The embryos survive the operation quite satisfactorily, but their term of life is limited because they do not possess the food supply normally contained in the yolky cells of the endoderm. The endodermless embryos show various defects in the ectodermal and mesodermal organs owing to the lack of inductive influences emanating from the endoderm. One of such defects is the complete absence of the heart, although the mesodermal layer, from which the heart rudiment is derived, may remain intact. (See also p. 435.)

After the end of the neurulation, the free edges of the mesodermal mantle gradually converge toward the middle of the mesoderm-free area and become thickened in the heart region, foreshadowing the formation of the heart rudiment. At this stage it can be noticed that between the free edges of the mesodermal mantle converging from the right and the left there lie a number of loose cells, similar to mesenchyme cells in their structure. These cells are derived from the ventral edge of the mesodermal mantle. They are the rudiment of the **endocardium**, that is, the endothelial lining of the cavity of the heart. The endocardial cells soon accumulate in the midline as a longitudinal strand and eventually become arranged in the form of a thin-walled tube. The lumen of the tube is the cavity of the heart (Figs. 219, 330). The endocardial tube bifurcates at both ends; at the anterior end its two prolongations are the ventral aortae, and at the posterior end it receives the two vitelline veins – the first venous blood vessels to reach the heart. All these vessels are at first similar to the endocardial tube in that they consist only of a thin layer of endothelium, produced by the mesenchyme cells joined together.

While the endocardial tube is being formed, the edges of the mesodermal mantle, which at this stage may also be called the edges of the lateral plate mesoderm, close in along the midline and fuse with each other. The fusion first occurs under the endocardial tube, between it and the ectoderm. Very soon, however, the visceral layer of mesoderm envelops the endocardial tube on the dorsal side as well. By fusion of the mesodermal layers of the

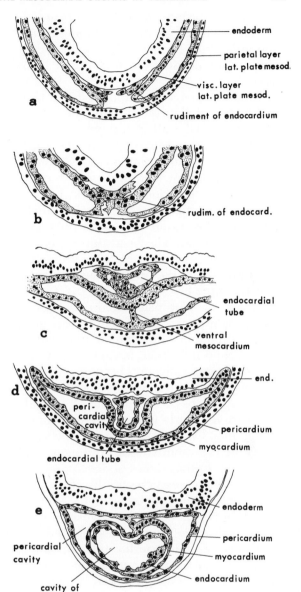

Figure 330. Development of the heart in amphibian embryos. *a, d, e, Triturus; b, Salamandra; c, Rana.* (From Mollier, in Hertwig, 1906.)

right and left side, epithelial partitions are formed above and below the endocardial tube. In analogy to the dorsal and ventral mesentery, these are called the **dorsal** and **ventral mesocardium**. The ventral mesocardium is of a very ephemeral existence; it is very soon perforated, and the coelomic cavities of the right and left side become continuous underneath the endocardial tube. The dorsal mesocardium persists longer but is also dissolved at a later stage. The coelomic cavities expand in the heart region to form the pericardial cavity. The pericardial cavity is initially only a part of the general body cavity, the coelom. It becomes completely separated from the remainder of the coelom, largely owing to the failure of the coelom to develop in the region of the branchial pouches, which lie immediately dorsal to the heart rudiment.

Posteriorly the connection of the pericardial cavity with the rest of the coelom becomes occluded by the developing liver, to which the posterior end of the endocardial tube becomes closely connected. A connective tissue wall developing in this position (at the anterior boundary of the liver) is the **septum transversum**.

From the above description, it will be clear that the pericardial cavity is lined by lateral plate mesoderm. The parietal layer of this mesoderm persists as the epithelial wall of the pericardial cavity, or the **pericardium** proper. The visceral layer adheres to the endocardial tube. This layer differentiates as muscle tissue and thus gives rise to the **myocardium** of the heart.

The heart is at first an almost straight tube and does not show a subdivision into its various chambers. Later the tube becomes inflected in a very characteristic way. Starting from behind, the tube first runs forward, then bends downward and to the right and eventually again to the left, upward and forward. The heart thus becomes coiled in the shape of an S. The degree of the twisting in higher vertebrates is greater than in lower ones, so that in the former the tip of the second inflection comes to lie well posterior to the tip of the first inflection (Fig. 331). The tubular heart rudiment becomes constricted in some places and dilated at others and is thus subdivided into its four main parts. The sinus venosus lies posteriorly; the atrium develops at the tip of the first inflection of the heart; the descending part, from the first to the second inflection, becomes the ventricle; and the part going forward from the second inflection becomes the conus arteriosus.

Before this subdivision is performed, however, the functioning of the heart starts; it begins to pulsate at a regular rhythm. The pulsations of the heart start very early in the development of the embryo, even before the peripheral blood vessels are ready to receive the blood stream.

As the presumptive heart rudiment is being formed, its capacity for performing the further stages of development independently of the normal surroundings increases perceptibly. If the heart rudiment is excised after the end of neurulation and transplanted into an abnormal position or allowed to develop *in vitro*, enclosed in a vesicle of skin, the differentiation goes much farther than in the experiments referred to above. Not only pulsating muscle tissue develops but a cardiac tube is formed, and the tube becomes inflected just as does the heart in normal development (Stöhr, 1924). The rudiment of the heart in this stage, however, is by no means strictly determined in all its parts. The left or right half of the heart rudiment may be excised, and the

30 HOURS   38 HOURS   44 HOURS   47 HOURS   76 HOURS

Figure 331. Twisting of the heart rudiment in a chick embryo (ventral view). A, Atrium; V, ventricle; C, conus arteriosus. (Modified from Patten, 1958.)

remaining half then develops into a complete whole (Ekman, 1925; Copenhaver, 1926). What is more, half of the heart rudiment may be explanted or transplanted, and it still develops into a complete heart. The ability of a half of the heart rudiment to form a whole heart may be used to produce two hearts in the same embryo. For this an incision should be made lengthwise before the two halves of the heart rudiment unite in the middle. Inserting a piece of extraneous tissue, a somite for instance, or leaving the wound to gape may prevent the halvès of the heart rudiment from coming together. Two complete pulsating hearts develop under these conditions (Ekman, 1925). The reverse can also be done: a complete heart rudiment may be superimposed on the intact presumptive heart mesoderm of a host embryo. The two rudiments then fuse into one whole and produce a normal heart (Ekman, 1925; Copenhaver, 1926).

The main points emerging from the foregoing will now be summarized:

1. The heart develops in a very anterior position, in the pharyngeal region. The position of the heart in the thorax (as in an adult tetrapod) is thus secondary and is due to a displacement of the organ in later development.

2. The heart develops from a paired rudiment, uniting in the midline secondarily.

3. Each half of the heart rudiment is able to differentiate even before the two halves fuse.

4. Two heart rudiments may fuse into one organ of normal structure.

5. The functioning of the heart begins at an early stage of development.

The Heart in Higher Vertebrates.   With all this in view, it is easy to understand the development of the heart in the vertebrates having yolky eggs and partial cleavage.

Because of the physiological requirements of the developing embryo (the necessity of establishing circulation), the heart in meroblastic vertebrates develops precociously, before the body of the embryo becomes separated from the yolk sac. The embryo in this stage is still lying flat on the surface of the yolk, and its lateral plate mesoderm is to be found toward the outer parts of the blastodisc. The lateral plate mesoderm is prevented from uniting on the ventral side of the embryo by the intervening yolk. As a result, the two halves of the heart rudiment begin differentiating independently of one another. Two endocardial tubes are actually formed; each becomes invested by the myocardium and surrounded laterally by the pericardial cavity. When the body folds undercut the anterior end of the embryo and the foregut becomes separated anteriorly from the yolk sac, the right and left heart rudiments become able to meet in the midline under the pharynx. The two endocardial tubes come to lie alongside each other and soon fuse into one tube in the cardiac region, while in front and behind the heart the endothelial tubes remain separate, thus leading to a state described earlier for the lower vertebrates (Fig. 332). The visceral walls of the right and left pericardial cavities also meet and fuse above and below the endocardial tubes, forming a single pericardial cavity. The single endocardial tubè is now completely surrounded by the myocardium. In view of the experimental results mentioned above, the fusion of two heart rudiments to form one single organ is not at all surprising.

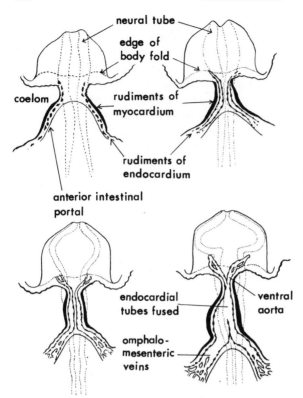

neural tube

edge of
body fold

coelom

rudiments of
myocardium

rudiments of
endocardium

anterior intestinal
portal

endocardial
tubes fused

omphalo-
mesenteric
veins

ventral
aorta

Figure 332. Development of the heart from a paired rudiment in the chick embryo, viewed from the ventral side (semidiagrammatic.) (After Patten, 1958.)

Of all the organs of a vertebrate, the heart is the one which starts its definitive function earliest. It is also greatly dependent in its development on function. It is essential for the development of the heart that a blood stream should actually flow through it. It is true that a heart of a typical shape with recognizable parts will develop even in complete isolation, as in the explantation experiments (Stöhr, 1924), but such an isolated heart soon stops developing further. Also, a heart in its normal position is arrested in its development if in some way or other (interruption of the afferent blood vessels) it is deprived of circulation. The degree of the heart's development and growth appears to be dependent on the volume of blood passing through it or on the size of the animal which the heart supplies with blood. Heart rudiments have been transplanted reciprocally between large and small species of salamanders (Copenhaver, 1930, 1933) and it was found that the hearts of small species grew beyond their usual size in large hosts, and the hearts of large species were undersized in small hosts. In every combination the transplanted heart grew to approximately the same size as the host heart should have grown.

In the vertebrates developing a pulmonary circulation, the heart becomes separated to a greater or lesser degree into a right half, carrying blood to the lungs, and a left half, receiving the blood from the lungs by way of pulmonary veins and sending it to the rest of the body. The first indication of this separation is found in the lungfishes (Dipnoi). In the amphibians, the atrium becomes subdivided by a partition wall arising between the points of entry into the atrium of the sinus venosus and pulmonary vein. After the separation is completed, the right atrium receives blood from the sinus venosus and the left atrium from the lungs by way of the pulmonary vein. Both atria, however, pour out their blood into the ventricle, which remains undivided.

The Mammalian Heart.   The most elaborate transformations are found to occur in the development of the heart in mammals. The task of directing the blood into its various channels is complicated not only by the presence in the adult state of a double circulation (the systemic and the pulmonary circulation) but also by the necessity of providing for a rapid change from fetal to postnatal circulation. The subdivision of the heart into right and left halves is dependent on the cooperation of several structures and carried out in stages.

The atrium is separated into right and left halves first by a primary partition wall (septum primum), which is similar to that found in amphibians. As soon as this partition wall subdivides the cavity of the atrium, however, it is perforated by an opening allowing for intercommunication between the right and left atrial cavities. Consequently, the left atrium is not deprived of a blood flow (on which, as we have seen, the development of the heart is dependent in a high degree) during the intra-uterine life, when the amount of blood passing through the lungs is very small.

At a later stage, a second partition wall (septum secundum) develops in the atrium just to the right of the first, but this remains incomplete, a large **foramen ovale** remaining open in its lower part (Fig. 333, *a*). The foramen ovale does not quite coincide in position with the opening in the primary partition wall; nevertheless, blood may pass through both openings so long as the blood pressure in the right atrium is greater than that in the left atrium, as it actually is during fetal life.

After birth, however, when the pulmonary circulation is fully established, the pressure in the left atrium becomes higher than that in the right atrium. The primary partition wall becomes pressed against the secondary wall, and as a result the previously existing passage becomes closed (see Fig. 333, *b*). Thus the atria become finally separated. Eventually the primary and secondary partition walls of the atrium fuse together.

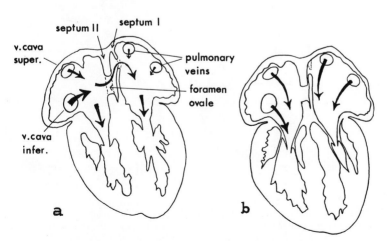

Figure 333.   Section of mammalian heart (diagrammatic), showing the changeover from fetal to postnatal circulation. Arrows show the direction and amount of blood flow.

The atrium originally communicates with the ventricle by way of the atrio-ventricular opening, which is a narrowed part of the heart tube. The separation of this single opening into two is performed by means of connective tissue outgrowths developing on the dorsal and ventral edges of the opening. The outgrowths, known as the **endocardial cushions**, fuse in the middle and are also joined by the lower edge of the primary interatrial partition wall; as a result two canals are left, one leading from the right atrium into the right ventricle and the other leading from the left atrium into the left ventricle. The endocardial cushions also participate in the formation of the atrio-ventricular valves (Fig. 334).

The ventricle becomes partially separated into left and right halves by an indentation of the myocardium at its tip (at the apex of the posteroventral inflection of the heart tube). The developing partition wall is therefore largely muscular but is incomplete. It is supplemented by a membranous (connective tissue) part arising in conjunction with a wall subdividing the conus arteriosus into two channels: one to serve for systemic circulation, and the other for pulmonary circulation. The latter partition wall cuts in backward between the origin of the fourth and sixth pairs of aortic arches in such a way that a ventral channel leads into the arches of the third (carotid) and fourth (systemic) pairs, while the dorsal channel leads into the sixth (pulmonary) pair of arches. The partition wall in the conus arteriosus is spirally twisted so that the ventral channel becomes connected to the left ventricle and the dorsal channel to the right ventricle.

It will be seen that the blood entering the right atrium from the sinus venosus, including the blood from the placental circulation (via the umbilical veins, pp. 272 and 285), is directed into the pulmonary arch (except for the volume of blood passing from the right into the left atrium via the foramen ovale). The pulmonary blood vessels, during the fetal life, cannot take all this blood, neither is there any necessity to have the blood pass through the

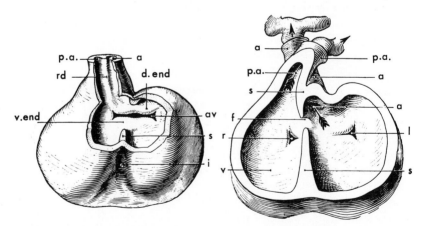

Figure 334. Subdivision of the atrio-ventricular canal in mammals. *a*, Aorta; *a.v.*, atrioventricular foramen; *d.end,* dorsal endocardial cushion; *f*, interventricular foramen; *i*, indentation of ventricular myocardium; *l*, left atrio-ventricular foramen; *p.a.*, pulmonary artery; *r*, right atrio-ventricular foramen; *rd,* ridge separating the conus arteriosus in two channels; *s*, parts of interventricular septum; *v.end,* ventral endocardial cushion; *v*, cavity of right ventricle. (After Kollmann, from Prentiss and Arey, 1917.)

lungs, as they are as yet not serving as respiratory organs. The greater part of the blood passing through the right half of the heart is therefore returned to the systemic circulation by way of the arterial duct (ductus arteriosus), which connects the pulmonary arch to the dorsal aorta. After parturition, the arterial duct becomes closed by a violent contraction of its muscular wall, and all the blood from the right part of the heart is forced into the blood vessels of the lungs. The double circulation thus becomes finally established.

It is a further peculiarity of the mammalian heart that the opening between the sinus venosus and the right atrium broadens out to such an extent that the sinus venosus becomes incorporated into the wall of the right atrium. As a result the main veins (anterior and posterior venae cavae, the coronary vein), which originally entered the sinus venosus, now have separate openings into the right atrium. Similarly, the proximal part of the pulmonary vein is incorporated into the wall of the left atrium, so that there are two, or sometimes even four, pulmonary veins entering the left atrium independently of each other.

14–6 DEVELOPMENT OF THE BLOOD VESSELS

In the adult vertebrate, blood vessels large and small permeate almost all parts of the body. Supernumerary parts of the body, whether they are grafts or results of induction, become vascularized, and the blood vessels, which in this case are additional to the ones produced in normal development, link up with host arteries and veins and are included in the host's blood circulation. It would appear that blood vessels are attracted to penetrate any parts which are in need of a blood vessel supply. Furthermore it appears that a suitable situation for blood vessels is duly reserved in the pattern of organization of any organ. It must be noted, however, that in vertebrates the blood vessels are invariably situated in spaces occupied by connective tissue or its derivatives. Where capillaries seemingly penetrate into epithelium, this is actually tantamount to the invasion of channels or other spaces between epithelial cells by connective tissue from which the endothelial cells of the blood vessels are derived.

The rudiments of the blood vessels are laid down as aggregations of mesenchyme cells. The cells participating in the formation of blood vessels are called **angioblasts**. They are probably always of mesodermal origin. We have seen that in the vascular area of amniotes the walls of the blood vessels are developed from the blood islands in conjunction with the development of the first blood cells (section 11–1). Similar, though more concentrated, blood islands occur in vertebrates with holoblastic cleavage (in particular in amphibians) on the ventral side of the abdomen. In the amniote body proper and in all areas except for the ventral body wall in the anamniotes, the blood vessels develop independently of blood corpuscles. The aggregations of angioblasts become arranged in the form of a flat epithelium surrounding a cavity. The epithelium is the endothelium of the blood vessel; the outer layers of the blood vessel walls are differentiated much later. A student of the anatomy of the adult vertebrates is accustomed to find the blood vessels in the form of tubes of a constant diameter over relatively long stretches. The first blood vessels laid down in the embryo are only rarely in the form of straight tubes. Over large areas the blood vessels are initially laid down in the form of a network (see Figs. 183 and 317). The further development of individual canals in the network depends on the amount and the direction of blood flow. Those channels which happen to come in the line of the greatest blood flow become increased in diameter, develop the connective tissue and the muscular layers and become arteries or veins. The channels that receive less blood remain in the form of capillaries or degenerate and disappear completely. Another form in which early blood vessels appear is as sinuses — extensive irregular spaces surrounded by endothelium. Large sections of some of the larger veins appear in this form (Fig. 335). Some of these sinuses later acquire a more regular tubular form; others remain as such in the adult animal — for instance, the postcardinal "vein" becomes a tubular blood vessel in urodeles but remains essentially in the form of a sinus in the dogfish.

Once the network of endothelial tubes — the rudiments of the blood vessels — has been established, new blood vessels continue to be formed by sprouting and outgrowth of those already present. Lateral branches may form on already existing capillaries, or a capillary may become interrupted and each free end grow out in a new direction. Two outgrowths from dif-

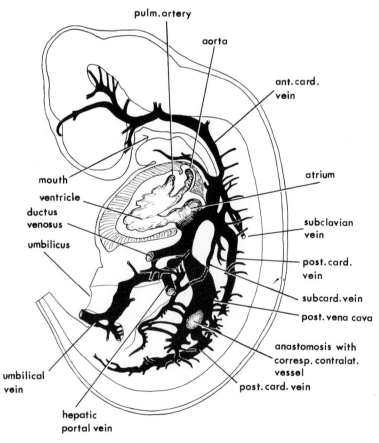

Figure 335.   Venous system of a 12 mm. pig embryo, showing irregular shape of blood vessels, especially in the posterior part of the body. (After Patten, 1958.)

Figure 336. Outgrowth of new capillaries, establishing new channels of circulation. (After Clark, from Arey, 1947.)

ferent blood vessels may contact each other and fuse, thus establishing a new channel for circulation (Fig. 336).

As a result of the extreme plasticity of the blood vessel system, the eventual arrangement of arteries, veins and capillaries in any part of the body is largely dependent on the amount and direction of blood flow in the part in question. In their first formation the embryonic blood vessels also appear in conjunction with other rudiments, suggesting a dependent mode of differentiation, though the dependence is not of a functional nature since the blood vessels develop prior to the establishment of circulation. If the heart rudiment in an amphibian embryo is removed before circulation starts, the main blood vessels continue to develop for some time, until the embryo dies. The exact position of the blood vessel rudiments is probably determined by a process similar to an induction, though this has not been shown conclusively.

Certain locations in the embryo offer preferential conditions for the development of blood vessels. These locations are: (1) between the visceral mesoderm and the endoderm (see Fig. 185); (2) around the kidneys, especially the pronephros and the mesonephros. Close networks of capillaries are always found in these two locations, and they are the site of development of some of the major blood vessels.

The heart obviously belongs to the first group. We have seen that the determination of the heart occurs at an early stage of development, and that as a consequence it shows a high degree of autonomy in its further differentiation. It is noteworthy, nevertheless, that the heart does not develop in embryos from which the endoderm has been removed (Mangold, 1936; Balinsky, 1939; see p. 426). The blood vessels which form the (paired) continuation of the heart tube anteriorly and posteriorly also develop in conjunction with the endodermal parts. The two posterior vessels are the vitelline veins, which collect the blood from the network on the surface of the gut and, in amniotes, from the network on the yolk sac. The anterior prolongations of the heart tube are the ventral aortae, which become connected along the partition walls between the endodermal branchial pouches (see section 15–3) with the dorsal aortae, a pair of blood vessels developing on the dorsal side of the endodermal gut (see Figs. 337 and 338). The vessels conveying blood from the ventral aortae to the dorsal aortae are the **aortic arches**.

The aortic arches develop in a cranio-caudal sequence, and the first to appear is the mandibular arch which ascends between the edge of the mouth and the first (spiracular) branchial pouch. The second aortic arch develops between the first spiracular and the second (first true branchial) pouch, and subsequent aortic arches develop between the more posterior branchial pouches. Six aortic arches are laid down in the embryos of all vertebrates

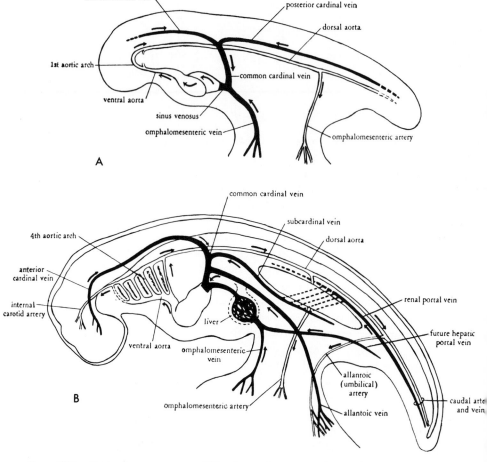

Figure 337.   General arrangement of blood vessels in an early amniote embryo *(A)* and the further development of the circulatory system *(B)*. The arteries are shown in white, the veins in black. (From Moog, 1949.)

except for some very archaic forms (cyclostomes and some selachians), whose number of gill clefts is larger than six (Figs. 339, 340). The dorsal aortae become extended forward into the head and backward throughout the length of the trunk and to the base of the tail. In the trunk region the two dorsal aortae later fuse into one unpaired dorsal aorta, while in the branchial and head region the two aortae remain separate. In the trunk, the dorsal aorta gives off at the level of each myocomma an intersegmental artery. Larger arteries convey blood from the dorsal aorta to the viscera, to the limbs and, in embryonic stages, to the yolk sac (vitelline arteries) and to the allantois (umbilical arteries).

    The blood vessels developing in conjunction with the excretory organs are the **cardinal veins**. The first rudiments of these appear, in Amphibia, in the form of a venous sinus around the pronephros. Very soon prolongations of this sinus are found anteriorly and posteriorly. The posterior prolongation is the postcardinal vein, which develops along the groove between the somites and lateral plates dorsolaterally to the nephrotomes and later becomes closely associated with the mesonephric kidney. The anterior prolongation is the

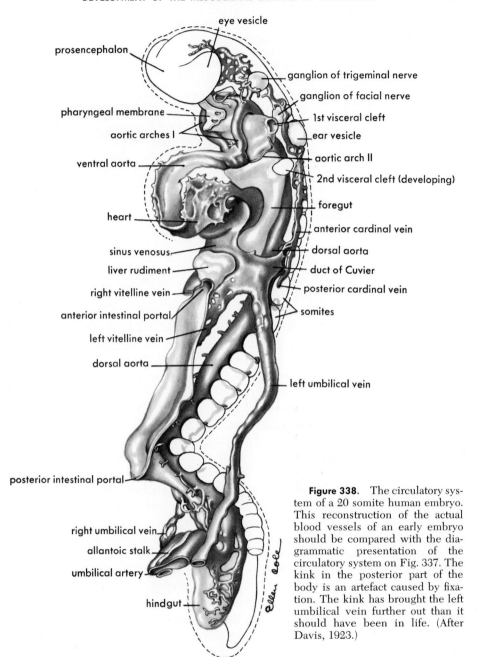

eye vesicle

prosencephalon

ganglion of trigeminal nerve

ganglion of facial nerve

pharyngeal membrane

1st visceral cleft

aortic arches I

ear vesicle

ventral aorta

aortic arch II

2nd visceral cleft (developing)

foregut

heart

anterior cardinal vein

sinus venosus

dorsal aorta

liver rudiment

duct of Cuvier

right vitelline vein

posterior cardinal vein

anterior intestinal portal

somites

left vitelline vein

dorsal aorta

left umbilical vein

posterior intestinal portal

right umbilical vein

allantoic stalk

umbilical artery

hindgut

Figure 338. The circulatory system of a 20 somite human embryo. This reconstruction of the actual blood vessels of an early embryo should be compared with the diagrammatic presentation of the circulatory system on Fig. 337. The kink in the posterior part of the body is an artefact caused by fixation. The kink has brought the left umbilical vein further out than it should have been in life. (After Davis, 1923.)

anterior cardinal vein. This runs forward on the same level as the postcardinal vein, just above the branchial pouches into the head. The anterior cardinal vein and postcardinal vein join at the level of the anterior edge of the pronephros forming the common cardinal vein (**duct of Cuvier**), which runs inward to join the vitelline veins where they enter the heart (see Figs. 337, 338).

At a later stage, a second pair of veins develops in tetrapods on the median side of the mesonephric kidney—the **subcardinal veins**.

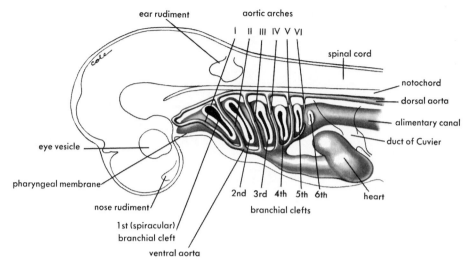

Figure 339.   Relation between the aortic arches and the branchial clefts in a dogfish embryo. (After Balfour, 1881, and Goodrich, 1958.)

This basic pattern of the main blood vessels is laid down with great regularity in embryos of all classes of vertebrates, but it becomes greatly modified as development goes on, especially in the higher vertebrates.

In the fishes and in the amphibian larvae, a number of aortic arches from the third onward supply blood to the gills. The blood flow from the ventral portion of each aortic arch involved is directed into a network of capillaries which develop in the gill lamellae attached to the gill septum or in the filaments of the external gills. From these, the blood then returns by way of collecting vessels into the upper part of the arch and through it to the dorsal aorta. The middle part of the aortic arch becomes greatly reduced in diameter. It becomes lost in the capillary network in the branchial septum but may not be completely interrupted, though the amount of blood which passes through it is small compared with the volume of blood going through the gills.

In amphibians which lose their gills on metamorphosing into the adult stage, the connection between the ventral and dorsal portions of the aortic arches is reinstated by the enlargement of the narrow blood vessels connecting them during the larval stages. The capillary system in the gills is reduced and disappears, and the aortic arches again assume the shape of simple tubes leading from the ventral aorta to the dorsal aorta.

Of the six pairs of aortic arches, the anterior two pairs become degenerate to a greater or lesser extent, but even in the higher vertebrates remnants of the ventral portions of these arches take part in the formation of the branches of the external carotid in the ventral region of the head. The anterior portions of the ventral aortae, which gave rise to the first and second aortic arch, become the **external carotids** (Fig. 340, *E, F*).

In the terrestrial vertebrates (including amphibians after metamorphosis), the third pair of aortic arches become the carotid arches (Fig. 341). The anterior parts of the dorsal aortae now serve to forward the blood from the carotid arch to the dorsal part of the head and to the brain. This blood vessel becomes the **internal carotid artery** (Figs. 340, 341). The sections of the ventral aortae

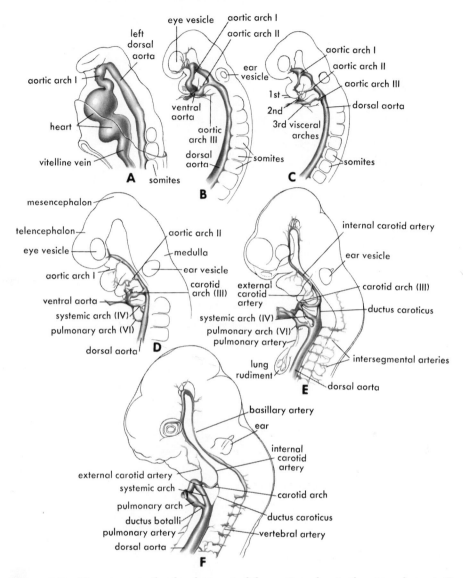

Figure 340. Five stages in the development of the aortic arches in the pig embryo. *A*, Embryo with 10 pairs of somites. *B*, Embryo with 19 pairs of somites. *C*, Embryo with 28 pairs of somites. *D*, Embryo with 36 pairs of somites, 6 mm. *E*, Embryo 12 mm. *F*, Embryo 14 mm. (*A*, enlarged 30 times; *B*, enlarged 14 times; *C*, enlarged 11 times; *D*, enlarged 8 times; *E* and *F* enlarged 6 times.) (After C. H. Heuser, 1923.)

between the points of origin of the fourth and the third (carotid) aortic arch carry blood both to the carotid arches (now the internal carotids) and to the external carotids. They thus become the **common carotids**.

The fourth pair of aortic arches becomes the main channel for the blood flow from the heart to the dorsal aorta and hence to the body. These are the systemic pair of arches (in amphibians and reptiles).

The fifth pair of aortic arches degenerates in all tetrapods except in urodeles, where they carry part of the blood to the dorsal aorta. The general direction of blood flow in the dorsal aorta is from the anterior to the posterior

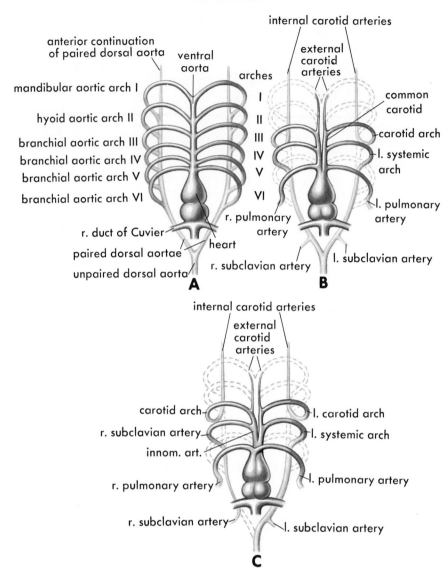

Figure 341. Diagrams of arterial arches (shown in ventral view) in a fish *(A)*, in a frog *(B)*, and in a mammal *(C)*.

end. This direction of blood flow is patent from the level at which the fourth (systemic) arches join the dorsal aortae. However, the anterior prolongations of the paired dorsal aortae serve for supplying blood to the head. This blood enters the dorsal aortae mainly through the carotid arches; the anteriorly directed flow of blood starts therefore from the point of entry of these arches. Between the level where the carotid arches join the dorsal aorta to the level where it is joined by the systemic arches, there is an area of blood stagnation. As in other cases, where a blood vessel is devoid of blood flow, the sections of the dorsal aortae between the carotid and the systemic arches tend to become atrophied; the vessels become attenuated or even completely interrupted. In some urodeles and reptiles this section of the dorsal aorta, known as the **ductus caroticus**, persists as a narrow vessel in the adult stage, but in most terrestrial vertebrates the duct becomes completely reduced and the anterior sections of the dorsal aortae, now becoming a part of the internal carotid artery, are completely separated from the remainder of the dorsal aorta (Fig. 341, *B*).

The sixth pair of aortic arches gives off blood vessels to the lungs (and to the skin in amphibians). It is thus the **pulmonary arch**. The upper part of the pulmonary arch, connecting the base of the pulmonary artery to the dorsal aorta, is known as the **duct of Botalli** (ductus Botalli or ductus arteriosus). In the larvae of amphibians and in the embryonic stages of amniotes, the whole of the pulmonary arch is a fairly large vessel carrying blood from the ventral aorta to the dorsal aorta. This condition changes drastically, however, when the lungs start functioning as respiratory organs. The pulmonary arteries, which had been insignificant blood vessels till that stage, greatly increase in size and take over the blood flow entering the pulmonary arch, while the ducts of Botalli become reduced. They remain as narrow blood vessels in adult urodeles and some reptiles, but in adult frogs and the majority of amniotes the ducts are closed and reduced to a fibrous strand connecting the pulmonary and systemic arteries.

In amniotes—and in mammals in particular—the pattern of aortic arches is modified still further (Fig. 341, *C*). The fifth aortic arch is already greatly reduced at the time of its formation. It is still recognizable as such in embryos of reptiles and birds but is completely lacking in mammals.

A characteristic feature of amniotes is the asymmetry in the development of their systemic arches. Although the aortic arches are laid down as symmetrical pairs of blood vessels, the left systemic arch degenerates in birds and the right systemic arch degenerates in mammals. In mammals, originally both systemic arches reach the paired dorsal aortae, and the latter fuse together posteriorly into the single dorsal aorta. Before their fusion, the paired aortae give off the subclavian arteries laterally. When the right aorta becomes reduced, it is interrupted at its posterior end after the origin of the subclavian artery and just before its connection to the unpaired aorta. In this way, the right systemic arch becomes the channel carrying blood to the right subclavian artery. In later stages, the distinction between the aortic arch and the right subclavian artery is lost, and the whole vessel is then known as the right subclavian artery. It is, therefore, not entirely homologous to the left subclavian artery, which starts, as in lower vertebrates, from the left paired dorsal aorta.

The section of the paired ventral aorta between the branching of the common aorta and the origin of the right common carotid artery becomes what is known as the **innominate artery**.

The reduction of the aortic arches is obviously dependent on the blood flow through these vessels, in the same way as the blood flow has been found to mold the development of vessels from the original capillary networks. The following experiments prove this. In frog tadpoles, all four (third to sixth) aortic arches persist up to metamorphosis, and only then the transformations occur which lead to the adult condition. In the tadpole of the clawed toad, *Xenopus laevis*, the systemic arch on one side was destroyed shortly before metamorphosis. The result was that the carotid arch of the

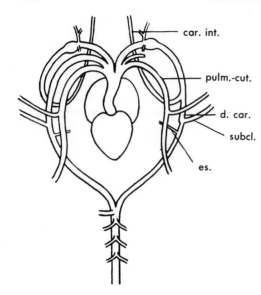

Figure 342. Arrangement of the arterial arches in a frog, *Xenopus laevis*, which had the fourth left aortic arch destroyed in the tadpole stage (ventral view). The blood flows to the dorsal aorta through the third (carotid) arch and the persisting carotid duct (d. car.), car. int., internal carotid artery; es., esophageal artery; pulm.-cut., pulmo-cutaneous artery; subcl., subclavian artery. (From Millard, 1945.)

same side took over the work of the systemic arch; the connection of the carotid arch to the dorsal aorta, which is interrupted in normal development, persisted, and the blood from the heart flowed to the dorsal aorta by way of the carotid arch (Fig. 342—Millard, 1945). Even more interesting, perhaps, is an experiment performed on the chick embryo: the normally persisting right systemic arch was ligatured. The effect was that the left systemic arch now took over the blood flow from the heart to the dorsal aorta and became permanent instead of degenerating (Fig. 343).

At the time of its origin, the ventral aorta is a paired blood vessel (see p. 426) diverging anteriorly from the heart. The two ventral aortae may be quite independent, each giving off a number of aortic arches. Subsequently they fuse in various degrees, forming a single unpaired ventral aorta, especially in fishes. In terrestrial vertebrates, however, the two aortae usually remain separate, except for the most posterior section, where the aortae are connected to the heart.

In diagrams, it is convenient to show the ventral aorta as being a long tube

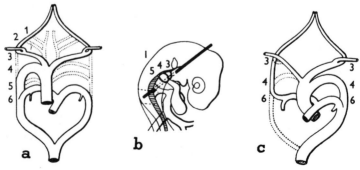

Figure 343. Ligating the aortic arches in a chick embryo. *a*, Normal arrangement of aortic arches in later stages of development (ventral view); *b*, thread in position to ligate the aortic arches on the right side; *c*, suppression of the fourth right aortic arch and retention of the fourth left arch. (After Stephan, from Waddington, 1952.)

extending forward from the heart (see Fig. 341). Actually this representation is not very accurate.

In adult fishes, the ventral aorta is a fairly long blood vessel extending in an anteroposterior direction, but in embryos of all vertebrates the heart is situated underneath (ventral to) the pharynx; the ventral aorta lies more or less in a vertical position and very soon splits to give rise to the roots of the aortic arches, of which only the first two or three pairs lie anterior to the heart, while the rest are developed on a posterior extension of the aorta (see Fig. 339). The pulmonary arteries, when these develop, may be described as being on the extreme backward prolongation of the ventral aortae (Fig. 253); when the last aortic arches are formed, the pulmonary arteries shift upward and can then be seen as originating from these last (sixth) aortic arches.

A further important change in the arterial system in higher vertebrates accompanies the separation of the heart into right and left halves. The pulmonary arteries acquire a separate connection to the right ventricle, while the systemic and carotid arteries are linked up to the left ventricle. The separation occurs from the branching points of these arteries backward toward the heart. The ventral aorta becomes split lengthwise by a partition cutting in at the point where the pulmonary arches branch off from the systemic arches, the latter carrying the carotid arteries with them.

In fishes, the heart remains in the pharyngeal region, but in terrestrial vertebrates the heart is shifted into a more posterior position in the thoracic cavity of the animal. The shift is, in part, owing to the emancipation of the heart from its connection with the gills and, in part, is a result of the development of the neck as a distinct region of the body (see Dalcq, 1960). The posterior position of the heart causes a considerable elongation of some of the blood vessels conveying blood to the head. The carotid arteries are the ones affected most. There is, however, some variety in the way that the elongation is achieved. In the amphibians, mammals, birds and most reptiles, the carotid arch is carried backward together with the heart (and the other aortic arches). It is then the external and internal carotids which become elongated. In snakes and some lizards, on the other hand, the carotid arches remain in the original position, just posterior to the head, and it is the common carotids which elongate. The systemic and pulmonary arches in all terrestrial vertebrates move into the thoracic cavity together with the heart.

The disappearance of the branchial respiratory apparatus, and the development of the neck, separate parts of a previously closely knit system and bring them in widely different positions in the body. The ganglia of the cranial nerves originally connected to the branchial apparatus and developing in part from epibranchial placodes (ganglia VII, IX and X) lie in the head, inside the brain case. The remnants of the visceral skeleton (hyoid and branchial arches) are to be found in the neck as the hyoid bone and the cartilages of the larynx and trachea. The aortic arches lie in the thoracic cavity, and close to them also lies the thymus, another derivative of the branchial pouches (see p. 482).

The vitelline veins on their way to the heart pass through the region in which the liver is developed at a later stage. When the rudiment of the liver is formed (see section 15–4), it envelops the vitelline veins. These break up into a system of hepatic sinusoids permeating the liver lobules and thus give rise to the hepatic portal system. The veins in front of the liver and the heart become hepatic veins, and the parts of the veins caudal to the liver give rise to the **hepatic portal vein**.

In amniotes, the development of the vitelline veins is asymmetric, the right vein tending to degenerate posteriorly and the left vein disappearing, in its most anterior part, in front of the liver. Through a system of anastomoses, however, the continuity of the blood flow is preserved, and a single blood vessel may eventually be built from parts of the two vitelline veins. The parts of the vitelline veins collecting blood from the yolk sac of the embryo disappear at the time of birth, but a branch from the vitelline veins — the **mesenteric vein** — takes over the drainage of blood from the intestinal tract and becomes the main component of the hepatic portal vein of the adult animal.

In embryos of reptiles and birds, the vitelline veins are not completely broken up into hepatic sinusoids as they pass the liver but preserve a large unpaired channel, the **ductus venosus**, by means of which blood passes through the liver and reaches the sinus venosus. After hatching, however, the ductus venosus is occluded, and all the blood of the portal vein is forced into the system of hepatic sinusoids.

The blood vessels of the cardinal system undergo extremely complicated transformations in the course of ontogenetic development and of evolution in vertebrates. The anterior cardinal veins are least changed; they become the internal jugular veins, and the common cardinal veins become the anterior venae cavae. In some mammals, including man, a transverse anastomosis is formed between the anterior cardinal veins of the right and left side, whereupon the connection of the left anterior cardinal to the heart disappears, and all the blood from the head, neck and forelimbs is directed into the right anterior duct of Cuvier which becomes the single anterior vena cava.

The transformations of the veins in the posterior part of the body are very much more drastic: the postcardinal veins, which are the main veins of the posterior trunk region in the fishes and in the early embryos of all vertebrates, are gradually reduced in the embryos of tetrapods.

The first stage in this reduction, as it occurs during the embryonic development in amniotes, is the formation of a venous network on the ventromesial side of the mesonephric kidneys (Fig. 344). This plexus gives rise to veins lying in the same position — the **subcardinal veins**. The subcardinal veins become linked to one another by anastomoses in the midline.

Initially, the subcardinal veins join the postcardinal veins anteriorly and use the latter as a channel for blood outflow. At a later stage, however, a connection becomes established between the network of the subcardinal veins, with their associated plexuses, and the system of veins in the liver. This opens a more direct route to the heart for the blood collected from the kidneys into the subcardinal veins.

At first, the blood from the subcardinal veins passes through the hepatic sinusoids in the tissue of the liver, but as more and more blood goes through, the sinusoids enlarge and develop into one straight channel, passing through the liver directly to the sinus venosus. This channel is the anterior portion of the **posterior vena cava**. (As result of the reduction of part of the hepatic tissue, the posterior vena cava later comes to lie on the edge of the liver.) The middle portion of the posterior vena cava is formed by the joining

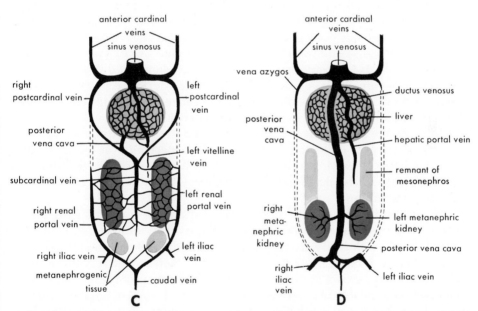

Figure 344. Stages in the transformations of the postcardinal veins in embryos of terrestrial vertebrates (diagrammatic). *A,* Early stage, slightly later than that shown on Figure 337, *A;* the vitelline veins have already given rise to the hepatic sinusoids. *B,* Stage corresponding to that in Figure 337, *B;* allantoic veins not shown. *C,* First appearance of posterior vena cava formed from a connection between the right subcardinal vein and the venous system of the liver. *D,* Posterior vena cava fully developed.

together of smaller vessels belonging to the subcardinal vein system. Eventually, the posterior vena cava, through a system of intermediate smaller vessels, establishes a connection with the iliac veins which collect the blood from the hindlimbs. The posterior vena cava is then established in its final form as it is found in adult amniotes.

The postcardinal veins, in the meantime, lose their significance as channels conveying blood from the posterior part of the body, and their anterior halves leading to the ducts of Cuvier degenerate, leaving behind only insignificant remnants. The posterior parts of the postcardinal veins remain intact as renal portal veins, in amphibians throughout life, and in embryos of reptiles and birds so long as the mesonephric kidneys remain functional. By means of these veins, the mesonephric kidneys are supplied with blood returning from the hindlimbs through the iliac veins and from the caudal vein (where it is present). With the replacement of the mesonephric kidney by the metanephros, the renal portal veins degenerate and disappear, and the iliac veins gain direct connection to the posterior vena cava, as has been explained.

The development of the posterior vena cava is a good illustration of the formative influence of the blood flow on the differentiation of blood vessels: we can observe how the blood flow is not restricted by the arrangement of existing blood vessels but causes the blood vessels to be fashioned in correspondence with the direction and amount of blood flow. Thus, the largest vein of the vertebrate body develops from blood vessels of capillary dimensions where they lie in the line of movement of the blood.

It may be noted that in adult amphibians we may find conditions representing consecutive stages in the development of the posterior vena cava.

Salamanders still possess a pair of postcardinal veins which carry part of the blood from the kidneys to the heart via the ducts of Cuvier. At the same time, they have also a posterior vena cava which is connected at its hind end to the system of veins between the kidneys. The posterior vena cava is a much larger vessel than the postcardinal veins and carries the greater volume of the blood from the kidneys direct to the sinus venosus.

In frogs, the postcardinal veins are reduced in the adult, and all the blood from the kidneys is collected on their mesial aspect into the posterior vena cava. The latter, however, is not yet linked up with the veins of the hind legs. This last stage in the development of the posterior vena cava is completed only in the amniotes.

In addition to the hepatic portal vein and the inferior vena cava, a third system of veins becomes associated with the liver in amniotes. The allantoic (or umbilical) veins go toward the heart in the body wall and enter the ducts of Cuvier. Before joining the latter, the allantoic veins pass very close to the liver. As the liver grows, it makes contact with the allantoic veins, whereupon a connection is established between these and the system of hepatic sinusoids in the liver. More and more blood from the allantoic veins enters the liver, until the main channel into the ducts of Cuvier becomes reduced and obliterated, so that all the blood from the allantois (from the placenta in mammals) goes to the heart by way of the liver. The right allantoic vein later degenerates in all amniotes, the left remaining as the only functional one.

The large amount of blood entering the liver from the left allantoic vein cannot be accommodated in the hepatic sinusoids and eventually makes for itself a broad direct channel which joins the posterior vena cava near the point where it leaves the liver at its anterior end. This direct channel is referred to by students of mammalian (especially human) development as the **ductus venosus**, although it is not homologous to the ductus venosus of reptiles and birds, where it is a section on the pathway of the vitelline veins. After birth and the cessation of placental circulation, the ductus venosus degenerates and becomes transformed into a strand of connective tissue (the **ligamentum venosum**), as often happens with large blood vessels when they cease to be functional. (Compare the fate of the ductus Botalli, p. 441.)

14—7 DEVELOPMENT OF THE REPRODUCTIVE ORGANS

The gonads in vertebrates develop from the upper edge of the visceral layer of lateral plate mesoderm in the posterior half of the body. The first rudiment of the gonad appears as a longitudinal strip of mesodermal epithelium lining the body cavity immediately lateral to the dorsal mesentery. This thickening is called the **germinal ridge**. Initally the ridge is produced by the mesodermal cells, assuming a high columnar shape, but soon the cells become arranged into a compact mass several cells thick, and the ridge protrudes into the coelomic cavity (Fig. 345). Still later, the connection between this cell mass and the peritoneal wall becomes constricted laterally, and the gonad remains suspended from the peritoneal wall only by a double layer of peritoneum—the **mesorchium** or **mesovarium**.

The genital ridges are situated in the same region of the body as the rudiment of the mesonephros and in close spatial association with the latter, the genital ridge being medial to the mesonephros. Although in the later development of vertebrates the genital apparatus becomes associated with the excretory system, the initial stages of the two organ systems are completely independent of each other.

What has been said so far about the formation of the gonad rudiment refers only to its gross morphology. A more detailed microscopic examina-

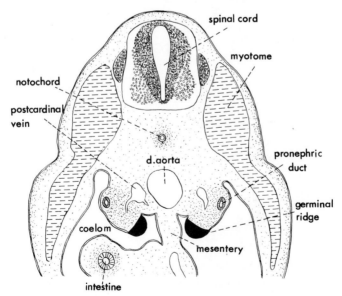

Figure 345.   Transverse section of a mouse embryo to show the position of the germinal ridges and their relation to the mesonephric rudiment and the dorsal mesentery.

tion of the germinal ridge epithelium discloses that it consists of two types of cells. The majority of cells are very similar to the other cells of the peritoneal epithelium, even though they may become columnar in the initial stages of the development of the ridge. The cells of the second type have a very different appearance. They are much larger than the ordinary mesodermal cells, they contain large, more or less vesicular nuclei and their cytoplasm differs from that of the surrounding cells in its staining properties (amphophil instead of acidophil in birds) and, in amphibians, in its higher yolk content. The shape of the cells is nearly spherical, and they do not participate in the epithelial arrangement of the typical mesodermal cells but appear to be interspersed between the cells of the mesodermal epithelium. Cells of this peculiar type are known as the **primordial germ cells** (Fig. 346).

The Origin of the Primordial Germ Cells.   According to views held by many embryologists, only the primordial germ cells are destined to give rise to the gametes (eggs and spermatozoa), while the ordinary mesodermal cells of the genital ridges differentiate into the somatic cells of the adult gonad: the Sertoli cells in the testes, the superficial epithelium and the follicle cells in the ovaries. Whatever their eventual fate, it appears certain that the primordial germ cells have a different origin from the rest of the cells in the germinal ridges, that they first appear in parts of the embryo other than those in which the germinal ridges lie, and that the primordial germ cells reach the germinal ridges after a more or less extensive migration.

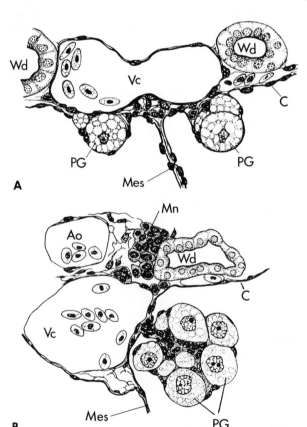

Figure 346. Early stages in the development of gonads in the frog. *A*, Primordial germ cells embedded in the genital ridges. *B*, Indifferent gonad stage. Ao, dorsal aorta; Mn, mesonephrogenic tissue; PG, primordial germ cells; Mes, dorsal mesentery; Vc, posterior cardinal veins; Wd, wolffian duct; C, coelomic epithelium. (From Witschi, 1929.)

In amphibians, the primordial germ cells may be traced back in microscopic sections to a position just above the dorsal mesentery. Here the primordial germ cells lie surrounded by mesenchyme before they migrate into the mesodermal epithelium of the germinal ridges. The median position of the primordial germ cells is probably already a secondary one. In the birds and reptiles, cells identical in their cytological properties with the primordial germ cells have been found in early developmental stages — before the beginning of segmentation of the mesoderm — in the endodermal layer of the extraembryonic part of the blastoderm (Fig. 347). Similarity of appearance cannot, however, be considered as proof that the cells found in the extraembryonic endoderm are the same cells as appear later in the germinal ridges.

To test whether the primordial germ cells are derived from the cells in the extraembryonic endoderm, the latter may be destroyed prior to their migration. In the chick, the cells in question occupy a crescentic area in front of the head end of the embryo (Fig. 348). This area can be destroyed in various ways, as for instance by cauterizing it with a hot needle or irradiating it with radium emanation (Dantschakoff, 1941). As the crescentic area lies well beyond the embryo proper, the development of the latter is unimpaired. At the time when the germinal ridges are formed, no primordial germ cells are to be found in and around the germinal ridges, although the area of the germinal ridges had not been tampered with.

The experiment shows that the peculiar cells of the extraembryonic endoderm are actually the primordial germ cells, which are later incorporated into the gonad.

This conclusion is further supported by the following experiment: if the primordial germ cells are exposed to very weak irradiation with x-rays, while still in the extraembryonic endoderm, they are damaged to a greater or lesser extent but not killed at once. Some of the damaged cells succeed in reaching the site of gonad formation and are to be found there for a short time. Then all the primordial germ cells perish, and there remains a gonad consisting of mesodermal cells only. The gonad may grow and develop further without showing any signs of producing generative cells (Dantschakoff, 1941). Such a gonad, devoid of generative elements, may be called a sterile gonad.

As to the means by which the primordial germ cells travel from the extraembryonic endoderm to their later position in the germinal ridges, it is supposed that they do so largely through the blood vessel system. The cells have been observed to leave the endodermal epithelium, to move slowly into the space between endoderm and mesoderm, and then to penetrate into the blood vessels of the area vasculosa. The primordial germ cells may actually be seen in the blood stream (Fig. 349). Although most of them eventually reach the germinal ridges, some go astray and are found in various parts of the body, where they eventually degenerate.

Further experimental work on the origin of primordial germ cells has been carried out in amphibians. According to the view held by the majority of embryologists, the cytoplasmic material included in the primordial germ cells in amphibians can be traced back as far as the uncleaved egg. Before cleavage begins, cytoplasmic inclusions of a particular kind can be found in the subcortical layer at the vegetal pole of the egg (Fig. 350, A). The inclusions are very rich in RNA. During cleavage, these inclusions move upward along the

Figure 347. *A* and *B*, Primordial germ cells of a chick embryo; two sections of extraembryonic endodermal layer of a chick embryo containing primordial germ cells. Some of these escape into the space between the endoderm and mesoderm and penetrate into the lumen of blood vessels. PG, primordial germ cells; E, endodermal cells. *C*, Germinal ridge of a 3-day-old chick embryo containing primordial germ cells, one of them in mitosis. R, cells of germinal ridge; (From Dantschakoff, 1941.)

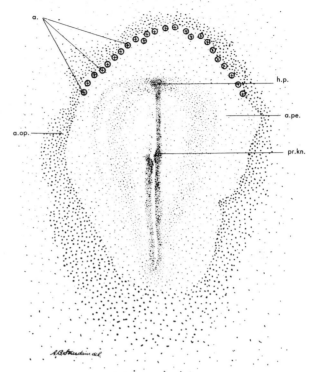

Figure 348. Surface view of a chick embryo in the head process stage, showing the original position of the primordial germ cells on the margin between the area pellucida and the area opaca: a, primordial germ cells (diagrammatic); a.op., area opaca; a.pe., area pellucida; h.p., head process; pr.kn., Hensen's node (primitive knot). (From Swift, 1914.)

cleavage furrows and surround the nuclei of a group of endodermal cells lying right in the middle of the mass of yolky endoderm (Fig. 350, *B, C, D*). The cells receiving this particular cytoplasmic substance are the primordial germ cells, and the substance of the cytoplasmic inclusions has been called the "**germinal plasm**" (Bounoure, 1934; see also Blackler and Fischberg, 1961).

By irradiating the vegetal pole of newly fertilized frog's eggs with ultraviolet light, it is possible to destroy the "germinal plasm" and in this way to greatly reduce the number of primordial germ cells formed in later stages (Bounoure, 1939). By removing the endoderm in the neurula stage, the embryos are completely sterilized (Monroy, 1939; Nieuwkoop, 1946). After the completion of neurulation, the primordial germ cells migrate first to the dorsal region of endoderm, to the dorsal crest, the part of the endodermal wall lying above the cavity of the gut. From here the primordial germ cells move into the mesenchyme of the dorsal mesentery and eventually into the germinal ridges.

The area containing primordial germ cells can be transplanted in the late neurula stage from one embryo to another (Fig. 351), and if the tissues of the donor embryo can be distinguished from the tissues of the host it can be shown that the eggs and spermatozoa are actually derived from the grafted material. In one experiment, the transplantation was made between two subspecies of the clawed toad *Xenopus laevis* differing, among other things, in the properties (size, color) of their eggs. Operated female embryos were reared to the adult stage and laid eggs which in color and size clearly showed

Figure 349. A, Migration of primordial germ cells in the chick embryo. Two primordial germ cells, together with a young erythroblast (Er), in a small blood vessel near the coelomic lining in the gonad area of a chick embryo. B, C, D, Three primordial germ cells in a chick embryo, one (in B) surrounded by mesenchyme, the other two (C and D) already embedded into the coelomic epithelium. One cell (in D) in mitosis; PG, primordial germ cells. (From Dantschakoff, 1941.)

the properties of the donor species. Thus the primordial germ cells transplanted with a section of endoderm at the end of neurulation not only found their way into the gonads but also preserved intact their genetic characters, in spite of the fact that during their development and maturation in the gonads they were surrounded by somatic cells of a different subspecies (Blackler, 1962).

Surprisingly, it appears that the primordial germ cells in urodele amphibians have an entirely different origin from those in frogs and also from those in amniotes. They develop not from the endodermal cells but from cells originally located in the posteroventral parts of the lateral plate mesoderm.

It has been stated earlier (section 14–5) that in salamander embryos it is possible to remove the whole of the endoderm in the neurula stage. The endoderm from another embryo may then be inserted into the empty ecto-mesodermal shell. If the operation is carried out heteroplastically, and if the two

Figure 350.   The germinal cytoplasm and its role in the development of the primordial germ cells in frog embryos *(Xenopus)*. *A*, Germinal cytoplasm (dark areas) near the vegetal pole in the two-cell stage. *B*, Primordial germ cell, near floor of blastocoel, in a midgastrula stage. The germinal cytoplasm (black) surrounds the nucleus, which is light colored. Above is an ordinary endodermal cell with small dark nucleus. *C*, Position of primordial germ cells (square) in a completed neurula (diagrammatic transverse section). *D*, Primordial germ cells in the interior of the endoderm of a completed neurula. Photograph corresponds to the diagram in *C*. (Courtesy of Blackler and Fischberg.)

species are chosen in such a way as to allow the cells of each to be distinguished by some peculiarity, then the derivation of the primordial germ cells, or any other cells, from the endoderm or the mesoderm respectively can be determined with certainty. The experiments were carried out with the purpose of investigating the origin of the primordial germ cells using *Triturus cristatus* as one of the components and *Triturus alpestris* or *Ambystoma mexicanum* as the other. The eggs of the latter two species contain in their cytoplasm considerable amounts of pigment granules, while in the eggs of *Triturus cristatus* pigment granules are either completely absent or very few in number. The operation is a rather difficult one, but a sufficient number of operated embryos survived (Nieuwkoop, 1946). The result was a very clear-cut one: all the primordial germ cells found in the operated embryos had the specific properties (pigmentation) of the species to which the ectoderm and mesoderm belonged and not of the species to which the endoderm belonged. The primordial germ cells were, in this experiment, embedded in germinal ridges consisting of cells of the same species.

Figure 351. Diagram of germ cell transfer operation in a *Xenopus* embryo. The black section of the left embryo, containing the primordial germ cells, is being transplanted into the same position in embryo on the right. (From Blackler and Fischberg, 1961.)

In another series of experiments, the lateral plate mesoderm was transplanted in the same heteroplastic combination (Nieuwkoop, 1946) and it was found that after such operations numbers of primordial germ cells develop from the graft. The primordial germ cells, although mesodermal, do not arise from cells in the germ ridges, but, as in the case of endodermal primordial germ cells, they migrate from their site of origin (ventrolaterally in the posterior part of the body) to the area above the dorsal mesentery and then into the germ ridges.

The conclusion seems inevitable that the primordial germ cells are derived from different germinal layers in the urodele amphibians and in the frogs. In many invertebrates, however (*Ascaris, Sagitta*, some insects), the primordial germ cells are known to be distinguishable in very early cleavage stages even before the germinal layers become segregated. The primordial germ cells can thus be considered as not belonging to any of the germ layers. This is in contrast to the somatic parts of the gonads and the auxiliary parts of the sexual organs (ducts, etc.) which are mesodermal.

As to the mechanism by which the primordial germ cells in the amphibians reach their destination, it is ameboid movement of the cells themselves. There is no reason to suppose that blood vessels play any part in their transport.

No experimental investigations have been carried out on the origin of the primordial germ cells in human embryos, but careful observations show that these are first found in the endodermal epithelium of the yolk sac in the vicinity of the allantoic stalk (Fig. 352), and that from there the germ cells

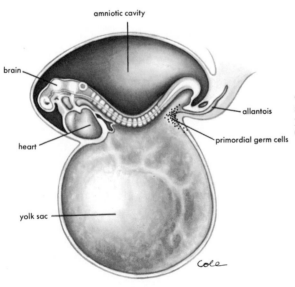

amniotic cavity

brain

allantois

heart

primordial germ cells

yolk sac

Cole

Figure 352. An early human embryo (3 mm. about 4 weeks), showing the original position of primordial germ cells (black dots). (From Witschi, 1948.)

migrate into the adjoining mesenchyme and eventually take up their position in the germinal ridges (Witschi, 1948).

In mice, on the other hand, investigations comparable to those done on birds and amphibians have been carried out. As in man, the primary germ cells first occur in the endoderm and later migrate into the germ ridges. These cells contain large quantities of alkaline phosphatase in early embryonic stages when this enzyme is absent from other cells of the embryo (compare p. 514). By using a special histochemical stain for alkaline phosphatase on sections, therefore, it is possible to distinguish the primary germ cells and to follow their migration from the gut into the dorsal mesentery and then into the germinal ridges. (Mintz, 1960). Originally there are less than a hundred primary germ cells in a mouse embryo, but during their migration the cells increase in number by repeated mitosis, so that eventually 5,000 or more cells are present. The primary germ cells are extremely sensitive to x-rays, and if the female mice are irradiated between the eighth and twelfth day of gestation with a dose of 400r, all or almost all the germ cells are killed off before they reach the germinal ridges. The germinal ridges develop nevertheless and differentiate into gonadal tissue which is, however, completely sterile — devoid of sex cells or their predecessors (Mintz, 1960).

Differentiation of the Gonads. After arriving in the germinal ridges, the primordial germ cells become embedded in the epithelium of the germinal ridge. At the same time, the germinal ridge epithelium becomes convex toward the coelomic cavity and, on its dorsal side, forms a hollow which is filled initially with loose undifferentiated mesenchyme. Subsequently, this loose mesenchyme is partly replaced by compact strands of cells migrating into the gonad from the mesonephrogenic cord — the **primitive sex cords** (Witschi, 1956; Nieuwkoop and Faber, 1956). (Students of human embryology, however, usually assume that the compact strands of cells are derived from the germinal ridge epithelium.) The epithelium of the germinal ridge (originally a thickening of the coelomic epithelium) which forms the surface of the gonad is known as the **cortex** of the gonad. The primitive sex cords (the strands of compactly arranged cells in the interior of the gonad) constitute its **medulla** (Fig. 353). The remainder of the loose mesenchyme serves as the pathway for the blood vessels supplying the gonad.

In the foregoing, no distinction has been made between the development of the ovaries and the testes. In the early stages of organogenesis with which we are concerned here, there is practically no difference in the development of the gonads of the two sexes, and the gonad in these stages may be called the **indifferent gonad.** Only with the onset of histological differentiation do the testes and the ovaries become increasingly different from each other.

In the male embryos, the primordial germ cells migrate from the cortex of the gonad, in which they were originally embedded, into the primitive sex cords of the medulla (Fig. 354), which forthwith become hollowed out and are thus converted more or less directly into the seminiferous tubules. The primordial germ cells give rise to the spermatogonia and subsequently to the spermatozoa, while the Sertoli cells are derived from the sex cords. The seminiferous tubules become connected to the **rete testis,** a system of very thin tubules developing in the dorsal part of the gonad, probably from the same

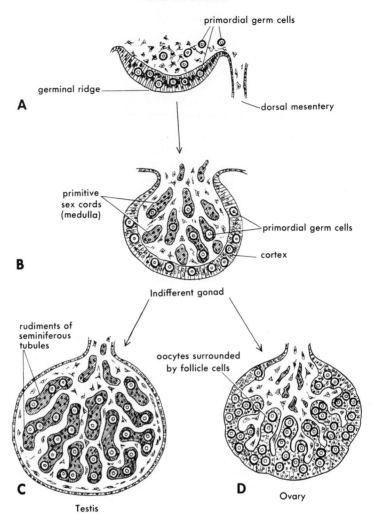

Figure 353. Diagram showing development of gonads in higher vertebrates. *A*, Genital ridge stage; primordial germ cells partly embedded in epithelium of the ridge and located partly in the adjacent mesenchyme. *B*, Indifferent gonad, germ cells in the cortex and in primary sex cords. *C*, Gonad differentiating as testis; cortex reduced; germ cells in sex cords (future seminiferous tubules). *D*, Gonad differentiating as ovary; primary sex cords reduced; proliferating cortex contains the germ cells.

material from which the seminal tubules have been built. The canals of the rete testis, in their turn, form connections to the adjoining tubules of the mesonephros. Thus a pathway is established from the male gonad, via the mesonephros, to the wolffian duct, which in vertebrates serves as the outlet for the sperm. While the medulla of the testis becomes its functional part, the cortex undergoes reduction and is converted into a thin epithelial layer covering the coelomic surface of the testis.

In female embryos, the medulla of the gonad becomes reduced, the primary sex cords are resorbed, and the interior of the mature gonad is filled with loose mesenchyme permeated by blood vessels. The primordial germ cells remain embedded in the cortex, which greatly increases in thickness. During the growth of the gonad, the masses of cortical cells become split up on the

Figure 354. Primordial germ cells embedded in the primitive sex cords (future seminiferous tubules) in a male, 11-day chick embryo. pr.o., primordial germ cells, str., mesenchyme, sc., sex cords; p.c., cell in sex cord. (From Swift, 1916.)

inner surface of the cortex into groups and strands of cells surrounding one or several primordial germ cells. These then become the primary oocytes which enter in the initial stages of oogenesis (see p. 56). The primordial germ cells lying nearer the surface of the cortex retain their undifferentiated state longer and serve for the production of eggs at a later stage in the female's life.

Special features in the development of gonads in some groups of animals will now be noted.

In the ovaries of amphibians, the degenerating medulla becomes cavitated, so that the mature gonad acquires the form of a sack with a hollow space (or rather with several hollow spaces) in the interior (Fig. 355). The mature eggs bulge into these internal cavities. When ovulation occurs, however, the external surface of the gonad becomes ruptured, and the eggs are shed not into the internal cavity but into the coelom.

In birds, with some rare exceptions, only the left ovary becomes fully developed. From the start, more primordial germ cells enter the left germinal ridge, and only here the ovarian cortex acquires a typical structure. The gonad on the right side remains in the state of an indifferent gonad, with the primary sex cords not reduced. The primordial germ cells in the right gonad eventually degenerate. However, if the left gonad is removed by operation, the right gonad enters into a stage of compensatory growth and differentiates progressively. The right gonad then acquires the general structure not of an ovary but of a testis and even starts to secrete male hormones. Under the influence of the male hormones, the bird shows some external features of the

Figure 355. Female gonad of a frog tadpole in early stages of differentiation: c, cortex of gonad; gc, germ cells; mo, mesovarium; cav, cavity of ovary; coel, coelom. (From Witschi, 1929; photograph retouched.)

male sex (especially in color and shape of the feathers) even though it was and remains a genetic female.

Something similar has been observed in male toads in which the anterior ends of the germinal ridges do not differentiate fully (as testes) but retain the state of an indifferent gonad. This part of the gonad is known as **Bidder's organ**. If the testes are removed, the Bidder's organs start growing and differentiate into fully functional ovaries. Sex reversal occurs here in the opposite direction to that in birds.

The sex conversions show that the primordial germ cells are not determined to become gametes of any sex in particular. Their ultimate fate depends on whether they remain in the cortex of the gonad or whether they are transferred to the medulla. Where the medulla develops progressively, the germ cells give rise to spermatozoa. Where the medulla is reduced and the cortex is retained and enlarged, the primordial sex cells develop into eggs.

Development of the Genital Ducts. An essential part of the genital organs are the **genital ducts** by means of which the sex cells (ova and spermatozoa) are passed to the exterior or to an other location where fertilization can take place.

The channels by which the spermatozoa are conveyed from the testes are the wolffian ducts (Fig. 356). The seminiferous tubules are connected to the wolffian ducts through the rete testis and a number of mesonephric tubules which become the **epididymis**. In fishes (except for the bony fishes, whose gonaducts are not comparable with those of other vertebrates) and in amphibians, the wolffian ducts serve simultaneously for the passage of urine from the mesonephros and of the spermatozoa from the testes. There may be, however, a certain degree of segregation between the genital and the excretory functions: the anterior part of the kidney and the corresponding part of the wolffian

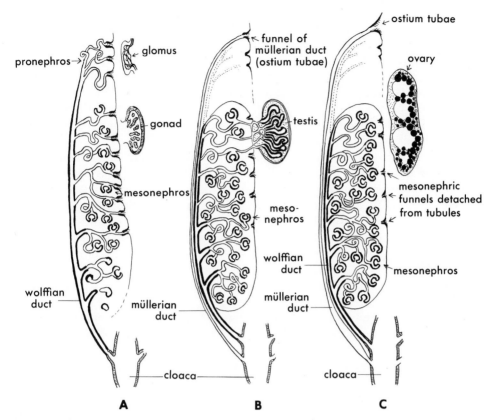

Figure 356. Diagrams showing the transition from the indifferent stage of the urogenital system *(A)* into the male condition *(B)* and the female condition *(C)* in frogs. Note the presence of the müllerian duct in both sexes.

duct serving mainly for reproductive functions, while the posterior part of the mesonephros carries out the main part of excretion (in selachians and in urodeles). Nevertheless, both the spermatozoa and the urine pass eventually into the cloaca through the same duct.

In amniotes, the mesonephros ceases to be an excretory organ and the only part remaining functional is that which in the males develops as epididymis. The wolffian duct becomes the vas deferens, serving only for reproduction.

In embryos of the female sex, the development of the wolffian duct starts in the same way as in male embryos. In anamniotes, it functions throughout life as the pathway for urine. In amniotes, the wolffian duct is laid down in connection with the development of the pronephros and mesonephros. When the mesonephros ceases to function as an excretory organ, the wolffian duct degenerates.

In addition to the wolffian ducts, a second pair of genital ducts, the **müllerian ducts** (Fig. 356), are formed in all vertebrates (again with the exception of bony fishes). At their anterior ends, the müllerian ducts open by a funnel-shaped **ostium tubae** into the coelomic cavity, and in adult females the müllerian ducts serve as channels for the eggs, that is, as **oviducts**. Although functional only in females, the müllerian ducts develop initially in embryos of both sexes. The development starts at the anterior end with the ostium tubae. In lower vertebrates (selachians, amphibians) the ostium tubae is the surviving funnel (nephrostome) of one of the pronephric tubules, which remains intact after the rest of the pronephros degenerates and is resorbed (there are indications that two or more pronephric nephrostomes may fuse to form the ostium). The deep end of the ostium starts growing in a backward direction retroperitoneally and reaches the wolffian duct. It then continues its growth alongside the wolffian duct until it reaches the cloaca and fuses with the cloacal wall.

In higher vertebrates, no nephrostomes remain after the degeneration of the pronephros, but the coelomic epithelium becomes thickened in the area where the pronephros was connected to the coelom. This thickening, which is elongated in a craniocaudal direction, sinks in, forming a longitudinal groove, and later it rolls into a tube. The tube remains open and in communication with the coelom anteriorly, but is completely closed posteriorly, where its free end is imbedded in the retroperitoneal connective tissue. At this stage, the rudiment of the müllerian duct becomes essentially similar to the initial stage of the duct in anamniotes, where it starts growing from a remnant of the pronephric nephrostome. The opening of the tube anteriorly, of course, becomes the newly formed ostium tubae. There follows a backward growth of the müllerian duct alongside the wolffian duct and its connection to the cloaca.

The details of the growth of the müllerian ducts are not very well known, and it appears that they vary to some extent in different animals. It is questionable to what extent the wolffian duct contributes to the development of the müllerian duct, if at all. It has been found, however, that if the wolffian duct

Figure 357. Diagram showing the relations between different parts of the urogenital system, based on experiments with bird embryos. The left side shows the normal urogenital system in the indifferent stage. The right side shows the effects of cessation of the growth of the wolffian duct at the point indicated by arrow. The undifferentiated nephrogenic tissues are stippled. *A*, adrenal gland; *G*, gonad; *K*, metanephric kidney; *M*, mesonephros; *MD*, müllerian duct; *U*, ureter; *WD*, wolffian duct. (From Gruenwald, 1952.)

is incomplete because its outgrowth was interrupted in early stages (see p. 419), the müllerian duct, developing at a very much later stage, grows backward only as far as the posterior end of the wolffian duct (Gruenwald, 1952; Fig. 357). It appears that the wolffian duct in some way provides a path for the subsequent growth of the müllerian duct, even if it does not itself contribute material for the elongation of the latter.

The müllerian duct initially develops in both male and female embryos, although it becomes functional in the latter sex only. In this way a most peculiar situation arises, namely, that embryos of both sexes possess a double set of genital ducts: the wolffian ducts, which in the male sex function as the vasa deferentia, and the müllerian ducts, which become the oviducts in the female sex. This condition of the genital ducts can be called the indifferent stage in respect of sex. In chick embryos this condition prevails up to the ninth day of incubation, and in a human embryo to the age of about two and one-half months. After this age, the ducts of the opposite sex regress (Fig. 358). The müllerian ducts in male embryos of amniotes disappear practically completely. The wolffian ducts in female embryos are reduced to a lesser degree: in birds, the wolffian ducts persist as rudimentary structures even in the adult state, and in mammals and man small remnants of wolffian ducts may

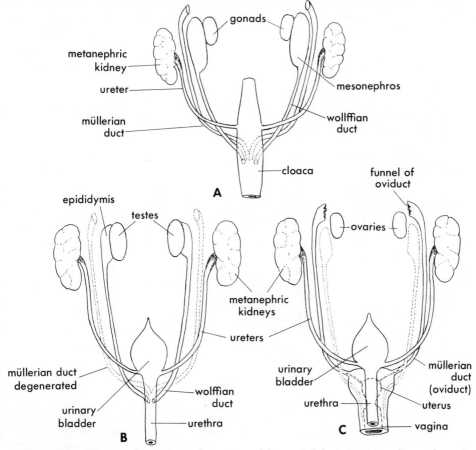

Figure 358. Diagram showing transformations of the genital ducts in mammalian embryos in transition from an indifferent stage (A) to the male (B) and female (C) condition.

also remain. In birds, the right müllerian duct becomes reduced in correspondence with the reduction of the right gonad, while the left duct becomes the functional oviduct.

The progressive development of the genital ducts, corresponding to the sex of the embryo, and the reduction of the genital ducts of the opposite sex are the result of the action of sex hormones which start being secreted by the gonads when these emerge from the indifferent state and differentiate into either testes or ovaries. The hormones are secreted not by the germ cells (future eggs and spermatozoa) but by the somatic cells of the gonads. The female hormones are believed to be secreted by cells of the cortex; the male hormones are produced by some of the cells of the medulla (the future interstitial cells).

A proof that the differentiation of the genital ducts is under hormonal control has been provided by experiments in which sex hormones were injected into embryos of birds or mammals, or sex hormones were added to water in which the larvae of amphibians were being reared. Figure 359 shows the result of one such experiment performed with chick embryos. The injection of a female hormone into a male embryo caused the retention and hypertrophy of the müllerian ducts (compare with normal male of same age; Fig. 359, B and C. Injection of a male hormone into a female embryo caused the müllerian ducts to disappear almost completely and the wolffian ducts to increase greatly in size. In these experiments the gonads were not affected, so that the original sex of the treated embryos could be easily ascertained. Essentially similar results were produced in numerous experiments on other animals. (For a review see Willier, 1955.)

The results of sex hormone injections may be checked by experiments of castration of early embryos. In birds, castrated embryos, female as well as male, retain both müllerian and wolffian ducts and remain thus in an indiffer-

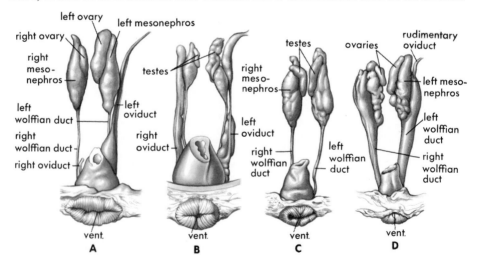

Figure 359. Development of the sex ducts in chick embryos after treatment with sex hormones. A, Normal female embryo incubated for 18 days. B, Male embryo treated with female hormone; both oviducts are present and greatly hypertrophied. C, Normal male embryo of 17 days, showing complete absence of oviducts. D, Female embryo treated with male hormone; the oviducts are absent except for small fragments anteriorly, and the wolffian ducts are greatly hypertrophied. (From Willier, Weiss and Hamburger, 1955.)

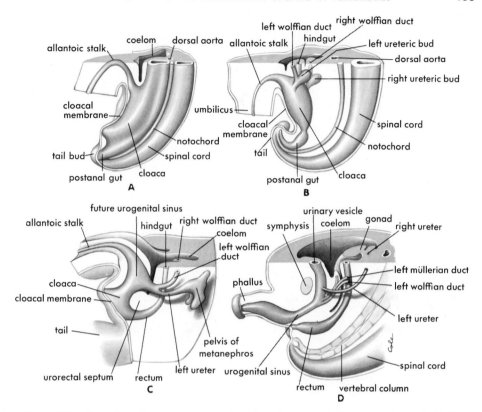

Figure 360.   Transformations occurring in the cloacal region of a human embryo. *A*, Embryo at 15 days, with cloaca connected to hindgut and allantoic stalk and closed ventrally by cloacal membrane. *B*, Embryo at 25 to 27 days; the wolffian ducts have established connection with the cloaca and produced ureteric buds on their dorsal side. *C*, Embryo at 32 to 33 days; cloaca is being subdivided into the urogenital sinus and the rectum. *D*, Embryo at nine weeks; subdivision of cloaca into the urogenital sinus and the rectum is completed; the ureters enter the urogenital sinus independently of the wolffian ducts; müllerian ducts have been formed and are fused near their entry into the urogenital sinus (compare with Figure 361). (From Kollmann, 1907.)

ent condition as regards the genital duct system. Castrated mammalian embryos of both sexes tend to develop according to the female sex pattern: their müllerian ducts develop progressively, but the wolffian ducts degenerate. This is interpreted as showing that in mammals it is the male hormone which mainly causes differentiation of the secondary sex characters, while the female characters do not need special stimulation for their development (see Willier, 1955).

The dependence of the development of sexual characters on hormones has been the subject of very numerous investigations, which could not be reviewed here. For further information on this subject the student is referred to Burns, 1961.

Differentiation of the Cloacal Region and the External Genitalia in Mammals. In amphibians, reptiles and birds, the ducts carrying excretory products (the wolffian ducts and ureters) as well as the genital ducts carrying eggs and sperm (the oviducts and vasa deferentia) open into the posterior section of the endodermal gut—the **cloaca**. The cloacal opening thus serves, in these animals, for the exit of feces, urine and the sex cells. In mammals, the cloaca becomes subdivided so that the channel for feces is separated from the pathway serving for the conveyance of urine and sex products (see Fig. 360).

In early mammalian embryos, the cloaca is a widened posterior end of the hindgut, which does not open to the exterior but is closed by the cloacal membrane. On its ventral side the cloaca gives off the allantoic stalk, which enters the umbilicus, and laterally it receives the wolffian ducts coming from the mesonephros. The subdivision of the cloaca is achieved by the backward growth of a mass of mesenchyme lying in the angle between the ventral surface of the hindgut and the dorsal surface of the allantoic stalk, which is known as the **urorectal** or **cloacal septum**. As the urorectal septum extends backward the cloaca is split into a dorsal and a ventral part. In the process of this subdivision, the openings of the wolffian ducts become assigned to the ventral part, which becomes the urogenital sinus, while the dorsal part becomes the rectum. The urorectal septum eventually reaches the cloacal membrane and fuses with it, thus completing the separation of the two parts of the cloaca. The perforation of the dorsal part of the original cloacal membrane gives the rectum an opening to the exterior (the anus). The perforation of the ventral part of the membrane forms an opening for the urogenital sinus. The external surface of the wall separating the two openings becomes the **perineum**.

The pair of wolffian ducts which enter the urogenital sinus is later joined by two further pairs of ducts. The first of these is the pair of ureters. Originally, the ureters develop as branches sprouting out from the wolffian ducts. In later stages, however, the terminal portions of the wolffian ducts become incorporated into the wall of the cloaca, with the result that the ureters now enter the cloaca directly and independently of the wolffian ducts. (Compare similar changes in the veins entering the heart, p. 433.)

Once they have become independent of the wolffian ducts, the ureters shift in a cranial direction, and their openings come to lie considerably farther forward than the openings of the wolffian ducts.

Lastly, the müllerian ducts reach the cloaca. During their initial development and growth, the müllerian ducts are situated laterally to the wolffian ducts. The posterior ends of the müllerian ducts, however, pass over the wolffian ducts and contact the urogenital sinus mid-dorsally, between the wolffian ducts. The terminal sections of the müllerian ducts closely approach one another and fuse partially (Fig. 361).

The urogenital sinus is continuous anteriorly with the stalk of the allantois. After the ureters have become separated from the wolffian duct and have moved to a more anterior position, the part of the urogenital sinus with the openings of the ureters, together with the adjacent part of the allantoic stalk, expand to form the **urinary bladder**. The canal leading from the bladder to the umbilicus (the **urachus**) later closes and degenerates. The portion of the urogenital sinus immediately following the bladder becomes narrow and develops as the **urethra**.

The external opening of the urogenital sinus is flanked on two sides by elongated thickenings — the genital folds. Anteroventral to the opening of the urogenital sinus, the genital folds join and form a median outgrowth, the **genital tubercle**, which is the rudiment of the **phallus** (Fig. 362).

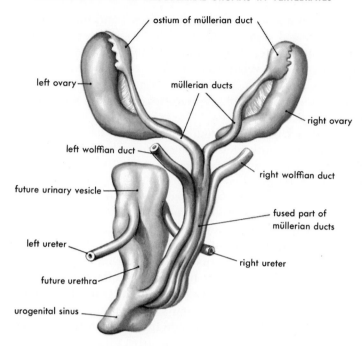

Figure 361. Connections of the genital and urinary ducts in a female human embryo of 29 mm. (beginning of third month) in which the genital ducts are still in the indifferent stage. (From Kollmann, 1907.)

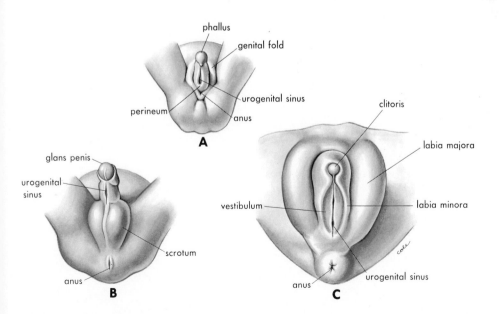

Figure 362. Development of external genitalia in human embryos. *A*, Indifferent stage in an embryo of 29 mm. (beginning third month). *B*, Male embryo of 145 mm. (16 weeks). *C*, Female embryo of 150 mm. (16 weeks). (From Kollmann, 1907.)

Just as did the gonads in the earliest stages and the genital ducts some-what later, the cloacal region with its associated structures, as described so far, represents an indifferent condition which does not allow for the distinction of the two sexes. When the secretion of sex hormones from the differentiating gonads begins, the urogenital sinus and the rudiments of the external genitalia undergo specific changes together with the changes occurring in the genital ducts.

In the male sex, the müllerian ducts degenerate; the rudiment of the phallus grows rapidly and becomes the penis. The genital folds fuse on the posterior surface of the penis, closing the original opening of the urogenital sinus and forming the urethral canal of the penis (Fig. 362, *b*). The urethral canal of the penis is continuous proximally with the part of the urethra developed from the urogenital sinus and bears in its most anterior portion the openings of the wolffian ducts (now the vasa deferentia).

In the female sex, the approximated portions of the müllerian ducts fuse and from these develop the **uterus** and the **vagina** (Fig. 358, *c*), while the upper parts of the müllerian ducts become the **fallopian tubes**. The wolffian ducts degenerate. The phallus grows only slightly and becomes the **clitoris**. The posterior portion of the urogenital sinus widens out to the exterior, so that the short urethra and the vagina open independently into the **vestibulum**, which is the widened posterior part of the urogenital sinus. The genital folds do not fuse and remain as the **labia minora** (Fig. 362, *c*).

15

Development of the Endodermal Organs in Vertebrates

15–1 THE RELATION BETWEEN THE ARCHENTERON AND THE DEFINITIVE ALIMENTARY CANAL

The relation between the archenteron and the definitive alimentary canal is very different in vertebrates with complete cleavage from that in those with incomplete (meroblastic) cleavage.

The Relation in Lower Vertebrates. The archenteron in *Amphioxus* is originally lined with presumptive endoderm, presumptive mesoderm and presumptive notochord cells. When the notochord and the mesoderm are segregated from the endoderm, the latter closes the gap on its dorsal side (see section 8–3), and the resulting cavity becomes the cavity of the alimentary canal.

In holoblastic vertebrates—cyclostomes, ganoid fishes, lungfishes, and amphibians—the presumptive notochord and mesoderm also participate in the lining of the archenteron, forming its roof. This roof is segregated from the endoderm and the endodermal cavity which is closed by the fusion of the free edges of the endodermal layer.

The resulting endodermal cavity consists of three unequal portions. The anterior portion is dilated and lined by a relatively thin endodermal epithelium. This part is usually referred to as the **foregut**. The following portion is called the **midgut**. The cavity of the midgut is narrower. Dorsally it is lined by a rather thin epithelium, but the ventral wall consists of a mass of large cells containing abundant yolk; the wall here is therefore very thick. The most posterior part of the cavity which adjoins the blastopore may be distinguished as the **hindgut**.

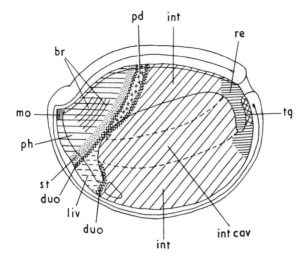

Figure 363. Fate map of the endodermal organs in the neurula of a frog. The embryo is represented as being cut in half in the median plane and viewed from side of the cut surface. br, branchial pouches; duo, duodenum; int, small intestine; int cav, region in which the cavity of the intestine will later develop; liv, liver; mo, mouth; pd, dorsal pancreas; ph, pharynx; re, rectum; st, stomach; tg, postanal gut. (From Tahara and Nakamura, 1961.)

The fate of the various parts of the endodermal lining of the fore- and midgut in amphibians has been elucidated by the method of local vital staining (in newts by Balinsky, 1947; in frogs by Nakamura and Tahara, 1953; Tahara and Nakamura, 1961 — Fig. 363). To stain the inner surface of the gut, cuts were made through the body wall (in some experiments through the neural plate) and pieces of agar soaked in vital stain were applied to the endoderm from the inside. After the stain was taken up by the endodermal cells, the agar was removed; the wound healed easily, and the embryos continued to develop apparently quite normally.

In the neurula stage, the ventral wall of the foregut becomes flattened out and later even folded slightly upward. The cavity is thus subdivided into two pocketlike recesses. The larger anterior one, lying immediately underneath the brain, gives rise to the cavities of the mouth and of the branchial region. The posterior pocket, bordering on the mass of the yolk-laden cells of the midgut, is known as the **liver diverticulum** (or hepatic diverticulum), although in addition to giving rise to the rudiments of the liver and the pancreas it also participates in the formation of the stomach and the duodenum (Balinsky, 1947). It is rather remarkable that in frogs the liver diverticulum is extended downward and backward until the endoderm is perforated, and the cavity of the gut opens into the space between the endoderm and mesoderm on the ventral side of the embryo. The significance of this perforation is not known.

The liver diverticulum becomes extended as a funnel-shaped invagination farther and farther in a posteroventral direction (compare Fig. 364, *c*, *d*, *f*), drawing into it the rudiments which were originally located in the walls of the broadened cavity of the foregut (such as the rudiments of the anterior part of the duodenum, stomach and esophagus). These rudiments become reshaped in the form of a narrow tube. This can best be shown by considering the development of the stomach in the frog embryo. In the neurula stage, the presumptive material of the stomach is arranged in the form of a narrow ring (Fig. 365, *a*), the ventral part of which lies just in front of the liver diverticulum; the dorsal part occupies the roof of the gut just at the mouth of the midgut, and the right and left parts obliquely cross the lateral

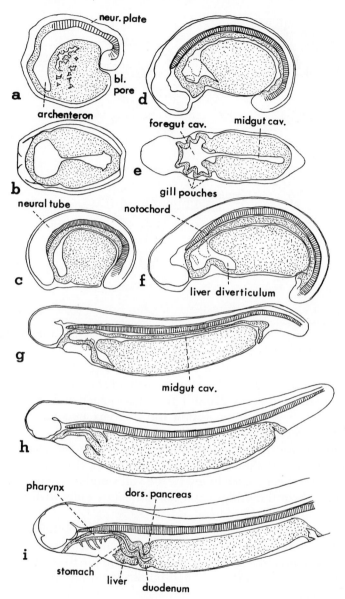

Figure 364. Development of the endodermal organs in the newt *Triturus taeniatus*, from the neurula stage to swimming larva. *b*, *e*, Frontal sections; all others are median sections. (From Balinsky, 1947.)

walls of the foregut. Figure 365, *b*, shows how this ring contracts and at the same time broadens until eventually the rudiment of the stomach becomes more or less barrel-shaped, with a fairly narrow cavity. The tube is constricted to an extreme degree between the pharynx and the stomach and may even be temporarily occluded in this region, which becomes the rudiment of the esophagus; a very short section of the gut in the embryo.

The part of the gut in front of the stomach rudiment also elongates, but instead of becoming tubular it is flattened dorsoventrally and expanded sideways. Most of this cavity becomes the pharynx. The floor of the pharynx

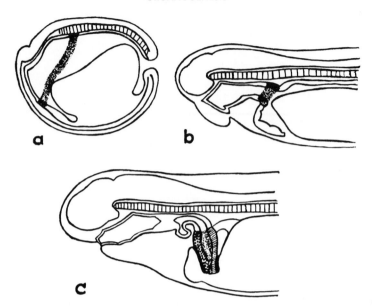

Figure 365. Development of the stomach in a frog embryo (after experiments with vital staining). *a*, Position of the presumptive gastric endoderm (stippled) in the neurula stage; *b*, constriction of the alimentary canal in the stomach region; *c*, elongation of the stomach rudiment. (From Nakamura and Tahara, 1953.)

is raised, partially as a result of the increase of the heart rudiment, which develops just underneath. The lateral edges of the pharynx are drawn outward even more and form the gill pouches, which will be dealt with in section 15–3. The epithelium lining the pharynx becomes rather thin, in contrast to the lining of the rest of the alimentary canal.

The part of the liver diverticulum posterior to the stomach retains a fairly broad cavity. At the same time, the cavity of the midgut (in urodeles and in most frogs) become occluded by the yolky endodermal cells. For a time there is no cavity in the midgut and the gut cavity ends with the liver diverticulum.

Subsequently, the centrally lying yolky cells of the midgut break down and become resorbed, and the remaining cells are rearranged around a new cavity which extends in a posterior direction from the liver diverticulum. The liver diverticulum thus becomes incorporated into the main channel of the alimentary canal.

This mode of development of the alimentary canal of the amphibians was first described for urodeles (Balinsky, 1947), and the findings were confirmed in all essential points by work done on frogs (Tahara and Nakamura, 1961). In some frogs, however, as in the clawed toad *Xenopus laevis,* the midgut cavity is not completely closed at any stage and later expands to form the intestinal cavity (Balinsky, in Nieuwkoop and Faber, 1956).

At the time when the midgut becomes occluded, the hindgut does not lose its cavity and the latter persists as the cavity of the cloaca. The dorsal wall of the hindgut becomes extended into the tail rudiment as a postanal gut (Fig. 138, A). The postanal gut has only an ephemeral existence and is soon broken up and disappears. The hindgut also gives rise in amphibians to the urinary bladder, which develops as a ventral evagination of the gut in late stages of larval life.

As the main portions of the alimentary canal begin to take shape, the canal as a whole becomes twisted in a characteristic way. At an early stage, the stomach has already assumed a slanting position (see Fig. 365). Subsequently, the posterior end of the stomach is shifted to the left, while the adjoining part of the duodenum comes to lie transversely, going from left to right. The distal part of the duodenum is then bent in such a way that it leads to the anterior end of the intestine, which is more or less in a dorsal position. The alimentary canal thus performs a complete spiral revolution, which may be referred to as the gastro-intestinal loop and which occurs with greater or lesser modifications in all vertebrates. Where the loop is in its lowest position, it leaves a space or saddle on the dorsal side, and this space is taken up by the rudiment of the pancreas (see also section 15–4). The posterior part of the alimentary canal also becomes twisted into folds and loops as the result of the elongation of the alimentary canal which exceeds the elongation of the body. The folding and twisting of the duodenum and intestine is especially prominent in the tadpoles of frogs which, in connection with their herbivorous diet, have a very long intestine (Fig. 366). The pattern of the twisting varies somewhat in different frogs and need not be followed here. In urodeles and also in fishes, the intestine does not elongate to the same degree and its folding may be very limited, though the gastro-duodenal loop is always present.

The Relation in Higher Vertebrates.   In vertebrates having a meroblastic type of cleavage, the development of the alimentary canal presents very different problems, and the processes leading to the formation of the definitive cavity of the alimentary canal are quite peculiar. In the following we will describe this process as it occurs in birds and mammals.

It must be noted, in the first instance, that in birds the archenteric cavity is often lacking altogether, and if it is present, as a canal leading forward from Hensen's node, it is very small and its walls are not endodermal. The starting point for the development of the alimentary canal proper is a sheet of endoderm lying flat under the ectodermal and mesodermal parts of the embryonic region of the blastodisc. The sheet of endoderm lies flat on the yolk of the yolk sac or forms the roof of the mammalian yolk sac, which is a space

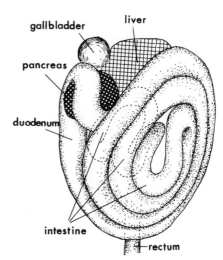

Figure 366.   Coiling of the intestine in a tadpole of the frog *Xenopus laevis* (ventral view).

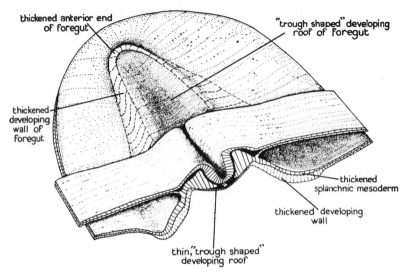

thickened anterior end
of foregut

"trough shaped" developing
roof of foregut

thickened
developing
wall of
foregut

thickened
splanchnic mesoderm

thickened developing
wall

thin,"trough shaped"
developing roof

Figure 367. Stage in the development of the foregut in a chick embryo. Ectoderm with neural folds and the parietal mesoderm are shown as being cut away at the anterior end of the embryo. (From Bellairs, 1953.)

filled with fluid. In both cases, the cavity of the alimentary canal is separated from the cavity of the yolk sac by a process of infolding.

During this infolding, the median strip of the endoderm lying immediately under the notochord and somites remains in this position, while the immediately adjoining strips on the right and left become inflected downward, and the crests of the folds converge toward the middle and eventually fuse (Fig. 367). The inner surfaces of the folds contribute to the formation of the floor of the gut, while the outer surfaces of the folds are continuous with the endodermal lining of the yolk sac. Concurrently with the movement of the endodermal layer in a transverse plane, a complicated shifting has been found to occur longitudinally: the median strip which forms the dorsal wall of the gut slides forward, while in the folds closing the gut laterally and ventrally endodermal material moves obliquely backward. During their movement downward, the lateral strips of endoderm are accompanied by the visceral layer of the lateral plate mesoderm, which closely adheres to the endoderm throughout this whole series of formative movements. It is probable that the dynamic force of the movement is due to the endoderm and mesoderm jointly (Bellairs, 1953).

As a result of the downward movement of the visceral layer of the lateral mesoderm, the coelomic cavity becomes considerably expanded locally. The coelom is reduced again, however, when the body folds undercut the embryo, as explained on page 267. The alimentary canal becomes separated from the yolk sac cavity first of all at the anterior end of the embryo. This part corresponds to the foregut of the amphibian embryo. Somewhat later, the posterior part of the endodermal groove closes into a canal, and this becomes the posterior part of the alimentary system which in the amniotes is called the **hindgut**, although most of it corresponds to the midgut of amphibian embryos. Between the foregut and the hindgut there remains a gap where the endoderm does not close to form a canal, or even a groove, and where it is in open

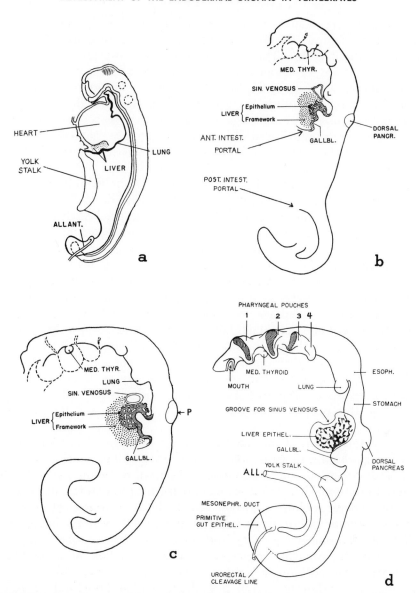

Figure 368.   Development of the endodermal organs in a human embryo (semidiagrammatic). (From Streeter, 1942.)

communication with the yolk sac (Fig. 368). This part, in amniotes, is referred to as the **midgut**.

The edges of the folds separating the foregut from the yolk sac where they meet in the middle form a ridge, known as the **anterior intestinal portal**. A similar edge at the anterior end of the hindgut is the **posterior intestinal portal**. The gap between the two is very large at first, but its relative size diminishes with the growth of the embryo, and eventually it is reduced to the opening of the **yolk stalk**, connecting the cavity of the gut to the cavity of the yolk sac.

From the beginning the foregut is much broader than the hindgut and is flattened in cross-section. As in the amphibians, the foregut gives rise to the endodermal lining of all anterior parts of the alimentary canal, including most of the duodenum, the liver and pancreas developing just in front of the anterior intestinal portal. The oral and especially the pharyngeal parts of the foregut remain expanded in a transverse direction, and the pharynx becomes drawn out to form the branchial pouches, but the posterior part of the foregut, corresponding to the esophageal, gastric and duodenal parts of the alimentary canal, eventually becomes round in cross-section. The esophagus in higher vertebrates is soon greatly elongated, in connection with the development of the neck. The hindgut is from the start narrower than the foregut and soon becomes round in cross-section too.

Although the foregut in higher vertebrates is quite different in shape from the foregut of amphibians, it develops the gastro-duodenal loop in much the same way. The anterior (cardiac) end of the stomach is displaced to the left side, the posterior (pyloric) end is turned downward and toward the middle, while the anterior part of the duodenum assumes a transverse direction, thus bringing about the familiar position of the stomach in adult mammals and birds. The intestine becomes convoluted in a pattern that varies greatly not only as between different classes but even in one class, as in various mammals. A peculiarity occurring in mammals is that sections of the intestine adjoining the yolk stalk, both anteriorly and posteriorly, sink down into the umbilical cord and lie for a time practically outside the body of the embryo proper as a sort of umbilical hernia. The convolutions of the intestine begin forming inside the umbilical cord, but well before birth the definitive intestine is withdrawn into the body and only the yolk stalk remains in the cord (this occurs in the human embryo during the third month of pregnancy).

The posterior end of the hindgut gives rise to the cloaca and also to a postanal gut, which disappears later. The ventral wall of the cloaca produces the allantoic diverticulum (the endodermal part of the allantois), as has been indicated in section 11–1. In higher mammals (in particular in man), however, the allantoic diverticulum is formed very early as an outgrowth of the yolk sac at the posterior end of the embryo, even before the embryo becomes subdivided into the embryonic body and the extraembryonic parts. Later, the allantoic diverticulum is incorporated into the ventral floor of the midgut and assumes the same position as it has in lower amniotes (Fig. 204).

At the time of their formation, both the foregut and the hindgut are blind diverticula, without openings to the exterior at the front and hind end of the embryo. The formation of the mouth opening at the anterior end of the foregut occurs in much the same way in both holoblastic and meroblastic vertebrates. It will be dealt with summarily in the next section (15–2). The development of the anal or cloacal opening is, however, different. In some vertebrates with holoblastic cleavage, the blastopore (or part of it) persists as the anal (cloacal) opening. In others the anus is formed early in embryonic life near the spot where the blastopore opening had been (see p. 198). As, in higher vertebrates, there is no patent blastopore leading into an endodermal archenteron, the cloacal opening has to develop by a perforation of the body wall at the posterior end of the hindgut. The point at which this perforation occurs is discernible as early as the primitive streak stage and lies at the posterior end of the streak (see Fig. 204, a). When the primitive streak shrinks in the late gastrulation stages, it leaves in front the three germinal layers:

the ectoderm, the mesoderm and the endoderm, lying one above the other. At the posterior end, however, the separation of germinal layers does not occur; the ectodermal and endodermal layers do not become separated by the intervening mesoderm and remain in close contact with one another. The resulting double-layered plate is the **cloacal membrane**. When the hindgut becomes separated from the yolk sac by folds, the cloacal membrane is incorporated into the wall of the gut. The ectodermal side of the cloacal membrane is originally dorsal, but this position is inverted by the development of the tailbud, occurring just anterior to the cloacal membrane (see Fig. 204, b). The tail rudiment protrudes backward, and the hindgut above the cloacal membrane develops a diverticulum entering the tail rudiment —the postanal gut. As a result, the cloacal membrane now comes to lie at the root of the tail with the ectodermal side facing downward. The part of the hindgut adjoining the cloacal membrane is somewhat dilated and becomes the rudiment of the cloaca into which open the wolffian ducts. The ectoderm is slightly depressed in the region of the cloacal membrane, forming the **proctodeum**. The cloacal membrane separates the cavity of the cloaca from the cavity of the proctodeum till late in embryonic development, but it is eventually ruptured and thus a free passage from the alimentary canal to the exterior is allowed.

15−2 DEVELOPMENT OF THE MOUTH

In all vertebrates, the mouth opening appears rather late in the embryonic life after all the primary organ rudiments have already been formed. The mouth opening breaks through where the anterior end of the endodermal part of the alimentary canal touches the ectodermal epidermis beneath the front end of the neural tube. The ectodermal epidermis here sinks in to form a pocketlike depression, the ectodermal mouth invagination or the **stomodeum**.

The ectodermal epithelium and the endodermal epithelium fuse here and become a **pharyngeal membrane** (see Fig. 204, b). The membrane becomes very thin, and eventually disappears. Forthwith, the boundary between the ectodermal and endodermal epithelia becomes indistinguishable, and it is not an easy matter to determine later which part of the oral cavity is derived from the stomodeum and which from the endodermal gut. There are, however, indications that the stomodeal epithelium reaches (in mammals) to about the middle of the tongue ventrally and to the beginning of the pharynx on the dorsal side.

The determination of the stomodeum begins at the end of gastrulation, and the development of the ectodermal mouth invagination is induced by the endoderm when the anterior end of the archenteron comes in contact with the ectoderm of the presumptive mouth region (Ströer, 1933). No mesoderm ever penetrates here between the ectoderm and endoderm, and the endoderm remains in contact with the ectoderm throughout the subsequent stages until the rupture of the pharyngeal membrane. After the endoderm and ectoderm come into contact in the oral region, the oral ectoderm acquires, to some extent, an ability to differentiate as stomodeum. The anterior part of the archenteron may now be removed, and the remaining ectoderm produces a

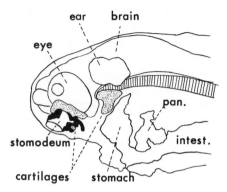

Figure 369. Development of the mouth and stomodeal invagination in a newt embryo after removal of the anterior endoderm in the neurula stage. (From Balinsky, 1939).

mouth invagination, although there are no endodermal oral and branchial parts behind it. The mouth invaginations thus developed are small, and their shape is not normal. If, however, the operation is performed a bit later, in the neurula stage, the stomodeum may develop in an almost completely normal way, with the sole reservation that it does not lead into the endodermal alimentary canal (Fig. 369). As the oral ectoderm acquires the ability for self-differentiation, all the rest of the epidermis loses the competence for development into stomodeum. If the region where the mouth is to develop is covered with a flap of epidermis taken from a different part of the body, the development of the stomodeum is suppressed, in spite of the presence of oral endoderm.

Presumptive epidermis of the stomodeum may develop a mouth invagination in an abnormal position, but this it can do only under certain conditions. In newts, stomodeal epidermis of a neurula, when transplanted alone, will not develop a mouth, but when it is transplanted together with some adjoining endoderm, and if the site of transplantation is not too far from the oral region of the host, an additional stomodeal invagination is formed by the graft, and this invagination may break through into the endodermal cavity of the host (Fig. 370) (Balinsky, 1948).

In frogs, the determination of the mouth ectoderm proceeds more rapidly than in urodeles, and the capacity for differentiation in the determined direction is higher. Already, in the early neurula, the removal of oral endoderm

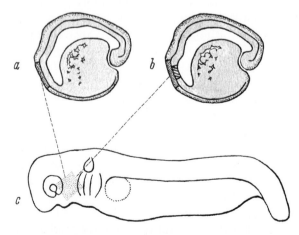

Figure 370. Transplantation of the oral ectoderm alone *(a)* and with the underlying endoderm *(b);* diagram of operation. *c*, Position of the graft on the host embryo several days after operation. The position indicated is favorable for development of a stomodeum from grafted tissue.

does not interfere with mouth development, and transplants of presumptive mouth ectoderm may develop in a typical way, producing the characteristic horny jaws and horny teeth not only in the vicinity of the normal mouth but also in other locations, such as on the belly. It was found, however, that for the mouth to be developed in abnormal regions it is necessary to transplant a piece of the transverse neural fold, together with the presumptive mouth ectoderm. Only a narrow median piece of the neural fold can support mouth development; lateral neural fold does not have this ability (Fig. 371). Together with the mouth, there also develops the adhesive organ (Cusimano, Fagone and Reverberi, 1962).

The transplantation experiments show that the oral endoderm is not the only part which induces the development of the ectodermal mouth invagination. Another factor operating in the immediate environment of the mouth — namely, the transverse neural fold — is also involved. There seems to be here some analogy to the dual dependence in the development of the lens: the dependence on the head mesoderm, on the one hand, and dependence on the eye cup on the other hand (see p. 379). In the case of mouth differentiation, as in the case of the inductor of the lens, a certain variation in modes of development in different animals may be attributed to the relative strength of one or the other inducing factor.

Besides giving rise to a part of the oral epithelium, the stomodeal invagination furnishes the cells which become the rudiment of the anterior lobe of the **hypophysis**. The rudiment is formed as a solid bud, or a small pocket (**Rathke's pocket**), on the dorsal side of the stomodeal invagination, just in front of the pharyngeal membrane (see Figs. 215, 218 and 244). The rudiment pushes backward through the connective tissue and eventually comes to rest underneath the diencephalon (see Fig. 254). The original connection with the stomodeum becomes interrupted, while the floor of the diencephalon furnishes the posterior lobe of the hypophysis.

One of the most characteristic differentiations of the oral cavity is the **teeth**. The rudiments of the teeth consist of an epithelial cap (the **enamel organ** which secretes the enamel), and a connective tissue **papilla** which produces the dentine (Fig. 372). The enamel organs of the teeth may develop from both the ectodermal and the endodermal epithelium. This can be proved by experiments similar to the ones already described, in which either the stomodeum or the endodermal oral epithelium is prevented from developing. The mouth invaginations, developing in the absence of the anterior end of the archenteron and the parts derived therefrom, often have well-differentiated teeth. When the endodermal oral cavity develops without a stomodeum being formed, or when the two are not in contact, teeth can be found developing in the endodermal epithelium.

In cyprinid fishes, one or two rows of teeth develop on the inner surface of the last branchial arch (the pharyngeal teeth). There can be no doubt that the enamel organs in these teeth are of endodermal origin.

In the lower vertebrates, the fishes and amphibians, the connective tissue papillae of the teeth project from the inside into the stratified epithelium lining the mouth, and the enamel organs of the teeth are developed from the malpighian layer of this epithelium. In mammals, however, the epithelium sinks down at the edges of the jaws into the connective tissue in the form

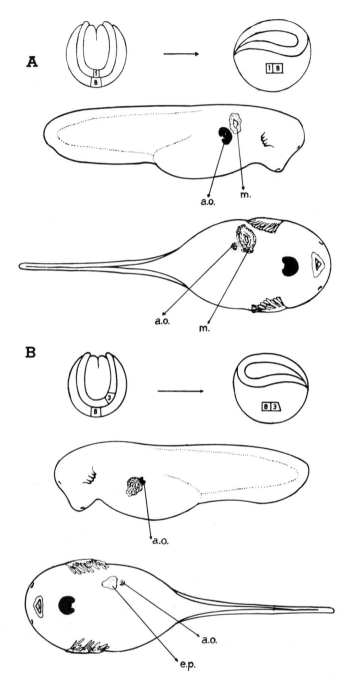

Figure 371. Experiments proving that in frogs the transverse neural fold plays a part in causing the development of the mouth. In A, the oral ecto- and endoderm were transplanted together with the medial part of the transverse neural fold. In B, the oral ecto- and endoderm were transplanted together with a part of the lateral neural fold. In A, the graft developed a perfectly formed mouth and adhesive organ. In B, only the adhesive organ developed as well as some skin epidermis; no mouth was formed. In both A and B, drawings above show diagrams of the operation, and below are the host embryos after 4 and 6 days of development respectively. *a.o.*, Adhesive organ; *b*, presumptive buccal ectoderm; *e.p.*, transplanted epidermis; *m*, mouth; *1,3*, parts of the neural fold. (From Cusimano, Fagone and Reverberi, 1962.)

tooth papilla   rudiment of
                                 palatine bone

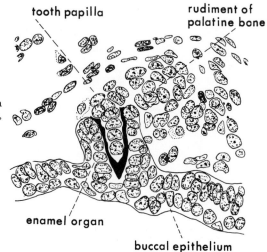

Figure 372. Rudiment of tooth in a salamander embryo. (After de Beer, 1947.)

enamel organ

buccal epithelium

of ridges. The rudiments of the individual teeth are formed at the edge of the dental ridges, at the expense of a connective tissue papilla and of the layer of innermost cells of the dental ridge which adjoin the papilla and form the enamel organ. The teeth are thus formed and begin to grow deep in the tissue of the jaw, and they erupt to the surface only when they have almost reached their full development.

While the cells of the enamel organ may be ectodermal or endodermal, the connective tissue cells of the dental papillae are derived from the neural crest. The neural crest is also the source of skeletogenous cells for the development of the mandibular arch: the quadrate and the Meckel's cartilage (see section 13–3). The development of the mouth as a whole depends therefore on the harmonious cooperation of cells coming from different primary rudiments — the foregut, the epidermis and the neural crest.

The development of the mandibular arch is, in part at least, directly dependent on the influence exercised by the ectodermal mouth invagination: if the ectodermal mouth invagination fails to be formed, the ventral part of the mandibular arch is not formed. An additional Meckel's cartilage can develop in connection with a mouth invagination resulting from the transplantation of the presumptive stomodeal ectoderm. The quadrate, on the other hand, may develop even in the complete absence of any sort of oral cavity; it is thus not dependent on the latter (Balinsky, 1948).

The development of structures surrounding the edges of the mouth contributes very much to the formation of the face in man and of corresponding parts in higher mammals. The structures in question are a number of swellings, consisting of actively growing mesenchyme and covered by ectoderm, which are formed around the stomodeal invagination (Fig. 373). At the dorsal edge of the stomodeum medially there is a slight swelling — the **medial frontal process**. Lateral to the frontal process on each side there develops a U-shaped swelling encircling the nasal pit. The free ends of the U are directed downward. The inner branch lies just alongside the frontal process and impinges on the edge of the mouth as the **medial nasal process**. The outer branch, lying lateral to the nasal pit, is the **lateral nasal**

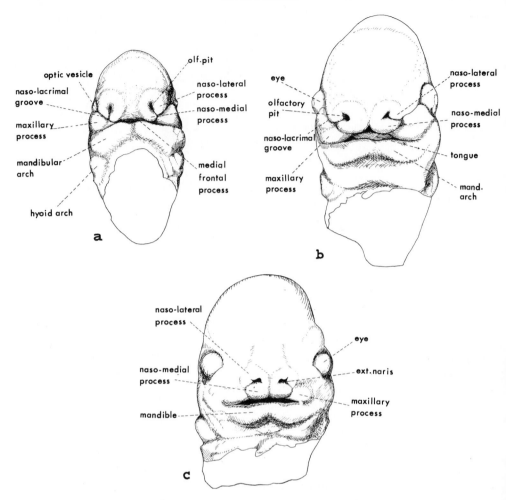

Figure 373. Development of the face of a pig embryo. (After Patten, 1944.)

process, and it does not quite reach to the edge of the mouth. Around the angle of the mouth on each side, another U-shaped swelling develops, with the upper branch ending on the edge of the mouth as the **maxillary process**. The lower branch spreads along the lower edge of the mouth as the **mandibular process**.

The two medial nasal processes grow downward and toward the midline until they fuse and exclude the frontal process from participating in the formation of the edge of the mouth. The maxillary processes grow forward and eventually fuse with the lateral edges of the medial nasal processes, thus completing the upper edge of the mouth. The opening of the nasal pit remains just above the line of fusion of the maxillary and medial nasal processes. The upper edge of the maxillary process also fuses with the lateral nasal process. The furrow lying between the maxillary process and the lateral nasal process, as can be seen in Figure 373, leads from the angle of the eye to the nasal pit. The infolded epidermis lining this furrow gives rise to a ridge of epithelial cells, which later becomes hollowed out and establishes a communication between the space underneath the eyelids and the nasal cavity. This is the **nasolacrimal duct**.

The lower edge of the mouth acquires its final shape after the median fusion of the two mandibular processes.

The nasal, maxillary and mandibular processes, as has been stated, are essentially proliferating masses of mesenchyme covered externally by ecto-dermal epithelium. The mesenchyme later ossifies and gives rise to some of the most important parts of the facial skeleton. The mesenchyme in the lower portions of the medial nasal processes ossifies as the pair of premaxillary bones. The maxillary bones are produced by the ossification of the mesen-chyme of the maxillary processes. The mesenchyme of the mandibular processes gives rise to the mandibular bones. The upper parts of the medial nasal processes together with the medial frontal process develop into the back of the nose.

15–3 DEVELOPMENT OF THE BRANCHIAL REGION

The development of the branchial region is no less dependent on the cooperation of parts of different origin than is the mouth region. The leading part in this development belongs to the endoderm. The endodermal cavity in this region, from its beginning, is distended in a transverse direction. In the amphibians it is derived from the inflated part of the foregut. In the stage immediately following the closure of the neural tube, the lateral walls of the pharyngeal cavity bulge out and produce a series of outwardly directed pockets on each side. These pockets are the **gill pouches** or **branchial pouches**. The gill pouches are developed one after another, beginning with the first pair, that is, the one lying just posterior to the mandibular arch. As the endo-dermal gill pouches reach the epidermis, having pushed aside the intervening mesoderm, the epidermis becomes folded inward, to meet the gill pouches. A series of branchial grooves is thus developed on the surface of the embryo, each groove corresponding to an endodermal pouch (Fig. 374). The outer wall of the endodermal pouch and the inner wall of the epidermal groove fuse into a **closing plate**, similar to the pharyngeal membrane. A **branchial cleft** is formed when the closing plate becomes perforated, so that an open communi-cation is established between the pharyngeal cavity and the outer medium. In aquatic vertebrates gill filaments are then developed on the walls of the gill clefts; these are the **internal gills**.

The development does not always reach the final stage – the formation of the gill filaments serving for respiration. Even in aquatic vertebrates, some of the gill pouches may not develop into gill clefts: thus in bony fishes and the amphibians, the first pair of gill pouches (the one lying behind the mandibular arch) does not reach the epidermis and remains a blind diverticu-lum of the pharyngeal wall. In the amniotes, the gills never function as respiratory organs, but four pairs of branchial pouches nevertheless develop (see Figs. 213 and 214). Branchial grooves and closing plates are formed, and in the first three pairs of branchial pouches the closing plates are broken so that branchial clefts are formed (see Fig. 368, d). The fourth pouch does not open to the outside. The existence of open branchial clefts is, however, of very short duration, and the clefts are again closed by membranes. The new closing membranes develop farther out than the original closing plates and are produced as folds of ectoderm only, whereas the original closing mem-

Figure 374. Frontal section of an embryo of a skate, *Raja*, showing branchial pouches and clefts, which are indicated by Roman numerals. *a*, Eye; *c*, cavity of brain; *Kd*, cavity of pharynx; *o*, esophagus. (After Maurer, in Hertwig, 1906.)

branes consisted of a layer of ectoderm on the outside and endoderm on the inside.

The whole system is later reduced to a greater or lesser extent, and its remnants are used up for the development of parts having nothing to do with the respiratory function; thus the first pair of branchial pouches becomes the eustachian tube in the terrestrial vertebrates. The third and fourth gill pouches give rise to a series of glands of internal secretion: the **thymus** and the **parathyroids**. These organ rudiments develop from masses of cells that become detached from the walls of the branchial pouches and are then shifted downward and backward until they come to lie in the neck or in the anterior trunk region.

It has been generally believed that the cells giving rise to the parathyroid glands and the thymus are derived from the endodermal part of the branchial pouches. There are indications, however, that at least a part of the thymus rudiment is derived from the ectodermal cells of the branchial grooves (for recent data and a survey see Ruth, Allen and Wolfe, 1964).

The importance of these glands for the well-being of the animal gives a possible explanation for the persistence of the branchial pouches in the embryos of terrestrial animals, although they have long since lost their original functional significance.

A further important gland of internal secretion associated with the pharynx in its development is the **thyroid gland**. The thyroid gland develops in vertebrates as a ventral pocket in the floor of the pharynx. Subsequently the pocket becomes closed and separated from the pharyngeal wall. The thyroid rudiment is then displaced in a caudal direction, until, in terrestrial vertebrates, it comes to lie ventral to the trachea.

It has already been stated that the endodermal gill pouches are the initiators of all the developments in the branchial region. The epidermal branchial grooves are induced by the endodermal pouches when they touch the epidermis; without the endodermal gill pouches, the epidermal grooves do not develop. Neither do they develop if the endodermal pouch, though present, does not reach the epidermis (as in the case of the first pouch in amphibians and bony fishes).

The relations between the endoderm and the external gills have been discussed already (section 13–4). For the development of the external gills in the urodeles, it is also necessary that the endodermal gill pouch reach the epidermis; otherwise the gills fail to appear. The external gills in the urodeles are later supplemented by internal gills – gill filaments developing on the branchial arches. Both external and internal gills function simultaneously, until both are reduced during metamorphosis. In the anurans, the external gills function only temporarily, during a short period after the hatching of the larvae. Soon after the little tadpoles begin to swim, a fold of skin appears anterior to the external gills – the **opercular fold**. The opercular fold spreads backward over the gill region, covering both the external gills and the gill slits. Both are thus included in a branchial cavity. The posterior edge of the opercular fold becomes attached to the skin behind the branchial region, so that only a narrow opening – the **branchial aperture** – leads from the branchial cavity to the exterior. At the same time, the external gills are reduced in size, and the internal gills develop on the branchial arches beneath the external gills and function throughout the whole period of larval development.

The visceral skeleton is an important integral part of the branchial region. As has been stated, the visceral skeleton develops from cells of the neural crest. In their downward migration, the neural crest cells are split by the gill pouches into several streams, moving in between the adjacent gill pouches. Later, the branchial arches are formed by the chondrification of the neural crest mesenchyme in about the same position as the masses of migrating cells were to be found. The dependence of the visceral arch development on the branchial clefts is, however, a more intimate one than would follow from this description. In the absence of the gill pouches, the neural crest mesenchyme does not chondrify, and no branchial arches are formed (Balinsky, 1948). If the number of branchial pouches is reduced (after an operation in which part of the endoderm of the branchial region has been removed), the number of visceral arches is similarly reduced; one skeletal arch is developed on each side of the remaining branchial pouches. Thus the number of arches is one more than the number of pouches present.

The hyoid arch shows the same kind of dependence on the visceral pouches as the branchial arches proper.

For the development of the visceral arches, it is not necessary for the endodermal gill pouches to establish a connection with the epidermis and for the gill cleft to break through; the presence of the endodermal pouches, even if they are represented by blind pockets, is sufficient to induce the development of the skeletal arches.

We can now review the dependence of the development of the various parts of the visceral skeleton on the adjoining parts of the alimentary canal (see Fig. 375).

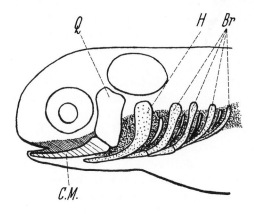

Figure 375. Diagram of the head of a urodele amphibian, showing the dependence of parts of the visceral skeleton on different sections of the alimentary canal. The ectodermal stomodeum and that part of Meckel's cartilage (C.M.) that is dependent on it are hatched; the endodermal foregut and the visceral arches dependent on the endoderm are stippled. Q, quadrate; H, hyoid arch; Br, branchial arches.

1. The upper part of the mandibular arch (the quadrate and the region of articulation with the lower jaw) develops independently of parts of the alimentary canal.

2. The lower part of the mandibular arch is dependent on the ectodermal mouth invagination.

3. The hyoid arch and the branchial arches are dependent on the endodermal gill pouches.

A very peculiar feature in the development of the amphibian visceral skeleton is presented by the second basibranchial. This skeletal element is developed from mesodermal mesenchyme, not from neural crest mesenchyme, and it is also independent of the endodermal gill pouches; it is formed even if the whole of the endoderm of the branchial region has been removed.

The visceral arches, which are dependent in their development on the epithelial parts of the alimentary canal, appear to exercise some influence on the development of the teeth. The tooth rudiments, consisting of the ectodermal or endodermal enamel organ and the papilla, derived from neural crest mesenchyme, are formed in connection with certain skeletal elements: Meckel's cartilage, the rudiments of the vomer and palatine bone, and later of the premaxilla, maxilla and dental bone.

With the reduction of the branchial pouches in adult terrestrial vertebrates, the visceral skeleton becomes modified. The lower end of the hyoid arch persists as the body of the hyoid bone; the lower part of the first branchial arch becomes utilized in the formation of the horns of the hyoid bone. Parts of the subsequent branchial cartilages contribute to the formation of the thyroid cartilages and cartilages surrounding the trachea.

15—4 DEVELOPMENT OF THE ACCESSORY ORGANS OF THE ALIMENTARY CANAL: LUNGS, LIVER, PANCREAS

The Lungs. The lungs develop from a rudiment which is a pocketlike evagination of the endodermal epithelium on the ventral side of the alimentary canal, just posterior to the branchial region. The pocket at first projects straight downward. At its tip it bifurcates, and the two branches grow out to the sides and backward. The unpaired medial part of the rudiment becomes the trachea; the two branches give rise to the two bronchi and to the lungs themselves.

In the lower vertebrates, the lungs are developed as saclike expansions at the ends of the bronchi, the walls of which become folded to various degrees. In the warm-blooded vertebrates, birds and mammals, in which the lung respiration attains the highest efficiency, the greater degree of differentiation of the air spaces in the lungs already becomes manifest in the earlier stages of lung development. In mammals, the distal ends of the bronchi as they grow out become branched in a more or less dichotomous fashion, the branches representing the secondary, tertiary, etc., bronchi and the bronchioles. The alveoli are eventually developed on the terminal branches of this system (Fig. 376).

The unpaired part, the rudiment of the trachea, may elongate greatly by subsequent growth. Although the first visible rudiment of the lungs is ventral and unpaired, there is good reason to believe that the lungs are derived from originally paired and lateral rudiments. By local vital staining in amphibians, it has been ascertained that the presumptive epithelium of the lungs lies, in the neurula stage, in the lateral walls of the foregut, just posterior to the presumptive endoderm of the gill pouches. The presumptive lung endoderm later shifts downward toward the midline (Balinsky, 1947).

In the clawed toad *Xenopus* (and possibly also in other frogs), the lung rudiments first become noticeable as two separate lateral pockets in a stage when the parts of the alimentary canal are not yet clearly separated from one another. When the gastric part of the gut becomes inflected downward, the lung rudiments are found just behind and ventral to the crest of the transverse fold separating the pharyngeal section of the gut from the esophagus. Following this, the part of the gut cavity connected to the lateral lung rudiments protrudes forward and becomes a distinct pocketlike evagination (Fig. 377). This cavity is the rudiment of the trachea (which is very short in

Figure 376.   Branching of the lung rudiment in a 35-day-old human embryo. (From Streeter, 1948.)

BRONCHIAL TREE
FRONT VIEW

STEM BRONCHUS

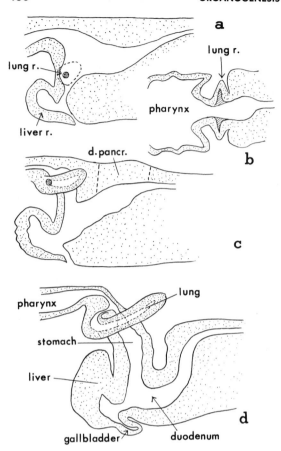

Figure 377. Development of the lungs in a frog, *Xenopus laevis* (semi-diagrammatic). *a, c, d,* Projection on the median plane; *b,* frontal section.

frogs). The cavity of the trachea, which is continuous with the cavities of the lung rudiments, becomes temporarily separated from the esophagus and later opens into the pharyngeal cavity. This new opening is the glottis — it does not coincide with the mouth of the original invagination which gave rise to the trachea (Nieuwkoop and Faber, 1956).

The lateral and independent origin of the lung rudiments in amphibians makes it probable that in the early history of the terrestrial vertebrates the lungs developed from the last pair of gill pouches, which failed to break through to the exterior and became adapted to the retention of air gulped in through the mouth; thus they became an organ in which the oxygen could diffuse into the blood vessels supplying the organ.

The swim bladder of fishes is similarly a pocket, growing out from the endodermal wall of the alimentary canal posterior to the branchial region. In many fishes the cavity of the swim bladder remains permanently in communication with the esophagus, and air can be taken into the swim bladder through this canal. It is fairly obvious that the unpaired lung of the lungfish *Neoceratodus* is the same organ as a swim bladder but adapted to respiration. Whether the rudiment of the swim bladder may be compared to a gill pouch has not been investigated.

The Liver.   The liver in all vertebrates develops from the endodermal epithelium on the ventral side of the duodenum.

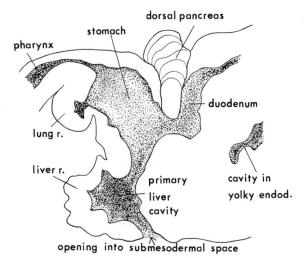

Figure 378. Reconstruction of the lung, liver and pancreas rudiments of the frog *Xenopus laevis* (median section).

In amphibians, the site of liver development is the anterior wall of the liver diverticulum, referred to on p. 468. At the stage when the main parts of the alimentary canal begin to take shape, the anterior wall of the liver diverticulum bulges forward, so that the slitlike cavity of the diverticulum enlarges locally. This pocketlike enlargement of the gut cavity is the **primary hepatic cavity** (Fig. 378). At the time when this occurs, in frogs, the liver diverticulum is still in communication with the space between the endoderm and the mesoderm. Next, the front wall of the hepatic rudiment becomes thrown into folds, and the folds occlude most of the primary hepatic cavity, leaving only the most posterior part open. At the same time, the original communication between the primary hepatic cavity and the duodenum is constricted and becomes gradually transformed into the **bile duct**. Simultaneously, the opening into the submesodermal space becomes closed by a sheet of cuboidal endodermal epithelium, and the adjoining posterior remnant of the primary hepatic cavity becomes the cavity of the gallbladder. The epithelial folds of the anterior wall of the liver rudiment soon break up into strands of cells, which for a short time may appear as tubules, with their lumen opening into the remainder of the primary hepatic cavity and thus also communicating with the rudiment of the bile duct and the gallbladder. The strands of liver cells become interwoven with blood vessels and sinuses produced by ramifications of the vitelline veins (see p. 443).

In the embryos of amniotes, the structure of the gut in early stages is very different from that of amphibians, owing to the absence of the yolk in the endoderm, and the liver rudiment accordingly has also a very different appearance, but it develops in a corresponding position, namely, in the ventral wall of the gut posterior to the section which gives rise to the stomach. The first visible rudiment of the liver can be found as a pocketlike evagination on the anterior intestinal portal (see p. 473; Fig. 368, *a*), at a stage when the opening from the yolk sac into the definitive gut is still quite wide. As the floor of the gut continues to close in an anteroposterior direction, the liver rudiment is later found some distance in front of the anterior intestinal portal, well within the foregut. The endodermal cells then begin migrating forward from the original pocketlike evagination, in the form of solid strands or cords of cells (see Fig. 368, *b*, *c*). The strands of liver cells form a meshwork and enclose the blood vessels (the vitelline veins and their ramifications) lying in the region posterior to the heart. From an interaction of the cords of liver cells and the blood vessels, there emerges eventually the complicated structure of the adult liver. A fine lumen may be seen sometimes running along the length of the strands of epithelial cells, so that they may appear as thin tubules.

The gallbladder is formed as a secondary hollow outgrowth at the posterior edge of the original hepatic rudiment.

The liver increases in size very rapidly and soon becomes a large and massive organ, although the part of the duodenal wall from which it develops is relatively a very small one, and, even of that, a large proportion is used up for the formation of the gallbladder and cystic duct.

The Pancreas. The pancreas develops from two rudiments—a ventral rudiment (or two ventral rudiments) and a dorsal one. The ventral rudiment develops from a part of the ventral wall of the duodenum just posterior to and in close association with the rudiment of the liver. It may appear as a pocketlike evagination and very soon becomes subdivided distally into a system of proliferating epithelial tubules. The original evagination becomes the duct of the ventral pancreas.

The dorsal pancreatic rudiment in amniotes is also a pocketlike evagination of the duodenum, but it appears on its dorsal side slightly in front of the liver rudiment.

In frogs, the dorsal pancreas develops from a section of the roof of the midgut, posterior to the rudiment of the stomach. A part of the roof becomes cut out by transverse crevices reaching from the cavity of the gut right into the submesodermal space above the gut. At the same time, that part of the gut wall which is destined to become the pancreas makes an abortive attempt to form a pocketlike evagination, but eventually the dorsal pancreatic rudiment in amphibians, as well as the ventral rudiment, is a solid mass which becomes transformed into a system of alveoli and ducts secondarily by rearrangement of cells.

The dorsal and ventral pancreatic rudiments may remain completely independent throughout life, as in the dogfish, but in amphibians and amniotes the two rudiments approach each other and fuse completely. The system of pancreatic ducts becomes reorganized in later life and is very variable in different vertebrates.

15—5 DETERMINATION OF THE ENDODERMAL ORGANS

Experimental investigation of the endoderm in early stages of development shows that the endodermal organ rudiments, like those derived from other germinal layers, are not determined right from the start, but that the endodermal cells destined to participate in the formation of the various organ rudiments are no more determined for their respective fates than are the cells of the other germinal layers. In the earlier stages of development, their fate is a function of the position that each cell or group of cells occupies in the embryo as a whole. This can be proved by isolating parts of the presumptive endoderm and cultivating them apart from the rest of the embryo or by transplanting them into an abnormal position.

In an extensive series of experiments, pieces of presumptive endoderm of young gastrulae were cultivated in the "Holtfreter solution." Various tissues were observed to differentiate from such isolated pieces; some conformed to the normal destiny of the isolated parts, and some did not. The range of differentiations included not only oro-branchial epithelium, stomach epithelium, liver, pancreas and intestine, but also notochord and muscle, which should not have developed from the presumptive endoderm if it were to keep to its prospective significance (Holtfreter, 1938a, 1938b). Thus the fate of the endoderm is not laid down finally in the early gastrula stage. Much greater deviations from the prospective significance of the various endodermal parts could be observed when these parts were placed in surroundings which, unlike the saline solution, could actively influence the differentiation of these parts.

In the early neurula stage, it is possible to separate the whole of the endoderm of a newt embryo from the ectoderm and mesoderm. The endoderm is removed as a whole through a slit on the ventral side of the embryo, leaving the ectoderm and mesoderm as an empty shell. The isolated endoderm can then be inserted again into the ecto-mesodermal shell of the same embryo, or of another embryo of the same species, or even into the ecto-mesodermal shell of an embryo of another species; the endoderm of the small *Triturus taeniatus* has been successfully implanted into the ecto-mesodermal shell of the larger *Triturus alpestris* (Mangold, 1949).

The implantation may be carried out so that the orientation of the endoderm is in harmony with the orientation of the ecto-mesoderm, or the endoderm may be implanted in an inverted position. In the first case, a completely normal larva has been observed to develop. A normal embryo also develops if the endoderm is implanted with its dorsoventral orientation reversed. This shows that the determination of the dorsal and ventral parts in the endoderm is not fixed in the endoderm itself but is imposed on the endoderm by the surrounding ecto-mesoderm. However, if the anteroposterior axis of the endoderm was inverted with respect to the axis of the ecto-mesodermal shell, the development was highly abnormal, thus showing that the differentiation of the endoderm along the anteroposterior axis cannot be dominated by the ecto-mesoderm. Here we may recall that in the experiments with the transplantation of the dorsal lip of the blastopore (primary organizer) the endoderm is often observed to develop a secondary lumen of the midgut, just underneath the notochord developed from the transplanted organizer. This secondary lumen is of course part of the dorsal differentiation of the endoderm.

A similar result emerged in experiments in which small pieces of endoderm taken from a late gastrula or early neurula stage were implanted in various positions into another embryo. When the pieces of endoderm were taken from embryos in the gastrula stage, the grafts were often smoothly incorporated into the endoderm of the host. The use of heteroplastic transplantation made it possible to distinguish the grafted cells from the host cells (differences in cell size in grafts between *Triturus taeniatus* and *Ambystoma mexicanum*) and thus to make sure that the graft was not destroyed but had fitted into the construction of local tissues. Thus presumptive oro-branchial endoderm was found to be able to develop into intestinal epithelium and *vice versa*. Stomach epithelium was developed from endoderm having a different prospective significance. Occasionally, however, grafts differentiated out of harmony with their surroundings, and the later the stage of the embryo from which the graft was taken, the oftener this occurred. After the end of the neurulation the grafts differentiated, in the main, according to their prospective significance (Balinsky, 1948).

In another experiment, different parts of the neurula endoderm were transplanted into parts of the ecto-mesodermal shell, either from the anterior part of the neurula or from the posterior part (Fig. 379; Okada, 1955a, 1955b). The endoderm taken for this experiment was either a part of the foregut endoderm, mainly destined to become pharynx, or endoderm from the midgut, normally differentiating as stomach and intestine. It was found that midgut endoderm grafted into the anterior ecto-mesoderm produced pharynx (in addition to other parts). Foregut endoderm surrounded by posterior ecto-mesoderm was in part differentiated as intestine. In both cases, endoderm produced parts which were not in accord with the prospective significance of the endodermal cells, and it seems plausible that these differentiations were induced by the adjoining mesoderm. Again we find that the endoderm, as well as the ectoderm, is dependent on the mesoderm in its differentiation.

In all experiments with explantation and transplantation of endoderm, it may be observed that liver tissue very rarely develops outside its normal position. In isolation experiments, liver differentiated only as a rare exception, and then only atypically. In transplantation experiments, liver often differentiated if endodermal grafts came to lie in the liver region, but even presumptive liver endoderm did not differentiate as liver heterotopically unless taken in rather late stages of development, that is, toward the end of neurulation. Even then, only small fragments of liver tissue could be seen to develop heterotopically, although other endodermal tissues, such as stomach epithelium, oro-branchial epithelium, pancreas and intestinal epithelium,

Figure 379. Testing the determination of parts of the neurula endoderm in the newt *Triturus pyrrhogaster* (diagram of operation). A, Anterior endoderm; M, middle endoderm. (From Okada, 1955.)

developed heterotopically just as well as in their normal position, if a sufficiently old graft were taken for the transplantation. All this indicates that quite special conditions are necessary for the development of the liver rudiment, and that these special conditions are found only in the region where the liver develops normally. This is another instance (besides the dorsoventral differentiation of the endoderm) where the development of the endodermal rudiments is definitely shown to be dependent on the influence of the surroundings.

There is as yet very little information concerning the earliest determination of endodermal organs in higher vertebrates. In birds, some information has been derived from experiments in which parts of the chick blastoderm were grafted to the chorio-allantoic membrane of another chick embryo. Various endodermal organs were seen to differentiate from the grafts, namely, pharyngeal epithelium, thyroid, lung, liver, large and small intestine. However, these tissues developed without a very definite relationship to the origin of the grafts, if the grafts were taken from early blastoderms up to the head-process stage. In other words, the endodermal differentiations in grafts were by no means strictly in accord with the prospective significance of the areas transplanted. Figure 380 shows the relation between the prospective significance of parts of the blastoderm, in so far as the endodermal organs are concerned, and the differentiation obtained by explanting these same parts. The lack of correspondence is obvious. The interpretation of these experiments is complicated even more by the fact that the endoderm (or hypoblast),

Figure 380. Diagrams showing the development of prospective as compared with potential areas of the blastoderm: *1*, Prospective areas for thyroid, lung, liver, pancreas (dorsal) and intestine in the definitive streak stage. The blastoderm is represented as folded longitudinally so that median structures appear in their future dorsal position. Data from marking experiments. *2*, Potential areas for the above organs in the definitive primitive streak stage: from results of differentiation in chorio-allantoic grafts. All three germ layers included in transplants. *3*, Potential areas as in Diagram 2 when hypoblast was not included in the grafts. *4*, Prospective areas as in Diagram 1, for the late head-process stage. *5*, Potential areas in the head-process stage. *6*, Diagram of the nearly closed gut tube of the three-day chick. At this stage most organ rudiments are visible, and potencies correspond with prospective significance. (From Rudnick, 1952.)

taken alone, differentiates extremely poorly. Information on the differentiation of endodermal organs is obtained by grafting sections of the blastoderm containing all the germinal layers.

It has been concluded (Rudnick and Rawles, 1937; Rudnick, 1952) that in itself the endoderm has a very low power of differentiation, and that it needs interaction with mesoderm for its development, at least until the completion of gastrulation. It was noted that liver and thyroid usually differentiate in explants which also show the presence of the heart (Willier and Rawles, 1931), and that intestine is accompanied by mesoderm forming coelomic spaces (Rudnick and Rawles, 1937). This would be broadly in correspondence with what has been found in the amphibian embryo. The role of the upper layers of the blastoderm may possibly go even beyond that. It has been observed that the epiblast alone, without the hypoblast, when cultivated on the chorio-allantois, will produce various endodermal tissues such as thyroid, liver, pancreas and intestine, almost in the same way as a whole blastoderm consisting of both epiblast and hypoblast. This may mean that the actual formative cells of the endodermal organs are derived from the epiblast in conformity with what has been said about migration of cells from the primitive streak into the hypoblast (Rudnick, 1952). (See p. 210.)

Only when the endodermal gut becomes separated from the yolk sac during the second day of incubation does the differentiation of endodermal explants correspond to their prospective significance.

Experiments have been reported concerning explantation of parts of early mammalian embryos to the chick chorio-allantois (Nicholas and Rudnick, 1933), to omentum or under the connective tissue capsule of the kidney of adult rats (Waterman, 1936). Only grafts from fairly advanced embryos (ten-day embryos of rats, eight- to nine-day embryos of rabbits) produced endodermal tissue (in particular, liver and pancreas). The earliest embryos whose endodermal tissues showed signs of differentiations in grafts were rabbit embryos already in the eight-somite stage. A regular and clear differentiation of pancreas and liver was found to occur in still older (nine-day) embryos, in which the foregut had already been developed. The visible rudiments of liver and pancreas appeared one day later.

PART VI

DIFFERENTIATION
AND GROWTH

Prefunctional and Functional Periods of Development. With the formation of all or of most organ rudiments of the embryo, the main features of the organization of the animal have already been indicated. What may be called the **morphological plan** of the animal is established; by morphological plan is meant here the kind and number of the organs, their relative position and the general features of structure of each organ. However, organ rudiments at this stage are not capable of performing their specific functions, on which depends the ability of the animal to lead an independent existence. The cells of the organ rudiments lack the peculiar structures that are necessary for specific functions; the organ rudiments are usually too small, and the animal as a whole is likewise far from the adult size. All the developmental processes dealt with so far may be grouped together as the **prefunctional** stages of development. Now a new phase of development sets in, which brings the animal to its **functional** state. The main processes involved are **growth** and **differentiation.** Some new organs may appear in late stages of development, especially in animals passing through a larval stage, and minor morphological adjustments may occur in the organs formed earlier, but the processes of growth and differentiation are predominant.

Growth and differentiation may proceed concurrently, or growth may precede differentiation, so that the cells first proliferate and then differentiate, growth ceasing with the onset of differentiation. The functioning of the organs usually begins before growth has come to a standstill and very often before the final stage of differentiation has been achieved—the initial stages of differentiation making the cells already capable of function. Once differentiation has started, and often even somewhat earlier, the parts of the embryo in question are as a rule irrevocably determined for their future fate. This determination concerns, however, only the general type of organ or tissue which is to be developed; the details are "polished" in the process of development, and sometimes the functioning of the organs plays a part in the final adjustments in the various organs. For convenience's sake differentiation will be discussed before growth.

Nutritional Requirements for Differentiation and Growth. As the development of the embryo progresses, its nutritional requirements increase; this is due to quite a number of factors, all working in the same direction.

First, in the course of time the original supply of reserve materials stored in the egg, as yolk, glycogen, lipid granules and the like, becomes exhausted, and new supplies from without become necessary if development is to continue. (If new supplies are not furnished, as for instance when larvae emerged from the egg are kept under conditions of starvation, large amounts of proteins may be used up, which should otherwise be utilized in a different way; this, however, is an abnormal condition—see Løvtrup and Werdinius, 1957.) In meroblastic eggs, even with maximal separation of active cytoplasm and yolk, restricted amounts of food supplies in the form of glycogen and small yolk granules may be present in the cytoplasm and are used in the early stages of development, but later the embryo must draw for its food requirements on the main yolk depot, which is extraembryonic (yolk sac).

The second factor increasing the nutritional requirements of the embryo is the rise in respiration with development, which has been dealt with in section 9–3.

Lastly, a third and most important factor comes in at the beginning of growth, which is practically absent during cleavage, very restricted during gastrulation, but becomes predominant in the later stages of development. Growth, which may be considered as equivalent to synthesis of new cytoplasm (for a more accurate definition see Chapter 17), can proceed only if large amounts of materials are made available to the embryo in some way or other.

What are the materials which have to be supplied? It is not possible to deal here with the mechanisms of nutrition and growth in general; this is a subject which falls into the field of general physiology. Some facts relating to the nutritional requirements of the early embryo will, however, be relevant.

The nutritional requirements of the embryonic tissues cannot be very well studied in those forms in which reserve materials are stored inside the cells, as it is not easy to determine what particular substances are being utilized and in what order and in what form (some data, however, have been given in Chapter 5 and in section 9–3). A much more favorable object is an embryo developing after meroblastic cleavage; such an embryo can be separated from the yolk and cultivated *in vitro*. Experiments of keeping blastodiscs of birds on plasma clots have been referred to repeatedly in the preceding text. The question naturally suggests itself whether the blood plasma + embryo extract, used in the above experiments, may not be replaced by a synthetic medium. A complete synthetic medium was accordingly worked out (Spratt, 1948). (See Table 12.)

TABLE 12. COMPOSITION OF "COMPLETE" SYNTHETIC MEDIUM
FOR CULTIVATION *IN VITRO* OF CHICK BLASTODERMS.
COMPONENTS SHOWN IN MILLIGRAMS
PER 100 CC. OF THE SOLUTION

Salts:		Vitamins:	
NaCl	700.0	thiamine	0.01
KCl	37.5	pyridoxine	0.05
$Ca(NO_3)_2 \cdot H_2O$	21.0	niacin	0.05
$MgSO_4$	27.5	riboflavin	0.01
$Fe(NO_3)_3 \cdot 9H_2O$	0.14	inositol	0.05
$Na_2HPO_4 \cdot 12H_2O$	24.5	biotin	0.01
KH_2SO_4	2.6	Ca-pantothenate	0.01
$NaHCO_3$	55.0	choline-HCl	0.50
Carbohydrates:		carotene	0.01
Glucose	850.0	vitamin A	0.01
Agar	250.0	ascorbic acid	0.05
Amino acids:		cysteine HCl	0.10
dl-lysine-HCl	15.6		
dl-methionine	13.0		
dl-threonine	13.0		
dl-valine	13.0		
l-arginine-HCl	7.8		
l-histidine-HCl	2.6		
dl-isoleucine	10.4		
dl-phenyl-alanine	5.0		
l-leucine	15.6		
dl-tryptophane	4.0		

The agar was added to provide a solid substrate for the embryo and in some cultures was omitted without deleterious effect.

On this "complete" medium the chick embryo, explanted in the primitive streak or head-process stage, will develop just as well as on a blood plasma + embryo extract medium. Not all of the components of the synthetic medium are of equal importance, as could be ascertained by omitting some of them in special experiments. Deleting glucose from the medium, with all the other components present, immediately stops all developmental processes and leads to a rapid disintegration of the embryo (see Fig. 381).

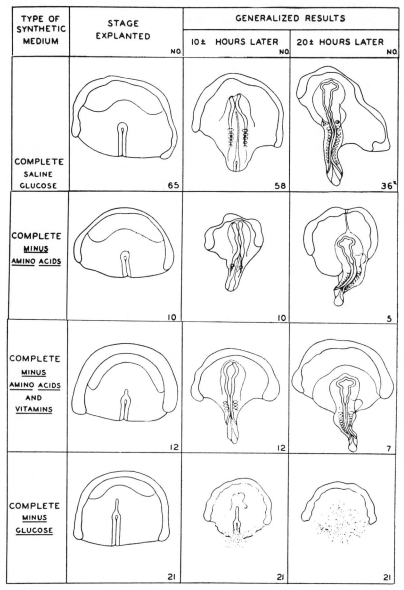

Figure 381.   Growth and differentiation of chick embryos cultivated on different synthetic media. Figures in the lower right-hand corner of each square indicate number of cases observed. (From Spratt, 1948.)

Obviously, of all the substances included in the complete medium, glucose provides the only source of energy for the embryo, and it cannot be dispensed with. The exclusion of all the amino acids, on the other hand, permitted development to proceed, but there was practically no growth of the embryo. Some morphogenetic processes were also retarded, such as the development of the ear vesicles and of the posterior end of the embryo (the latter is perhaps mainly due to the absence of growth). The withdrawal of the vitamins from the medium, in addition to the absence of amino acids, did not further affect development; growth was stopped but differentiation proceeded (see Fig. 381).

From these experiments it can be seen that morphogenesis and differentiation may be carried out by means of reorganization of the substances already present in the embryo, provided that an energy source is available to carry out this reorganization, but that the intake of additional building materials is required for growth. Incidentally, the experiments also show that morphogenesis (the elaboration of structure) may proceed without growth; we have already reached the same conclusion before when analyzing the role of "morphogenetic movements" in early development.

CHAPTER

16

Differentiation

16 – 1   DEFINITIONS

Differentiation is a term that is somewhat ambiguous, as it is used at least in two senses: a broader, more general sense and a narrower sense. In the broad sense, differentiation is the process in which the cells or other parts of an organism become different from one another and also different from their previous condition. For example, while the neural plate as a whole is being induced by the roof of the archenteron, its cells become different from both the presumptive epidermis and from the parts of blastoderm which gave rise to the neural plate. In this broad sense, almost the whole of development may be said to be essentially a process of differentiation, and if an understanding is gained of how cells of the embryo become different from one another and from their original condition, such an understanding would be equivalent to understanding development, or at least a very essential part of it.

At the same time, the term differentiation is also used in a narrower sense, in the sense of **histological differentiation**. Histological differentiation is the process as the result of which the parts of the organism acquire the ability to perform their special functions. In the case of multicellular animals, the parts in question are the cells and groups of cells.

The special functions of cells in this definition are distinguished from the basic functions of life which are common to all living cells. Every cell is capable of performing the processes of metabolism (respiration, synthesis, and so on), possesses to a certain degree the ability for ameboid movement, shows irritability and is able to react to external stimuli. These functions are found in both undifferentiated and differentiated cells. Differentiated cells, however, are able to perform special functions, or to perform them in such a way as other cells cannot. Thus the nerve cells are capable of conducting nervous impulses to great distances and at a high speed. The liver cells secrete bile (besides their other functions). The melanophores produce granules of pigment in their cytoplasm. These are the special functions of nerve cells, hepatic cells and melanophores.

The neural plate of the early embryo, although differentiated in a general way, having become different from other parts of the embryo, is not differentiated histologically, since its cells are not yet capable of functioning as nerve cells.

The ability to perform special functions is dependent on the existence of specific mechanisms in the differentiated cells. These mechanisms are sometimes visible in the form of organoids of the cell, such as the myofibrils of muscle cells, cilia of epithelial cells of the trachea, long processes of nerve cells. These tangible morphological properties of the cells are also called **differentiations,** a practice that is legitimate as they are actually the visible expression of the process of differentiation. In other tissues, the differentiation becomes visible not so much as a change in the structure of the cell itself but as the result of the production by the cells of intercellular structures, such as fibers in the connective tissues, matrix of cartilage and bone, cuticle on the outer surface of the skin in invertebrate animals. These extracellular parts are called differentiations in the same sense as the organoids of the cells. The special function of a cell may be the secretion of some substance that does not remain in the tissue as a permanent part but is removed or dissolved in the surrounding medium. In this case, granules of secretion may sometimes be seen in the histological preparations as a morphological expression of the function of the cell.

The functional mechanisms of histologically differentiated cells are cytoplasmic. The building up of these mechanisms therefore causes a shift in the relative volume of the nucleus and the cytoplasm. As has been stated before, the nuclei of the cells are their conservative part; they do not change essentially with the onset of development (section 7−5). It is believed that even in the case of fully differentiated cells, the nuclei in all the various tissues of the animal's body have the same chromosomes and genes. In differentiated cells, the mass of cytoplasm increases while the nuclei do not increase, or do not increase in the same proportion. The ratio−mass of cytoplasm to mass of nucleus−increases with differentiation. This ratio gives a rough quantitative estimate of the degree of differentiation. The estimate may be made even more exact if chemical substances and not morphological parts are taken into consideration. The basic substances of the nucleus are the chromosomes, with deoxyribonucleic acid as their essential component. The cytoplasmic structures are built up of proteins. Furthermore, the enzymes, which are the essential part of the functional mechanism of a cell, are of a protein nature. It is thus possible to substitute the amount of deoxyribonucleic acid for the basic structure of the cell and the amount of protein for its changing functional mechanisms. Direct measurements show that the relation protein/deoxyribonucleic acid changes with differentiation in agreement with expectation (Davidson and Leslie, 1950).

In the developing chick embryo, the amounts of protein nitrogen and of deoxyribonucleic acid phosphorus were determined every day between the eighth and the nineteenth days of incubation. The organs were brain, heart, liver and leg muscle. In all these tissues, the ratio of nitrogen to phosphorus increased steadily throughout the period of observation. The highest increase was in the brain, the organ which can rightly be called the most highly differentiated of all the organs of a higher vertebrate. The next highest increase of nitrogen was found in the leg muscle—a tissue which is rapidly differentiating in the chick embryo. The liver showed a rather slow increase of nitrogen, which is understandable, as the embryonic liver does not attain full functional differentiation. Furthermore it remains a blood-forming organ in the embryo and contains therefore masses of proliferating, undifferentiated cells. The lowest increase of nitrogen was found in the heart. This can be accounted for by the fact that the heart starts functioning very early. By the eighth day it has already achieved a degree of histological differentiation which changes but little during the further twelve days of incubation.

16—2   THE CHEMICAL BASIS OF DIFFERENTIATION

Whatever the type of differentiation of the cell, it is doubtless based on the chemical constitution of the cell. In every case where the function of the cells consists in the elaboration of some substances, whether in the form of structural elements or in the form of secretions, there must be a specific enzyme or specific combination of enzymes responsible for the reaction. As the substances produced by cells are very diverse, a correspondingly varied assortment of enzymes may be postulated as being present in different tissue cells. It may therefore be said that "differentiation is the production of unique enzymatic patterns" (Spiegelman, 1948; see also Boell, 1948, 1955).

All enzymes are known to be proteins, so that the last sentence may be paraphrased to read: "differentiation is the production of unique protein patterns." This wording is a more general one, as it includes not only proteins having enzymic properties but also the proteins which are not enzymes. An important group of the latter kind are the structural proteins, which are particularly prominent in some differentiations of cells and tissues. Some of the structural proteins are permanently intracellular, such as the keratin produced in the epidermis cells of terrestrial vertebrates. Other structural proteins, although produced by the cells, are eventually extruded from the cells and accumulate in the intercellular spaces. Collagen is the best known of such proteins.

Other organic substances, such as lipids and carbohydrates, alone or in conjunction with proteins, play a very important role in the life of cells, but between these substances and the proteins there is a very important difference. The synthesis of carbohydrates, lipids and also smaller molecules, such as organic acids (including amino acids), occurs under the control of enzymes and enzyme systems, which are of a protein nature. Given a certain pattern of proteins in a cell, the other components are then determined by the enzymic activities of the proteins (provided, of course, that the necessary precursors are present and the environmental conditions are of a specified nature).

The proteins of the cell, on the other hand, are not produced by the action of other proteins, but are synthesized under the direct control of nucleic acids, as has been explained in section 2–3. Ultimately, the structure of every protein in the cell is determined by the sequence of nitrogenous base pairs in the chromosomal DNA.

Genes Determining Protein Structure: the Hemoglobins. The relationship between gene structure and protein structure has so far been best studied in the case of hemoglobins contained in the red corpuscles of human blood.

By applying methods of chemical analysis (stepwise fractionation and analysis of fractions) on the one hand, and of methods of x-ray diffraction (analysis of x-ray scattering by hemoglobin in crystalline form) on the other, it has been possible to get a complete picture of the organization of the molecules of human hemoglobin. The hemoglobin—or, to be more exact, hemoglobin A—which makes up about 95% of the hemoglobin of normal human blood, has a molecular weight of about 65,000. The molecule is complex and consists of four subunits: there are two identical α subunits and two identical β subunits, lying in a tetrahedral arrangement. The whole molecule is roughly spherical (Fig. 382). Each of the subunits is a polypeptide chain, folded in a complicated three-dimensional figure, to which is attached a disc-shaped "hem" group carrying in its center an atom of iron, which serves for the binding of oxygen in oxyhemoglobin. The polypeptide chain consists of a number of amino acids linked by typical peptide bonds. The exact composition—the sequence of amino acids—is now known for both kinds of subunits. The subunit α, apart from the hem group, consists of 141 amino acids; the subunit β consists of 146 amino acids. (For a list of the amino acids in each chain see Perutz, 1961.)

In addition to the normal hemoglobin A, other kinds of hemoglobins also occur in man. Of particular interest in connection with gene action are the hemoglobins called hemoglobin S and hemoglobin C. Hemoglobin S has

Figure 382. View of the complete hemoglobin molecule, reconstructed on the base of electron density distribution. The molecule consists of four subunits; two on top are shown white and the two below, black. Two hem groups are shown as discs (on one of them is the mark O_2, indicating the oxygen combining site). (After Cullis et al. from Perutz, 1961.)

been found to occur in persons suffering from an inheritable condition known as sickle-cell anemia, a disease which in some cases may be fatal. The red blood corpuscles of persons suffering from sickle-cell anemia have a shrunken, irregular shape often resembling a sickle — hence the name. The condition is inherited in a typical mendelian fashion and is dependent on a recessive gene, which is allelic to one of the genes involved in determining the normal condition of the red blood corpuscles.

It was found (by Pauling and collaborators, 1949) that the hemoglobin S contained in the blood of persons suffering from sickle-cell anemia differs from the normal hemoglobin A. The difference is, however, only in one kind of the subunit in the hemoglobin molecule, namely, in the subunit β which is changed from β^A to β^S, while the subunit α is identical with the subunit of normal individuals. Further, it was found that persons heterozygous for the gene of sickle-cell anemia do not show the symptoms of this abnormality either in their physical state or in the shape of their red blood corpuscles, but their blood contains both hemoglobins A and S in roughly equal proportions. The presence of subunits β^A and β^S in the two kinds of hemoglobin indicates that in the heterozygous state the sickle-cell gene and its normal allelomorph produce polypeptide units independently of one another, and these then combine with the α polypeptide units which are not affected by the sickle-cell gene. This situation indicates a direct relationship between the gene and the protein (or polypeptide) chain which is synthesized under the gene's control, presumably through the separate emission of a specific messenger RNA by each gene, which then serves as a template for the assembly of the protein chain.

Another abnormal hemoglobin, hemoglobin C, does not cause any deficiences in persons carrying the gene but can be only discovered by a physicochemical investigation of the blood. The action of the gene causes an alteration of the component β of hemoglobin, while component α remains unchanged, as in sickle-cell disease. The inheritance of the condition closely resembles the inheritance of sickle-cell anemia: the gene is allelic to the gene responsible for the formation of component β of normal hemoglobin. In persons homozygous for gene Hb-C, most of the hemoglobin molecules have the composition $\alpha_2^A + \beta_2^C$; in heterozygous persons, roughly half[*] the molecules have the abnormal composition as above, and the other half have the normal structure $\alpha_2^A + \beta_2^A$. Again, the presence of both kinds of β chains in heterozygous persons shows that each gene acts independently in producing the specific kind of polypeptide molecule in the cell containing such a gene.

A further understanding of the close relation between the gene structure and the structure of the corresponding protein emerges from a study of the amino acid composition of the abnormal hemoglobins S and C. By comparing the amino acid sequence in the β chain of normal hemoglobin A and the abnormal hemoglobins S and C, it was found that the latter two differ from the normal only in one amino acid, (see Gerald, 1961).

---

[*]Actually, somewhat less than half, in the case of both hemoglobin C and hemoglobin S, thus suggesting that the rate of production of hemoglobin by different genes is not exactly the same.

In sickle-cell hemoglobin, the glutamic acid residue which is the sixth from the beginning of the β chain is replaced by a valine residue. In hemoglobin C the same glutamic acid residue is replaced by lysine. The section of the β chain in which the replacement occurs can be shown as follows:

Normal hemoglobin A, β chain: val.-his.-leu.-thr.-pro.-*glu.*-glu.-lys.
hemoglobin S, β chain: val.-his.-leu.-thr.-pro.-*val.*-glu.-lys.
hemoglobin C, β chain: val.-his.-leu.-thr.-pro.-*lys.*-glu.-lys.

According to what has been said in Chapter 2, each amino acid residue in a protein chain is coded by a base triplet in the chromosomal DNA, which is "translated" into a complementary base triplet of messenger RNA.

The (RNA) code for glutamic acid is AGU   and GAA

The (RNA) code for valine   is   UGU

The (RNA) code for lysine   is AAU, AAG and AAA

It is evident that a change in one base only could account for the transformation of the normal hemoglobin into one or another of the alternative forms. In the case of sickle-cell hemoglobins, a uracil nucleotide could have been substituted for an adenine nucleotide; in the case of hemoglobin C, an adenine nucleotide could be substituted for a guanine nucleotide.

The abnormal hemoglobins S and C most probably owe their origin to mutations. It thus becomes likely that "point" mutations (mutations of a single gene) may, at least in some cases, result from a change in only one base pair of DNA, which changes a code triplet in such a way that it determines a different amino acid from the one coded by the previously existing sequence of base pairs in the chromosomal DNA. As result of a change of one code triplet, the resulting protein would have one amino acid residue in the chain replaced by a different one. Sometimes such a replacement might not seriously affect the functional properties of the protein concerned, but occasionally the change may be very considerable: we have seen that the substitution of only one amino acid residue in the β chain of human hemoglobin not only leads to a distinct morphological expression, in the shape of the red blood corpuscles, but also changes the metabolism of the whole organism. The change in one base pair in the chromosomes may become a matter of life or death for the carrier of the abnormal gene.

Selective Action of Genes in Differentiation. We now have to consider a very serious contradiction between the properties of cleavage nuclei and the fates of cells differentiating in various directions. In section 7–5 it has been shown that during cleavage and also in subsequent stages the nuclei of all the cells of the embryo retain the ability to support the development of a whole embryo with all its various differentiations. When nuclei of endodermal cells are taken from swimming frog larvae and transplanted into enucleated eggs, the eggs can develop into perfectly normal frogs which do not lack any kind of tissues or cells. This is a clear indication that the cells in embryos which have advanced far in development still contain in their nuclei the full set of information necessary for any differentiation occurring normally in that particular kind of animal. The same conclusion may be reached by a consideration of processes of regeneration and asexual reproduction, which will be dealt with in Chapters 19 and 20. It will be shown that in repair of damage to the body of adult animals and in the production of new individuals from somatic cells, already differentiated cells may participate in the production of tissues of a different type.

If we accept—as it appears that we must—that the whole genotype with a complete set of information covering all possible differentiations of a certain kind of animal is contained in the nucleus of every cell, or at least in most cells, even when the adult stage is reached, then how is it that in any given cell only part of its potentialities is revealed, while others do not manifest themselves; in other words, how is differentiation of cells possible?

The obvious solution of this contradiction is that, while the nucleus of every normal cell contains the full complement of genes, not all of them are in an active state. In terms of the mechanism of gene action outlined in section 2–3, this means that not all genes are producing messenger RNA in any given tissue at any given time. An alternative explanation would be that all genes produce messenger RNA continuously, but that some species of messenger RNA are in some way debarred from being used for protein synthesis.

The latter explanation may be rejected, firstly because it would involve an enormous wastage of RNA, which seems to be very unlikely, and secondly because there are definite indications, gained from work on microorganisms, that chromosomal mechanisms are involved in the regulation of gene action (Jacob and Monod, 1961). It is thus more likely that during the development of animals only some of the genes produce RNA in any kind of cell at any given time. Such genes can then be considered as being in an active state, while the rest of the genes are in an inactive state. While they are present all the time in the form of sequences of DNA triplets in the chromosomes and are capable of self-replication preceding cell division, they do not produce messenger RNA.

The transition of a gene from an inactive to an active state may well be called "activation"; however, a consideration of all relevant evidence seems to make the use of this term inadvisable.

The use of the term "activation" assumes implicitly that the genes taken by themselves are passive and that an additional ("activating") factor must cooperate with a gene before it can produce messenger RNA. As a matter of fact, the synthesis of RNA does require additional factors, namely, the enzyme RNA-polymerase (as mentioned on p. 33), and also, of course, a pool of RNA precursors (the triphosphoribopurines and triphosphoribopyrimidines), without which the RNA synthesis is impossible. These factors, however, are assumed to be present at all times, and furthermore, they are available to all genes in a nucleus in equal degree, so that the inactivity of some genes and not of others cannot be explained by the lack of enzyme or precursors.

The more acceptable interpretation is that the genes are prevented from being active continuously by a *repressor,* which may be a product of a special gene ("regulator" gene). A gene becomes active when the repressor is removed in some way or other. A gene is thus not "activated" when it starts producing messenger RNA, but rather it is "derepressed." We know that at the beginning of development, during cleavage, there is no indication that the nuclear genes are directly involved in the control of the properties of the cells; no new proteins are formed during this period, indicating that no messenger RNA is being produced (see Chapter 7). With the beginning of gastrulation, new proteins appear, showing that some genes have become active — that they have become derepressed. It is not the same genes which are derepressed in different parts of the embryo, with the result that different kinds of enzymes and other proteins are synthesized in different tissues.

The conclusions so far are almost self-evident. To complete this interpretation, however, two further questions must be answered, which at present pose the greatest difficulties for the investigators, namely:

1. What is the actual mechanism of derepression of a gene?
2. What is the cause or causes of particular genes becoming derepressed at specific times and in certain groups of cells?

At present there is no definitive answer to the above questions, and only very tentative suggestions can be made in the following pages.

In connection with the first question, it may perhaps be relevant to point out that DNA, although the most important, is not the sole constituent of the chromosomes. The chromosomes as they are seen in ordinary microscopic preparations consist of nucleoproteins, the nucleic acid component being mainly DNA; the protein components are mostly a particular class of proteins known as histones. (In some cells, such as spermatozoa, protamines — a simpler kind of polypeptide — are associated instead of histones with the DNA.)

The histones are proteins with an unusually high proportion of basic amino acids (arginine, lysine and histidine). The double-stranded molecules of DNA have free acidic groups of phosphoric acid on their outer surface, and these can establish firm bonds with the NH_2^+ groups of the basic amino acids of histone chains. Hence the association of the histones with deoxyribonucleic acids may be a very close one. It is likely that the molecule of histone may be wrapped around the double-stranded DNA molecule, following the shallow groove on its surface (Fig. 383). It has been suggested (Stedman and Stedman, 1950; Bloch, 1962) that by associating themselves with the DNA molecules (either by wrapping themselves around them, as shown in Figure 383, or in some other way), the histones prevent the DNA from interacting with other substances in the cell and thus from serving as templates for the production of messenger RNA. There are some experimental results which are relevant to this hypothesis.

Cell-free preparations containing DNA (from calf thymus) and RNA polymerase from *Bacillus megagaterium*, in the presence of RNA precursors, will synthesize RNA. If histones (also derived from calf thymus) are added to this mixture, the synthesis of RNA is inhibited. Different fractions of histones prepared by chromatography and various precipitation and extraction procedures inhibit RNA synthesis in an unequal degree, one particularly active fraction inhibiting the synthesis completely. The experiment proves that histones can actually "repress" the DNA-dependent synthesis of RNA. On the other hand, it could not be shown that histones show specificity for certain particular genes, as could be expected if histones controlled which of the genes are allowed to act and which are to be repressed (Barr and

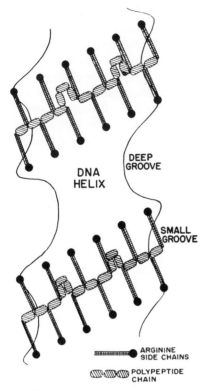

DNA
HELIX

DEEP
GROOVE

SMALL
GROOVE

ARGININE
SIDE CHAINS

POLYPEPTIDE
CHAIN

Figure 383. Diagram showing how a protamine molecule becomes wound around a double DNA molecule, following the small groove between the two strands of DNA. The phosphate groups of DNA are at the black circles and coincide with the basic ends of the arginine side chains. Nonbasic residues are shown as folds in the polypeptide chain. (From Wilkins, 1956.)

Butler, 1963). Further work may change these results (see Bonner, Huang and Gilden, 1963).

A different type of experiment consists in treating isolated calf thymus nuclei with a proteolytic enzyme, trypsin. The treatment removes most of the histone associated with the nucleic acid in the chromosomes. The trypsin-treated chromosomes are then used as primers in preparations containing RNA precursors. It was found that the amount of RNA synthetized is increased roughly threefold when 70 per cent of the histones were removed (Allfrey, Littau and Mirsky, 1963). In an experiment on plant material, removing all the histone from chromosomal DNA resulted in a fivefold increase of the synthesis of RNA (Huang and Bonner, 1962). The conclusion seems justified that histones associated with the DNA in the chromosomes repress their ability to serve as RNA templates.

The answer to the second question in a very general form can be derived from two facts dealt with in earlier chapters of this book.

One fact is that **cytoplasmic differences in the egg** determine which path differentiation will take in different cells of the embryo. As the differentiation of cells in the various parts of the embryo involves production of different proteins, and this presupposes a selective derepression of the genes responsible for the manufacture of the corresponding kinds of messenger RNA, it follows that the kinds of cytoplasm present in the cells determine in the last instance which genes are to come into action.

The second relevant fact is that the induction of the neural plate and other embryonic parts by the "primary organizer" is carried out by means of emission of a protein, or nucleoprotein, which in the first place penetrates into the cytoplasm of the reacting cells. If dissolving of the surface layer of yolk platelets is indeed the first stage in changing the reacting cells, as has been indicated by Yamada (see p. 255), then the importance of the cytoplasm as the starting point which leads eventually to a change in the functioning of the nuclear genes becomes even more impressive.

The particular composition of the cytoplasm, whether inherited from the egg during cleavage or produced as result of induction at a later stage, must be somehow transmitted from the cytoplasm into the nucleus. As a pure speculation, one could suggest that what is transmitted is an enzyme or set of enzymes, which destroy or change the histones repressing the activity of particular genes. The result would be the emission of quantities of messenger RNA from such genes. Once this mechanism was set in motion, it is not difficult to imagine that when the messenger RNA reaches the cytoplasm it would cause new proteins to be synthesized there. Some of these might be enzymes capable of attacking further histones on the chromosomes, thus causing yet new kinds of messenger RNA to be released into the cytoplasm. In this way more and more genes would be derepressed as development goes on, and of course the kinds of genes put into an active state would depend upon what direction the differentiation had already taken in the previous stages. More variety in the results of this nucleo-cytoplasmic interaction would be introduced by the influences on one another of already distinct parts of the embryo, the activity of "organizers of higher degrees" (p. 381), tissue interactions (which will be dealt with on pages 523-528), actions of hormones, etc.

16–3 CONTROL OF THE REACTIVE ABILITY OF TISSUES BY THE GENOTYPE

While the initial step in the differentiation of cells is made by the cytoplasm, it can be shown that the final result cannot be achieved without the involvement of hereditary factors — the nuclear genes. This is true in particular in the case of differentiations caused by induction. It has been shown (p. 244) that inducing substances are not highly specific, and tissues of one species of animal may induce structures in another species even if the two are, systematically, very wide apart. The structure induced on the other hand is, as a general rule, one that is peculiar to the reacting species.

In section 13–4 it was indicated that the balancer of salamander larvae develops as a result of an induction, the stimulus being given off probably by the roof of the archenteron, and the reacting system being the epidermis in the neurula stage. The balancers are found in most newts and salamanders, but a few species do not possess them. Experiments have been performed to determine the cause of this difference. If, in the neurula stage, the epidermis of a species possessing a balancer (viz., *Triturus taeniatus*) is taken from any part of the body and transplanted to the side of the head of a species which does not have balancers (viz., *Ambystoma mexicanum*), the transplanted epidermis will develop a balancer in exactly the same position in which it is usually found, that is, underneath the eye near the angle of the mouth. A reverse transplantation, that is, transplantation of epidermis from *Ambystoma mexicanum* to the site of balancer development in *Triturus taeniatus*, results in the absence of a balancer on the operated side of the head (Mangold, 1931a; Rotmann, 1935).

These results show that the absence of balancers in *Ambystoma mexicanum* is due to the failure on the part of the epidermis to react to the stimulus of the inductor, or in other words that the epidermis lacks an appropriate competence. The inducing stimulus, on the other hand, is present both in species possessing balancers and in species not having these organs. As the inability of *A. mexicanum* to develop balancers is genetically fixed, it is to be concluded that the hereditary factors (genes or their combinations) responsible for this particular peculiarity of *A. mexicanum* directly affect the competence of the ectoderm, while the inducing systems remain unchanged.

Another example illustrating the same principle is found in the development of the mouth in anurans and urodeles. The larvae of urodeles (salamanders and newts) have typical teeth consisting of the pulp and the layers of dentine and enamel. The teeth are situated inside the mouth and attached to the jaws and the bones of the palate. The tadpoles of the frogs and toads have no true teeth; instead, the edges of the jaws are covered by horny sheaths, and rows of small horny teeth and epidermal papillae are developed on an oral disc surrounding the mouth. It has been shown in section 15–2 that the ectodermal mouth parts develop under the influence of an induction from the oral endoderm. The inductor, however, determines only the position of the ectodermal oral invagination, not its specific peculiarities. It is possible to transplant ectoderm from an early frog embryo to a salamander embryo in such a way that the grafted ectoderm covers the mouth region. As a result, the graft is induced to develop a mouth. This mouth is, however, in every respect the mouth of a frog, with horny jaws and rows of horny teeth and oral papillae (Fig. 384 – Spemann and Schotté, 1932).

It is thus evident that the influence of the mouth inductor is similar in the salamanders and the frogs, or at least sufficiently similar for frog ectoderm to be able to react to a salamander's inductor. What is different is the competence of the ectoderm; to the same stimulus, the ectoderm of different animals reacts in its peculiar way. It is the competence or nature of reaction of the ectoderm that is affected by the hereditary factors responsible for the differences in the development of the mouth in urodeles and anurans. The power of the inductor is limited: it can only evoke such differentiations as are provided by the hereditary constitution of the reacting cells. As this constitution is embodied in the structure of the nuclear DNA, it may be concluded that induction eventually is consummated by changing the activity of the genes in the reacting cells.

It is also possible, however, for the hereditary factors to modify an inducing system without changing the competence of the reacting tissues. It has been proved that the dorsal fin fold in amphibians is induced by the neural crest (section 13–4, The Fin Fold). In most salamander larvae, the fin fold reaches anteriorly almost to the occipital region, but in *Eurycea bislineata* it is present only on the tail, the trunk being devoid of a fin fold. This peculiarity is not a result of the inability of the trunk epidermis to develop a fin fold. If the trunk epidermis of *Eurycea bislineata* is transplanted to the back of an embryo of *Ambystoma maculatum* (a species having a fin fold in the trunk

Figure 384. Larva of a newt in which the ectoderm in the oral region was replaced by ecto-derm of a frog embryo. The grafted ectoderm developed horny jaws and teeth and the adhesive organ found in frog tadpoles. (After Schotte, from Spemann, 1938.)

region), the transplanted epidermis will participate in the formation of a fin fold (Bytinski-Salz, 1936). The peculiarity of the fin fold of *Eurycea* is thus due to a failure of the trunk neural crest to act as inductor.

We have seen that the position of the external gills found in amphibian larvae, and the very fact of their development, is dependent on the endoderm, while both the epidermis which covers the gills and the mesenchyme which forms the connective tissue and the blood vessels of the gills react to the inducing influence of the endoderm. Now the number of pairs of external gills in tadpoles of frogs and toads varies in different species from one to three. In the South African toad *Bufo carens* there are three pairs of external gills, while in another species, *Bufo regularis*, only two pairs are formed. If the presumptive epidermis of *Bufo regularis* is transplanted to an embryo of *Bufo carens*, and if it lies in the branchial region, it will form gills in response to an induction from the host endoderm. It was found that three gills were formed on the operated side, the number typical for the host and not for the reacting epidermis (Fig. 385). In the reciprocal transplantation, that is, transplantation of the presumptive epidermis from *Bufo carens* to *Bufo regularis*, two external gills develop, again the number typical for the host. It is evident that the epidermis can form any number of external gills, and the number that

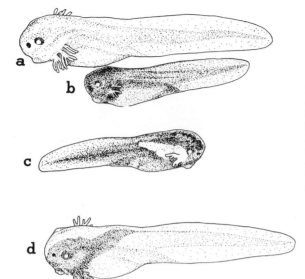

Figure 385. Results of exchanging ectoderm between two species of toads differing in the number of external gills. *a*, Normal tadpole of *Bufo carens*; *b*, normal tadpole of *Bufo regularis*; *c*, tadpole of *B. regularis* with grafted ectoderm of *B. carens*; *d*, tadpole of *B. carens* with grafted ectoderm of *B. regularis*.

actually develops is determined not by the reacting system (grafted epidermis) but by the inductor—the host endoderm (Balinsky, 1956). The ability of a part of the embryo to act as inductor may thus be affected by the specific genetic constitution of an animal.

There is no contradiction between these results and the experiments showing that an induction can only produce such differentiations as are provided for by the genotype of the reacting cells. Although in the last two experiments quoted the inductor was responsible for some features of the induced structure (extent of fin fold, number of gills), the result of the induction did not go beyond changing the spatial distribution of certain structures. The heteroplastic inductor did not produce any qualitatively new differentiations that were foreign to the species supplying the reacting tissue.

16—4 CHANGING PATTERN OF PROTEIN SYNTHESIS

In this and the next sections, the changing pattern of processes of differentiation will be shown in examples taken from the development of vertebrates.

Hemoglobins. An illustration of how specific genes change their activity during development is given by the composition of hemoglobins in man. It has been explained earlier (p. 501) that the hemoglobin in adult humans is in the form of composite molecules consisting of four units (polypeptides), two of which are of the type α and two of the type β. Each type of polypeptide is produced by a separate gene. The human fetus, however, has a different hemoglobin, which has been shown to consist of four polypeptides, two of which are identical with the α chains of adult hemoglobin; the other two have a different polypeptide sequence (not yet known in every detail) which has been designated as chain γ. Having a different polypeptide sequence, the γ chain is produced by a separate gene. The amounts of fetal hemoglobin in blood diminish sharply after birth and are reduced to about 1 per cent for the rest of life. Instead, there appears the adult hemoglobin composed of the α and β chains. In view of the very direct relationship existing between the genes and the hemoglobin components, it is evident that after birth the gene producing the γ chain is "switched off" and the gene producing the β chain is "switched on," while the gene for the α chain continues to be active both before and after birth (Gerald, 1961).

Lactate Dehydrogenases. A somewhat similar situation to that of the hemoglobins is presented by the production, in mammals, of the enzyme lactate dehydrogenase (see Markert, 1961, 1963). The enzyme has a molecular weight of 135,000, and the molecule can be split into four component polypeptides of about equal size. The isolated subunits do not have any enzymatic action. It has been found that the enzyme is commonly found in five forms, differing in electrophoretic behavior but having practically an identical enzymatic capacity. The five enzymes have therefore been called **isozymes**. It has been further found that the subunits of the five isozymes are of two kinds only, and that the subunits, named subunit A and subunit B, combine at random to produce the five complete isozymes. The composition of the isozymes can be represented in the following way:

Isozyme	I	II	III	IV	V
Subunits	A^0	A^1	A^2	A^3	A^4
	B^4	B^3	B^2	B^1	B^0

The isozymes I and V are built up of four subunits of one kind only; the isozymes II, III and IV contain both kinds of subunits in different proportions.

Unfortunately, the genetic background of the formation of the two subunits of lactate dehydrogenase is not yet known, but it is a reasonable assumption that each of the two kinds of subunit is coded by a separate gene. The subunits are then produced on ribosomes independently of each other and combine to form the five active isozymes.

If the combination of the subunits were random, and if both subunits were available in equal quantities, the five isozymes should be produced in the proportion 1:4:6:4:1. This has actually been confirmed experimentally by mixing together equal quantities of subunits A and B. In the tissues, however, the proportions of the enzymes are not random, but, depending on the particular tissue, either the enzymes contain more of component B or of component A. The first case is found in the skeletal muscles, while the kidney has a more balanced proportion of B and A. Further, there is a general increase of isozymes with a high proportion of component B during life.

It is thus seen that although both of the genes responsible for the production of dehydrogenase isozyme components are active practically in all cells of a mammal, the degree of activity changes from one tissue to another and in the course of an animal's life.

Myosin. The manufacture of specific substances may be correlated with visible changes in the organization of tissues in the embryo. This can be illustrated by considering the build-up of the protein **myosin**, which is the specific substance of muscle tissue. In the adult muscle, myosin amounts up to 10 to 12 per cent of the fresh weight or nearly 50 per cent of the dry weight.

The amount of myosin in the protoplasm of the cells undergoing differentiation into striated muscle fibers has been estimated and compared with the morphological differentiation of the muscle (Nicholas, 1950). In the rat embryo, the differentiation of striated muscle proceeds in the following way:

12th–13th day after fertilization: the myotomes expand into the lateral and ventral body wall.

14th day: the syncytial muscle fibers have been formed; on the same day the muscles become functional: they start contracting.

17th day: transverse striation of the myofibrils becomes visible.

The changes in the chemical constitution of the muscle tissue during embryonic and postembryonic development are shown in Table 13.

TABLE 13. CHANGES OF CHEMICAL COMPOSITION OF MUSCLE TISSUE DURING DEVELOPMENT IN THE RAT. (THE FIGURES HAVE BEEN RECALCULATED FROM THE DATA OF NICHOLAS AND HIS COLLABORATORS; SEE NICHOLAS, 1950, HERRMANN AND NICHOLAS, 1948, 1949)

Stage	Dry weight in % of fresh weight	Deoxyribo-nucleic acid in % of fresh weight	Myosin in % of fresh weight
13th day after fertilization	5.5	0.57	0.1
At term (21 days after fertilization)	9.0	0.34	1.0
At weaning	14.0	0.22	4.5
Adult rat	20.0	0.08	10.0

Several conclusions can be drawn from the above data:

1. In the prefunctional stage, the amount of myosin in the presumptive muscle cells is very small, and this amount increases greatly in the period when the functioning of the muscle begins (between the thirteenth and the twenty-first day after fertilization).

2. The differentiation of the muscle tissue is by no means accomplished when the tissue begins to function. This is shown by the tenfold increase of myosin in the postembryonic stages of development. This increase is due mainly to the elaboration of additional quantities of myofibrils in the muscle fiber. As a result, the strength of the fiber increases greatly. As measured by the breaking load of the fibers, their strength increases more than 400 fold between the seventeenth day after fertilization and the adult stage.

The specific physical organization of the myofibrils can be studied by testing the differentiating muscle for birefringence. Positive birefringence was found to be present in muscle tissue on the fourteenth day after fertilization. The birefringence is a definite proof that the myosin molecules are arranged in long chains. This arrangement thus precedes the appearance of contractility, while the transverse striation of the fibrils appears after the muscles have started to contract.

The data on the development of striated muscle bring out again the change in proportions between the nuclear apparatus and the functional mechanism of differentiating cells. While the amount of myosin (the functional substance) increases, the amount of the deoxyribonucleic acid decreases as compared with the other substances of the cells (fibers).

There is another lesson to be learned from the development of muscle tissue. It concerns the relationship between organ rudiment formation and histological differentiation. The organ rudiments—the myotomes, in this case—are formed in an early stage of embryonic development, about the seventh or eighth day after fertilization. The cellular materials for the development of the muscles take up their final position in the lateral and ventral body wall during the twelfth to thirteenth day of development. The elaboration of myosin and its arrangement in long chains (as shown by positive birefringence) follows only two days later.

Digestive Enzymes. The development of enzymic mechanisms may be illustrated by the appearance of the proteolytic enzymes pepsin and trypsin in the digestive tract of the salamander, *Ambystoma punctatum* (Dorris, 1935). The gastric glands which secrete pepsin are developed in the walls of the stomach after all the parts of the alimentary canal are already clearly recognizable (see section 15–1). In stage 40 the walls of the stomach consist of columnar epithelium, with a large number of yolk platelets in the cells (see Fig. 386, *a*). At stage 41 the deeper lying cells of the epithelium become clumped together, each clump representing the rudiment of one gastric gland (Fig. 386, *b*). In stage 42 the cells of the gland rudiments are clearly arranged in a spherical layer, and a cavity appears in the middle—the lumen of the gland (Fig. 386, *c*). In stage 43 the lumen of the gland is lined by a smooth cuboidal epithelium and communicates by means of a narrow duct

Figure 386. Development of the gastric glands in the stomach of *Ambystoma punctatum* embryos, stages 40(*a*), 41(*b*), 42(*c*) and 43(*d*). GL, cavity of gastric gland; M, visceral mesoderm lining alimentary canal; SL, stomach lumen. (From Dorris, 1935.)

with the cavity of the stomach (Fig. 386, *d*). The yolk granules in the cells have disappeared by this time.

Pepsin first appears in the gastric glands between stages 42 and 43. Prior to and in stage 42 no trace of pepsin can be found in the stomach, and at no stage either earlier or later is pepsin present in other parts of the body. We see that the glands are already clearly distinguishable morphologically (in stage 42) before they can perform their specific function — the production of pepsin. The morphological differentiation of the glands is, however, not quite completed by that stage, as there is some further progress till stage 43, when the glands attain their final structure. The presence of trypsin in the pancreas can first be discovered in stage 43, very slightly later than pepsin. The pancreatic acini first become distinguishable in parts of the organ (especially in the dorsal pancreas) at stage 41; they are more distinct in stage 42 and well differentiated in the dorsal pancreas in stage 43. As in the gastric glands, the structure of the secretory parts is laid down first, and the specific function (production of trypsin) sets in after that. It may be added that the mouth in salamander larvae breaks through at about stage 42 and feeding begins normally in stage 44.

Alkaline Phosphatase.   We shall now consider an enzyme which is more widely distributed in the body of the animal, namely, alkaline phosphatase, the enzyme which causes hydrolytic splitting of monoesters of the phosphoric acid in an alkaline medium (Moog, 1946) and which may also function as a phosphotransferase — that is, it transfers the phosphate radical from one molecule to another. In early mammalian embryos, the enzyme is present in only small quantities and in a diffuse state, except that it seems to be always present in the nuclei of the cells (Danielli, 1953).

At the time of the onset of differentiation, it appears in large quantities but in only a few tissues. It is found to be concentrated in the subcutaneous tissue of the embryo in cells concerned with the development of the subcutaneous connective tissue layer. A little later, alkaline phosphatase is found in cartilages and in the hair papillae (Hardy, 1952). In all these three sites the enzyme is supposed to be connected somehow with the elaboration of fibrous proteins — collagen fibers in the connective tissue and cartilage matrix, fibers of keratin in developing hairs.

In later stages of development, the enzyme is very abundant in the periosteum of bone and in the matrix of bone. In the latter position (where the enzyme is extracellular), the alkaline phosphatase splits off the phosphoric acid from glucose phosphates in the form of calcium phosphate, which impregnates the bone matrix. Further sites of alkaline phosphatase concentrations are in the brush border of proximal convoluted tubes of the kidney and in the cells of the intestinal mucosa. In both of these sites, the alkaline phosphatase is concerned with the transfer of glucose from the lumen (of the renal tubule and the intestinal lumen respectively) into the internal medium of the body. In the adult, the quantities of alkaline phosphatase in the kidney, the intestinal mucosa and the bone surpass by far the quantities found in other tissues, as may be seen from Table 14.

It is worth while tracing the timing of the appearance of the alkaline phosphatase in the hair papillae. The rudiments of hairs in the mouse embryo first appear 14 days after fertilization in the form of epithelial thickenings. There is no trace of the connective tissue papilla in this stage. In

TABLE 14. DISTRIBUTION OF ALKALINE PHOSPHATASE IN DIFFERENT TISSUES (AFTER GREENBERG, FROM SPIEGELMAN, 1948)

Tissue	Enzymatic Activity of Alkaline Phosphatase (in arbitrary units)
Liver	4
Hyperplastic breast	9
Lymph nodes	8
Bone marrow	23
Spleen	17
Kidney	1072
Skeletal muscle	2
Cardiac muscle	12
Skin	5
Lung	36
Intestinal mucosa	2789
Gastric mucosa	17
Thymus	3
Pancreas	1
Brain	12
Bone	420

15-day-old mouse embryos, mesenchyme cells accumulate under the epithelial thickenings, thus forming the rudiments of the future papillae. The differentiated papilla, as has been previously indicated, contains large amounts of alkaline phosphatase, which is connected with the function of the papilla as the organ supplying the materials for the formation of the hair itself, which largely consists of fibrous keratin (see Birbeck and Mercer, 1957).

In the rudiment of the papilla, when it is first detectable, there is no alkaline phosphatase. Only in the more advanced hair rudiments of a 15-day-old embryo can small amounts of alkaline phosphatase be demonstrated. In the hair papillae of 16-day-old embryos, large quantities of the enzyme may already be found (Fig. 387; Balinsky, 1950).

The formation of the rudiment of the hair papilla thus precedes the appearance of the specific substance (enzyme) which is a part of the functional mechanism of the differentiated organ.

Detection of New Proteins by Immunological Methods. In cases where the specific substances of differentiated tissues cannot be determined chemically, they can still be traced by the use of immunological methods. A suitable experimental animal, usually a guinea pig or rabbit, is immunized against the tissue that is being studied. For this purpose the tissue, crushed into a brei or in the form of an extract, is injected into the animal that is to be immunized. The injected animal develops **antibodies** against the protein of the tested tissue in its blood plasma. The proteins which are used for immunization are called **antigens**. If the antibodies are again brought into contact with the same antigens, a reaction of a high degree of specificity will take place—the antibodies reacting only with the same antigen or with very closely related substances (and then to a weaker degree).

If a tissue extract containing antigens is mixed with the blood plasma of the immunized animal, a reaction of precipitation takes place: the antigen is agglutinated by the antibodies and forms a precipitate. (For review see Cooper, 1948; Tyler, in Willier, Weiss and Hamburger, 1955; Holtzer, 1961.)

Figure 387. Distribution of alkaline phosphatase (shown by dark stippling) in developing hair follicles (*a, b, c, d, e*) and in a fully differentiated hair follicle of a mouse (*f*). (Fig. 387, *f*, from Hardy, 1952.)

The following experiment may serve as an example of the results obtained by the precipitation method (Burke, Sullivan, Petersen and Weed, 1944). Experimental animals were immunized by injecting tissues of the adult chick. In this way anti-organ sera were prepared against brain, lens, kidney, bone marrow, erythrocytes, ovaries and testes. The antisera were then tested against tissue extracts from organs of the chick embryo at different stages of development. A reaction between the two proves that the specific tissue substances (antigens) of the adult animal are already present in the organs of the embryo. The following list shows the earliest stage (expressed in days of incubation) at which the specific adult tissue antigens could be discovered:

Brain	11 days
Lens	7 days
Kidney	9 days
Erythrocytes	4 days
Ovaries and testes	11 days

In every case the antigen was found to be present when the tissues were well on their way to histological differentiation. Some "cross reactions" were also found, that is, reactions of an antiserum with tissue other than the one used for immunizing the donor of the serum. This means that the substances of the various organs could not be completely told apart.

The technique used in this experiment appears not to have been up to the highest standard of perfection possible by means of the precipitation method, as was shown by subsequent work (Ten Cate and Doorenmaalen, 1950). The latter work, however, was restricted to the development of the specific substance of the lens. Rabbits were immunized by injecting extract of chick and frog lens respectively.

Tables 15 and 16 show the results obtained.

TABLE 15. ADULT LENS ANTIGEN IN CHICK EMBRYOS

Age of Embryo (Hours)	Number of Experiments	Number of Lenses	Result of Reaction
60	3	40	+ + ++
58	1	60	+
54	3	50, 30, 30	± ± −
51	1	50	−
48	1	50	−

TABLE 16. ADULT LENS ANTIGEN IN FROG EMBRYOS

Stage of Development[*]	Antigen	Result of Reaction
25	lens + eye cup	+
23	lens + eye cup	+
23	rest of embryo	−
21-22	lens + eye cup	+
21-22	ventral epidermis	−
19-20	lens + eye cup	+
19	lens + eye cup	+
19	lens + eye cup	+
19	lens + eye cup	−
17-18	presumptive lens ectoderm	−

[*]Shumway, 1940.

In the chick, the earliest unambiguously positive reaction was with lens tissue of a 58-hour-old chick; in the frog, with the lens of an embryo in stage 19.

The first positive reactions were obtained in these experiments with lenses in a very early stage of differentiation. The lens of a 58- to 60-hour-old chick embryo is in the form of a vesicle which is still connected with the epidermis, with the inner wall not yet thickened by the initial stages of fiber differentiation. The lens rudiment of a frog embryo in stage 19 is still less developed; it has not yet even formed a vesicle but only a thickening lying in the pupil of the eye cup. It is thus shown that the organ-specific substance may be present as soon as the organ rudiment is formed and before it shows any visible traces of histological differentiation.

16−5 CONDITIONS FOR DIFFERENTIATION

The Problem of Reversibility of Differentiation. Differentiation may be reversible to a certain extent. The morphological and physiological peculiarities of tissues require for their maintenance the environment which surrounds them in the normal organism. Except for manifestly nonliving parts, such as the chitin cuticle in insects or the hairs in mammals, all other animal structures may become changed or may even dissolve and disintegrate if the normal conditions in the organism are changed. A disintegration of the animal's morphological organization is even more to be expected if the integrity of its body is interfered with, as in the case of wounding or in experiments with explantation of parts of the animal's organs and tissues.

The cultivation of small portions of tissues in a clot of blood plasma or any other suitable medium (tissue culture) is an especially effective method of investigating the extent to which the histological differentiation of tissues may be reversed. In tissue cultures, intercellular structures (fibers of connective tissue, matrix of the bone and cartilage) become destroyed, the normal arrangement of cells in the tissues becomes dissolved, and the specific organoids of cells may also disappear (myofibrils, cilia). Cells derived from different tissues may acquire a very similar appearance, an appearance not unlike that of cells which have not yet undergone differentiation. These phenomena may be conveniently called **dedifferentiation**.

We have seen that in differentiation there is an increase of proteins in the cells in relation to nucleic acids. The reverse is true in the case of dedifferentiation. Dedifferentiation involves a breakdown of functional mechanisms of cells (composed of protein), and it can be expected that the amount of protein in the cells would diminish as compared with the amount of nuclear material. This is actually the case. Determinations of protein nitrogen and deoxyribonucleic phosphorus were carried out on a culture of fibroblasts taken from a chicken's heart and grown *in vitro*. After six days of cultivation, the amount of protein nitrogen per unit of deoxyribonucleic acid phosphorus was diminished by one-half (Davidson and Leslie, 1950).

The dedifferentiation of cells under conditions of tissue culture, or the retention of a lower state of differentiation, if embryonic cells are being cultivated, is the result of the change of environment in which the cells are being kept. The separation of a part of the body from other parts and the damage to the tissues caused by cutting them may contribute toward these changed conditions (the latter factor will be dealt with in the discussion on regeneration, Chapter 19). However, the main factor which causes the cells to lose their differentiation and to start growing and proliferating instead is the medium which surrounds them in tissue culture, and which is different from the medium (the fluid bathing the cells) in the intact organism.

The standard medium for tissue cultures consists of blood plasma, embryo extract and some modification of the Ringer saline solution. The salts are necessary for the upkeep of ionic balance between the cells and the surroundings. The blood plasma contains fibrin, which clots and forms the solid substrate on which the cells can spread out and which also becomes slowly dissolved and supplies some of the necessary nutrients for the cells. The embryo extract is added as a growth-stimulating agent. Without embryo extract, on blood plasma and saline alone, the cells grow only very slowly, if at all. With embryo extract added, the cells start growing and proliferating rapidly, and dedifferentiation occurs, as previously described.

The embryo extract naturally contains some of the substances surrounding the cells in the early embryo. The behavior of cells in tissue cultures may thus be attributed to the fact that the medium bathing the cells tends to keep them in a condition characteristic of the embryo in the stage from which the extract had been taken. In a seven-day-old embryo, often used for the preparation of embryo extract, growth is rapid (see section 17–3) and there is as yet not much histological differentiation. If this interpretation were essentially correct, it should be possible to produce progressive differentiation of cells by exposing them to media containing extracts from consecutively older embryos.

This has been done in the following experiment (Gaillard, 1942). Osteoblasts derived from a 16-day-old chick embryo were kept in cultures in two series. The tissues were grown in flasks (Carrel flasks) on the surface of a blood plasma clot and suffused with embryo extract, which was changed every two days. In one series the embryo extract was always the same, prepared from seven-day-old chick embryos. In the other series, older embryos were taken to prepare the extract at each subsequent change, namely: 10-day, 12-day, 15-day, 18-day embryos, then the extract from the heart of a newly hatched chick and lastly blood serum of an adult hen. The changing extracts were to imitate the changes in the tissue fluids with progressing development. The experiment gave results according to expectation; the first culture grew and proliferated without any differentiation, while bone developed in the second culture.

In spite of the apparent simplification of the cells which have undergone dedifferentiation, they do not revert to the state of embryonic cells. Evidence from numerous experiments, which cannot be considered here in detail, proves that dedifferentiated cells retain their histological specificity and do not acquire new competences. If cultivated alone, renal tissue may become disintegrated and its component cells grow out in the form of a disorganized sheet or layer, but the cells remain kidney cells and, given suitable conditions, they again arrange themselves into the shape of tubules (see also p. 523).

Similarly, cartilage may be dedifferentiated and the cartilage cells grow as a disorderly mass, scarcely distinguishable from a mass of connective tissue cells. But if the culture is kept under conditions which do not favor rapid growth, as when the culture medium is poor in growth-promoting substances (small amounts of embryo extract) or if it is not changed often enough to a fresh medium, a new differentiation becomes possible. When this happens, the former cartilage cells again secrete cartilage matrix, thus showing that they retained their functional specificity in spite of morphological simplification.

In tissue cultures, cells are dissociated from one another as a result of the breakdown of the bonds which bind them together in a normal tissue. The dissociation is not complete, especially in the case of epithelial tissues, which remain joined in a sheet even when cultivated *in vitro*, nor is it quite under the control of the experimenter. Therefore the attempt was made to separate tissue cells by more direct methods so as to test how far individual cells can retain the peculiarities that they had acquired previously in conjunction with other cells. By grinding tissues — especially embryonic tissues — in a specially prepared small glass mortar, they may be disaggregated, and a sufficient number of individual cells remain alive and may be used for further study (Weiss and Andres, 1952). A more delicate method is to treat tissues with a weak solution of trypsin in a calcium- and magnesium-free saline. This treatment causes the cells to separate from each other. A suspension can be obtained in this way consisting almost exclusively of completely separated individual cells which appear to be quite healthy (see Fig. 388 — Moscona, 1952). The suspension may then be put into a medium in which the cells can reaggregate and, under favorable conditions, resume differentiation. In some experiments, the medium was that used for tissue culture with reduced embryo extract to facilitate differentiation (see above). In other experiments, the cell suspension was injected into the veins of chicken embryos, and the cells became disseminated through the vascular route. Individual cells or small clusters of cells then settled at various sites in the body of the embryo or on the chorio-allantois and were either incorporated in the tissues of the host or gave rise to small local growths — teratomas (Andres, 1953).

The main result of these experiments is that the cells, which had passed through a condition of complete disaggregation, were able to resume specific tissue differentiation, whether on a plasma clot or on the chorio-allantois of a living embryo. Masses of brain tissue, muscle, cartilage, bone, nephric tubules, glandular tissue or epidermis, usually in the form of cysts with clearly differentiated feather germs, were observed in various experimental series. The assortment of tissues appearing in any experiment depended on the origin of the cell suspension, the stage of the embryo from which the cells were derived, and the part of the embryo taken. The results available so far are compatible with the assumption that every type of cell differentiates after disaggregation in conformity with its previous differentiation. So if

Figure 388. Suspension of completely dissociated cells, produced by treating chick embryo tissues with trypsin. (Courtesy of Dr. A. A. Moscona.)

cell suspensions were prepared from whole embryos, the teratomas contained a very wide variety of tissues including nervous tissue, musculature and glands. If only limb-buds were used for preparing the suspension, the teratomas contained epidermis, cartilage, bone and mesenchyme but no nervous tissue, muscle or glands (Andres, 1953).

It is remarkable that structures developing from cell suspensions do not present a chaotic assemblage of different types of differentiation. Rather, they produce parts resembling organ rudiments of a normal embryo, with the various tissues segregated from each other and each tissue arranged into a recognizable morphological unit: nerve cells form brain vesicles with a central lumen; cartilage cells are sometimes arranged into elongated rods with perichondrial ossification; epidermis cells are arranged in layers with a clear distinction between proximal and distal surfaces; feather germs may show a very high degree of internal organization (Fig. 389). As it is unlikely that each unit of tissue is always derived from one single cell, it follows that the cells sort themselves out in some way—that cells of any one kind join together and group themselves anew in an order similar to what they had before they had been separated. This is the same process that we have found in relation to cells at the time of gastrulation and neurulation (section 12–3) and is a further evidence of the "affinities" between particular kinds of cells.

Control of Differentiation by Chemical Substances. Since the actual differentiation of tissue cells is dependent on conditions in their environment, it is possible, as we have seen (p. 519), to direct their development along definite pathways by exposing them to appropriate treatments. Some further experiments along these lines will now be described, first of all in relation to the control of differentiation by such chemical substances as vitamins and hormones.

Stratified epithelium in vertebrates appears to be a suitable object for experiments of this kind. Under normal conditions, stratified epithelium takes on various forms, both in different groups of vertebrates and in different parts of the same animal. In terrestrial vertebrates, stratified epithelium is squamous and cornified on its surface, but in fishes the epidermis, though stratified, is not squamous and contains mucus-secreting cells. The degree of cornification in terrestrial vertebrates varies, being very strong on the surface of the body but weak in that lining the oral cavity, the pharynx and the esophagus. In the vagina, the stratified epithelium undergoes cycles of cornification accompanying the menstrual cycle. The epidermis gives rise to a number of glands, among them the mammary glands, in which the epithelium becomes simple columnar, but under pathological conditions it may revert to the cornified type, as in some kinds of cancer (Pullinger, 1949). Lastly, in the endodermal part of the alimentary canal of mammals the esophagus is lined with stratified epithelium, while the posterior parts, starting with the stomach, are lined with columnar mucus-secreting epithelium.

The transformation of stratified epithelium from the cornified to the noncornified type may be achieved by purely chemical methods under conditions of explantation *in vitro*. If small pieces of vaginal wall of juvenile female mice are cultivated in the standard media for tissue cultures, the epithelium remains without any traces of cornification. If, however, the female sex hormone 3,17β-estradiol is added to the culture medium, the epithelium be-

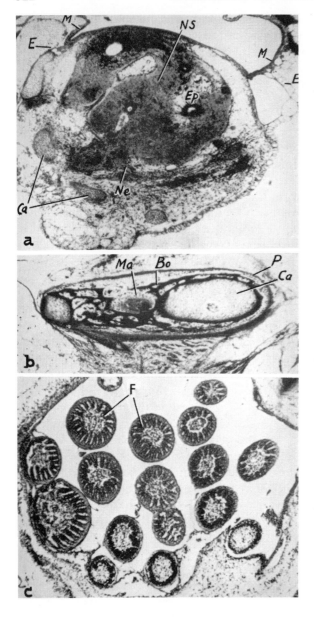

Figure 389. Teratomas developed from completely dissociated cells of a chick embryo and injected into the blood vessels of an intact chick embryo. *a*, Teratoma consists mainly of a large mass of brain tissue *(NS)* surrounded by some muscle tissue and cartilages *(Ca)*: M, visceral mesoderm of the host; E, endodermal epithelium of the host; Ne, nerves; Ep, ependyma. *b*, Teratoma consists of an elongated piece of skeleton with cartilage *(Ca)* and bone *(Bo)*, surrounded by a layer of perichondrium *(P)* and also of masses of muscle and adipose tissue; Ma, bone marrow. *c*, Teratoma is a large epidermal cyst with feather germs *(F)* seen in cross-section. (From Andres, 1953.)

comes squamous and cornified on its surface. Other preparations of estrogens have a similar effect (Hardy, 1953).

The opposite transformation may be achieved by treatment of the cells with vitamin A. If the skin from young seven- to eight-day incubated chicken embryos is grown in the ordinary tissue-culture medium (blood plasma + embryo extract), it develops a squamous cornified layer on the surface of the epithelium. An addition of vitamin A to the medium causes a complete transformation of the epithelium, which now becomes a cuboid or columnar mucus-secreting one. It is remarkable that the cells do not need to be continuously in a vitamin A-enriched medium to be converted into the non-keratinized type: a short treatment with the vitamin suffices to switch the development from the one channel into the other. To enable the vitamin to reach each epithelial cell in a short time, the skin of a chick embryo was dissociated into single cells by trypsin treatment (as described on p. 520), and these were then immersed into a 0.06 per cent solution of vitamin A for 15, 30 or 60 minutes. After this, the cells were put onto a plasma clot and cultivated for several days. The cells reaggregated and in the best cases formed cysts or vesicles, with the distal surface of the epithelium turned inward and the outer surface surrounded by connective tissue. Typical stratified squamous epithelium developed in controls not exposed to vitamin A (see Fig. 390, *a*). As to the vitamin A-treated preparations, it was found that even a 15-minute sojourn in the vitamin solution was sufficient to transform the cells into the nonkeratinizing type, while additional periodic washings (30 minutes every two days) furthered the development of the epithelium into a typical columnar epithelium with goblet cells (Fig. 390—Weiss and James, 1955).

A special type of condition for the differentiation of some tissues is the interaction between epithelium and mesenchyme. The organized growth of many epithelial structures and the very preservation of the epithelial arrangement of cells is dependent on the presence of connective tissues on one (the proximal) surface of the epithelium. An example of this is presented by the embryonic epidermis of the early amphibian embryo (see p. 236). When isolated without mesoderm or mesenchyme of any kind, embryonic epidermis soon loses its epithelial arrangement; the cells acquire a reticulate arrangement and eventually degenerate and die off. In the presence of mesodermal mesenchyme, the epithelial arrangement is preserved; the ectoderm remains healthy and differentiates as normal skin epidermis.

When epithelial tissues are grown in tissue culture they tend to grow as sheets of cells which, though preserving contact with each other, do not follow the arrangement that was present in the original tissue or that should have arisen in the course of development, if the part taken for cultivation was the early rudiment of some epithelial structure. For example, if epithelial cells of renal tubules are cultivated alone, they form a disorganized sheet or layer spreading out on the surface of the plasma clot. If, however, some connective tissue cells are added to the culture, the spreading out of the sheet of renal cells is arrested, and they become reconstituted into tubules, reminiscent of the normal tubules of the kidney (Drew, 1923).

The dependence of epithelia on the connective tissue can be demonstrated very clearly when rudiments of glands are cultivated *in vitro* with or without connective tissue. The submandibular glands of a mouse embryo appear on the thirteenth day of gestation in the form of a pair of solid, club-shaped buds, growing from the buccal epithelium down into the connective tissue layer, one on each side of the tongue. Soon the epithelial bud becomes surrounded with dense mesenchyme forming a "capsule." On the fourteenth day, the tip of the epithelial bud becomes indented; this is the beginning of the branching of the gland rudiment, and the two primary branches grow out, each bearing a knoblike thickening at its end. The end knobs divide repeatedly and eventually give rise to the secreting acini of the gland, while the more proximal parts likewise become split and form the ramified system of ducts. While this outgrowth and branching of the epithelial parts goes on, the capsule mesenchyme surrounds the branches and penetrates between them, forming the connective tissue of the gland. The ducts and acini become hollowed out at a later stage.

Figure 390.   Influence of a short treatment with vitamin A on the differentiation of dissociated and reaggregated epidermal cells. *a*, Control culture, differentiating as typical stratified squamous epithelium. *b*, Treated culture, developing into columnar epithelium with goblet cells. (From Weiss and James, 1955.)

This development can be observed on whole gland rudiments cultivated *in vitro* in a plasma clot (Fig. 391 – Borghese, 1950). By treatment of the early thirteenth day rudiment of the submandibular gland with a 3 per cent solution of trypsin for three to five minutes in the absence of calcium and magnesium ions, the cohesion of the mesenchyme with the epithelium can be

Figure 391. Camera lucida drawings of the capsule and the epithelial part of a mouse's submandibular gland growing *in vitro*. (From Borghese, 1950.)

destroyed and the two components of the rudiment may be separated from each other. On placing them in a culture medium, both components are found to be fully viable but their differentiation is no longer normal: the capsule connective tissue produces a typical culture of mesenchyme, with individual cells crawling out radially from the initial piece of tissue; the epithelial bud loses shape and becomes transformed into a sheet of growing cells. This behavior, however, does not show that the cells of either the capsule or the epithelial part have changed in their essential nature; if the two components are set in the culture medium near to one another, the mesenchyme comes to surround the epithelial rudiment, whereupon the latter starts sprouting and branching in a very nearly normal fashion. The interaction between the epithelium and mesenchyme has restored the system to its normal state (Fig. 392 – Grobstein, 1953a, 1953b).

The mutual influence of the epithelium and mesenchyme of the submandibular gland rudiment may be considered to be a special case of induction, and, as has been done with respect to inductions occurring in earlier stages, it may be questioned whether the influence of one component on the other is specific or not. To answer this question, isolated epithelium of the submandibular gland was cultivated with mesenchyme of different origins: mesenchyme from the rudiment of maxilla, from the somites, from the lateral

Figure 392. *a,* Epithelial part of the submandibular gland separated from the capsular mesenchyme and grown *in vitro*. *b,* Epithelial part of the submandibular gland separated from the capsular mesenchyme as in *a* but then reunited with the capsular mesenchyme in the culture. (*a,* From Grobstein, 1953a; *b,* from Grobstein, 1953b.)

plate, or from the lung rudiment. With all foreign mesenchyme, the epithelial rudiment of the submandibular gland failed to sprout and ramify; the sheet-like spreading out of the epithelial cells was arrested, however, and the rudiment developed eventually into an epithelial cyst. When the epithelial rudiment was implanted into a culture of capsular mesenchyme, which had been previously killed off by heat, the rudiment behaved very much the same as when it was surrounded by foreign mesenchyme; the flattening out and spreading of the epithelium was suppressed, but no growth or ramification took place. Apparently the stimulus necessary for the normal development of the duct and acini system of the submandibular gland can only be given off by the capsular mesenchyme of this organ and only in the living state (Grobstein, 1953b).

In another case of tissue interaction, the inducing stimulus has been found to be less specific. We have seen (p. 422) that the development of renal tubules of the metanephros is dependent on the presence of the growing and ramifying ureter bud. Under the influence of the latter, the loose mesenchyme of the metanephric rudiment (the metanephrogenic mesenchyme) becomes partially converted into epithelium and forms convoluted tubes—the renal tubules—which in normal development link up with the terminal ramifications of the ureteric ducts. The interaction of the ureteric bud and the metanephrogenic mesenchyme can be observed *in vitro* in the same way as the interaction of epithelium and mesenchyme of the submandibular gland, that is, after separating the epithelial and the mesenchymal components by trypsin treatment and reuniting them in the culture medium, though the results of the reaction here are of course essentially different. The experiment referred to previously (p. 523) differs from the ones described now in the stage at which the renal tissue was taken for cultivation: in the previous experiment the epithelium was derived from already differentiated renal tubules; in the present experiment it is the initial formation of the renal tubules that is under consideration.

By combining metanephrogenic mesenchyme taken from an 11-day-old mouse with other tissues, it was found that the ureteric duct is not the only part that causes the mesenchyme to be converted into renal tubules. The epithelial part of the submandibular gland cultivated together with metanephrogenic mesenchyme produces the same effect, although there was no reciprocal action; the gland epithelium remained unbranched. The epithelium of the submandibular gland can thus serve as an "abnormal inductor" of renal tubules, just as adult liver can serve as an abnormal inductor of a neural plate. Furthermore, the spinal cord, especially its dorsal half, proved to be a very efficient inductor of renal tubules, when placed in a culture of metanephrogenic mesenchyme (Grobstein, 1955).

The renal tubules in the above experiments always developed in the immediate vicinity of the inducing tissue. An attempt was therefore made to test whether immediate contact is necessary for the induction to take place. For this purpose, the inducing and reacting tissues were separated by thin membranes of various degrees of porosity. Cellulose ester membrane filters were used, varying in thickness from 20 μ to 150 μ, and with pores approximately 0.8 μ, 0.4 μ and 0.1 μ in diameter. The experiment consisted essentially in arranging for two tissue cultures to grow one on each side of the membrane filter. The inducing culture (spinal cord) was grown on one side of the membrane and the reacting tissue (the metanephrogenic mesenchyme) on the other side. It was soon discovered that the inductive influence could easily pass through the coarser filters (with pores 0.8 μ and 0.4 μ in diameter) of up to 60 μ in thickness, but not if the filter was 80 μ thick (or consisted of four or more layers each 20 μ thick) (see Fig. 393). With finer filters (pores *ca.* 0.1 μ in diameter) the induction became weaker, and the influence could cross only a thin membrane not exceeding 30 μ in thickness. A still finer filter, such as a cellophane membrane 20 μ thick, effectively stopped the inducing influence.

Figure 393. Induction of kidney tubule differentiation through cellulose ester membrane filters. Below the filters is the inductor, spinal cord tissue; above the filters is the reacting nephrogenic mesenchyme. *a,* Successful induction through one layer of filter (20 μ thick). *b,* Four layers of filter preclude induction. (From Grobstein, 1957.)

Positive results have also been obtained when the submandibular gland components were cultivated on the opposite sides of a membrane filter, the epithelial part on one side and the capsule mesenchyme on the other. The epithelial bud produced numerous ramified outgrowths, thus showing that the inducing principle could penetrate through the filter (Grobstein, 1953c).

The electron microscope was applied to see what was going on in the pores of the filter membrane separating the inductor and the reacting tissue. In ultrathin sections made perpendicular to the separating membrane, it could be seen that in the case of coarser membranes the pores contained cytoplasmic outgrowths of cells, coming both from the neural tissue and from the mesenchyme. The possibility was therefore not excluded that the processes of the two kinds of cells met somewhere inside the membrane and thus established a direct contact between the inducing and reacting cells. These processes were, however, more scarce when filters with 0.4μ pores were used, and in the filters with 0.1μ pores there was practically no penetration of the filter by cytoplasmic processes of the cells, except for a few small impocketings which did not go more than 1 to 2μ into the substance of the filter (Grobstein and Dalton, 1957).

The results of these experiments are very important: they show that the interaction of cells responsible for the normal differentiation of tissues can cross a narrow gap between the cells. The inducing principle is therefore a diffusible substance. Since this substance does not penetrate through cellophane, it must be a macromolecular substance, most probably a protein or a nucleoprotein. The similarity of these results to those obtained with the neural inductor in early amphibian development (see p. 242) is very obvious and very suggestive. Much remains to be done. We still have to learn why the inducing substance does not spread over greater distances — whether this is the result of extremely small quantities of the substance produced, of its instability or of some other unknown factor. The chemical nature of the inducing substance has to be elucidated. The way for further research is now open and new discoveries will probably not be long awaited.

16–6   SEQUENCE OF GENE ACTION IN DEVELOPMENT

It has been suggested at the beginning of this chapter that when development starts all the genes are in a repressed stage. During cleavage all genes are inactive, and whatever hereditary traits can be observed are due to gene action during the growth and maturation of the oocyte.

From gastrulation onward, some genes become derepressed and the action of individual genes becomes evident. By observing normal development, it is usually not possible to state whether a particular advancement in the organization of the embryo is due to the action of a gene or genes. (Some exceptions to this statement have been dealt with on pp. 228 and 511.) In a mutant, however, one or more genes become different from the "normal" allele, or the arrangement of the genes in the chromosomes is changed (in translocations), and this change comes to our notice by producing a deviation from the normal development of the organism. Quite often the deviation is of the nature of a developmental arrest, and from this it may be inferred that the gene or genes in their normal, unmutated state are somehow involved in producing the normal course of development. If, therefore, we find that in a mutant some process leading to formation of organ rudiments is disturbed, we conclude that this process is under the control of the normal allele of the mutated gene or is dependent on the normal arrangement of genes in the chromosomes.

Genes Affecting the Earliest Stages of Organogenesis.   There are several mutations in mice which produce a partial or complete duplication of the whole body. The duplication may be posterior, involving the tail, sacral and hindlimb region (Danforth's posterior reduplication, Danforth, 1930), or more generalized ("Kinky" homozygotes, symbol *Ki*, Gluecksohn-Schoenheimer, 1949). The duplications could not have been produced later than the time of primary organ formation, possibly even during the gastrulation stage. It is not known what is the mechanism by which duplication is achieved, but in this connection it is sufficient to know that the genetic constitution of the embryo may influence the morphogenetic processes involved in the formation of primary organ rudiments.

A mutant line is known in guinea pigs which shows various degrees of abnormalities of the head. The abnormalities are of the nature of cyclopic defects (see section 10–5); paired organs of the head tend to approximate each other on the ventral side and fuse into unpaired organs. In animals defective to a greater degree, the more anterior parts of the head disappear altogether, and even the whole of the head may be absent, while the organs of the trunk region are more or less normal (Fig. 394; Wright and Wagner, 1934). These defects are so similar to cyclopic defects which can be pro-

Figure 394.   Series of cyclopic defects of increasing severity in guinea pigs of the mutant strain studied by Wright. (From Needham, J., 1942.)

duced in amphibians by removing the anterior part of the archenteron that it is hardly possible to doubt that in the mutant guinea pigs the origin of the abnormalities is a similar one; the abnormal genetic constitution in some way inhibits the action of the primary organizer (the chordo-mesoderm and the endoderm of the head region). The external ear is also involved in abnormal guinea pigs, and this is a direct indication that the branchial region of the foregut developed abnormally, as the external ear is connected in its development with the first branchial pouch, and its abnormal position could only arise if the arrangement of the branchial pouches was defective right from the start. A similar mutation is known in mice (Little and Bagg, 1924), and it probably occurs in other animals as well.

Genes Affecting Organ Rudiments in Later Organogenesis. An example of genetic control of organogenesis in a later stage is presented by Danforth's short tail mutant in the mouse (symbol Sd). Externally, the mice carrying this gene differ from the normals by having a shortened tail or by the complete absence of the tail. Another feature which interests us here is the reduction in size or complete absence of one or both kidneys found in these mice. As has been explained previously (section 14–4) the metanephros in mammals develops from two separate rudiments: the metanephrogenic tissue and the ureter, which sprouts from the wolffian duct. In Danforth's short-tailed mice, the ureter buds off from the wolffian duct, as usual, but it tends to remain shorter and sometimes does not reach the metanephrogenic tissue at all. If the ureter does not reach the metanephrogenic tissue, the kidney does not develop, as the induction from the ureter is necessary for the kidney tubules to be differentiated. If the ureter reaches the metanephrogenic tissue, then at least a small kidney develops. The size of the developing kidney depends on the degree of branching taking place at the end of the ureter, as only those parts of the metanephrogenic tissue become differentiated into renal tubules which lie in the immediate vicinity of the tip of the ureter or its branches (the latter becoming the collecting tubules of the differentiated kidney). Thus the cause of the kidney defect is the arrest of development of the ureter as a result of the changed genetic composition of the affected animals. The arrest in the development of the ureter prevents the establishment of the spatial relationship between inductor and reacting system (the ureter and the metanephrogenic tissue), which is necessary for the induction of the kidney to take place (Gluecksohn-Schoenheimer, 1943, 1945).

The genes causing excessive development may be represented by the genes causing the increase in the number of digits on the forelimb or hindlimb. Quite a number of such genes are found in different animals. The development of this condition has been studied in a mutation of the mouse called "luxate" (symbol lx — Carter, 1954). In these mice additional toes, one or two, appear on the preaxial side of the foot, that is, on the inner side of the hallux. The anomaly can be traced back to the limb-bud stage, when the hindlimb-bud is excessively broad on its anterior edge. When, in the next stage, mesenchyme condensations appear indicating the rudiments of the digits, the number of these condensations is greater than normal. As the size of each digit rudiment corresponds to the size in normal limbs, it seems plausible that the excessive number of digit rudiments is the result of the excessive amount of material provided for the digit development in the abnormally broad limb-bud.

Effects of Genes on Growth. Differences in the sizes of animals are hereditary, and this means of course that the process of growth is controlled by the genotype. There may be, however, very different ways of such control.

TABLE 17. COMPARISON OF NUMBERS OF CELLS IN EARLY EMBRYOS OF A LARGE AND A SMALL BREED OF RABBIT

Hours After Fertilization	Average Number of Blastomeres	
	Flemish Giant	Polish Breed
32½	4.41	4.06
40	9.04	8.29
41	11.64	8.62
48	21.75	14.00

In one well-investigated case (Table 17) the genetic constitution acts directly on the ability of cells to grow and proliferate. The case is not one of single gene action but concerns the differences betwen the growth of two breeds of rabbits, probably due to a number of genes. In the Flemish giant breed the average adult weight is 4750 gm.; in the Polish breed the average weight of the adult is only 1680 gm. In both breeds the eggs are of the same size, but in the cleavage stage a difference already appears: the Flemish giant embryos cleave at a quicker rate than the Polish breed, so that at any given time there are more cells in the embryo of the Flemish giant (Castle and Gregory, 1929; Gregory and Castle, 1931). The blastocyst of the Flemish giant at the age of six days is 47.8 microns in diameter, that of the Polish race 40.5 microns in diameter. At the age of 12 days the embryo of the large race is 23.1 mm. long, the embryo of the smaller race is 18.1 mm. long.

The rate of cleavage is of course not to be confused with the rate of growth. After 12 days of development, however, the size of the embryo actually is the result of growth, supported by an intake of foodstuffs from without (through the placenta). It is thus evident that the early stages of growth in the two breeds already proceed at different rates. The difference in the rate of growth persists throughout the later days of gestation and during the postembryonic development. The unequal rate of cleavage serves to support the conclusion that the different rates of growth are due to intrinsic properties of the cells and are not the secondary effect of some other distinctions.

The dwarf mutation in mice (pituitary dwarf, symbol *dw*) presents an example of quite a different nature. The character is dependent on a single recessive gene. The homozygotic mice, which alone show the character, are born indistinguishable from normal individuals. At the end of the first week of postembryonic life, however, the dwarf individuals begin to show a slightly retarded growth as compared with the controls. In the third, the dwarfs become conspicuously smaller than normals, and after weaning they increase in weight only slightly. The adult dwarfs are only one-third to one-fourth of the weight of normal mice. The retardation of growth in this case has been traced to an abnormality of the hypophysis, which is reduced in size and fails to produce the **growth hormone**. This has been proved experimentally by transplanting pieces of fresh rat hypophysis subcutaneously into dwarf mice. The result was that the treated mice resumed growth and reached the size of normal individuals (Smith and Macdowell, 1930). In this case, therefore, the gene does not directly affect the intrinsic growth rate or the cells' ability to proliferate, but the primary effect of the gene is to modify in a certain way the differentiation of one of the organs (the anterior lobe of the hypophysis). The arrest of growth is then the visible expression of the deficiency of a growth-stimulating substance normally produced by the hypophysis.

The genetic constitution may affect the growth of different parts in unequal proportion. The mutant gene short ear (symbol *se*) in the mouse will serve to illustrate such a case. The pinnae of the newborn mice are the same size in normals and mutants. Subsequently the growth of the pinna in the mutant is retarded, as shown by the following figures (after Keeler, from Gruneberg, 1952):

	Length of the Pinna	
Age	*Normal*	*Short Ear*
14 days after birth	7.1	6.0
28 days after birth	11.6	7.6
Percentage increase	63%	27%

The most affected part of the pinna is its distal part, while the proximal part is hardly changed at all. The defect has been traced to an abnormality in the development of the cartilage supporting the pinna. The cartilage in the mutant mice is laid down as a collection of mesenchyme, but this does not differentiate beyond the precartilage stage. A true perichondrium is not formed, and the rudiment eventually dissolves altogether. Without the cartilage to support it, the pinna of the ear does not grow out. In short-eared mice, the ear cartilage is not the only one that fails to differentiate; parts of the cartilaginous skeleton of the ribs, sternum and vertebral column (in the tail region) do so as well. As a result multiple defects are present.

There are two points to note in the case of the short-eared mice:

1. The growth of the ear is affected not directly, but through the derangement of differentiation. This is in agreement with the concept (see section 17–3) that rates of growth are dependent on the differentiation of the organs and tissues.

2. A single primary abnormality (in this case a failure of part of the precartilage to differentiate into cartilage) may cause deviations in the structure of many parts of the animal. This is what in genetics is known as the **pleiotropic effect** of a gene.

The Pleiotropic Effects of Genes.   Whereas the term pleiotropic effect refers to the multiplicity of the manifestations of a gene, from the point of view of embryology it is important in this connection to distinguish between the primary effect and the secondary effects of a gene. If there are several manifestations of a gene, these different manifestations are often reducible to one primary cause. This principle will now be illustrated by examples concerned with histological differentiation rather than growth.

The gray lethal mutant in the mouse (symbol *gl*) is produced by a single recessive gene. The heterozygotes are normal. The homozygotes, as the name of the mutant implies, are not viable and die at the age of three or four weeks after birth. The gene causes multiple defects of the whole skeleton, arrest of the growth of bones, failure of the teeth to erupt. All the defects may be traced back to the incapacity for secondary bone resorption. Normally the bones containing an internal cavity (including the long bones of the limbs) grow in such a way that layers of bone are deposited on the surface, while inside the bone is destroyed (resorbed) by osteoclasts. The solid bones also undergo a secondary resorption of part of their matter during the process of growth. In the gray lethal, this resorption does not occur, although osteoclasts are present. The interior of the long bones of the limbs remains filled with spongy bone instead of developing cavities filled with bone marrow. The shape of the bones is abnormal, as well as the shape of the skull (Gruneberg, 1936). The teeth are prevented from erupting, because in normal development the alveoli containing the tooth rudiments have to be partially resorbed at the edges, so as to let the teeth grow out and cut through the gums. The resorption of the bone is, however, impossible and the teeth remain encapsulated in the bony matter of the jaws.

The normal bone resorption is dependent on the activity of the parathyroid glands. It is supposed, therefore, that the primary effect of the gene may consist either in preventing the parathyroid glands from producing their hormone or in some sort of inactivation of the parathyroid hormone.

Another gene causing widespread defects by interfering with a process of differentiation is the "emphysemic" gene in the rat (Gruneberg, 1938). The primary effect of the gene is to cause an abnormal thickening of most of the cartilages, especially those of the ribs, the trachea and the nasal region (Fig. 395). The thickened ribs immobilize the thorax and so interfere with normal breathing. Thickened cartilages of the nose and trachea create further difficulties in respiration. The result is an emphysema of the lungs. As a further tertiary effect, the right ventricle of the heart is hypertrophied to compensate for the insufficient aeration of the lungs. Abnormal individuals eventually die from one of several causes: inability to suckle due to the blockage of the nostrils, slow suffocation due to defective respiration, heart failure, or hemorrhages from lung capillaries due to increased blood pressure.

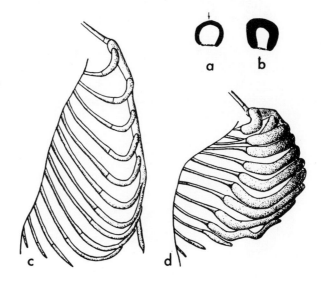

Figure 395. Cross section of trachea (a, b) and profile view of thorax (c, d) of normal rats (a, c) and rats with "emphysemic" gene. (From Gruneberg, 1938.)

Most of the characters caused by genes referred to so far are of the nature of defects or developmental arrest. We shall now consider a case in which an apparently new structure is produced. The structure in question is the peculiar crest of feathers found on the head of the Houdan fowl (Schmalhausen, 1949). The crest or tuft of feathers takes the place of the fleshy crest found in the ordinary fowl. The abnormality is by no means restricted to the integument: the skull is abnormal; the roof of the skull bulges upward and is perforated by numerous openings; the bulge of the skull encloses a bloated brain. The primary effect of the gene appears to be the increased secretion of the cerebrospinal fluid by the cells of the forebrain. The fluid is found in vacuoles lying under the ependyma, and the anterior ventricles of the brain become swollen. The cerebrospinal fluid apparently penetrates through the thin roof of the third ventricle and causes a dissolution of the skeletogenous tissue destined to differentiate into the bones of the cranial roof (parts of the frontal bones). Only the lateroventral parts of the frontal bones develop, and the skull remains open dorsally. The skeletogenous mesenchyme from the disorganized bone rudiments concentrates under the skin epidermis and gives rise to the rudiments of feathers (the feathery crest). Finally, during postembryonic development, islands of bone develop underneath the crest. They fuse into a network of bony trabeculae and so form the new roof of the skull, adapted to the shape of the bloated brain (Fig. 396).

The Cooperation of Genes. The examples of multiple secondary effects produced by one primary action of a gene illustrate one principle of genetic control of development. Another principle involved is the cooperation of several genes to produce one final effect.

The coloration of insects is produced by several groups of pigments, and the actual color is usually dependent on the combination of more than one pigment, as well as upon the structure of the surfaces bearing the pigment and the position of the pigment granules in respect of the surface. Any of the various pigments may appear independently of the others, and genes are known which affect certain pigments or groups of pigments and do not affect

Figure 396. Skull of a Houdan fowl with a dome-shaped reticulated protuberance in the frontal region (a), and skull of a normal fowl (b). (Modified from Schmalhausen, 1949.)

the others. One group of dark pigments, known as the ommochromes, is found in the eyes of insects (the fruit fly *Drosophila*, the meal moth *Ephestia*, and a number of other moths, flies and wasps). Similar or identical pigments are also present in the internal organs of the same animals, as in the gonads or the brain. In the meal moth, one pigment of this group, an **ommin**, gives a black color to the eyes of both the adult moth and the caterpillar, while a related pigment, an **ommatin**, is found in the skin of the caterpillar. In *Drosophila*, the brown pigment of the eye is an ommatin.

It has been found (for a review see Kühn, 1941; Ephrussi, 1942) that all the pigments of the ommochrome group are derived primarily from the amino acid tryptophan, which is processed by a series of steps, controlled by several genes. The same genes — that is, genes with an identical chemical activity — are found in different insects having the ommochrome pigments. All the genes of a series have to be present in an active state if the final pigmentation is to be normal.

The first gene of the series is the vermilion (symbol v^+) gene of *Drosophila*, or the corresponding a^+ gene of *Ephestia*. If the gene mutates to a state v or a, the dark pigment of the eyes is not formed, no matter what the remaining genetic constitution of the animal. The color of the eyes in the mutants becomes light red, this color being produced by a different pigment, unrelated to the ommochromes and masked in normal insects by the presence of the darker ommochrome. It is now known that the normal genes v^+ and a^+ are instrumental in transforming tryptophan into the related substance, **kynurenin**. The defective coloration in mutants not possessing the normal v^+ or a^+ genes can be restored to normal if the necessary quantities of kynurenin are introduced from without. This can be done in several different ways:

1. By transplanting into the mutant larva or early pupa tissue from an animal bearing the normal gene v^+ (or a^+). The rudiment of the eye or the gonad has been used for such transplantation. The kynurenin is produced by the cells of the graft possessing the necessary normal gene. Kynurenin, being a diffusible substance, can spread into the tissues and cells of the host and there be used for the development of pigment, provided that the other mechanisms for this development are available.

2. By injecting into a mutant individual an extract from a normal individual. This method, by the way, has been used to prove the identity of the substances produced by the gene v^+ in *Drosophila* and the gene a^+ *Ephestia*: an extract from a normal *Drosophila* individual caused an *a Ephestia* mutant to develop black eyes, and an extract from a normal *Ephestia* caused a *v* mutant of *Drosophila* to develop wild type eye coloration.

3. By feeding the larvae (in the case of *Drosophila*) on cooked pupae of the insects possessing the normal gene. The kynurenin, contained in the boiled tissue and taken in with the food, can be used by the larvae for producing pigment.

4. By cultivating eye rudiments of mutant individuals in an extract from insects (whether of the same species or a different one) possessing the normal gene. The eye rudiment attained normal color *in vitro*.

5. By cultivating eye rudiments of mutant insects in a saline solution to which kynurenin had been added.

6. By adding kynurenin to the food of mutant *Drosophila* larvae.

7. By injecting kynurenin into *v* mutants of *Drosophila* or *a* mutants of *Ephestia*.

In all the variations of these experiments, a substance which could not be produced by the tissues of the animals, and which is necessary for the further development of the pigment, was introduced in some way or other so that the broken chain of reactions could be restored and the later processes of pigment development could then proceed in an apparently normal fashion. The experiments listed under 5, 6, and 7 prove that the substance in question is kynurenin.

Kynurenin is a colorless substance, and further transformations are necessary before the actual pigment is formed. These transformations can be broken off at the next stage by the failure of the gene cinnabar (symbol *cn*⁺) in *Drosophila*. An analogous gene must exist in other insects. The mutation of the gene *cn*⁺ into *cn* does not prevent the formation of kynurenin, but kynurenin is not processed into the next link in the chain of substances leading to pigment formation. The ommochromes are thus not produced.

The failure of the *cn*⁺ may be compensated in the same way as the failure of the *v*⁺ gene by implanting into the body of mutants tissues of individuals bearing the normal gene. The action of the normal *cn*⁺ gene has also been replaced by a chemical substance, which is sometimes found as an impurity with kynurenin. It has not been possible to separate this substance from kynurenin in a pure form. This prevents an exact analysis of the substance but at the same time suggests that it is a very nearly related substance and probably a product of transformation of kynurenin.

The next gene which is known to participate in the development of ommochromes is the gene white (symbol *w*⁺) found in *Drosophila* and in many other insects. The mutation of *w*⁺ into *w* removes all eye pigments from the eye. The tissues of mutant *w* individuals may be used as a source of the substances restoring to normal the pigment development in *v* and *cn* individuals. This proves that the earlier stages of pigment development proceed normally in the white mutant individuals but that the chain is broken at a later stage.

The pigmentation of the eye of a *w* mutant cannot be restored by the implantation of tissues of a normal *w*⁺ animal, nor can this be done by introduction of extracts or chemical substances. The gene *w*⁺ must actually be present in the cells of the tissue (the eye rudiment) which is to become pigmented. Under no known circumstances can the actual colored substance be elaborated unless the tissues in which the pigment is found normally have been present. It is concluded, therefore, that the link of the chain controlled by gene *w*⁺ is intimately connected with the cellular structures, and that the substances involved cannot diffuse beyond the limits of the cells. It is possible that the final chemical modeling of the pigments occurs in the granules in which they are found in the fully differentiated cells.

There is hardly any doubt that the three genes mentioned above are not the only ones that are involved in the transformation of tryptophan into ommochrome pigment. Very many more genes would be needed to account for the whole chain of reactions. All these genes must thus cooperate to produce the normal differentiation of the eye. The picture becomes still more complicated if it is considered that the eye rudiment itself must be there for the pigments to be deposited. The development of the eye rudiment is dependent on other genes having nothing to do with the genes of coloration. Thus in *Drosophila* a mutation is known which prevents the development of the eyes (eyeless). In such a mutant no eye pigments are produced, although all the genes otherwise necessary for the elaboration of pigment in the eye may be present.

Sequence of Gene Action and the "Biogenetic Law." The sequence of gene action in the course of development throws a new light on some generalizations which have played a considerable role in embryology in the nineteenth century, namely, the "laws" of Behr and of Müller-Haeckel (see p. 9). Essentially, both "laws" stress the greater conservatism of the earlier stages of ontogenetic development rather than that of the later stages, as a result of which the earlier stages show features general to large groups of animals while the more specialized features distinguishing lower taxonomical units become apparent during later stages. These features distinguishing closely related animals may be considered as later acquisitions in the course of evolution.

We have seen that mutations can affect all stages of ontogenetic development and that even the earliest stages may thus become changed. In spite of this, the cumulative effect of mutations must necessarily show a greater influence on the later than on the earlier stages. If a mutation occurs which changes any developmental process in an earlier stage, and if the embryo nevertheless remains viable, then a number of later processes might also be modified, owing to the pleiotropic effect of the initial change, as explained on pp. 532-534. Mutations of genes which normally become derepressed during later stages of ontogenesis obviously cannot affect the earlier stages. In this way, the earlier stages of development would be modified only by a minority of mutant genes, while the great majority of the genes, both those acting in earlier stages and those acting later, would leave a mark on the later stages. The greater conservatism of the earlier stages can thus be given a rational genetic explanation.

It is obvious, however, that exceptions to the general rule are always possible. One obvious exception is presented by the structure of the egg: lying, as it does, at the end of a life cycle (as well as at the beginning of a new one), the structure of the egg may be under the influence of genes becoming active throughout a lengthy period of life; it is of course well known that the structures of eggs, including egg membranes, show a great amount of variation. It is sufficient to point to the endless variety of sculpture found on the surface of insect eggs.

CHAPTER

17

Growth

Growth is the increase in size of an organism or of its parts due to synthesis of **protoplasm** or of **apoplasmatic substances**. Protoplasm in this definition includes both the cytoplasm and the nucleus of cells. Apoplasmatic substances are the substances produced by cells and forming a constituent part of the tissues of the organism, such as the fibers of the connective tissue, the matrix of bone and cartilage, and so on, as opposed to substances produced by the cells and subsequently removed from the organism, such as the secretions of digestive and skin glands, or substances stored as food, such as fat droplets in cells of the adipose tissue. Imbibition of water or the taking of food into the alimentary canal before the food is digested and incorporated into the tissues of the animal, although it may increase the weight of the animal, does not constitute growth.

Growth is the result of the preponderance of the anabolic (synthetic) over the catabolic (destructive) processes in the organism. If synthesis and decomposition go on at the same rate, there is no increase in the bulk of the organism—no growth. In certain conditions, decomposition dominates over synthesis, as for instance in prolonged inanition, when synthetic processes are impossible because of lack of food supply, while catabolic processes (oxidations, etc.) continue to satisfy the current requirements for energy. After the internal food reserves (fat in the adipose tissue) have been exhausted, the energy is produced at the expense of the proteins of the protoplasm, and the result is a decrease in the mass of living matter which may be called **degrowth** (Needham, 1942).

In ordinary life, growth is often identified with increase in height. From a biological viewpoint, however, growth is an increase of mass of living substance; only the weight can therefore be considered as an index of growth. The increase in linear dimensions (height, length) may accompany increase of mass, but the connection is by no means a simple one, and this must always be borne in mind, if for any reason the height or length of a growing animal is measured instead of its weight.

By weighing a growing animal at regular intervals and plotting the weight against time on a diagram, we get a **growth curve**, showing the increase of the mass of the animal with time. The shape of the growth curve very often resembles the letter S: there is an initial part, where the curve rises very gradually, then a middle part, where the curve rises steeply, and the last part, where the rise of the curve is again slowed down and it asymptotically approaches a horizontal line signifying the limit of growth in each particular case. A curve of this shape is known as the **sigmoid curve** (Fig. 397).

If the increments of growth for equal time intervals are measured, the increase in different periods of life of the same individual may be estimated. The increase, taken as a difference between the final and initial size (weight) of an animal for any period of time, irrespective of other factors, is called the **absolute increase**. The sigmoid curve is actually a graphic representation of the absolute increase, and it shows that the absolute increase per unit of time is, in this case, greatest in the middle part of the growth cycle. The absolute increase is, however, not a correct indication of the rate of growth and cannot well serve for comparing the growth at different periods of life and for comparing the growth of different organisms. It is obvious that if a small animal and a big animal show the same absolute increase in a given

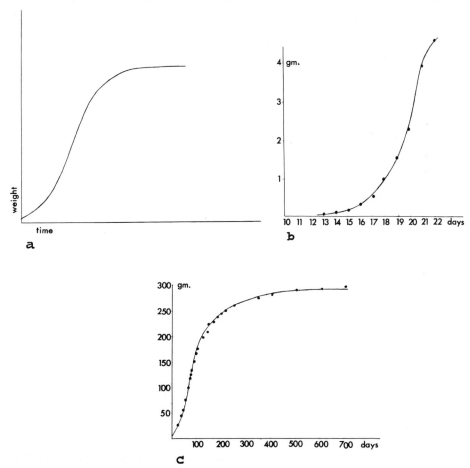

Figure 397. Sigmoid growth curves. *a*, Ideal sigmoid curve, after Robertson. *b*, Intrauterine growth of the white rat. *c*, Postnatal growth of the white rat. The points show the actual measurements. (After Donaldson, Dunn and Watson, from Fauré-Fremiet, 1925.)

time, their rate of growth is not the same: the small animal has to grow at a greater rate to have the same absolute increase as the big one. The rate of growth is measured as the relative increase — the increase related to the initial mass of growing substance. The exact definition of the rate of growth is then

$$v = \frac{dW}{dt} \cdot \frac{1}{W} \qquad (1)$$

where v is the rate of growth and W is the size (weight) of the animal at any given time, t.

Growth thus defined is, in its essence, an increase in geometrical progression, the increase being proportional to the initial quantity of growing substance.

Increase in geometrical progression is called exponential; growth is thus an **exponential process**. The general formula for exponential growth, showing the increase of the growing mass with time, is

$$W = e^{vt} \qquad (2)$$

where W as before is the weight of the animal at any given time t, v is the observed rate of growth, and e is the base of natural logarithms (equal to 2.71828 . . . , accurate to the fifth decimal place). The above formula is correct if the initial quantity of growing matter is infinitely small and very nearly accurate if the initial size is negligible. If the initial size of the growing animal cannot be ignored, the formula must be slightly changed by the introduction of a constant, as follows:

$$W = be^{vt} \qquad (3)$$

where b is a constant and is equal to the initial size of the growing organism.

The rate of growth may be calculated from the same data as those on which the sigmoid curve of growth is based.

17—1   GROWTH ON THE CELLULAR AND INTRACELLULAR LEVEL

The essentially exponential nature of the growth process can best be verified by considering growth on the cellular level. In a mass of growing cells, other conditions being equal, the increment of growth will be greater, the greater the number of growing cells. If each cell produces, by mitosis, two cells after a certain period of time, then the total number of cells will be doubled, and the same will occur after another similar interval, provided that all the time neither the cells nor the conditions for their existence change. Such conditions are very nearly fulfilled in the case of cells growing in tissue cultures with sufficiently frequent transfers of cells to new portions of nutritive medium. Cell divisions under these circumstances have been observed in some experiments to occur at intervals of from 10 to 23 hours. The exponential growth is thus based on the ability of the cells to duplicate themselves.

A similar case is the growth of unicellular organisms (bacteria, protozoa and unicellular plants) in constant and favorable conditions. The principle of exponential growth applies in the same way to the increase of populations of multicellular animals reproducing in optimal conditions, provided that the food supply is infinite and that the animals can disperse themselves in space to avoid overpopulation. Theoretically, the growth of living matter (in this case proportionate to the number of animals) may continue indefinitely, always having an exponential nature. Practically, of course, such an indefinite increase can never occur, since the conditions for it cannot be provided.

Matters become more complex if growth is considered on the intracellular level. Even when growth is not complicated by differentiation, the anabolic processes in the cell are of an extremely involved nature. If we consider a clone of cells undergoing mitosis from time to time and growing in between to attain that state, both qualitatively and quantitatively, which the cells had at a time immediately preceding the previous mitosis, we will be able to distinguish several aspects of the process.

1. The chromosomes must be brought up to the same state as they were in the mother cell.

2. Proteins in the nucleus and the cytoplasm must be doubled so that their amount would equal that in the mother cell.

3. Other cell components must be replenished accordingly.

The three aspects are satisfied by entirely different mechanisms which have to be considered separately.

The necessity of (1) follows from the postulate that all cells during development are supplied with a full complement of hereditary information; therefore, they must possess at least one set of double-stranded DNA molecules. We may thus expect that the amount of chromosomal DNA per cell will remain constant in spite of repeated mitotic divisions. This can be actually proved by direct measurement. The amount of this acid per cell may be estimated either chemically or spectroscopically (by ultraviolet light absorption owing to the presence of nucleic acid), and it was found that in any species of animal all somatic cells having a diploid set of chromosomes possess the same amount of deoxyribonucleic acid. Table 18 shows the amounts of deoxyribonucleic acid per cell found in different vertebrates.

TABLE 18. AMOUNTS OF DEOXYRIBONUCLEIC ACID IN SINGLE NUCLEI IN VARIOUS ANIMALS (IN mg $\times$ 10^{-9}) (VENDRELY AND VENDRELY, 1949; MIRSKY AND RIS, 1949)

Bull	6.4
Pig	5.1
Guinea pig	5.9
Dog	5.3
Man	6.0
Rabbit	5.3
Horse	5.8
Sheep	5.7
Mouse	5.0
Duck	2.2
Fowl	2.4
Turtle	5.1
Toad	7.3
Frog	15.7
Carp	3.3
Trout	5.8

The average quantities of deoxyribonucleic acid per cell found in different somatic tissues of the same animal are the same. The figures apply to the nuclei in the resting stage.

Between two mitotic divisions the amount of deoxyribonucleic acid is doubled, as the daughter cells show the same amount of the substance generation after generation (Swift, 1950). By using radioactively labeled DNA precursors in a way explained on p. 27, the part of the life cycle of a cell during which the DNA synthesis occurs has been ascertained with a high degree of exactness.

It is believed that molecules of DNA isolated *in vitro* and provided with precursors and the enzyme DNA polymerase can replicate very rapidly, perhaps in a matter of a few minutes or less. The replication of DNA in intact chromosomes, however, takes quite a considerable time. This is because different parts of the chromosomes replicate asynchronously, groups of genes or possibly even individual genes replicating' at different times (Taylor, 1960a).

As a result, the duplication of chromosomes takes a considerable part of the life cycle of a cell. This part of the cell's life is called phase S, and it is found to lie toward the second part of the interphase. Straight after mitosis, which may be called phase M, the nucleus enters a phase in which it does not incorporate DNA precursors and thus does not make new DNA. This is phase G_1. The duration of this phase depends on the length of the whole cycle, but it continues in any case for several hours. Next follows phase S, during which all the DNA in the chromosomes is replicated. The duration of this phase is again variable; times from six to eight hours have been recorded in different kinds of cells. After the completion of DNA replication, the cells enter a second period during which no new DNA is made and which is designated as phase G_2. It continues for another two to six hours and is terminated by the onset of the next mitosis (Taylor, 1960a; Kuyper, Smets and Pieck, 1962; Prescott and Bender, 1963).

Figure 398. The length of different phases during the life cycle of cells grown in tissue culture. *A*, Embryonic Chinese hamster cells; *B*, embryonic Chinese hamster cells; *C*, fetal calf liver cells. *M*, mitosis; G_1 and G_2, phases in which there is no synthesis of DNA; *S*, phase of DNA synthesis (duplication of DNA strands). (*A*, From Taylor, 1960a, 1960b. *B*, From Prescott and Bender, 1963. *C*, From Kuyper, Smets and Pieck, 1962.)

Figure 398 shows the approximate length of the phases during a cell's life cycle in several kinds of cells grown in tissue culture.

To the question why the DNA double-stranded molecules separate and duplicate themselves at a particular moment during phase S in the life cycle of a cell, there is practically no answer, although many factors are known which stimulate growth and division of cells in general. None of the conditions favoring growth and division can be connected directly to the duplication of DNA as the causative agent of such a duplication. The formation of new, complementary strands of DNA requires the presence of an enzyme, DNA polymerase. The latter, being a protein, falls under the next section.

As for the second aspect (2), the synthesis of proteins in the growing cell, including all the proteins with enzymic action, requires the following conditions to proceed: messenger RNA, transfer RNA, ribosomes, and precursors in the form of a full complement of amino acids. It is thus evident that rapid growth requires considerable amounts of RNA to be present in the cytoplasm. The amount of ribonucleic acid per cell is by no means constant; the ratio of ribonucleic acid to the deoxyribonucleic acid varies in different kinds of cells from 0.2 in the thymus to as much as 8.1 in the pancreas (Davidson, 1947). The observation has been made (Brachet, 1941) that the ribonucleic acid content is highest in those cells which are especially active in synthesizing proteins. Such are some of the secretory cells (pancreas), but also the actively growing cells. Cells that cease growing lose their ribonucleic acid. This has been directly demonstrated in the development of some tissues, in which growth and reproduction of mother cells ("stem cells") precedes the specific histological differentiation of the cells produced in this way. The differentiated cells lose the ability to grow and divide, as in the case of red blood corpuscles or of the permanently growing teeth of rodents, where the dentine is perpetually produced at the expense of a group of reproducing cells at the root of the tooth. In the stem cells, from which the red blood corpuscles are eventually produced, the content of ribonucleic acid is 5 per cent. As the differentiation progresses, the percentage of ribonucleic acid drops almost to zero (Thorell, 1947).

On the other hand, if cells are stimulated to more intensified growth and reproduction, the percentage of ribonucleic acid goes up. This happens when differentiated cells are explanted in vitro and allowed to grow as a tissue culture. Measurements of the ribonucleic acid have been made on explants of chick heart tissue, and the amount of ribonucleic acid was compared with the amount of deoxyribonucleic acid, which as we know remains constant per cell. The measurements showed that at explantation the amount of ribonucleic acid was about double that of deoxyribonucleic acid, but it rose to about five times the amount of deoxyribonucleic acid after four days of cultivation in vitro (Davidson and Leslie, 1950).

All these earlier data refer mainly to the ribosomal RNA. There are very few data on the amounts of messenger RNA and transfer RNA in different types of cells. As the life of the messenger RNA is a limited one, it is to be assumed that most if not all of the messenger RNA used by the growing cell between two mitotic divisions is produced during this same period. By using radioactive tracers, it has been shown that there is no synthesis of RNA in the chromosomes while these are in the strongly spiralized and contracted form, that is, from the late prophase to middle telophase. RNA synthesis is resumed in late telophase, when the chromosomes become despiralized, continues through the interphase and becomes gradually diminished and eventually ceases during the prophase (Taylor, 1960b; Prescott and Bender, 1962).

Table 19 shows the incorporation of H³-labeled uridine into RNA and also the incorporation of H³-labeled histidine into cellular proteins during interphase and mitosis of cells grown in a tissue culture.

TABLE 19. INCORPORATION OF TRITIATED URIDINE INTO RNA AFTER A 5-MINUTE EXPOSURE AND INCORPORATION OF TRITIATED HISTIDINE INTO PROTEINS AFTER A 10-MINUTE EXPOSURE OF CHINESE HAMSTER CELLS GROWN in Vitro. FROM PRESCOTT AND BENDER, 1962. FIGURES SHOW AVERAGE COUNTS OF SILVER GRAINS IN PHOTOGRAPHIC EMULSION OVER THE CELLS.

Stage, Site	H³ Uridine	H³ Histidine
Interphase nucleus	39 ± 2	45 ± 2
Interphase cytoplasm	0	. .
Early prophase, nucleus and cytoplasm	29 ± 2	40 ± 2
Late prophase, nucleus and cytoplasm	0	25 ± 1
Metaphase, nucleus and cytoplasm	0	15 ± 1
Anaphase, nucleus and cytoplasm	0	11 ± 1
Early telophase, nucleus and cytoplasm	0	10 ± 1
Late telophase, nucleus and cytoplasm	4 ± 1	17 ± 1

The incorporation of RNA precursors is initially into the nucleus only, showing that synthesis of RNA is carried out in the nucleus. After some time, the newly synthesized RNA passes out into the cytoplasm. The passage of the RNA into the cytoplasm is fairly slow and takes 20 to 60 minutes. However, toward the end of prophase there is a more rapid release of RNA from the nucleus, and most of the remaining nuclear RNA passes into the cytoplasm in a short time.

RNA synthesis does not stop during the S phase when chromosomal DNA is being replicated, though there are indications that it may be retarded and that, at the points where DNA is replicating, no RNA synthesis is taking place (Prescott and Kimball, 1961). The synthesis of RNA continues probably because at any time during the S phase only a part of the genes in the chromosomes are actually in the process of replication—the rest are available for use as templates for the RNA. The RNA synthesis is, however, completely blocked when the chromosomes are in a condensed state. Although the synthesis of RNA is blocked during mitosis, the synthesis of protein goes on, though at a diminished rate, as shown by the continued incorporation of labeled histidine. This protein synthesis is due to the survival in the cytoplasm of messenger RNA produced during the preceding interphase.

With regard to (3), the synthesis of nonprotein components in the cell is presumably not directly dependent on the nuclear DNA but is regulated by the enzymes which have been produced on the messenger RNA templates in cooperation with the ribosomes. The proteins do not have a very rapid turnover; therefore, a cell emerging from a mitosis would have supplies of enzymes inherited from the mother cell and capable of carrying out synthetic processes in a continuous fashion. Among the nonprotein cell constituents which are synthesized in the cytoplasm are the nucleic acid precursors — the phosphoribonucleotides and also the nonessential amino acids. (The essential amino acids, that is, those which cannot be synthesized by animal cells, have to be provided in ready-made form from the environment.)

Growth being the result of the preponderance of anabolic over catabolic processes, the rate of growth would depend on the factors controlling each of these. The anabolic processes, as has just been shown, are very complex and depend on the interplay of a number of factors. The degradation of substances in the cells through oxidation and fermentation is similarly due to a number of factors — in the first place the enzymes present in the cell but also the conditions of its environment. No general rule governing the rate of catabolic processes in the course of the life cycle of the cell is known.

The actual measurements of growth of single cells between two mitoses have been carried out on unicellular organisms. The growth of infusorians with elongated bodies was studied by measuring their length at regular intervals between two divisions (Schmalhausen and Syngajewskaja, 1925), and in a heliozoan, *Actinophrys*, which has a spherical shape, the growth was estimated by measuring the diameter of the cell (Syngajewskaja, 1935). Recently the remarkable achievement has been performed of weighing individual cells of *Amoeba* throughout its life cycle (Prescott, 1957). The results of all these measurements conform very well with one another and show that in these unicellular organisms growth is most rapid after a cell division and slows down later (see Fig. 399).

It is reasonable to assume that the course of growth of cells in multicellular organisms follows the same general course; this, however, is an extrapolation, which needs further experimental confirmation.

17—2 GROWTH ON THE ORGANISMIC LEVEL

The relation between growth of cells and growth of whole organisms is not the same in every case. It will be convenient to distinguish three types of such relationships.

Type 1. The volume of the animal's body increases owing to the growth of the individual cells, without an increase in their number (**auxetic growth,** after Needham, 1942). This rather rare case is found in nematodes, in rotifers, and Larvacea among the tunicates. In the development of the nematodes, the cell divisions stop in the early stages of organogenesis. The number of cells in the fully grown nematode is thus the same as in a young one just emerged from the egg (see Hyman, 1951). The number of cells in each rudiment may be definitely fixed in this type of development. Thus the whole excretory system of a nematode consists of only three cells. In the rotifer *Hydatina senta* the total number of somatic cells of the body could be estimated and was found to be 959 (Martini, 1912). The gonads, however, are an exception among the other organ rudiments; the mitoses in the sex glands are not

Figure 399. Growth curves of three protozoans. *Paramecium*—growth in length, in arbitrary units (divisions of ocular micrometer) (after Schmalhausen and Syngajewskaja, 1925). *Actinophrys*—growth in volume, recalculated from original measurements of diameter (after Syngajewskaja, 1935). *Amoeba*—growth in weight, in millimicrograms (after Prescott, 1957). In *Actinophrys*, growth could not be measured during division, which takes about three hours to complete, and is interpolated for that period.

restricted to the early embryonic period, and the gametocytes continue to proliferate in the adult animals.

While the number of the cells is restricted, owing to the cessation of mitoses, the growth of the individual cells continues, and the growth of the animal is proportional to the increase in size of its constituent cells.

Type 2. The animal's growth may be a result of the increase in number of its constituent cells (**multiplicative growth**, after Huxley, 1932). The increase in number is brought about by mitotic division of all the cells, while the average size of the cell remains the same or nearly so. This type is found quite commonly in the growth of embryos; it is especially characteristic of the prenatal growth of the higher vertebrates. If the size of the cells remained strictly constant and no other processes were involved, growth of the animal's body would be directly proportional to the number of its constituent cells. Actually the size of the cells does not remain constant; as the embryo develops and its tissues become differentiated, the cells, or many of them, increase in size. This increase in size of the individual cells is, however, very limited and can account for only a very small proportion of the over-all increase of the body. As the animal develops, the mechanism of its growth becomes modified by the differentiation of its tissues, so that a further type of growth should be recognized.

Type 3. In this type, the growth of the animal is based to a greater or lesser degree on the activity of special cells, retaining their ability to divide mitotically, while other cells have lost this ability more or less completely and so cannot proliferate any more (**accretionary growth**, Huxley, 1932). These latter cells are the differentiated cells of the body, performing various physiological functions necessary for the maintenance of the animal's life. The former may be called the reserve cells, for they provide a supply of new cells, capable of reinforcing and replacing, in case of necessity, the functioning differentiated cells. The multiplying cells can also be called undifferentiated cells, inasmuch as they lack the specific morphological and physiological properties of functioning cells. However, the competence of the proliferating cells may be already curtailed to a large extent, so that they can differentiate only into one type of functioning cell, or only into a limited number of types.

The epidermis of terrestrial vertebrates may serve as an example of this type of growth. In the outer layers of the epidermis, the cells do not divide and do not grow. Their cytoplasm becomes keratinized, thus forming a protective layer on the surface of the skin. The fully keratinized cells are no longer vital and are perpetually being peeled off. The malpighian or generative layer of the epidermis consists of cells which are not keratinized and which possess the capacity to proliferate; later, the outermost cells of the layer replace the keratinized cells, undergoing keratinization in their own turn.

The cells of the bone tissue (the osteocytes) do not grow and do not proliferate. The growth of the bones is dependent on the activity of the cells of the periosteum, which are capable of proliferation and can become osteocytes, while they secrete additional quantities of intercellular bone matrix.

In a number of organs centers are found, regions or layers which alone contain proliferating cells. In the vertebrate eye, the proliferating cells are found in a ring in the region of the ciliary body. From there new cells are added onto both the retina and the iris. In the intestine of vertebrates, proliferating cells are found at the bottom of the intestinal glands, and the same is true in other organs.

17-3 GROWTH CURVES AND THEIR INTERPRETATION

If the growth of an animal were a strictly exponential process, the growth curve would have the shape of a hyperbola, the curve produced by an exponential increase of a quantity. The curve would begin at a point near zero of the coordinate system and rise with an ever-increasing steepness.

A prerequisite for the growth being truly exponential is that the rate of growth should be constant. This in turn is possible only if neither the animal itself nor the environmental conditions change as growth proceeds. Such conditions apply to the growth of populations in perfectly favorable conditions, as has been mentioned previously. Purely exponential growth has been found in rod-shaped bacteria (Schmalhausen and Bordzilowskaja, 1930). In round bacteria—cocci—growth becomes retarded as the organism increases in size, presumably because the relative decrease of the surface in relation to the mass of protoplasm places the coccus in a worse position with regard to exchange of substances with the surrounding medium.

In multicellular organisms, exponential growth is never found in a pure form. The nearest approach to it is the growth of larvae of insects having a complete metamorphosis. In caterpillars of moths, growth starts at about the same rate after each molt; the absolute increase, therefore, is most rapid toward the end of larval development, as would be expected with exponential growth. However, the growth curve in this case is not a smooth hyperbola, as growth is very much retarded before and during molting. The curve is thus broken up into a series of spurts and level portions (Levitt, 1932).

In most animals, the rate of growth does not remain the same but diminishes quite regularly from the beginning to the end of the cycle of growth. The resulting curve, as has already been mentioned, in many cases is in the shape of a letter S — the sigmoid curve. The absolute increase is small at the beginning, becomes greatest in the middle of the period of growth and diminishes again later, until growth ceases altogether. If, however, the rate of growth is calculated for the various parts of the growth cycle, it is found that the rate of growth is highest at the beginning and declines throughout the period of growth. The low absolute increase at the beginning is due to the fact that only a small mass of living substance is growing. In the middle part of the cycle, the mass of growing substance has increased, and the absolute increase is, therefore, greater even though the rate of growth is not so high as at the beginning. In the last part of the growth period, the growing mass is even greater than at the middle of the cycle, but the rate of growth has sunk so low that the absolute increase slows down and comes to a standstill. The growth curve approaches asymptotically to a horizontal line, which is the limit of growth or, in other words, the maximal size that can be attained by the animal whose growth is being considered.

The limit to growth is very distinct in such animals as birds and mammals, but not in some of the lower vertebrates such as reptiles and fishes. In these animals growth can go on indefinitely, although with ever retarded rate. As a result, some individual fishes and reptiles may attain an extraordinarily large size if they escape accidental death which puts an end to the growth of other members of the same species. The growth curve in these animals approaches the shape of a parabola: it starts a little above the zero point (the initial mass of growing substance can never be 0) and gradually rises. The concavity of the curve is greatest near the starting point, and the curve flattens out as growth proceeds, approaching asymptotically a straight line inclined at an angle to the axes of the system of coordinates. This type of growth has been called **parabolic growth** (Fig. 400; Schmalhausen, 1927, 1930a).

It is interesting to note that the sigmoid curve is also found in the growth of populations. Animal populations under ideally favorable environmental conditions should increase exponentially, but under actual conditions a shortage of food and space soon causes a decline in the rate of reproduction, with the result that the growth curve of the population becomes sigmoid. In the end the population may stop increasing further, having achieved the limit which is permitted by the environment given in each case.

The progressive decline in the rate of growth has attracted much atten-

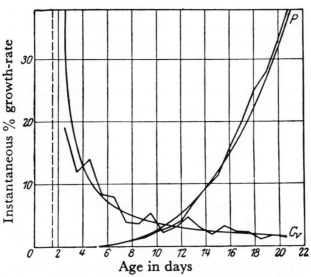

Figure 400. Increase in weight (P) and true rate of growth (Gv) in parabolic growth (growth of the chick embryo). The curves based on actual measurements and the smoothed theoretical curves are shown side by side. (After Schmalhausen, from Needham, 1931.)

tion, and several theories have been proposed to account for this decline. The theories fall into two main groups, depending on whether the sigmoid curve or the parabolic curve has been considered as better representing the nature of the growth in metazoa.

The first interpretation, mainly propounded by Robertson (1908) and more recently followed by L. von Bertalanffy (1948, 1949), starts with the assumption that the organisms possess an intrinsic potential growth rate. This potential growth rate is curtailed by obstacles arising in the process of growth and setting a limit to it. As the organism approaches the limit of growth, the growth rate diminishes, and eventually growth stops altogether. These relationships have been given the following mathematical form:

$$\frac{dW}{dt} = bW \frac{L-W}{L} \qquad (4)$$

where W is the size of the organism at any given time t, b is the potential growth rate and L is the maximum size (limit of growth or asymptote of the growth curve). The equation (4) is known as the **logistic equation**. The sigmoid curve is also sometimes referred to as the logistic curve.

The logistic equation represents growth as an essentially exponential process, the increase $\left(\dfrac{dW}{dt} \right)$ being proportional to the growing mass (W).

On the other hand, the potential growth rate can actually be observed only in the initial stages of growth, while W is very small in relation to L (the actual size being very small as compared with the final size). At this stage the factor $\dfrac{L-W}{L}$ is near unity. As W increases, this factor becomes less than unity, and when W = L, it becomes 0. The increase then also becomes zero.

The logistic equation has been applied both to the growth of individuals and to the growth of populations. It appears, however, that the equation is much more fitted to the latter case. Several objections may be brought against the application of the equation to the growth of individuals.

1. The nature of the limiting factor has not been made clear. Bertalanffy suggests that the decline in the rate of growth is due to a discrepancy between the increase of surfaces and volumes. (The surfaces increase as the square of linear dimensions, the volumes as the cube of linear dimensions.) The ultimate growing unit, however, is the cell, and the sizes of cells as a rule do not change so as to account for the retardation of growth. The change in the relative size of any other surfaces in the animal's body would not explain the universal nature of the slowing down of growth.

2. Animals having no upper limit of size (having a parabolic growth curve) still show a retardation of growth. The logistic equation is not applicable in this case.

3. Holometabolic insects do not show a retardation of growth, although their growth is limited. The existence of a growth limit thus does not cause in itself a slowing down of growth during the earlier periods of development.

The second way of interpreting the growth curve makes use of the fact that the rate of growth (specific rate of growth) is inversely proportional to the time that elapses since the beginning of growth:

$$v = \frac{k}{t} \qquad (5)$$

$$\text{or } v \cdot t = k \qquad (6)$$

where v is the growth rate, t is time and k is a constant which is different for each organism.

The time since the beginning of growth is an indicator of the age of the animal. Minot (1891, 1908) was the first to make this observation, and he accordingly stated that the decrease of the rate of growth is due to increasing age of the animal. The decline of growth is thus one of the many expressions of **aging**. Minot also showed the connection between aging and the differentiation of cells in the developing animal. The more the tissues of the animal become differentiated, the less they are able to grow. This aspect of Minot's theory has been further elaborated by Schmalhausen.

According to Schmalhausen (1930b), the differentiation of parts of the developing animal, and not age as such, is the cause of retardation of growth. Inasmuch as the degree of differentiation of some cells of the animal's body may be preserved at a certain level, their rate of growth may remain constant, and exponential growth would take place in such groups of cells or tissues. This would account for the type of growth found in caterpillars: the caterpillar of a later instar is not more differentiated than one of the first instar so far as its larval organs are concerned. The organ rudiments of the adult moth (the imaginal discs) do not change very much until the pupal stage, and anyway they form only an insignificant part of the bulk of a caterpillar and do not essentially influence the growth curve. Given equal levels of differentiation at the start of every instar, the growth rate remains constant, and this has actually been observed.

Growth may also be exponential in the growth centers of a vertebrate's body (malpighian layer of the epidermis, ciliary body of the eye), but the proportion of proliferating cells to those which have partially or completely lost their ability to proliferate may diminish with age, and this becomes noticeable in the decrease of the over-all rate of growth. Besides, the cells of the growth centers are already partially differentiated and do not proliferate as rapidly as the cells of an early embryo. Lastly, growth centers may disappear altogether. The growth of the long bones of the limbs in vertebrates is dependent on the presence of an actively proliferating layer of cells between the diaphysis of the bone and its epiphyses. At about the time of sexual maturity the proliferating layer disappears, and the bony cores of the epiphyses are firmly joined onto the diaphysis. The result is that the growth in length stops.

The residual growth centers are, however, an exception rather than the rule among the tissues of a higher animal. Most of the cells become differentiated, which is of course essential for the functioning of the various organs, and this leads to a retardation of growth.

There appears to be an inverse proportion between the degree of differentiation and the rate of growth: the more highly an organ or tissue is differentiated, the slower it grows. The most highly differentiated tissue of the vertebrate's body is the tissue of the brain and spinal cord. The nerve cells in the adult state completely lose the ability to proliferate, and in the brain and spinal cord there is no residue of undifferentiated cells functioning as a growth center. The result is that the brain and spinal cord, throughout life, grow more slowly than other parts of the body. The sense organs have a degree of differentiation that is scarcely lower than in the brain tissue. These also grow very slowly. Organs like the heart and the kidneys grow at a higher rate than the brain and sense organs. The heart and the kidney, however, are rather highly differentiated organs, with no growth centers consisting of undifferentiated cells to provide for proliferation, and their growth is consequently not very fast. Higher rates of growth are found in the muscle and skeletal system. Although bone tissue has no growth of its own, and the striated muscle possesses a highly specialized differentiation, in both cases there are residues of undifferentiated cells providing for rapid growth. There is the periosteum in the case of bone (perichondrium for cartilage, in addition to a certain degree of interstitial growth). New elements of muscle tissue—new cells or muscle fibers—are not normally produced after the earlier part of the embryonic period has passed, but the individual muscle fibers, or muscle cells, in the case of the smooth muscle tissue, have the ability to increase in size to a very great extent and thus produce a rapid growth of the muscular tissue.

The highest rates of growth are found in parts of the intestinal tract and in the skin of vertebrates. The skin possesses a permanent growth center in its malpighian layer. There are groups of growing and proliferating cells in the gut (at the bottom of the intestinal glands and crypts); furthermore, the epithelial cells of the intestinal tract do not have a complicated morphological differentiation. The connective tissue is also capable of rapid growth;

while the products of differentiation in this tissue are the various inter-cellular fibers, the cells themselves (fibroblasts and histiocytes) do not become highly differentiated, and even in the adult animal they can at any time be mobilized to proliferate and produce new connective tissue fibers. Such a mobilization of the connective tissue cells takes place in wound healing.

In any given organ, the rate of growth is highest before histological differentiation has set in, or at least when it has not progressed very far. Even in the case of very highly differentiated organs, such as the brain, the early rudiment of the organ may possess and actually does possess a very high growth rate, as is shown in Table 20.

TABLE 20. GROWTH OF ORGANS OF THE CHICK EMBRYO FROM THE FOURTH DAY OF INCUBATION TO HATCHING (AFTER SCHMALHAUSEN, 1927)

	Initial Weight in Milligrams	Final Weight in Milligrams	Weight Increased by a Factor of	Growth Constant $k = v \cdot t$
Brain	10	1,020	× 102	2.10
Lens	0.08	8.8	× 110	2.10
Forelimb	0.75	540	× 720	2.93
Metanephros	1.4 (on ninth day)	130	× 93	3.58
Whole embryo	53	41,000	× 773	

The inverse relationship between growth and differentiation can also be shown in experimental conditions. In the intact organism, the tissue cells differentiate and their growth becomes restricted. When bits of tissue are cultivated *in vitro*, the tissues become dedifferentiated, and at the same time they regain the ability to proliferate at a rapid rate. It is possible, however, to retard the growth of a tissue culture by supplying it with a medium poor in growth-promoting substances or by keeping it longer on the same plasma clot. Under these circumstances, the cells may show signs of renewed differentiation; intercellular fibers (or cartilage matrix) are produced in the culture, depending on the nature of the cultivated cells. Differentiation goes hand in hand with reduced proliferation.

Dedifferentiation and a concomitant increase of the proliferation rate of cells also occurs during regeneration of lost parts, as will be described in Chapter 19.

The contention that progressive differentiation is the actual cause of the decline in the growth rate of animals with time is thus very well substantiated. On the other hand, this does not quite explain the existence of a definite growth limit found in many animals, such as birds, mammals and also insects. The nature of the limitation of growth may perhaps be different in the arthropods and in the vertebrates. In the arthropods (insects), the limit to growth is quite obviously connected with the mechanism of metamorphosis and will be discussed in Chapter 18. In the higher vertebrates, a regulation of growth by means of hormones exists. The hypophysis is known to produce a growth-stimulating hormone. Animals (dogs) treated with this hormone may be caused to grow in excess of the usual size (Evans and collaborators, 1933). In humans, dwarfism is attributed to an insufficient production of the growth hormone by the hypophysis. The thyroid hormone is also necessary for normal growth, and the removal of the thyroid in a young animal causes the growth to be below normal. The cessation of growth in mammals and probably also in birds) seems to be the result of an interplay of perhaps numerous hormones controlling growth. The details of this mechanism are not yet completely understood.

17—4   PROPORTIONAL AND DISPROPORTIONAL GROWTH OF ORGANS

The growth of different organs and of parts of the same animal (embryo) very seldom goes on at the same rate. As a rule, some grow faster and some grow slower. The result is that the proportions of the animal change with growth. In the case of vertebrates, the central nervous system and the sense organs are distinguished by their particularly low rate of growth, and the size of these organs diminishes relatively throughout the whole embryonic and postembryonic development. In the early embryo (of a chick, for instance), the head is at first quite as large as the rest of the body, and a large portion of the head is made up by the relatively enormous eyes. At the time of hatching, the head is already much smaller than the body, and in the adult fowl the head is relatively small.

To compare the growth of different organs, their rates of growth may be estimated. However, the rate of growth changes with age, so that it is not a very convenient quantity for purposes of comparison. The growth constant k (see preceding section) may be calculated for each organ as well as for the whole animal, and the constants of different organs may be conveniently compared.

A different method of analyzing the unequal growth of organs has been proposed by J. Huxley (1932). Huxley found that if two parts of an animal grow at different rates, their sizes at any given moment stand in a very simple relationship to each other. The relationship is expressed by the following formula, known as the formula of **allometric growth:**

$$y = bx^k \qquad\qquad (7)$$

where y is the size of one of the organs, x is the size of the other organ, b is a constant, and k is known as the **growth ratio,** because it shows the relation of the rates of growth of the two parts which are being compared. If the growth ratio equals 1, the two organs grow proportionally or **isometrically.** The constant b in this case shows the proportion of one organ to the other: $b = \frac{y}{x}$. If the growth ratio is $\neq 1$, the growth is disproportional or **allometric,** the relative size of the two organs changing as the growth proceeds. If the growth ratio is > 1, the organ y grows at a quicker pace than the organ x. The organ y is called **positively allometric** to the organ x. If the growth ratio is

< 1, the organ y grows at a slower pace than the organ x; it is **negatively allometric** to x.

The formula for allometric growth can be given in a logarithmic form:

$$\log y = \log b + k \log x \quad (8)$$

In other words, the logarithms of the sizes of two organs growing at different rates are proportional to each other. This form of the equation is especially instructive, as it allows for a very simple graphic representation of allometric growth (Fig. 401). If the logarithms of the sizes of one organ are plotted against the logarithms of the sizes of the other organ, the points lie on a straight line crossing the ordinate axis at a distance from the zero point = log b and ascending with an inclination a, determined by the equation:

$$\tan \angle a = \frac{\log y - \log b}{\log x} = k \quad (9)$$

The latter formula discloses the true significance of the exponent k, and also shows how this exponent can be determined in practical work.

A great advantage of the formula for allometric growth is that it eliminates time, which enters into all the other growth equations as the independent variable. As a result, the formula can be applied for the analysis of growth of parts in groups of specimens whose timing (age) is not known, as when a series of animals of different sizes is collected in nature and not bred and reared under permanent observation. The formula of allometric growth is also applicable to linear dimensions, as well as to volume or weight, and is in this respect more pliable than the other equations used for analysis of growth.

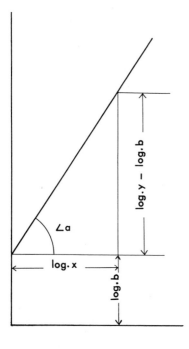

Figure 401. Graphic representation of allometric growth (in logarithmic transformation).

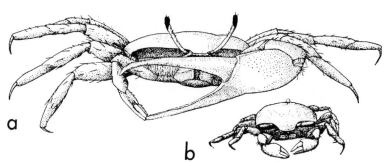

a

b

Figure 402.   Positive allometric growth of the left chela in a fiddler crab *Uca*. *a*, Adult male with disproportionately large left chela. *b*, Young male crab with both chelae of equal size. (From Morgan, 1927.)

The organs to be compared, x and y, may be chosen at will. A special case of the application of the formula is when the size of an organ is compared with the size of the body less the size of the organ, the growth of which is being investigated. It can then be learned whether an organ grows in excess of the other parts (the remainder of the body) or not.

It has been found that organs attaining especially large proportions in certain animals often owe their increased size to positive allometric growth. In the fiddler crab *Uca pugnax*, one of the chelae in the males attains an extraordinarily large size, up to 38 per cent of the weight of the body as a whole. The large chelae are positively allometric in respect of the rest of the body, with a growth ratio of 1.62. This means, by the way, that in a young male crab the chelae are very nearly equal in size, and that the relative size of the larger chela increases as the crab grows (Fig. 402).

In most mammals the facial region of the head, including the jaws, grows at a greater rate than the cranial part of the head. The length of each of these parts of the head has been measured and the growth compared during the postembryonic life of sheep dogs. In a puppy, the length of the cranium is almost double the length of the facial region (42 mm. and 22 mm.). In the adult dog the cranial region is only slightly longer than the facial region (120 mm. and 112 mm.). The facial region is thus positively allometric in respect to the cranial region. The growth ratio is in this case 1.49. The lower rate of the growth of the cranial region is mainly due to the rate of growth of the brain, which is enclosed by the skull and which is noted for its low rate of growth; it is negatively allometric in respect to the body as a whole.

The formula of allometric growth can be used not only for the comparison of the growth of morphologically definable parts of the animal's body but also for the increase of various chemical components of the body. In differentiating tissues, the amount of protein increases in respect to the amount of nuclear chromatin, as has been indicated in section 16–1. This can be represented as a case of allometric growth; in Table 21, the quantities that have been compared are the deoxyribonucleic acid phosphorus and the protein nitrogen in several organ rudiments of the chick embryo.

The high rate of increase of the protein nitrogen (large growth ratio) corresponds, according to what was said before, to a rapid rate of differentiation. The high figures for the brain and the leg muscle can therefore be easily understood. The heart shows little increase of differentiation because

TABLE 21. COMPARISON OF INCREASE OF PROTEIN NITROGEN AND DEOXY-RIBONUCLEIC PHOSPHORUS IN DIFFERENT ORGANS OF THE CHICK EMBRYO (AFTER DAVIDSON AND LESLIE, 1950)

Organ	Incubation Period in Days	Growth Ratio of Protein Nitrogen to Deoxyribonucleic Phosphorus
Brain	8–13	2.55
Brain	15–19	1.05
Heart	10–19	1.05
Liver	8–19	1.10
Muscle (leg)	12–19	1.40

in the 10-day chick the heart is already fully functional, that is, already differentiated. The liver is an example of an organ which becomes differentiated late, and even there the level of morphological differentiation is in this case rather low.

PART VII

MORPHOGENETIC PROCESSES IN THE LATER PART OF ONTOGENESIS

Taken as a whole, ontogenetic development appears to slow down with the increasing age of the individual animal. In the later periods of life, spectacular changes such as those occurring during cleavage, gastrulation and organ formation do not take place. When histological differentiation starts, it gives rise to various tissues, but further differentiation serves mainly to support and only sometimes to increase the already established initial differences. Even growth, as has been stated, diminishes in rate with age. There are, however, special cases in which morphogenetic processes may be aroused again at a late stage of ontogenesis, so that the changes produced by these processes may equal in volume those observed in the earlier stages of the individual's development. These special cases will now be considered.

18

Metamorphosis

The first case in which morphogenetic processes may be reactivated after development has almost reached a standstill is observed in animals in which the embryo develops into a larva, and the larva is transformed into the adult by way of **metamorphosis**. Larval forms and an accompanying metamorphosis are found in most groups of the animal kingdom, though by no means in all representatives of each group. The larvae usually have special names distinguishing them from the adult forms. The following is a survey of the occurrence of larval forms, with their names:

1. Porifera — amphiblastula
2. Coelenterata — planula
3. Platyhelminthes
   Turbellaria polycladida — Müller's larva
   Trematodes — miracidium, cercaria, redia, sporocyst
   Cestodes — onchosphaera
4. Nemertinea — pilidium
5. Annelida — trochophore
6. Mollusca — trochophore and veliger
7. Crustacea
   Entomostraca — nauplius
   Malacostraca — zoea
8. Insecta — nymphs of insects with incomplete metamorphosis; caterpillars, grubs, etc., of insects with complete metamorphosis
9. Bryozoa ectoprocta — the cyphonautes larva
10. Echinodermata — pluteus, bipinnaria, auricularia, etc.
11. Enteropneusta — the tornaria larva
12. Ascidiacea — the tadpole larva
13. Cyclostomata — ammocoete
14. Amphibia — tadpoles of frogs; aquatic larvae of salamanders

The morphogenetic processes in all these groups differ both in the nature of transformation and in the mode of causation of the whole sequence; it is thus impossible to describe them in common terms. Two cases are chosen here for closer study: the metamorphosis in amphibians and the metamorphosis in insects.

18−1 CHANGES OF ORGANIZATION DURING METAMORPHOSIS IN AMPHIBIANS

In amphibians, metamorphosis is associated in typical cases with a transition from an aquatic to a terrestrial mode of life. Superimposed on this change of environment is, in the anurans (frogs and toads), a change in feeding. The tadpoles of most frogs and toads feed on vegetable matter — particles of plants, living and decaying — which they scrape off submerged objects with the aid of the horny teeth surrounding their mouths. Some are detritus feeders, passing through their guts the mud and detritus collected from the bottom, and others, as the tadpole of the clawed toad *Xenopus,* are plankton feeders. Adult frogs are carnivorous, living on insects, worms and the like, but sometimes also on larger prey, such as smaller frogs and even little birds and rodents, which they catch, overpower and swallow. In the case of urodeles, there is no substantial change of diet, the larvae being as carnivorous as the adults though naturally feeding on smaller animals (mainly crustaceans and worms). The changes in the organization of the animals during metamorphosis are in part progressive and in part regressive, and may be grouped into three categories:

1. The organs or structures necessary during larval life but redundant in the adults are reduced and may disappear completely.
2. Some organs develop and become functional only during and after metamorphosis.
3. A third group of structures, while present and functional both before and after metamorphosis, become changed so as to meet the requirements of the adult mode of life.

In **anurans,** the differences between the mode of life of the larva and the adult are much more profound, and accordingly the changes at metamorphosis are more extensive than in the urodeles. We will consider them first.

The regressive processes occurring during the metamorphosis in frogs are the following: the long tail of the tadpole with the fin folds is resorbed and disappears without a trace. The gills are resorbed, the gill clefts are closed and the peribranchial cavities disappear. The horny teeth of the perioral disc are shed, as well as the horny lining of the jaws. The shape of the mouth changes. The cloacal tube becomes shortened and reduced. Some blood vessels are reduced, including parts of the aortic arches as indicated in section 14-6.

The constructive processes involve, first, the progressive development of the limbs, which increase in size and differentiation. The forelimbs, which in the frogs develop under cover of the opercular membrane, break through to the exterior. The middle ear develops in connection with the first branchial pouch (the pouch situated between the mandibular and the hyoid arch). The tympanic membrane develops, supported by the circular tympanic carti- lage. The eyes protrude on the dorsal surface of the head and develop eyelids. The tongue is developed from the floor of the mouth. The organs which function both in the larva and the adult, but change their differentiation during metamorphosis, are primarily the skin and the intestine. The skin of the tadpole is covered with a double-layered epidermis. During metamor- phosis, the number of layers of cells in the epidermis increases and the sur- face layers become cornified. Multicellular mucous and serous glands develop as pockets sinking from the surface into the subcutaneous connective tissue layer. The lateral line sense organs, present in the skin of tadpoles, disappear during metamorphosis in most frogs. The pigmentation of the skin is changed; new patterns and colors appear. The intestine, which is very long in tadpoles, as in most herbivorous animals, becomes greatly foreshortened, and most of the coils which it forms in the tadpole become straightened out. The metamorphosis is very rapid and takes only a few days.

In **urodeles**, the changes at metamorphosis are far less striking. The tail is retained; only the fin fold disappears. The branchial apparatus is reduced, the external gills become resorbed and the gill clefts close. The visceral skele- ton becomes greatly reduced. The head changes its shape, becoming more oval. The progressive changes are less conspicuous than in the metamorphos- ing frog tadpoles. They are restricted mainly to the changes in the structure of the skin and the eyes. The eyes bulge more on the dorsal surface of the head and develop lids. The skin becomes cornified, and multicellular skin glands become differentiated. The pigmentation of the skin changes. The legs, contrary to those of tadpoles, suffer hardly any change at all, and the same may be said of the alimentary canal. The metamorphosis is, on the whole, more gradual and may take up to several weeks (Fig. 403).

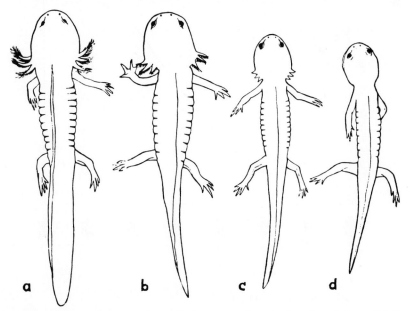

a   b   c   d

Figure 403. Metamorphosis in the axolotl. *a*, Animal in the larval condition; *d*, fully meta- morphosed animal; *b*, *c*, intermediate stages of metamorphosis. (From Roth, 1955.)

It is worth noting that the lungs do not undergo drastic changes during metamorphosis in both anurans and urodeles; they develop very gradually and become fully functional in the larval state. Long before metamorphosis, the larvae of frogs as well as of salamanders start coming up to the surface and gulping air into their lungs and thus supplementing their aquatic respiration. This may be of considerable importance where the larvae develop in stagnant and polluted waters, as is often the case.

Hand in hand with morphological changes during metamorphosis go physiological changes, of which we shall point out the following. In the frog tadpoles, the endocrine function of the pancreas starts at metamorphosis, and this is connected with the increased role of the liver in the turnover of carbohydrates (glycogen). (See Abeloos, 1956.) A profound change takes place in the excretory mechanism. In the tadpole, the end product of nitrogen metabolism is ammonia, which is easily disposed of (by diffusion) in an aquatic medium but which in a terrestrial animal might accumulate and become dangerous because of its high toxicity. Metamorphosed frogs, however, excrete most of their nitrogen in the form of urea and only small amounts as ammonia. The change-over occurs in the late stages of metamorphosis and is, of course, due to a changed function of the liver, which performs the synthesis of urea (Munro, 1939; Fig. 404).

The reduction of the gills and the tail in tadpoles is effected by autolysis of the component tissues of these organs, with active participation of ameboid macrophages which phagocytose the debris of the disintegrating cells. The

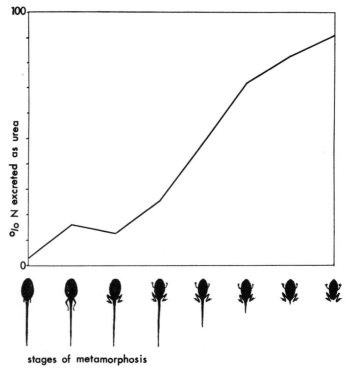

stages of metamorphosis

Figure 404. Changes in the amounts of ammonia and urea excreted by tadpoles of the frog *Pyxicephalus delalandii* during metamorphosis. (After unpublished data by J. Balinsky.)

same mechanism, though of a limited scope, is in action when the external gills and fin folds are reduced in urodele amphibians.

Since destructive processes play such a considerable role in metamorphosis and since, in addition, food intake may be interrupted during the crucial part of the transformation, especially in tadpoles, the mass of the body at the end of metamorphosis is smaller than at the beginning ("degrowth"—see p. 538). The reduction of the body mass is not only due to loss of some parts (gills, tail), but the remaining parts, excepting the actively growing organs, also appear to shrink during metamorphosis; the head and trunk of metamorphosed amphibians are smaller than in larvae just before the commencement of metamorphosis.

18—2 CAUSATION OF METAMORPHOSIS IN AMPHIBIANS

The concurrent changes in so many parts of the animal's body during metamorphosis suggest the existence of some common cause for all the transformations. It has been found that this common cause is a hormone released in large quantities from the thyroid gland of the animals entering the stage of metamorphosis. A first indication of this was obtained when Gudernatsch fed some frog tadpoles on dried and powdered sheep thyroid gland and observed that they metamorphosed precociously (1912). Feeding tadpoles with preparations of other glands did not have the same effect. This experiment made it very probable that tadpoles are capable of reacting to the thyroid hormone by metamorphosing.

The proof that the thyroid hormone is actually the cause of metamorphosis in normal development was further given by the following two experiments. The rudiment of the thyroid gland was removed in frog embryos in the tailbud stage (through an incision on the ventral side, Fig. 405, A). The operated tadpoles were fully viable and showed normal growth but failed to metamorphose (Allen, 1918), although they were kept alive almost a year after the control animals had become little froglets. The thyroidless tadpoles continued to grow and attained a much greater size than normally: total

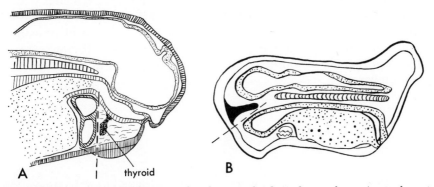

Figure 405. Removal of rudiments of endocrine glands in frog embryos (sagittal section). A, Late tailbud stage, showing how the rudiment of the thyroid was removed through a ventral incision (broken line); B, Early tailbud stage showing how the rudiment of the hypophysis (black) was removed through an incision indicated by a broken line. (From Allen, in Willier, Weiss and Hamburger, 1955.)

length up to 123 mm. instead of about 60 mm. as at the beginning of meta-morphosis in normal tadpoles. It was thus proved that metamorphosis can-not set in without a stimulus emanating from the thyroid gland. The final experiment consisted in supplying the thyroidless tadpoles with thyroid hormone from without, either by feeding them on dried thyroid gland (Allen, 1918) or by immersing them in water containing soluble extracts from thy-roid glands. The tadpoles treated in this way immediately proceeded to metamorphose, thus showing that their own thyroid glands are not necessary so long as they are supplied in some way or other with thyroid hormone (see Allen, 1938).

Similar experiments were carried out on urodeles. A very favorable animal for the experiments is the axolotl *Ambystoma mexicanum*, which under ordinary conditions does not metamorphose at all but may be induced to metamorphose by thyroid treatment (see Marx, 1935).

As already indicated, the active principle of the thyroid gland may be introduced into the animal's body in several different ways. Normally it emanates from the animal's own thyroid gland. The same effect may be produced by implanting bits of live thyroid gland, feeding the animals on thyroid gland, injecting them with preparations of thyroid gland, or keeping them in water containing soluble extracts of thyroid glands. The last fact clearly shows that the active principle of the thyroid gland is a chemical substance—a hormone.

A saline extract of fresh thyroid tissue contains protein, **thyroglobulin,** which retains the activity of the thyroid gland. An important characteristic of thyroglobulin is that it contains iodine, which, as we will see, is of great importance for the working of the thyroid hormone. Thyroglobulin has a molecular weight of about 675,000; its molecules are thus very large, and it is unlikely that thyroglobulin can penetrate as such through cellular mem-branes, which would be necessary if it were to leave the thyroid gland and reach the cells eventually reacting to the thyroid treatment.

To become active, the iodine-containing compounds are released from their connection to the thyroglobulin. Several compounds of smaller molec-ular weight are liberated in this way. In chemical structure, all these com-pounds are combinations of molecules of the amino acid tyrosine with one or more atoms of iodine. The most important of them are tri-iodothyronine and thyroxine. In both of these compounds two residues of tyrosine are joined together, and to these are attached three (in tri-iodothyronine) or four (in thyroxine) atoms of iodine. The structural formulas of these substances are as follows:

tri-iodothyronine:

thyroxine:

Of the two compounds, thyroxine is produced in very much greater quantities and is thus the main active substance released by the thyroid gland, although tri-iodothyronine has a higher activity on tissues.

It has been tested whether iodine alone can cause metamorphosis in amphibians, and positive results have been obtained either by keeping frog tadpoles or newt larvae in water containing the element iodine (in solutions as weak as 0.0000003833 per cent!), by injecting animals with iodine or by implanting iodine crystals into the body cavity. The element iodine caused metamorphosis even in thyroidectomized axolotls, so it must have been acting directly and not through the increased production of hormone by the animal's own thyroid gland. On the other hand, it appears that the degree of activity of the iodine atoms may be greatly influenced by the type of amino acid with which the iodine is bound. This can be shown clearly by comparing the activity of the two amino acids di-iodotyrosine and thyroxine. By placing tadpoles in solutions of each amino acid separately, it was found that the same amount of iodine was 300 times more active when forming a part of the thyroxine molecule than when incorporated into the di-iodotyrosine molecule. The activity of tri-iodothyronine is three to five times as high as that of thyroxine (L. Wilkins, 1960).

The thyroid gland is not the only one whch is involved in the causation of metamorphosis in amphibians. It has been discovered that the hypophysis plays an important part as well. If, in frog tadpoles, the hypophysis is destroyed (Adler, 1914) or if the rudiment of the hypophysis in a late frog embryo is excised (Fig. 405, B—Allen, 1929), the tadpoles do not metamorphose, just as if their thyroid glands had been removed. The removal of the hypophysis rudiment may later be compensated by implanting pieces of hypophysis from metamorphosed or adult frogs, but only if the thyroid gland of the animal is intact. If the thyroid gland has been removed, no amount of hypophyseal tissue implanted can induce metamorphosis. From this it may be concluded that the hypophysis does not act upon the tissues directly, but only by way of stimulating the thyroid gland. In fact, the thyroid gland of hypophysectomized animals remains underdeveloped and does not accumulate the thyroid hormone (in the form of "colloid") in its follicles. Implantations of active hypophyses can also be used to stimulate metamorphosis in the axolotl.

The agent necessary for activating the thyroid gland is produced in the anterior (epidermal) lobe of the hypophysis and has been isolated in the form of a **thyrotropic hormone**.

In the case of larval amphibians, the hypophysis does not produce the thyrotropic hormone until the time when metamorphosis normally occurs. This has been proved by taking hypophyses from tadpoles of various ages and transplanting them into tadpoles whose own hypophyses had been removed previously. Whereas hypophyses taken from tadpoles in stages of metamorphosis or from metamorphosed frogs compensated for the removal of the animal's own hypophysis and restored the tadpole's ability to metamorphose, hypophyses taken from younger stages were not effective.

The following pattern of amphibian metamorphosis emerges from these studies. The initial signal for metamorphosis is given by the anterior lobe of the hypophysis when it reaches a certain degree of differentiation and becomes capable of producing the thyrotropic hormone. The thyrotropic hormone activates the thyroid gland, which builds up and releases the thyroid hormone. The thyroid hormone (of which thyroxine is the most important component) affects the tissues directly, causing the degeneration and necrosis of some cells and stimulating the growth and differentiation of others.

18−3 TISSUE REACTIVITY IN AMPHIBIAN METAMORPHOSIS

One of the most intriguing aspects of amphibian metamorphosis is the diverse nature of reactions in different tissues to one and the same condition—the presence of the thyroid hormone. Whereas some of the tissues (the tail, the gills) become necrotic owing to the action of the hormone, others (the limbs) react to the hormone by increased growth and progressive differentiation. It can easily be shown that the character of the reaction is not due to the position of the parts in question, nor to an uneven distribution of the active principle, but solely to the nature of the reacting part. Parts of a tadpole's tail transplanted to the trunk undergo metamorphosis together with the host's tail and become absorbed. On the other hand, an eye transplanted to the tail of a tadpole before metamorphosis remains healthy while all the surrounding and underlying tissues undergo necrosis. As the tail shrinks, the eye is brought nearer to the trunk and eventually becomes fused to the body in the sacral region after the whole of the tail has disappeared (Fig. 406—Schwind, 1933). The same experiments, incidentally, prove that the stimulus of the thyroid gland is carried through the blood vascular system, as it is only by this route that it can reach any part independently of its actual position. The secretion of the thyroid gland is thus a hormone in the narrow sense of the term. What happens to a tissue under the influence of the thyroid hormone is determined by the reactive properties of the tissue itself, or by what we have earlier called its **competence** (see p. 236). The competence of tissues to react to the thyroid hormone is not directly dependent on their histological differentiation; in tadpoles, while the myotomes of the tail become resorbed during differentiation, the myotomes of the trunk are not so affected.

It has further been noticed that different parts of the body reacting to the thyroid hormone (whether by degeneration or progressive development) are not equally responsive to the dosage of the hormone. Very weak dosages

Figure 406. *a*, Metamorphosing frog (*Rana sylvatica*) tadpole with a grafted eye in the tail. *b*, Metamorphosed froglet: the tail has disappeared, but the eye is retained in the sacral region. Eye indicated by arrow. (From Schwind, 1933.)

applied to frog tadpoles cause an acceleration of the growth and differentiation of hindlimbs and a shortening of the intestine. Further processes may not be set into motion at all or follow only after a lengthy treatment. A higher dose of the thyroid hormone causes the breakthrough of the forelegs. An even greater dose of the hormone is necessary to cause the resorption of the tail. There is evidently some kind of threshold value for each part which has to be attained before the reaction sets in. Different parts of the tail have different threshold values, the tip of the tail reacting more readily than the proximal parts. In general, the degree of sensitivity to the thyroid hormone is reflected in the order in which the metamorphic changes proceed in normal development: the parts which have a low threshold (legs, reacting by growth) respond earlier than the parts having a high threshold value (tail, reacting by reduction). (See Etkin in Willier, Weiss and Hamburger, 1955; Abeloos, 1956.)

When heavy dosages of thyroid hormone are supplied to young tadpoles, all processes start at once and the normal sequence of events becomes upset, the destructive processes being capable of proceeding faster than the constructive processes: the forelimbs break through before becoming differentiated; the tail becomes reduced before the legs are sufficiently developed to take over locomotion. The result is, of course, the death of the animal.

In urodeles, the bulging of the eyes seems to be the reaction which may be elicited by the weakest doses of the thyroid hormone. Next follow, more or less concurrently, the reduction of the fin fold and the shortening and disappearance of the external gills. The closure of the gill clefts and the transformation of the skin are the result of a maximal stimulation and accompany complete metamorphosis in the course of normal development. The earlier stages of metamorphosis, including the shortening of the external gills, are partly reversible: if the thyroid treatment is stopped, the gills may elongate again to a certain extent.

18–4 PROCESSES OF INDUCTION DURING AMPHIBIAN METAMORPHOSIS

Although, as a general rule, the processes of metamorphosis are a direct reaction to the thyroid hormone which reaches each tissue, there are some notable exceptions to this rule. The skin covering the tail of a tadpole, although subject to necrosis in normal metamorphosis, remains healthy if transplanted to the body, provided that it is transplanted without the underlying muscles. Skin transplanted with underlying tail muscle will necrotize in any position on the body. It is thus evident that the direct action of the thyroid hormone is on the muscle tissue, and the overlying skin becomes involved in the process of resorption secondarily.

A more complicated case is presented by the development of the tympanic membrane in frogs. The middle ear, with its cavity connected by the eustachian tube to the pharynx, is one of the structures that develop progressively during metamorphosis. The tympanic membrane first becomes differentiated toward the end of metamorphosis. It is supported in frogs by a cartilaginous ring, **the tympanic cartilage**, which develops as an outgrowth from the posterior edge of the quadrate cartilage. The skin which later participates in the formation of the tympanic membranes is originally no different from the skin covering the rest of the body. During metamorphosis, the

Figure 407. Dependence in the development of the tympanic membrane on the tympanic cartilage. *a*, Stage of operation: skin *(S)* turned back to reveal tympanic cartilage *(ATC)*. *b*, Normal tympanic membrane *(TM)* developed on control side. *c*, No tympanic membrane developed after tympanic cartilage had been removed *(EC*, scar from operation). *d*, Tympanic cartilage transplanted subcutaneously on the back has caused development of tympanic membrane from local skin. (From Helff, 1928.)

connective tissue layer of the skin in the area of the tympanic membrane becomes reorganized, the original layer of fibers — the stratum compactum — is broken up with the participation of phagocytes, and a completely new, somewhat thinner fibrous layer is developed in its place. In the fully differentiated tympanic membrane, the skin is less than half the thickness of ordinary skin but much more compact, and it also differs in its pigmentation.

It has been found that the differentiation of the tympanic membrane is not due to a direct action of the thyroid hormone but that it is induced by the tympanic cartilage (Helff, 1928). If the tympanic cartilage is removed before metamorphosis, the tympanic membrane does not develop. If the area in the otic region is covered by skin from the flank or from the back, the skin will develop a tympanic membrane. Lastly, if the tympanic cartilage is inserted under the skin on the flank or the back in tadpoles approaching metamorphosis, the local skin becomes differentiated as tympanic membrane (Fig. 407).

We can draw up a complicated chain of interactions that must take place before a tympanic membrane becomes differentiated. The first step is the formation of the rudiment of the hypophysis. The latter is developed in conjunction with the stomodeal invagination (see p. 477) and presumably is induced by the oral endoderm (p. 475). The hypophysis in due time secretes the thyrotropic hormone and activates the thyroid gland. The thyroid gland releases the thyroid hormone, and this causes the posterior edge of the quadrate to become differentiated as the tympanic cartilage. Lastly, the tympanic cartilage induces the skin to differentiate as tympanic membrane.

18—5 MOLTING AND ITS RELATION TO METAMORPHOSIS IN INSECTS

In any consideration of metamorphosis in insects, it has to be taken into account that metamorphosis in these animals is a special form of molting (the periodic shedding of the cuticle of the skin which necessarily accompanies growth, because the strongly sclerotized parts of the cuticle cannot stretch or cannot stretch sufficiently to accommodate the growing mass of the body). A large proportion of the external features of an insect is embodied in the sclerotized parts of the cuticle, such as the details of shape of parts of the body, the hairs and spines on the surface of the skin, the sculpture of the surface of the cuticle and, to a certain extent, the pigmentation. In the process of molting, these features are lost with the discarded cuticle. The external characters of the insect, in so far as they find their expression in cuticular structures, have to be produced anew at each molt, though on a larger scale. The new cuticle is secreted by the epidermis of the skin, and it is therefore this layer of cells which is directly responsible for the external features of the insect emerging from a molt, whether the molted insect is an enlarged copy of the previous stage or whether it shows some new characters.

The molt in every case is quite a complicated process. In between two molts the cells of the epidermis are quiescent, they are more or less flat, and the epithelial layer may be rather thin. The epidermis cells adhere closely to the inner surface of the cuticle. Before each molt, however, the cells of the epidermis become activated; they detach themselves from the cuticle and enter a phase of rapid growth and proliferation. Numerous mitoses are observed. (Proliferation of epidermal cells is not observed, however, during the larval molt of cyclorraphe dipteran larvae, in which the cells of the larval epidermis do not divide between the stages of the egg and the pupa and are eventually discarded and replaced by imaginal epidermis.)

The number of epidermal cells produced by mitosis may be in excess of what is necessary, and some of the cells at this stage undergo degeneration by pycnosis. In spite of the degeneration of some of the cells, the layer of epidermis becomes thicker and the remaining cells become arranged in a regular columnar epithelium. The surface of this epithelium foreshadows the shape of the animal emerging from the molt. In those parts of the body which are to be increased as the result of the molt, the epidermis is thrown into folds which expand and straighten out after the insect has emerged from its old skin. The folding is especially great where new or greatly increased appendages (such as the wings) are to be developed.

The epidermal cells now produce on their surface a thin layer of hardening secretion which becomes the outermost layer of the new cuticle—the **epicuticle**, consisting of a substance of lipoprotein nature, **cuticulin**. A fluid produced mainly by special molting glands is now poured into the space between the surface of the new epicuticle and the innermost surface of the old cuticle (Fig. 408). The fluid contains enzymes which digest the inner layers of the old cuticle until little more than the old epicuticle is left. The fluid with the substances digested from the old cuticle later becomes reabsorbed into the body of the insect. At the same time as the old cuticle is being digested, the epidermis produces further layers underneath the new epicuticle: the **exocuticle**, containing large quantities of cuticulin and also phenolic substances which are later oxidized to produce the dark pigment in the cuticle, and eventually the **endocuticle**, consisting of protein and chitin, which is a nitrogenous polysaccharide.

When the old cuticle is reduced to a thin shell, it is ruptured at the back of the head and thorax, and the insect crawls out of its old coat. The new cuticle is by no means quite completed at this stage; after molting the cuticle hardens and visible pigment is produced in the cuticle from colorless precursors (phenolic substances). Further layers of endocuticle are deposited by

Figure 408. Two stages of molting in an insect. *A*, Old cuticle separated from epidermis which has produced a new epicuticle (thick black line). *B*, Deep layers of old cuticle dissolved, and layers of new endocuticle produced beneath the new epicuticle. *d*, Molting glands; *c*, molting fluid. (From Wigglesworth, 1939.)

the epidermal cells on the inner surface of the cuticle for days and even weeks after the molt has taken place.

It will be seen that some elements of amphibian metamorphosis, namely, destructive processes (resorption of the old cuticle, necrosis of part of the epidermal cells) as well as constructive processes (rearrangement of epidermal cells, formation of new cuticle), are present in an ordinary molt in insects. It depends on the condition of the epidermal layer whether the new structures produced during the molt are similar to the old ones or different. In the first case the molt contributes to the growth of the animal; in the second it becomes a mechanism for progressive development. If the changes achieved after a molt are considerable, the result is metamorphosis. In the primarily wingless archaic insects, the Apterygota, the young insect emerging from the egg is essentially similar to the adult, differing only in size and in the immature state of the sexual organs. Molting in these insects leads only to growth, and the advent of sexual maturity is not related in any way to molting; in fact, molting and growth continue even after the attainment of reproductive ability.

In all other insects, the Pterygota (winged or secondarily wingless forms), there is a distinct imaginal stage, which is attained after a specific imaginal molt, after which the insect does not molt any more. Except for secondarily wingless insects, the imaginal stage differs from the larval stages by the presence of wings. The imago also differs from the larval stages by the full development of external genital organs. (The gonads, on the other hand, may become fully functional only some time after metamorphosis.) In the more primitive winged insects the wings appear gradually, the rudiments of the wings in the form of flat outgrowths of the second and third thoracic segment being visible in the later larval, or as they are often called, **nymphal** stages. These rudiments increase with every subsequent molt, but at the last imaginal molt there is an abrupt and very marked increase in the size of the wings, and after this molt the wings become functional (only in the mayflies the first winged stage, the **subimago**, molts again before it turns into an imago). The insects in which the rudiments of the wings develop on the surface of the body are called Exopterygota; these comprise the locusts, cockroaches, dragonflies, mayflies, bugs and other related groups. In the most advanced orders of insects, however, the wings develop internally, as folded appendages concealed during the larval stages in deep pockets (infoldings) of the epidermis (see Fig. 409). The epidermis covering these wing rudiments

Figure 409. Longitudinal section through the imaginal discs of the wings in full-grown larva of the ant *Formica*. (After Perez, from Wigglesworth, 1954.)

retains an embryonic character throughout larval life, and although the rudiments continue growing slowly their epidermis does not participate in the formation of the external cuticle of the larva and comes into action only when the larval stage is drawing to an end. Such rudiments, concealed under the surface of the body in the larval stage and reaching full differentiation in the imago, are called **imaginal discs**. The insects in which the wings develop internally as imaginal discs are called Endopterygota; here belong caddis flies, beetles, butterflies, bees and wasps, mosquitoes and flies.

Although the development of the wings in the adult insect attracts the greatest attention, the other parts of the body also change at the time of metamorphosis from a larva or nymph to the adult (imago). Even where the larva or nymph leads the same mode of life as the adult and has a fairly similar general appearance, as in the locusts or bugs, many finer features of structure change. In the bug *Rhodnius prolixus*, for instance, which has been studied by Wigglesworth (1954), the fine structure of the cuticle and the pigmentation of the adult bug are very different from the last larval stage, so that even small areas of skin of the larva and the adult can be easily distinguished.

In the endopterygote insects, the difference between the larvae and adults is much greater. Not only wings but also mouth parts, antennae and legs may be developed from imaginal discs, while the larval appendages become discarded as in the case of butterflies (Fig. 410). In some parasitic wasps and in flies such as *Drosophila* and *Musca*, the whole larval epidermis is discarded and replaced by the imaginal epidermis derived from a series of imaginal discs (Fig. 411). Concurrently with the formation of appendages and other external parts, the internal organs are also reorganized. As the locomotion of the winged adult is so completely different from the locomotion of a crawling larva, the muscle system may have to be radically changed. During metamorphosis of higher insects, the larval muscles become broken down and their remnants are consumed by phagocytes. The adult muscles, in particular the muscles operating the wings (the flight muscles), are then developed.

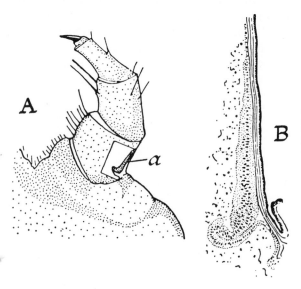

Figure 410. A, Position of the imaginal disc (*a*) in the leg of caterpillar of the butterfly *Vanessa*. B, Detail of the imaginal disc. (After Bodenstein, from Wigglesworth, 1939.)

Figure 411. Imaginal discs in the last stage larva of the parasitic wasp *Encyrtus*. *an*, Antennae; *e*, compound eyes; *m*, mandibles; *g*, genital organs; *mx1*, *mx2*, first and second pairs of maxillae, *l*, legs; *w*, wings. (After Bugnion, from Kühn, 1955.)

The eyes of the adult insects in the more advanced orders are very different from those of the larvae and are developed from special imaginal discs. Most of the cells of the alimentary canal of the larva may undergo resorption, and the alimentary canal of the imago is lined by a new epithelium produced at the expense of pockets of small reserve cells, which are found between the functioning cells of the larval intestine.

While the moderate amount of transformations that occur in exopterygote insects can be performed in one molt, the reorganization that is needed to produce the imago in most endopterygote insects is so profound that a resting stage – the pupa – is intercalated between the larval and the adult condition. In the pupa, the pockets containing the imaginal discs – wings, limbs, antennae, etc. – are brought to the surface. Internally, the formation of adult parts is, however, not yet completed, and while the reorganization takes place in the pupal stage the insects do not take food and are very restricted in their movements, if they move at all.

When the reorganization is completed, another molt takes place, and the imago emerges from the pupa. Metamorphosis which includes a pupal stage is called complete metamorphosis, and the insects having this type of metamorphosis are called Holometabola; those not possessing a pupal stage and thus having an incomplete metamorphosis are Hemimetabola. The holometabolous insects are the Endopterygota; the terms, so far as systematics are concerned, are synonyms, though they stress different properties of the same group of insects.

18–6 CAUSATION OF MOLTING AND METAMORPHOSIS IN INSECTS

In an ordinary molt (**larval molt**) all parts of the body must participate in the process and carry it out at the same time, if the molting is to be successful.

This suggests a common cause to which all parts of the insect are subjected. The existence of a common cause is even more obvious in the case of metamorphosis in which the involvement of both external and internal organs may be more far reaching and radical. This common cause may be expected to be either external or internal. Cases are actually known in which under natural conditions an external factor is necessary to start a molt. In the bloodsucking bug *Rhodnius,* such a factor is the intake of food. The bugs of this species feed only once in the interval between two molts, taking up so much blood that their body weight may increase many fold. Molting occurs regularly 12 to 15 days after a feed in the case of the first four larval stages. The same dependence of molting on food intake holds true for the last, the fifth larval stage, only the interval is somewhat longer, namely, about 28 days, and the result is different: the molt transforms the larva into a winged imago. Another example in which an external factor is necessary to initiate a molt is the case of the pupa of the moth *Platysamia cecropia.* After pupation, the insect falls into a quiescent state with reduced rate of metabolism — the **diapause** — which continues throughout winter. It is essential that during this time the pupa be exposed to cold, otherwise the diapause is prolonged indefinitely. However, the diapause may be broken precociously if the pupa is treated with cold (3 to 5° C.) for at least two weeks. The temporary cooling activates the vital processes in the pupa and on return to a warmer environment the pupa molts, and so the development is completed with the emergence of the imago.

In the overwhelming majority of insects, however, no external cause of any molt can be found, and the molts follow each other at intervals which appear to be determined entirely by internal processes in the animal. In many insects the body weight increases in a fixed proportion between two molts, often by a factor of two, and it would appear that a certain amount of synthesis has to be performed after each molt before the stimulus for a new molt is generated in the organism. However, even in cases where an external factor triggers the mechanism of molting, it can be shown that the factor in question does not affect all parts of the body directly, but that it is mediated by the brain of the insect. If a larva of *Rhodnius* is decapitated within a day or two after feeding it does not molt, although it may remain alive for over a year. If, however, it is decapitated five or more days after a meal, molting takes place; by that time a stimulus generated by the brain reaches beyond the level of decapitation and is able to spread throughout the body and cause the molt to proceed (Wigglesworth, 1954). A corresponding experiment in the moth *Platysamia* consists in activating one pupa by exposure to cold and then transplanting parts of the body of the activated pupa into an untreated pupa. The transplantation of the brain but not of other organs will cause the second pupa to molt and the adult moth to emerge, thus showing that the cold directly affects only the brain but that the rest of the body is stimulated to molting through the mediation of the latter (Williams, 1946).

The question naturally arises how the brain affects the rest of the body. It is now established that, as with amphibian metamorphosis, the molting and metamorphosis in insects is controlled by hormones, and that at least three organs of internal secretion are involved: the brain (**protocerebrum**), the **corpora allata** and the **prothoracic gland.** In the brain, a hormone is produced

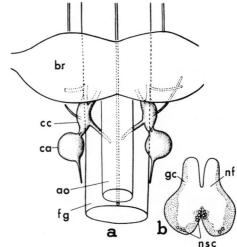

Figure 412. The endocrine glands associated with the brain in moths. *a*, Dorsal view of the brain in a hawk moth pupa. *b*, Transverse section of the protocerebrum in a caterpillar of the meal moth. *ao*, Aorta; *br*, brain; *ca*, corpora allata; *cc*, corpora cardiaca; *fg*, foregut; *gc*, ganglionic cells; *nf*, nerve fibers; *nsc*, neurosecretory cells. (After Cazal and Rehm, from Kühn, 1955.)

by **neurosecretory cells**, which are arranged in four groups: two groups near the midline and one group on each side (Fig. 412). Behind the protocerebrum, alongside the dorsal aorta, there are to be found in most insects two pairs of bodies connected by nerve strands to the protocerebrum: first the **corpora cardiaca**, which are of the nature of nerve ganglia, and, more posteriorly, the **corpora allata**, consisting of secretory cells. The corpora allata may be fused into one body in some insects. The third endocrine gland, the **prothoracic gland**, is an irregular branching mass of glandular cells located in the thorax, in close association with the tracheal tubes (Fig. 413). The glandular cells of all three centers show regular secretory cycles preceding each molt, and the three types of secretion are necessary for the normal course of larval molts. The molt is initiated by the neurosecretory cells of the protocerebrum, but all that the hormone of the protocerebrum does is to activate the prothoracic gland. The prothoracic gland then produces a hormone which sets in motion the mechanism of molting in the epidermis: the growth and proliferation of the epidermal cells, the shedding of the old

Figure 413. Prothoracic gland in the moth *Saturnia*, and its associations with the ventral nerve cord and the tracheal system. (After Lee, from Wigglesworth, 1954.)

cuticle and the production of the new one. The hormone produced by the prothoracic gland is called therefore the growth and molting hormone or ecdysone.

We have described some of the evidence proving that the initial stimulus for molting is given off by the brain (or the neurosecretory cells of the proto-cerebrum). One of the experiments consisted in transplanting the brain of an activated pupa of *Platysamia* into an untreated pupa, whereupon the latter molted and produced the moth. A variation of the same experiment has been used to prove that the secretion of the brain cannot act directly but only through the activation of the prothoracic gland. Instead of transplanting the activated brain into a whole pupa, it was implanted into the posterior half of a pupa cut in two (the cut surface was sealed with paraffin wax). Under these conditions the graft was powerless; no metamorphosis took place. The reason for this is that the prothoracic gland is absent in the posterior half of the pupa. If in addition to the brain the prothoracic gland was also grafted, metamorphosis occurred (Williams, 1947; Wigglesworth, 1954). An analogous experiment has been performed on the bug *Rhodnius* (Fig. 414). After the neurosecretory cells of the brain had been activated by the bug's having a meal of blood, the brain was transplanted into the abdomen of a decapitated specimen. A decapitated larva is still in possession of the prothoracic gland, which could react to the implanted brain and cause the molt to proceed. If, however, the activated brain was implanted into an isolated abdomen (Fig. 414, *C*), no molting occurred. On the other hand molting could be induced in the isolated abdomen by the implantation of a thoracic gland (Wigglesworth, 1954).

The role of the brain and the thoracic gland as causative agents of molt-ing can also be demonstrated in insects in which the time of the molting is not dependent on any particular external factor. If the brain is removed from caterpillars sufficiently early before the next expected molt, the caterpillars may remain alive for over two months but do not molt and do not pupate. The implantation of a brain from another caterpillar restores the ability of a brainless caterpillar to complete its development (Kühn and Piepho, 1936).

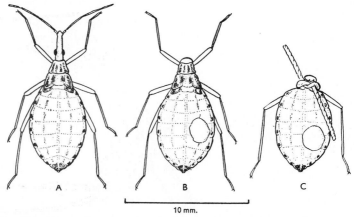

Figure 414. Experiment showing necessity of thoracic gland for molting and metamorphosis. A, Normal larva of *Rhodnius*. B, Decapitated larva with an implant in the abdomen. C, Larva ligated through metathorax, with implant in isolated abdomen. (From Wigglesworth, 1954.)

Figure 415. Experiment showing necessity of thoracic gland for pupation. *a*, Normal pupa of the meal moth *Ephestia kühniella*. *b*, Result of ligating the caterpillar before the hormone of the thoracic gland has been released: the part posterior to the ligature remains in the larval stage. *c*, Result of ligating the caterpillar after the molting hormone has been released: both parts pupate. (After Kühn and Piepho, from Kühn, 1955.)

a *b* *c*

Once the thoracic gland has become activated, the brain is no longer necessary for initiating the molt; only those parts molt (or pupate), however, to which the hormone of the thoracic gland has been able to gain access. If a caterpillar in the last larval stage is constricted behind the thorax, the anterior part of the body will pupate but the posterior part, which the molting hormone could not reach, remains in the larval state (Fig. 415). A little later, when the hormone has already spread throughout the body, a transverse constriction does not prevent pupation of the posterior end of the caterpillar.

The hormones emitted by the protocerebral neurosecretory cells and the thoracic gland induce an insect to molt but they do not determine whether it will be a larval molt producing the next larval stage, the pupal molt, converting the larva to pupa, or the imaginal molt, leading to the eclosion of the imago. The third endocrine gland, the corpora allata, controls the nature of the change that is going to take place at the time of the molting. Curiously enough, the first two glands, the protocerebral neurosecretory cells and the thoracic gland, when acting alone cause immediate metamorphosis—the development of the imago in hemimetabolous insects or of the pupa in holometabolous insects.

It is possible to remove the corpora allata from caterpillars of moths. Independently of the stage in which the operation is performed, the caterpillars proceed to pupate at the next molt. In due course the moth emerges from the pupa, although it may have reached only a fraction of the normal size (Fig. 416; Bounhiol, 1937). Apparently the presence of the corpora allata is necessary to **prevent** metamorphosis, to keep the insect in the larval state. Accordingly, the secretion of the corpora allata has been called the **juvenile hormone.** Now, at every larval molt the cells of the corpora allata show signs of secretory activity (swelling of cells, appearance and discharge of vacuoles, etc.), but no such activity is present during the pupal or im-

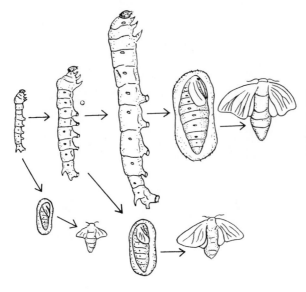

Figure 416. Precocious metamorphosis in the silkworm, caused by the extirpation of the corpora allata in the third or fourth stage, respectively. The larva pupates normally after the fifth stage. (After Bounhiol, from Abeloos, 1956.)

aginal molt. Accordingly it would seem that, at the time metamorphosis takes place, the corpora allata do not produce their secretion or at least are less active. That it is actually the absence of the juvenile hormone that is the necessary condition for metamorphosis can be proved by implanting corpora allata from a young larva into the last stage larva which should be metamorphosing with the next molt. The larva may molt in due course, but, under the influence of the juvenile hormone secreted by the graft, it is not transformed into an imago (in the case of a hemimetabolous insect) but instead produces an abnormally large larva (Fig. 417).

In the case of holometabolous insects, the conditions are more complicated inasmuch as there are two molts accompanied by profound morphological changes—the pupal molt and the imaginal molt. The removal of the corpora allata from caterpillars causes the caterpillar to be transformed into a pupa. Some experiments, the details of which cannot be related here, indicate that the subsequent transformation of the pupa into the imago is probably connected with a further decrease of the juvenile hormone in the

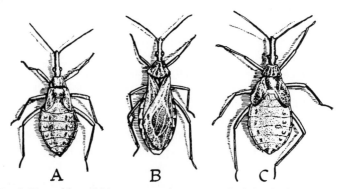

Figure 417. *A*, Normal last (5th) stage nymph. *B*, Normal adult *Rhodnius*. *C*, Giant 6th stage nymph produced by implanting the corpus allatum from a 4th stage nymph into the abdomen of a 5th stage nymph. (From Wigglesworth, 1939.)

blood of the insect. After the ablation of the gland, small amounts of the juvenile hormone could have still been present in circulation but would have been used up by the time of the second molt (see Wigglesworth, 1954).

18—7   NATURE OF THE FACTORS CONTROLLING MOLTING AND METAMORPHOSIS IN INSECTS

In the previous section, it has been assumed that the agents produced by the thoracic gland and the corpora allata are hormones, that is, chemical substances emitted by the cells and circulating in the body fluids. This could be deduced from the fact that the effect of the gland does not depend on whether it is in its normal position, with all its connections to neighboring organs and to the nervous system intact, or on whether it had been transplanted to an abnormal site. Further evidence in favor of a diffusible substance being the means of action of the gland will now be presented.

An equivalent to the glands' independence of their position is the independence of the position of the reacting organs in the reaction. When molting or metamorphosis occurs, not only do all parts of the body of the intact animal react together but transplanted parts also do the same. Imaginal discs and other parts of the body may be transplanted between animals in different developmental stages, and they always molt and metamorphose together with the organs of the host and independently of their own age. A very elegant experiment of this kind, carried out on the developing moth *Ephestia kühniella*, consists in transplanting pieces of skin into the body cavity of another individual (Kühn, 1939; Piepho and Meyer, 1951; Kühn, 1955). The edges of the implanted piece of skin curl so as to form a cyst, with the original distal surface of the skin turned inward. The proximal surface of the epidermis is bathed by the body fluids of the host and by the host's hormones if any are present in the body fluids. The necessary conditions are thus provided for the graft epidermis to react to any hormones circulating in the body of the host. It was found that with every molt of the host the cyst epidermis molted also, discarding the old cuticle into the cavity of the cyst. Not only was the molting of the graft simultaneous with that of the host, but the nature of the new cuticle was always the same as that of the host. When a larval molt occurred, the cyst epidermis produced a thin cuticle like the one that covered the body of the caterpillar. When the host pupated, the cyst produced a thick pupal cuticle. When the host metamorphosed into the adult moth, the epidermis of the cyst developed an imaginal cuticle with scales! All the successive cuticles could be seen later one inside the other, on sectioning the cyst (Fig. 418).

Even after reaching the stage of producing the cuticle of the adult moth, the epidermis does not lose its capacity for molting, provided that ecdysone (the molting hormone) or both ecdysone and the juvenile hormone are present in the surrounding fluid. A cyst which had gone through the pupal and imaginal molts may be excised from the first host and transplanted into a second one. If the second host is a caterpillar, the cyst will undergo a new molt simultaneously with the pupation of the host, will shed the imaginal cuticle with scales and will again produce a thick pupal cuticle. This may be

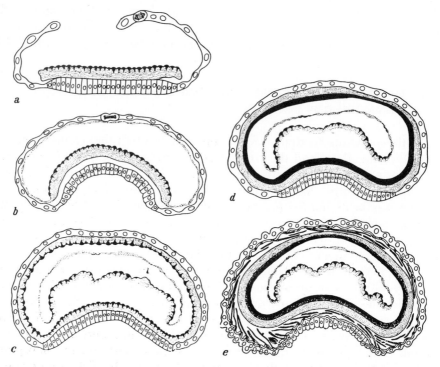

Figure 418. Hormones in the development of a moth. Molting in the interior of an implanted epidermal cyst under the influence of hormones circulating in the host's body. *a,* Cyst in the process of formation. *b, c,* Shedding of a larval cuticle. *d,* Production of a pupal cuticle. *e,* Pupal cuticle shed, an imaginal cuticle with scales produced underneath. (From Kühn, 1955.)

followed, at the time of metamorphosis of the host, by a second imaginal cuticle with a new set of scales (Fig. 419).

Apparently metamorphosis is fully reversible, at least in regard to the skin epidermis, and the nature of differentiations produced by the latter is solely dependent on the balance of hormones present in the blood. A re-

Figure 419. Control of metamorphosis by hormones in the moth *Galleria melonella*. Reversal of metamorphosis in an epidermal cyst transplanted into a second, younger host. The consecutive cuticles are: larval (*i. Rc*); pupal (*Pc₁*); imaginal (*Ic₁*) with scales (*Sch₁*); then again pupal (*Pc₂*); and, lastly, imaginal for a second time (*Ic₂*), with a second generation of scales (*Sch₂*). *Ep,* Epidermis. (After Piepho and Meyer, from Kühn, 1955.)

versal of metamorphosis, even a partial one, can occur, however, only under experimental conditions. In the normal life of an insect, metamorphosis marks the end of morphogenesis and of growth (except for the growth of the gonads, which may continue in the adult). The reason for the cessation of further development is that the thoracic gland degenerates and breaks up after causing the last (imaginal) molt. With the thoracic gland gone, no other factors can reawaken the morphogenetic activity of the epidermis, and no further molting can occur. This is also an explanation for the existence of a growth limit in insects which was referred to at the end of section 17–3.

The action of the juvenile hormone is not restricted to the control of qualitative changes in the body of the insect but it appears to have also a direct influence on growth. It is found that in the imago, after metamorphosis, the corpora allata resume their secretory activity, and that their secretion is necessary for the growth of the ovaries and the oocytes.

In vertebrates, the chemical nature of the agents emitted by the endocrine glands has been proved by preparing active extracts from the glands, containing chemically definable substances. The extraction of hormones from insects is much more difficult, owing to the small mass of the endocrine glands. However, some success can be noted in this field also. The molting hormone, ecdysone, (the hormone of the thoracic gland) has been prepared in a chemically pure form by Butenandt and Karlson (1954). Five hundred kilograms of silkworm pupae were used to isolate 25 mg. of the pure substance, and 0.0075 mg. of this material was sufficient to cause the pupation of a fly larva. The chemical analysis of the substance gave the empirical formula $C_{27}H_{44}O_6$ (Karlson and Hoffmeister, 1963). The substance belongs to the steroid group and its approximate structural formula is:

$$CH_3 \quad CH_2 \quad CH_2 \quad CH_3$$
$$O \quad CH \quad CH_2 \quad C$$
$$OH \quad CH_3 \quad + \; 4\;OH \text{ in unknown position}$$

The chemical analysis of the other two hormones—the brain hormone and the juvenile hormone—has not yet been as successful. The results obtained by different research workers are somewhat contradictory. It appears, however, that the juvenile hormone is chemically related to ecdysone and is also a steroid or a substance of the terpene group which is a possible precursor of steroids (Schneiderman and Gilbert, 1964).

As in the case of inducing substances in early amphibian embryogenesis, it has been found that the action of the juvenile hormone may be imitated by extracts of tissues of various animals (Williams, Moorhead and Pulis, 1959) and by certain substances of known chemical composition, such as the terpene farnesol. The latter was also able to stimulate the prothoracic gland, an effect normally produced by the brain hormone. It has been suggested, therefore, that all three hormones regulating growth and development in insects have something in common in their chemical structure and activity (Schneiderman and Gilbert, 1964).

18–8   MECHANISM OF ACTION OF INSECT HORMONES

The study of insect molting and metamorphosis has contributed some very interesting information on the way chemical substances act on cell differentiation.

It has been known for many years that, in the salivary glands of some insects in the order Diptera, certain cells grow to a relatively large size, and that in such cells the chromosomes become visible although the cells do not undergo mitosis. The "giant chromosomes" in such cells are the result of repeated duplication of the DNA molecules, so that many hundreds of DNA molecules lie side by side. Cells of malpighian tubules and some other tissues also grow excessively and produce giant chromosomes. The chromosomes show characteristic transverse bands which may be related to specific genes as known from breeding experiments. Even before the relation of the bands on the giant chromosomes to genes was known, it was found that conspicuous thickenings are to be found on some giant chromosomes. These thickenings were known for many years as the "Balbiani rings," so named after the scientist who discovered them first in salivary chromosomes of the midge *Chironomus*. Later it was found that the thickenings occur in all cases where giant chromosomes are found, though not all are as large as the Balbiani rings. The thickenings, large or small, are now called **puffs** (Figs. 420 and 421).

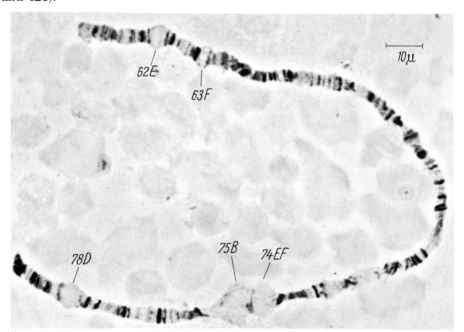

Figure 420. Giant chromosome from salivary gland of *Drosophila* larva showing several puffs as they appear in a period just preceding pupation. (Courtesy of Dr. H. J. Becker.)

74EF—

75B—

Figure 421. Drawing of part of the same giant salivary gland chromosome of *Drosophila* larva shown in Figure 420. (Courtesy of Dr. H. J. Becker, 1962.)

—78D

A puff is actually a section of the chromosome in which the numerous strands of DNA, of which the giant chromosome consists, become separated from one another and form loops, extending outward from the main axis of the chromosome. This loosening of the chromosome structure is favorable for the chemical interaction of the DNA strands with their environment inside the nucleus. As a matter of fact, it has been proved (by using radioactive precursors) that there is a very rapid synthesis of RNA on the puffs. The RNA synthesized on the puffs is different in base composition from the cytoplasmic ribosomal RNA and is believed to be messenger RNA (Edström and Beermann, 1962). In other words, the puffs represent sections of chromosomes in which the genes are in a derepressed state and are particularly active in producing messenger RNA (compare p. 504).

A further important discovery was made (Clever, 1961; Becker, 1962; Beermann and Clever, 1964) that the pattern of puffing changes with the stage of development of the insect: puffs appear at different points on the chromosomes and may disappear again at a later stage, while new puffs develop at other points.

The stage of metamorphosis is characterized by a specific pattern of puffs which can be recognized if the structure of the giant chromosomes of a species under investigation is known in detail.

The question now arises whether there is a connection between the structural changes in the chromosomes and the morphogenetic changes (molting, metamorphosis) of the whole animal. *A priori* one could expect that changes in the activity of genes must bear some relation to the transformations of the animal's organization. On the other hand, we have seen that the molting and metamorphosis in insects is under the control of hormones (ecdysone and juvenile hormone).

A breakthrough in this field was achieved when it was shown that injection of pure ecdysone into *Chironomus* larvae caused the giant chromosomes to acquire the puffing pattern which was identical to the one occurring during pupation (Fig. 422 — Clever and Karlson, 1960). The changes in the chromosomes occurred very rapidly: the first reactions were visible within 15 to 30 minutes from the injection, whereas the changes in the cuticle of the larvae leading to pupation occur in a matter of a few days (Clever, 1961). The conclusion seems reasonable that the hormone acts initially on the genes and that the changed activity of the genes then causes a changed behavior of the cells and tissues.

The action of the ecdysone can be observed not only when the hormone is injected into whole animals but also when isolated nuclei are treated with solutions of the hormone *in vitro*. This proves that the hormone acts directly on the nuclei of each individual cell and that the action is not mediated by an agency common to groups of cells or tissues. In a further experiment, isolated nuclei containing giant chromosomes were punctured and part of the chromosomes allowed to escape through the puncture. The nuclei were then exposed to an ecdysone solution, and it was found that the remaining chromosomes reacted by forming puffs in the same way as when the whole set of chromosomes was present. From this it may be concluded that each locus on the chromosome answers directly to the treatment and does not depend on other parts of the chromosomal set in order to react (Kroeger, 1964). It appears thus that the reacting unit is the individual gene.

Doubts have been expressed, however, whether ecdysone as such acts on the gene or whether it changes the intranuclear milieu, and a change of

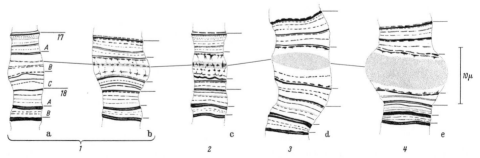

Figure 422. Induction of a specific puff on the giant salivary gland chromosome of *Chironomus tentans* by injecting the larva with ecdyson. *a, b, c,* Chromosomes of untreated (control) larvae; *d, e,* same region of the chromosome in a larva after ecdyson injection. (From Clever, 1961.)

intranuclear milieu then affects the gene. It was found that ecdysone causes a change in the permeability of the nuclear membrane to sodium and potassium ions, thus upsetting the balance of sodium and potassium in the intranuclear fluid. Similar changes may be produced by agents other than ecdysone (by zinc ions or by narcotics, for instance) and in that case the same puffs appear, which under physiological conditions are the result of ecdysone action (Kroeger, 1963, 1964). Whether this is the final explanation of the mechanism of ecdysone action still remains to be seen. The unspecific agents which have been used to produce chromosome puffs are not able to cause metamorphosis or molting.

It is interesting to note the close similarity of the results obtained in experiments on insect metamorphosis and of the conclusions which emerge from work on the primary organizer (neural inductor) in amphibian embryos. In both cases, the obvious reaction involves the activities of groups of cells, which change their behavior and acquire new differentiations (in insects, cells change from the larval condition to that of a pupa or an imago; in an amphibian embryo, gastrula ectoderm becomes differentiated as neural tissue). In both cases we have been led to the conclusion that the change is produced by a modification of the activity of nuclear genes. This modification is not a spontaneous change of the genes themselves but is evoked by an external factor: ecdysone in the metamorphosing insect, neuralizing substance in the amphibian embryo. Lastly, the inducing substance reaches the gene through the mediation of the nongenic parts of the cell: the change of permeability of the nuclear membrane in the insect cell (if this is indeed the deciding factor in ecdysone action) may be the counterpart of the solubilization of yolk platelets which occurs during neural induction. Here, however, we enter a field which probably is not sufficiently investigated to allow far-reaching generalizations to be made.

18—9 FINAL REMARKS ON METAMORPHOSIS

The metamorphosis of amphibians and insects is an excellent example of the control of morphogenetic processes by hormones. The dependence of differentiation on diffusible chemical substances, as revealed in studies on metamorphosis, should be compared with the results of experiments on the influence of diffusible substances on the differentiation of cells in tissue cultures (section 16–5).

When comparing the interrelation of different hormones in insect and amphibian metamorphosis, one is astonished to find that these two groups of animals have developed causative mechanisms having a distinct general similarity. In both cases, the transformation is initiated by a secreting organ closely associated with the brain: the hypophysis in amphibians, the neurosecretory cells of the protocerebrum in insects. In both cases, the secretion of this primary center does not act on the tissues directly but stimulates the activity of a second endocrine gland: the thyroid gland in amphibians, the thoracic gland in insects. The juvenile hormone of insects has, however, no counterpart in amphibians: there is no hormone checking or preventing precocious development, or at least we are not aware of the existence of such an agent.

There is very little information as to the causative agents of metamorphosis in animals other than amphibians and insects, and we do not know whether their transformations are controlled by hormones. One would expect that at least in the cyclostomes the transformation of the larva (Ammocoetes) into the adult should be caused by hormones, but this has not been found to be the case: thyroxine does not accelerate transformation of the Ammocoetes into a lamprey (see Gorbman and Bern, 1962).

In the ascidian tadpole, the absorption of the tail is in some way dependent on the anterior end of the body, since cutting off the anterior tip with the adhesive papillae will prevent the necrotization of the tail (Oka, 1943). Treating ascidian tadpoles with thyroid hormone accelerated the metamorphosis (Weiss, 1928), but this action is hardly specific, as the tadpole does not have a thyroid gland of its own, and treatment of the tadpoles with narcotics or even with distilled water has the same effect (Oka, 1958).

Numerous experiments have been carried out on the metamorphosis of larvae of various invertebrates (Tubularia, Bryozoa, sea urchins, molluscs). Treatment by various chemicals (salts of copper, for instance) has had a positive effect (for a review, see Lynch, 1961). However, it has not been possible to find what factors cause the metamorphosis under normal conditions, and there is so far no indication that in any of these organisms a hormone plays a decisive role in the process. An exception to the latter statement is apparently presented by the transformation of the asexual form of the annelid worm *Platynereis dumerilii* into the sexual form. This transformation is dependent on a neurosecretory hormone released in the prostomium of the asexual individual; the hormone is an inhibitor of the transformation, and the sexual form is developed when the prostomium hormone is eliminated (Hauenschild, 1964).

Regeneration[*]

The second mode of reawakening of the morphogenetic processes at an advanced stage of the ontogenetic cycle is by means of partial destruction of the system which has evolved as a result of the previous development. The animal organism possesses the ability to repair more or less extensive damage incurred by the body either accidentally in natural conditions or willfully imposed by the experimenter. The damage repaired may be a wound which severs or partially destroys the tissues of the animal's body, or the damage may involve the loss of an organ or larger part of the body. These can sometimes be renewed, and in this case the process of repair is known as **regeneration.**

19—1 TYPICAL CASE OF REGENERATION: THE RENEWAL OF A LIMB IN A SALAMANDER

The limbs of newts and salamanders, both in the adult stage and in larvae, are capable of regeneration to a very high degree and have often been used for various experiments on the subject. Limbs, especially those of larvae, are sometimes bitten off by other members of the same species, or the limbs may be cut off at different levels for research purposes. Whatever the cause of the loss of a limb, the first stage of repair of the damage is that the epidermis from the edges of the wound starts spreading over the wound and very soon covers the open surface. The closing of the wound is relatively a very rapid process, and it is accomplished in the course of one or two days, depending on the size of the animal. During the next few days, the epidermis covering the wound begins to bulge outward, becoming more or less conical

---

[*]Much of the recent work on the subject is reviewed in *Regeneration*, edited by D. Rudnick, 20th Symposium, Society for the Study of Development and Growth, New York, 1962.

Figure 423. Regeneration in the limbs of the newt *Triturus cristatus. a, b, c, d, e, f,* Consecutive stages of regeneration of a forelimb amputated above the elbow. *g, h, i, j, k, l, m,* Stages of regeneration of a hindlimb amputated above the knee. (From Schwidefsky, 1934.)

in shape (Fig. 423). A mass of cells accumulates under the epidermis. These cells are in a state of active proliferation, and together with the epidermal covering they form what is known as the **regeneration blastema** or **regeneration bud.** The blastema grows rapidly, at first retaining its conical shape, but later it begins to be flattened dorsoventrally at the end. The flattened part is the rudiment of the carpus or tarsus, called the hand- or footplate, depending whether a forelimb or a hindlimb is regenerating. Soon the rudiments of the digits appear, separated by slight indentations at the edge of the plate (Fig. 423). In the meantime, the mass of cells in the interior of the limb-bud becomes segregated to form the rudiments of the internal parts of the limb—the various bones of the limb skeleton and of the arm (or leg) muscles. These then undergo histological differentiation. The rudiments of the digits elongate, and the whole regenerating limb continues to grow until it attains the size of a normal limb. As the tissues of the regenerating limb differentiate, the limb resumes normal function (movement). Eventually the regenerated limb becomes completely indistinguishable from a normal limb. The time necessary for the completion of the process depends on the size and stage of development of the animal; regeneration is most rapid in small larvae, and here the regenerated limb may be complete after three weeks (in the case of an axolotl larva). In older and larger larvae the process may take a longer time, and in the adult salamander the completion of regeneration takes several months.

It is seen that the new limb is produced from a rudiment, the regeneration blastema, which, when formed, acquires the potentiality for development otherwise found only in the organ rudiments of the early embryo. There is the obvious difference, however, that the cells of the regeneration blastema develop into parts of one organ only (the limb), whereas the cells of the early embryo produce the whole animal. Reversion to a state somewhat similar to that of early embryonic cells obviously takes place in the formation of a regeneration blastema. How far this "rejuvenation" goes will be discussed later.

What is developed by regeneration supplements the residue of the animal's body (in our case by far the major part). The regenerated organ is thus an addition to the other parts. A type of regeneration exemplified by the renewal of limbs in salamanders is therefore called **epimorphosis** or **epimorphic regeneration** (Morgan, 1901). It is the common type found in higher animals.

19—2 REGENERATIVE ABILITY IN VARIOUS ANIMALS

Although present throughout the whole of the animal kingdom, the ability to regenerate lost parts differs both in scope and in its course in the various groups of animals.

In the coelenterates, the regenerative ability is exceedingly high. It was the regeneration of the fresh water polyp *Hydra*, first discovered by Trembley in 1740, that attracted the scientists' attention to this phenomenon. A hydra may be cut in two or more parts and each part will reconstitute itself into a new and complete individual of diminished size. The posterior end of a cut hydra regenerates the mouth and tentacles; the anterior part of the body regenerates the posterior end with the foot and adhesive disc. Even small sections of the body, comprising as little as 1/200 part of the original individual, can regenerate a complete whole. In the latter cases, it is especially clear that the new individual is produced not by addition of parts to the remaining piece (**epimorphosis**) but by remodeling the whole available mass of cells into a new whole. This thus differs from the epimorphic regeneration of an amphibian limb. A type of repair involving a reorganization of the remaining part of the body of an animal is known as **morphallaxis**, or **morphallactic regeneration**. If only smaller parts are removed from the hydra, the remodeling of the remaining body is not so extensive, and with very small defects the regeneration approaches the epimorphic type, even though a typical regeneration bud cannot be clearly distinguished.

Other coelenterates regenerate to varying extents, the regenerative power being highest in the polypoid forms and much reduced in the medusoid forms.

The next group remarkable for their high regenerative ability are the planarians. Planarians may be cut across or lengthwise, and each part of the body will regenerate the missing half. Any part of the body may be replaced in this way: the head, the tail or the middle part with the pharynx. When the cut is made, a regeneration blastema is formed at the cut surface, and the missing part is developed from the blastema. The remaining part is, however, reorganized on a diminished scale, so that the individual resulting from regeneration is smaller than the original one. The regeneration is thus carried out in a way that combines epimorphosis and morphallaxis. Other platyhelminths do not regenerate to any great extent.

The nemerteans have a high regenerative ability, and a complete worm may be formed even starting from very small fragments.

Many experiments have been carried out on regeneration in the annelids. Both polychaetes and oligochaetes regenerate anterior and posterior ends after an amputation. If an earthworm or other oligochaete is cut in two halves, the posterior half regenerates the anterior end with the mouth, and the anterior end regenerates a new posterior end. Two new individuals may thus be produced from the original one. In the majority of the annelids regeneration is, however, somewhat restricted; at the anterior cut surface only a limited number of segments are formed, the number being typical for every species (see Berrill, 1952). In the earthworm *Allolobophora foetida*, this number is four or five. If five segments or less are cut off from the anterior end of the worm, the regeneration is complete; if more than five segments are removed, only four or five segments will be regenerated, and the worm will thus not attain the same over-all number of segments as it had before the operation. If the cut is carried out behind the genital segments (tenth to fourteenth), only four or five anterior segments are regenerated; the genital organs are thus never renewed. On the other hand, there is no restriction in the regeneration of posterior segments, and about as many are formed as have been removed. The process of regeneration is an epimorphosis, a regeneration bud being formed and the new parts developing at the expense of this bud. Hirudinea do not regenerate at all (Weiss, 1939).

In molluscs, the regeneration is relatively poor. In gastropods, eye stalks with eyes may be regenerated as well as parts of the head or of the foot. The whole head does not regenerate, and if the cerebral ganglia are removed together with a part of the head these will not regenerate. The arms of cephalopods may regenerate but not other parts of their body.

In nematodes, the regenerative ability is very low; this may be connected with the high degree of differentiation of the cells of their bodies and the fixed limit to the total number of cells (*cf.* section 17–2). Only the closure of superficial wounds is still possible.

In arthropods, regeneration is limited to the renewal of lost appendages, but this form of regeneration is fairly widespread. In most crustaceans, the limbs may regenerate at any stage of development, including the adult. In insects, limb regeneration occurs only in the larval stages, and the regenerated limb often does not reach the size of a normal limb. The legs of crabs and some spiders are readily shed if seized by an enemy (or the experimenter). The legs break off at a preformed breaking point, across the second leg joint. There is here a constriction which is a modified joint. The leg is broken off by the violent contraction of a muscle (the extensor muscle of the leg). This self-mutilation is known as **autotomy**. Autotomy is probably a special adaptation helping the animal to escape being caught by a predator; if the predator gets hold of one limb, he succeeds in capturing only the limb but not the animal, the latter escaping at the expense of the loss of a limb.

After the amputation or loss of an appendage in an arthropod, the wound is covered by a chitinous plug. Underneath this, a regeneration bud is formed which later reproduces the limb by way of epimorphic regeneration. The new limb does not, however, become apparent until the next molt. The regenerated limb is small at first and attains normal proportion as a result of accelerated growth in the course of several molts.

Among the echinoderms, the starfishes, brittle stars and sea lilies can regenerate arms and parts of the disc. The arms appear to be lost rather often in natural conditions, as individuals regenerating one or more arms are found quite frequently. The Holothuroidea are capable of ejecting through the anus parts of their internal organs—the respiratory tree and the alimentary canal. These can be regenerated later.

In vertebrates, the regenerative power is most spectacular in the urodele amphibians. In newts and salamanders, and especially in their larvae, not only limbs can regenerate (as has been described) but also tails and external gills, and furthermore the upper and lower jaws. Parts of the eye can likewise regenerate, such as the lens and the retina. If most of the eye is removed, it can be regenerated so long as a small part is left, and the new eye develops at the expense of the remaining fragment. In the anuran amphibians, the faculty for regeneration is restricted to the larval stage of their development. Frog and toad tadpoles are able to regenerate their limbs and their tails. The legs of adult frogs and toads do not normally regenerate at all.

In fishes, regeneration is very restricted. The fins can regenerate if cut off or damaged, but the tail (apart from the tailfin) does not regenerate.

The lizards are known to regenerate their tails. This regeneration follows autotomy. The tails are broken off at a preformed level near the base of the tail. To release the mechanism of autotomy, the distal part of the tail must be injured or grabbed with such force as to cause the animal discomfort. After the tail is shed, a regeneration bud is formed on the wound surface, and this gives rise to a new tail. The latter, however, differs from the original tail; the vertebral column is of a simplified structure, and the scales covering the regenerated tail differ from the normal ones. The legs and even the digits in the same animals cannot regenerate completely, though very rudimentary structures are sometimes formed on the site of an amputation. Parts of the beak can be regenerated in birds, but otherwise their regenerative ability is rather poor.

In the mammals, the regenerative ability is reduced to tissue regeneration, that is, the restoration of defects and lesions in various tissues, but not the restoration of lost organs. Tissue regeneration is often equivalent to wound healing. Thus skin wounds may be covered by newly formed epidermis and connective tissue. In the case of large skin wounds, however, the newly formed connective tissue differs from the normal dermis and can be distinguished as scar tissue. The skeletal tissue has a high regenerative ability. Large defects in the bones, especially those of the limbs, can be made good. If parts of individual muscles are removed, the defects can be repaired by a proliferation taking place at the expense of the remaining part of the muscle. Lesions in the tendons can be replaced by connective tissue in the first place, the connective tissue later acquiring the structure and mechanical properties of the tendon. The tissues of some internal organs are able to proliferate to a very great extent and thus compensate for the loss of large parts of the organ. This is found to a striking degree in the case of the liver. The greater part of this organ may be removed; the remaining part then proliferates and restores the normal mass of liver parenchyme. The newly proliferated tissue does not, however, assume exactly the same shape as the liver before the operation.

From this survey it will be seen that, on the whole, representatives of the lower forms of animal life regenerate better — may restore their normal structure from smaller parts of the original individual than is possible for more highly organized animals. The rule is, however, not without numerous exceptions. Some exceptions may be explained by the high degree of histological differentiation in animals otherwise standing low in the scale of the animal kingdom (viz., the nematodes), a high degree of histological differentiation being antagonistic to the ability of cells to proliferate. In other cases this explanation does not hold; it does not tell us, for instance, why the fishes regenerate worse than the amphibians, although the latter are supposed to be derived from the former in the course of evolution.

With one and the same species of animals, the ability to regenerate may be greater in the earlier stages of the ontogenetic cycle. Legs may be regenerated in tadpoles but not in adult frogs. Adult insects cannot regenerate legs although the larvae or nymphs are capable of regeneration. It may be recalled in this connection that parts of early embryos are sometimes able to develop into whole animals whereas corresponding parts at a later stage are not even viable, as when the cleavage stage of an amphibian egg is compared with an adult amphibian, or even with an embryo after the end of gastrulation (see Chapter 10). It may be concluded that a renewal of the morphogenetic processes in regeneration occurs more easily if normal morphogenesis is still under way. If the morphogenetic processes of normal ontogenesis have come to a complete standstill, it is more difficult or even impossible to renew them again.

19–3 STIMULATION AND SUPPRESSION OF REGENERATION

Although the general level of regenerative ability of an animal is determined by its constitution, by the degree of differentiation of its tissues or the stages of ontogenetic development, and other factors, this ability may be increased or diminished by the environment or by the special treatment to which the animal is exposed.

The rate of regeneration is naturally dependent on temperature, as most biological processes are. Increase of temperature, up to a certain point, accelerates regeneration.

In *Planaria torva*, regeneration is scarcely possible at a temperature of 3° C. Of six individuals kept at this temperature, only one regenerated a head, and this was defective; the eyes and brain were not fully differentiated after six months. Regeneration was most rapid at 29.7° C.; at this temperature new heads developed in 4.6 days. A temperature of 31.5° C. was too high, and the heads regenerated after 8.5 days. A temperature of 32° C. proved to be lethal for the animals (after Lillie and Knowlton, from Morgan, 1901).

Food, on the other hand, does not affect regeneration very much. Even a fasting animal will regenerate at the expense of its own internal resources. In such diverse cases as rats regenerating parts of the liver, salamanders regenerating limbs or hydras and planarians regenerating parts of their body, depriving the animals of food does not prevent regeneration and may even accelerate it to a certain extent. If planarians are deprived of food for a long time, they can live by metabolizing constituents of their own body. The animal, of course, diminishes in size in consequence (degrowth, Needham, 1942). In this state a planarian can still regenerate. Although the over-all size decreases, the missing parts are gradually rebuilt so that a complete, even if very small, worm is eventually developed. Figure 424 shows the result of an experiment (Morgan, 1901) in which *Planaria lugubris* was cut lengthwise, and while the left half was fed the right half was left entirely without food. Both regenerated. It appears, therefore, that regeneration is given top priority in the utilization of resources available to the organism. Although restriction of feeding seems to be favorable for regeneration, if anything, extreme degrees of emaciation by starving prevent regeneration except in organisms such as the planarian which is able to utilize its own body as a source of energy without deleterious results.

From both theoretical and practical viewpoints, it would be very important to know whether it is possible to excite regeneration in organisms or their parts which do not normally regenerate. The legs of tailless amphibians are a very suitable object for experiments in this direction, since they regenerate in tadpoles but do not do so in adult frogs. The ability to regenerate disappears in the legs of tadpoles some time before metamorphosis sets in, at a stage when all the digits have been formed and the skeleton of the limb is in a state of chondrification (Polezhayev, 1946). At a later stage, when the cartilaginous skeleton of the limb is fully differentiated and the limb becomes bent in the knee joint, an amputated leg does not regenerate any more, but the wound is covered with skin and no regeneration bud develops. A regeneration bud may, however, be caused to be formed if after amputation the stump is traumatized by sticking a needle into it several times. This additional stimulus is sufficient to get the process of regeneration under way, and the regeneration bud subsequently develops into a limb in the usual manner (Polezhayev, 1946). In the adult frog, traumatization with a needle does not appear to be sufficient to incite regeneration, but treatment of the wound after amputation of the leg with a hypertonic salt solution may cause regeneration (Fig. 425; Rose, 1942). In all cases, the essence of the treatment used

Figure 424.   Regeneration of a planarian which was cut into two, lengthwise (A). The left half was fed (B, C, D); the right half was kept without food (E, F, G). (From Morgan, 1901.)

for inciting regeneration is to increase the destruction of tissue beyond that caused by the amputation. The resulting dedifferentiation of tissues favors the formation of a regeneration bud (*cf.* sections 19–4 and 19–5).

The experiments on regeneration of legs in older tadpoles and adult frogs are very promising and give some hope of the possibility of inciting the regeneration of limbs in other animals (such as mammals) in which they do

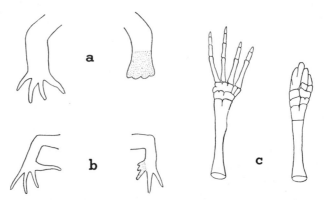

Figure 425.   Regeneration of limbs in the frog after chemical stimulation. *a,* In a one-year-old frog. *b,* In a frog one month after metamorphosis. Regenerated parts stippled. *c,* Skeletons of a normal and a regenerated forelimb. (From Rose, 1942.)

not normally regenerate. It must be remembered, however, that the legs of frogs present a special case, inasmuch as here we have an organ that normally regenerates during an earlier ontogenetic period.

The method applied to the legs of older tadpoles, i.e., traumatization by pricking with a needle, has been used to stimulate regeneration in the hydra (Tokin and Gorbunowa, 1934). Although a hydra is a paragon of high regenerative ability, the aboral tip of its body, that is, the foot with the adhesive disc, if severed from the rest of the body does not normally regenerate a new hydra but remains unchanged until it dies. Traumatization of an isolated foot in the manner described succeeded in causing it to reorganize itself into a complete new individual.

If the attempts to provoke regeneration where it does not naturally occur have been successful only in a few special cases, we possess some universally effective methods of preventing or inhibiting regeneration. One of the methods is by irradiating tissues with x-rays. If a leg or an arm of an adult newt is amputated, it readily regenerates. If, however, a newly formed regeneration bud of a limb is irradiated with x-rays, the development of the limb is either retarded or stopped altogether, depending on the amount of irradiation administered. There is some individual variation, but a dose of 5000 to 7000 r (r = roentgen, the unit of dosage of x-rays) suppresses regeneration in every case. An irradiated regeneration bud does not grow, and instead of developing the skeleton and muscle of the limb becomes filled with connective tissue. The bud may actually decrease in size and become partially or wholly resorbed (Brunst and Scheremetjewa, 1933; Butler, 1933). The mechanism of the action of x-rays on the regeneration bud is obviously connected with the action of the rays on mitosis. X-rays are known to inhibit or suppress the mitotic activity of cells. If the cells of the regeneration bud cannot divide by mitosis, the growth of the rudiment becomes impossible; the number of cells available remains too small for the development and differentiation of the organ.

It is still more remarkable that the irradiation of a limb with x-rays may precede the amputation of the limb by months and nevertheless make the regeneration impossible. A dose of 7000 r applied to a normal limb of an adult newt does not usually cause any visible effect. Neither in appearance nor in its function does an irradiated limb differ from a nonirradiated one. The treated animals may be kept for months without showing any deleterious effect of the irradiation. If, however, an irradiated limb is amputated, regeneration is completely lacking and the wound is instead covered by skin, leaving a permanent stump (Brunst, 1950).

It has been found that x-rays have the same effect on regeneration in all animals in which this effect has been tested. The effect is thus on some very fundamental property of living cells.

19—4 HISTOLOGICAL PROCESSES CONCERNED IN REGENERATION

Regeneration involves a complicated sequence of histological transformations in the stump of the amputated organ and later in the regeneration blastema.

The immediate effect of an amputation is that tissues and cells lying normally in the interior of the body emerge on the surface. Some of the cells are squashed, torn or otherwise destroyed; others become damaged by exposure to an unfavorable environment. The surface of the wound is thus covered with the debris of dead cells. In animals with a developed blood vessel system, the blood from the damaged vessels flows onto the surface of the wound and there coagulates, thus stopping further loss of blood.

The next stage is the covering of the wound surface with epithelium. Skin epithelium spreads over the wound surface, penetrating underneath the blood clot, between it and the intact living connective tissue. The spread of the epithelium is due to ameboid movement of the cells and does not involve growth at the edges of the wound. No mitoses are found in the epithelium at this time. The time needed for the epithelium to cover the wound surface depends on the size of the regenerating animal and the size of the wound, besides such external factors as temperature. In the salamander larva, after the amputation of a leg the wound becomes closed by the epithelium in about one or two days. In invertebrates, the closure of the wound may be assisted by the contraction of the subepidermal muscle layer, so that the surface which has to be covered by the epidermis is diminished.

After the closure of the wound, a very important step in the process of regeneration sets in: dedifferentiation of the tissues adjoining the cut surface. This dedifferentiation has been best studied in vertebrates and is here perhaps most pronounced. Dedifferentiation proceeds in conformity with what has been said on this subject in section 16–5. The intercellular matrix of bone and cartilage becomes dissolved, and the cells come to lie freely under the epithelium which has covered the wound. The connective tissue fibers likewise disintegrate, and the connective tissue cells become indistinguishable morphologically from cells derived from the disintegration of the skeletal tissues. The muscles also undergo dedifferentiation, the myofibrils disappear, and the nucleo-cytoplasmic ratio greatly increases. The cells of all tissues become similar in appearance to embryonic cells. Whether this similarity is a superficial one or whether the cells acquire the properties of embryonic cells in every respect is a different matter and will be dealt with in section 19–8.

The formation of the blastema or regeneration bud is the next step. Undifferentiated cells accumulate under the epidermis covering the wound, and together with it they form the regeneration bud, mentioned in section 19–1. There has been much argument as to the origin of the cells of the blastema. Two main theories on this subject have been proposed. According to one theory, the cells of the blastema are all of local origin, that is, derived from the tissues immediately adjoining the wound surface. Except for the epithelium covering the wound, the rest of the cells, according to this theory, are set free from the dedifferentiating connective tissue, skeleton and so on.

According to a second theory, the differentiated cells at the wound level have nothing to do with the formation of the blastema (except for the epithelium, which is obviously derived from the adjoining intact parts of the skin). The blastema is supposed to be derived from cells migrating to the regeneration site from more or less distant parts of the body by ameboid movement or brought there with the blood stream. These cells are supposed to be special "reserve" cells, which still possess a capacity for development that has been lost by the differentiated tissue cells.

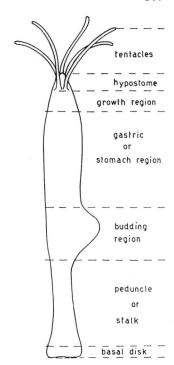

tentacles

hypostome

growth region

gastric
or
stomach region

budding
region

peduncle
or
stalk

basal disk

Figure 426. Diagram of *Hydra*, illustrating the different body regions of the animal. (From Burnett, 1962.)

It is now known that neither of these two theories has universal application but that both sources of cells of the blastema may occur in different animals. The problem thus resolves itself into finding what the local tissues contribute to the formation of the regeneration blastema and what is contributed by migratory cells in any given animal.

Hydroid polyps are normally in a continuous state of "physiological regeneration." The cells of which the tentacles and the hypostome are composed continuously become worn out and discarded and are replaced by the shifting of cells from a region lying below the hypostome (Fig. 426). This region is a "growth zone" in which most of the mitoses in the body of a hydra take place (except for the case of asexual reproduction which will be dealt with in section 20–2). The base of the polyp (peduncle and foot) also depends on the supply of fresh cells from the growth zone, so that from the growth zone a steady migration of cells goes on in both directions: to the hypostome and tentacles and to the peduncle and foot. On the hypostome and tentacles, the cells that need frequent replacement in the highest degree are the **cnidoblasts**, the cells producing the nematocysts which serve for the immobilization and capture of the small animals on which the hydroid polyps feed. A nematocyst can be used only once, so that the cnidoblasts degenerate after once having thrown out their thread and must be continuously replaced by new ones. The replacement of the cnidoblasts is performed by a special kind of cell, known as the **interstitial cells**, so called because they are found lying in the intercellular spaces at the base of the ectodermal epithelium and also in smaller numbers between the cells of the gut epithelium (Fig. 427). The cells are small with relatively very large nuclei (as in most undifferentiated cells) and basophilic cytoplasm.

In addition to their role in the replacement of cnidoblasts, the interstitial cells serve generally as a pool of undifferentiated cells which can be used for

Figure 427. Interstitial cells between two differentiated epitheliomuscular endodermal cells in *Hydra*. (From McConnell, 1936.)

various morphogenetic processes in the organism of the hydroid: they are supposed to give rise to the sex cells, are the leading elements in asexual reproduction and take part in processes of regeneration of lost parts. It appears that the role of the interstitial cells in replacement of lost parts has been somewhat overrated, however.

When a hydroid polyp is cut transversely, the open wound is initially closed by a contraction of the epithelio-muscular cells of the ectoderm. The ectoderm next covers the damaged surface with a sheet of epithelial cells. In the next few hours mitotic activity is increased in the growth zone, and more than the usual number of cells are given off toward the damaged area, be that at the oral or the aboral end òf the body. The cells thus mobilized at the site of the wound become molded to form the missing parts. Some of the interstitial cells moving toward the cut edge invade the endodermal layer and become converted into endodermal cells, thus supplementing the local endoderm. Others serve for the production of cnidoblasts for the regenerating parts (in the case of regeneration of the oral end). The epithelium of the newly built part is derived from similar epithelium adjoining the wound, and the endodermal epithelium nearest the wound contributes in part to the development of the regenerating structure (Burnett, 1962).

It has been repeatedly observed by many investigators that agents such as x-rays or mustard gas, which has a somewhat similar action, kill off interstitial cells of hydroids without causing immediate damage to differentiated types of cells. The animals continue living for a few weeks, but their ability to regenerate (and also to reproduce by budding) is severely reduced or even completely eliminated. This result has been interpreted as proving that regeneration is impossible without the participation of interstitial cells. In view of the moderate part played by interstitial cells in the restoration of lost parts, as shown by direct observation, the above conclusion seems doubtful, and perhaps a more cautious interpretation would be that the x-ray or mustard gas treatment precludes the growth and mitosis in all cells of the body, and of course this would make the formation of new parts impossible.

There is at present sufficient evidence to show that the interstitial cells are not the only ones that can be transformed into other cell types. Attempts have been made to test whether the ectoderm or the endoderm of a hydra alone can reconstruct a complete organism. In this connection some experiments with isolation of endoderm are of particular interest. In *Pelmatohydra oligactis* and *Hydra viridis*, the endoderm was isolated from ectoderm by treatment with trypsin which digests the mesoglea binding the two layers together. Isolated ectoderm degenerated after such treatment, but isolated endoderm underwent a progressive differentiation and produced a new complete animal. It is important that, in the species used, interstitial cells are present only in the ectoderm. In this way the new individual was produced at the expense of endodermal cells only. Some of these lost their differentiation and turned into ectodermal cells. Other dedifferentiating cells became transformed into interstitial cells, and the latter proceeded to produce cnidoblasts in the reconstituted polyp (Haynes and Burnett, 1963). It has also been claimed that isolated ectoderm of another hydroid, *Cordylophora*, is capable of producing a complete animal (Zwilling, 1963), but in the latter case the participation of interstitial cells has not been excluded.

It appears that in the hydroids the cells of various types show a very broad potentiality, an evidence that, in spite of being functionally differentiated, they retain a complete genotype and that all parts of their genetic information can be put to use (derepressed—see p. 504). Nevertheless, the existence of a cell type such as the interstitial cells which under normal conditions lend themselves especially readily for morphological transformations, is worth noting and leads us to the next example of the same kind.

In the planarians, the processes of regeneration take a somewhat similar course. The wound is initially covered by the epidermis of the skin. The cells move tangentially over the wound surface without proliferating. This occurs in the first 24 hours after infliction of the wound. The replacement of the lost parts occurs later at the expense of undifferentiated cells derived from the parenchyme (mesenchyme) of the worm. Whether these cells are "reserve" cells, as in the hydra, or are constituent cells of the normal connective tissue which undergo dedifferentiation and become capable of participating in new morphogenetic processes, is not known for certain. They form the blastema under the sheet of epithelium, proliferate and later differentiate into the various organs (Fig. 428). The blastema, and so in the last instance the migrating parenchyme cells, give rise to most of the regenerating organs: the connective tissue, the pharynx, the nervous system, as well as the muscle of the body. The skin epithelium is derived from the skin at the edge of the wound, and also, it is claimed, the intestine in the regenerated part is derived from the cut edge of the old intestine (Bandier, 1937).

That the blastema is formed by cells migrating from remote parts of the body is definitely proved by the following experiment. If a planarian is irradiated with x-rays prior to wounding, no regeneration occurs, as we know irradiation with x-rays makes the cells incapable of participating in the process of regeneration (see section 19–3). If, however, a small part of the worm is shielded from x-rays and then a part of its body is amputated, regeneration will proceed even if the wound is far away from the region which had not been irradiated. This can only mean that cells which had not been ex-

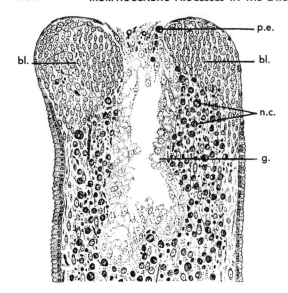

Figure 428. Regeneration in the land planarian *Rhynchodemus bilineatus*. *bl*, Regeneration blastema; *g*, gut; *n.c.*, necrotic cells; *p.e.*, proliferating endoderm cells. (From Bandier, 1937.)

posed to x-rays are capable of migrating long distances and then forming a healthy blastema on the cut surface (Fig. 429 – Dubois and Wolff, 1947).

In the annelids, there is a special type of cell called **neoblasts** which serve for the formation of regenerating parts. The neoblasts are large cells found normally in the peritoneum of the posterior surface of the intersegmental septa. When the body of the worm is cut, the neoblasts become activated and migrate toward the cut surface, following the course of the ventral nerve chain. The neoblasts accumulate under the epidermis which closes the wound and thus form the regeneration blastema. Not all the organs of the regenerated part are developed from the neoblasts, however, but only the mesodermal organs. The nervous system of the regenerated part is developed from the epidermis (from a thickening on its inner surface). Also the gut regenerates from the cut surface of the old gut. The competence of the neoblasts is thus more restricted than that of the mesenchyme cells in a planarian.

After treatement with x-rays, the neoblasts are the first to suffer damage and degenerate, and they may be destroyed with weaker doses of the rays, which leave the other tissues intact. Irradiated worms will not regenerate (Zhinkin, 1934). Epidermis and endoderm of the gut, which normally con-

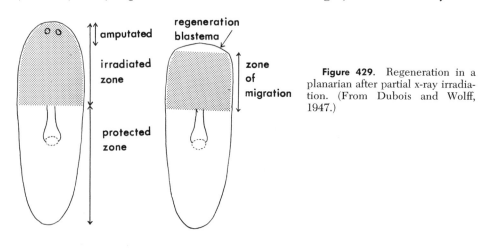

Figure 429. Regeneration in a planarian after partial x-ray irradiation. (From Dubois and Wolff, 1947.)

tribute to the formation of the regenerate, are not visibly damaged by x-rays, but they do not produce new parts in the absence of neoblasts. This may be either a result of the failure of some stimulating action normally exercised by the neoblasts or a result of direct damage by the x-rays, making these tissues incapable of proliferation even if this does not interfere with their normal activities.

The origin of the cells forming the regeneration bud in vertebrates is naturally of special interest to us. This has been most exhaustively investigated in the case of regenerating legs of newts and salamanders. A study of microscopical sections of regenerating stumps of salamander legs does not allow of an unequivocal solution to the problem. Whereas a dedifferentiation of tissues adjoining the wound can easily be observed, it is very difficult to prove that the cells from dedifferentiating tissues actually form the regenerating blastema. This leaves the way open to those who would like to claim that the regeneration blastema has a different origin, that the cells of the blastema are brought to the site of regeneration with the blood stream. The question has been settled, however, by the application of local irradiation with x-rays (Butler, 1935; Brunst, 1950). We have seen earlier (section 19–3) that irradiation with a sufficiently high dosage of x-rays suppresses the ability of salamanders to regenerate. A modification of this basic experiment could be used for the solution of the problem under discussion.

Two types of experiment have been applied. In the first experiment, the whole animal was shielded from the x-rays (with a sheet of lead) and only one leg was exposed to the rays. The leg was then amputated inside the irradiated area. There was no regeneration (Brunst and Chérémétieva, 1936). In another experiment, the whole animal was irradiated and an untreated leg was transplanted onto the irradiated body. Subsequently the leg was amputated (inside the untreated area) and it regenerated normally (Butler, 1935). It is thus obvious that the irradiation does not interfere with the powers for the regeneration of the animal as a whole, but only affects the cells which are directly exposed to the rays. If the regeneration cells had been brought to the site of regeneration from other parts of the body, the local irradiation of only one leg should not have prevented its regeneration. By careful application of the lead screen, it could be proved that even a very thin layer of normal (unirradiated) tissue is sufficient to ensure a normal regeneration of the leg (Fig. 430—Scheremetjewa and Brunst, 1938).

The irradiation of hydrae or annelids in the first instance causes the degeneration of the interstitial cells or the neoblasts, and the ability to regenerate disappears as a consequence. It may be questioned in the case of newts and salamanders whether there is a special type of cells which is destroyed when the animals are made incapable of regeneration by the action of x-rays. The answer to this question should probably be a negative one; it is impossible to find by histological methods any cells in the tissues of the newt or salamander which could be identified as "reserve cells" or "undifferentiated cells."

By the use of radioactive tracers, it has been possible to give positive proofs that all the dedifferentiating tissues are actually involved in the formation of the regeneration blastema, not one particular cell type. Tissues of amputated limbs of newts were supplied with tritiated leucin, a protein precursor, in one experiment (Anton, 1961) and with tritiated thymidine, a DNA

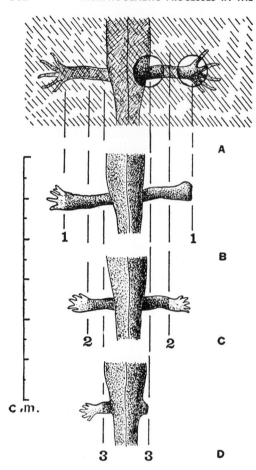

Figure 430. Local irradiation of parts of the limb in a newt, and results of amputation at different levels in the irradiated limb (right) and in control limb (left). Drawing above (*A*) shows shielding plate covering the whole animal except for two circular openings through which the rays could pass. The limb fails to regenerate when amputated inside irradiated areas. (From Brunst, 1950.)

precursor, in another experiment (Hay and Fischman, 1961). In both experiments it was observed that the radioactively tagged precursors were taken up by the cells adjoining the cut surface (to a depth of about 1 mm.). The intake started while the tissues had not yet lost their histological characteristics, and it was possible to ascertain that all kinds of tissues participated in the upsurge of synthetic activity; in particular this was found to be the case with muscle, fibroblasts, periosteum, endosteum, Schwann cells of the nerves, and the epidermis. The blastema was later found to consist of labeled cells. It follows that none of the tissues of the amputation stump are excluded from the participation in regeneration, but that all respond to the wounding by growth (synthesis) and later by proliferation.

While the processes of dedifferentiation of tissues underneath the covering epidermis are still going on, the next step in regeneration is inaugurated: cells in the region adjoining the wound start proliferating and dividing by mitosis. Mitotic activity starts as soon as tissues begin to dedifferentiate, and the rate of proliferation, as expressed by the proportion of cells in mitosis, rapidly increases (Table 22; Chalkley, 1954; Hay, 1962). This process reaches its peak at the time of the formation of the regeneration blastema in which, as Hay puts it (p. 186), "muscle and other cell types have given up their structural and functional complexities to engage wholeheartedly in the pleasures of proliferation." For a time the divisions of the cells outstrip growth, and this leads to a slight diminution of the size of the cells in the blastema. Later growth catches up with mitosis and both go hand in hand, so that a very distinct period of growth follows. The growth rate is at its highest immediately after the blastema has been formed, and subsequently the rate of growth diminishes inversely proportionally to the time that has passed since the beginning of growth (Syngajewskaja, 1936). As the growth diminishes, differentiation sets in; thus the inverse relationship between growth and differentiation holds good for regeneration as well as for normal development.

The reservation must be made that a local increase of mitotic activity is not observed where regeneration is by way of morphallaxis. In a hydra, as has been stated, an increase of mitoses does occur during regeneration, but these take place away from the wound surface, mainly in the growth center (Kanajew, 1926; Burnett, 1962).

TABLE 22. THE MITOTIC ACTIVITY IN THE MESODERMAL BLASTEMA AND THE ADJOINING PART OF THE STUMP DURING REGENERATION OF THE FORELIMB OF THE NEWT, *Triturus viridescens* (AFTER CHALKLEY, 1954).

Days after Amputation	No. of Cells Counted	No. of Mitoses	"Mitotic Index" (% of Cells in Mitosis)
1	52,487	4	0.0
7	78,533	415	0.53
13	111,705	748	0.67
19	139,322	900	0.65
25	180,043	953	0.53
31	215,035	625	0.29
37	213,432	365	0.17

The processes of histological differentiation taking place in the regenerating parts are as a rule similar to those occurring in normal ontogenetic development and need not be described here. In special cases, however, the processes may differ in two respects.

1. Certain tissues in regeneration may be developed from a source different from that in normal ontogenesis. An example of this has been mentioned previously: the regeneration cells of a planarian, which are derived from the parenchyme (mesenchyme) and are thus of a mesodermal nature, give rise in regeneration not only to the parenchyme and the muscles but also to the nervous system and the pharynx. In normal development from the egg, the nervous system and the pharynx are produced by the ectoderm. Similar cases are known to occur in some other animals.

2. Sometimes the regenerated structure is formed in a way different from the normal one. The notochord is the predecessor of the vertebral column during the normal development of a salamander larva. In an adult salamander, the notochord is reduced and replaced by the bony vertebrae and it does not reappear in a regenerating tail. During regeneration, the cartilages representing the rudiments of the vertebrae are formed around the spinal cord instead. The normal segmentation of the vertebral column is not restored in the regenerated tail of a lizard.

19—5   PHYSIOLOGICAL PROCESSES INVOLVED IN REGENERATION

The physiological state of regenerating animals allows us to distinguish two periods with a different type of metabolism: predominantly destructive metabolism in the first period and predominantly constructive metabolism in the second period. The period of destructive metabolism is naturally of greater significance in those animals in which there is considerable dedifferentiation at the beginning, as in amphibian regeneration. Most prominent is the abrupt increase in the activity of proteolytic enzymes. If a normal healthy tadpole tail is subjected to autolysis, a part of its own protein becomes decomposed by the action of the proteolytic enzymes contained in its tissues. This part can be measured by the amount of nonprotein nitrogen produced in this way. The actual quantity observed in an experiment of this kind was 58 mg. per 100 gm. in 12 hours. A stump of an amputated tail under the same conditions produced 233 mg. of nonprotein nitrogen per 100 gm. In the stump of the amputated tail, which undergoes dedifferentiation, the activity (or quantity) of proteolytic enzymes was thus four times as great as in the normal tissue (Bromley and Orechowitsch, 1934).

The proteolytic enzyme that is mainly responsible for this increase is kathepsin. A direct measurement of the kathepsin activity, with gelatin as substrate, showed a rapid increase of the activity in the very first days after amputation. A maximum, which was more than twice the normal level, was reached three days after the amputation (Orechowitsch, Bromley and Kozmina, 1935). After this the activity of the kathepsin slowly decreased, reaching the normal level by the twelfth day. The activity of the dipeptidases was also found to have increased sharply during the first few days after the amputation, but the increase was of a longer duration, and the maximum of the increase was reached only by the eleventh day.

Through the activity of proteolytic enzymes, the cells damaged by the operation are destroyed in the first instance, but the main result is the dedifferentiation of part of the healthy tissues adjacent to the wound surface: destruction of the intercellular substances and the highly differentiated parts of cells (such as the muscle fibrils). As a result of these catabolic processes, the amount of free amino acids increases to about double the amount in normal tissues—from 16.8 per cent to 35.1 per cent of the total nitrogen (Orechowitsch and Bromley, 1934). A qualitative change in the structure of the proteins and their products also takes place. This is shown by an increase in the amount of reduced sulfhydryl compounds, that is, compounds having a reduced –SH group, presumably owing to a reduction of the cystine in the tripeptide glutathione. This is important because reduced glutathione is known to increase the activity of kathepsin, and therefore this change may also be a contributing factor to the processes of dedifferentiation setting in after the infliction of a wound.

It is remarkable that catabolic processes after wounding are not necessarily restricted to the site of the injury but may occur throughout the whole body, as has been found in the case of mammals in which large amounts of proteins are broken down after the infliction of major wounds (see Needham, 1952).

Another phenomenon of a physiological nature following amputation is a change in the character of the oxidation in the tissues of the stump. The respiratory quotient, R.Q. (ratio of CO_2 produced to the amount of O_2 consumed), falls abruptly, reaching the level of 0.57 (Ryvkina, 1945). This may be considered a sign of incomplete oxidation in the tissues. Actually, lactic acid was found to increase in regenerating tissue as compared with normal tissue. The amount of lactic acid found in the regeneration blastema of the limb of a newt was 39 mg. per 100 gm., as compared with 18 mg. per 100 gm. in normal limb tissue (Okuneff, 1933). As is well known, lactic acid is formed when anaerobic glycolysis replaces oxidation. The enzymes which in normal tissues carry on the oxidation, such as cytochrome oxidase, show a low level of activity in regenerating tissues. The changes concerning the R.Q. and the lactic acid content reach their maximum toward the time when the regeneration blastema is fully formed, and during the later stages — the stages of differentiation — both the lactic acid content and the R.Q. gradually return to normal. The absolute amount of oxygen consumed may fall in the early stages of regeneration, but in the differentiation phase it is above normal.

The changes in the metabolic processes taking place in the earlier phases of regeneration — accumulation of free amino acids, of lactic acid, of free –SH groups — all lead to a lowering of the pH in the tissues of the stump and the regeneration blastema. This could be measured directly in the case of limb regeneration of salamanders. In normal limb tissues, the pH is 7.2. It becomes lower immediately after wounding and reaches a minimum of 6.6 at the time when the blastema is being formed. After this the pH slowly rises, reaching the normal level when differentiation sets in (Okuneff, 1928).

What has been said suffices to show the main features of the predominantly destructive phase of regeneration: the period when the damaged cells are destroyed and dedifferentiation takes place. Some indications will have been noted of the metabolism of the constructive phase of regeneration. This is characterized by an increase of oxidation, by a return of the pH to normal, by a higher R.Q., by a decrease in the amount of free –SH groups and of lactic acid.

We have previously noted the connection that exists between growth and cytoplasmic ribonucleic acid. This connection has also been found to be valid in the case of regenerative growth. The cells of the regeneration blastema become very rich in cytoplasmic ribonucleic acid, even if the cells from which the blastema is derived do not originally contain large amounts of this substance. When the stage of differentiation of the regenerating part is reached, the amount of ribonucleic acid in the cells diminishes again (Roskin, cit. from Brachet, 1950b).

19—6 RELEASE OF REGENERATION

According to definition, regeneration is the replacement of lost parts. One could have expected, therefore, that the loss of some part of the body would be the adequate stimulus to set in motion the mechanism which restores the part and thus restores the normal structure of the animal. This is by no means always the case. If a deep incision is made on the side of a salamander's limb, or on the side of the body in an earthworm or a planarian, a regeneration blastema may be formed on the cut surface. The blastema then proceeds to grow and develop into a new part, as in ordinary regeneration. In the case of a limb, the new part thus developed will be the distal part of the limb, from the wound level outward. The development of the regenerating part proceeds just as if the entire distal part of the limb were cut off.

In the case of a planarian, a lateral incision may cause the development from the wound surface of either a new head or a new tail, or both. If both a head and a tail are regenerated, the head forms from that part of the wound surface which faces anteriorly and the tail develops from the wound surface facing posteriorly. This results, of course, in the regenerated head lying more anterior than the regenerating tail. A somewhat similar reaction is produced by lateral incisions in the earthworm, with the restriction that lateral incisions near the head end of the worm give rise to additional heads, incisions in the middle part of the animal cause the development of both heads and tails, while incisions in the posterior part of the animal's body cause the formation of tails only. Another peculiarity in the case of the earthworm is that the incision must be deep enough to sever the ventral nerve chain if any regeneration at all is to take place (compare what will be said further, in section 19–7).

In each of these cases, the original parts of the animal (heads, tails, limbs) had not been removed, so that the regenerated parts are additional and therefore superfluous to the animal. The experiments allow us to draw the conclusion that not the absence of an organ but the presence of a wound is the stimulus for regeneration.

The development of a superfluous number of organs or parts of the body, as a result of regeneration, is called **super-regeneration**.

The clue given by super-regeneration has been followed up to analyze the stimulus leading to regeneration still further. It has been found that regeneration can be started even without inflicting an open wound. This has been performed by ligaturing a limb in a salamander (axolotl). (See Nassonov, 1930.) A tight ligature causes a considerable destruction of the tissues immediately affected by the pressure. The muscles and portions of the skeleton of the limb disintegrate, so that the part of the limb distal to the ligature becomes bent at an angle and is dragged about by the animal without being capable of movement of its own. The skin, however, turns out to be more resistant and preserves its integrity. After some weeks, the region of the limb just proximal to the ligature begins to swell, and it soon becomes evident that a regeneration blastema has been formed. The regeneration blastema then develops into the distal part of a new limb, although the old distal part of the limb is still present. With the processes of differentiation setting in, the skeleton of the old distal part of the limb may be joined again to the proximal skeleton.

The experiment with ligaturing the limb teaches us that the presence of an open wound is not essential for regeneration. What is really necessary is damage to the tissues of an organ that is capable of regeneration. Usually tissues are damaged by wounding, but if extensive damage to the tissues can be caused without an open wound, this suffices to start the sequence of processes leading eventually to regeneration.

Having reached so far we may suggest that damaging the tissues is necessary so that some substance or substances be released from the damaged and disintegrating tissues, which are the immediate cause of the processes that follow. Various types of experiments have been adduced in support of this concept.

It has been found that if a regeneration blastema of an axolotl limb is dried at low temperatures, so that the cells of the blastema are all killed, and this is then transplanted under the skin of an axolotl limb, it causes an outgrowth on the surface of the host limb. This outgrowth, which is covered by skin and has a cartilaginous axis in the middle, is comparable to a very rudimentary limb or at least to a digit. A similar outgrowth may be caused by an implanted piece of cartilage and also by introducing under the skin the products of alkaline hydrolysis of cartilage (Nassonov, 1936). These experiments immediately remind us of the experiments on the primary organizer in early amphibian development; there as here it was found that the stimulus for causing certain morphogenetic processes was not necessarily dependent on the integrity and vital activity of the cells of the inducing part, and that nonliving substances could exert a similar action.

Another line of research consists in the treatment of the amputation surface with a solution of beryllium salt (beryllium nitrate). Beryllium nitrate applied to the amputation surface of a tadpole tail or of the limb of an *Ambystoma* larva completely suppresses regeneration (A. E. Needham, 1941, 1952). It has been suggested that beryllium in some way binds the substances released from the damaged cells at the wound surface that would have normally initiated the whole sequence of the processes of regeneration—the dedifferentiation in the first place and subsequently the formation of the regeneration blastema. Such an interpretation is supported by the following details of the experiments with beryllium.

First, the beryllium treatment must be carried out immediately after the amputation; an hour later the treatment is without any effect. This might mean that the substances released from the damaged cells have already started off the next step of the reaction (the processes of dedifferentiation) or at least created the conditions in which this next step inevitably follows.

Second, if after treatment of the wound surface the stump is again amputated 0.5 mm. proximal to the original cut, regeneration proceeds normally. Thus the action of the beryllium is only very local. If new cells are damaged they may in their turn release the same substances and "trigger off" regeneration. The treatment of normal tissues prior to amputation does not have any effect, either; it is only after the cells are damaged that beryllium can in some way affect the results which could have been produced by the damaged cells.

In this respect there is a profound difference between the inhibition of regeneration by x-rays (see section 19–3) and the inhibition of regeneration by beryllium nitrate. X-rays make the cells incapable of growth and reproduction, and this makes regeneration impossible. The demolition processes are not checked by the rays. On the other hand, beryllium does not impair the ability of the cells to grow and differentiate, but it checks all the stages of regeneration by preventing the initial steps of regeneration from occurring. It is thus very probable that it interferes with the specific factor releasing regeneration, and that this factor is a substance or substances given off by the damaged cells at the wound surface.

Other factors besides the substances from disintegrating cells have been shown to be of importance for starting regeneration. In colonies of hydroids, the oxygen supply appears to be of major importance (Barth, 1940). If the concentration of oxygen in the surrounding sea water is below 1 cc. per liter, regeneration does not take place, even though the animals remain alive and will regenerate if they are placed again in normal sea water. The rate of regeneration, measured by the length of the hydranth blastema, or by the time necessary for the hydranth blastema to be formed, increases with increased concentration of oxygen, as can be seen from Table 23.

TABLE 23. EFFECT OF VARYING OXYGEN TENSION ON THE RATE OF REGENERATION OF THE HYDROID *Tubularia* (AFTER BARTH, 1940)

Oxygen cc./liter	Length of Hydranth Primordium	Time for Primordium Formation (in Hours)
2.4	1072	36.1
3.2	1284	28.1
4.1	1370	26.8
4.8	1365	26.3
8.2	1640	24.5
11.3	1809	24.6
14.3	1840	24.1
16.5	1846	23.7
Control in open dish	1370	26.2

The data so far show that oxygen is a necessary condition for regeneration, and that it can affect the rate of the process. Further experiments show, however, that an increased oxygen supply can start the regeneration process where it would otherwise have not occurred. One of such experiments consists in cutting away the perisarc from the middle of the stem of a *Tubularia* hydroid. The perisarc normally decreases the amount of oxygen reaching the cells of the stem from the surrounding water; therefore cutting away of the perisarc increases the oxygen supply to the stem, with the result that it starts to proliferate and forms a hydranth at each end of the exposed region.

Another experiment consists in cutting out a piece of stem of *Tubularia* together with the perisarc and tying the perisarc with a thread at both ends. The section of stem enclosed thus inside the perisarc will not regenerate, because the oxygen supply to it is cut off. If, however, a bubble of oxygen is now injected into the gastric cavity of the stem, regeneration starts in the vicinity of the gas bubble.

Even though oxygen may serve as a stimulus for starting regeneration in hydroids, this is to be regarded as a special case, whereas the release of substances by wounding or destroying the cells probably plays a part in the regeneration of the most diverse animals and possibly even in the case of hydroids, when regeneration follows amputation of a hydroid or a cut through the stem of the colony.

19—7 REGENERATION AND THE NERVOUS SYSTEM

Among the factors concerned with regeneration, the nervous system deserves particular attention, since it appears to have a special influence on regeneration.

Figure 431. Arrest of regeneration in limbs with transected nerves (left limb in each pair). Limbs with intact nerves regenerate normally. (After Schotté, 1926.)

In the amphibians, the early stages of regeneration cannot proceed normally in the absence of an adequate nerve supply to the region of the wound. If the nerves supplying the leg or the arm of a newt are destroyed simultaneously with the amputation of the limb or during the early stages of regeneration, the development of the regenerating limb is arrested, and the blastema ceases to grow or may even be resorbed (Fig. 431; Schotté, 1923, 1926). If the nerves are cut before amputating the limb, processes of dedifferentiation set in, but, instead of leading later to the formation of a limb blastema, they continue unchecked until most of the limb is destroyed. The constructive part of the regeneration does not start at all (Schotté and Butler, 1941; Schotté and Harland, 1943). The nervous system exerts its influence mainly on the earlier stages of regeneration. Once the regenerating limb has reached the stage when the differentiation commences, it can proceed with its development even in the absence of nerve supply (if the nerve is cut at that stage).

The action of nerves, however, can go even further than supporting the process of regeneration. In a newt, it is possible to deviate a nerve from its normal position. In the case of limb nerves, the experiment is done so that the nerve is transected at a distal level, then separated along part of its course, from the distal end to the shoulder or pelvic level. A cut is then made through the skin of the trunk, starting from the pelvis or the shoulder, and the nerve is placed in the cut, so that when the wound heals the free end of the nerve is in a position under the skin and away from the limb it normally supplies. It was found that if the end of the nerve was not too far from the base of the limb, a limb rudiment, similar to a regeneration blastema of the limb, was formed over the end of the nerve. In successful cases this grew out into a complete new limb (Locatelli, 1924). Thus the presence of a limb nerve may cause the formation of a limb at a spot where otherwise no limb development could have been expected.

That a stimulus causing growth and development can be exercised by a free nerve ending has also been shown in a somewhat different experiment. It has been mentioned previously that the limbs of an adult frog cannot normally regenerate, but that some degree of regeneration in adult limbs may be released by traumatization of the stump after the amputation of a limb (section 19–3). The sciatic nerve of a young metamorphosed frog was dissected as described and deviated into the forelimb, which was then amputated. The presence of the sciatic nerve exerted the same action as traumatization of the limb stump: a blastema was formed and this developed into an incomplete limb "with a tendency to hand or finger formation" (Singer, 1950).

The influence of the nervous system on regeneration is by no means restricted to the regeneration of limbs in amphibians. It is very obvious in annelids. After section of the body, when the neoblasts migrate to the surface of the wound to form a regeneration blastema, they follow the ventral nerve cord in their migration. If the nerve cord is excised some distance from the level at which an earthworm has been transected, no regeneration will occur at that level. A regeneration blastema may be formed, however, at the spot where the nerve cord ends, and a new anterior end of the worm will be formed some distance from the anterior cut surface (Morgan, 1901).

The anterior end of the nerve cord can also be deflected similarly to the deviation of a limb nerve in a newt. The free end of the deflected nerve cord then causes the formation of a regeneration blastema and a new head (*cf.* Berrill, 1952). Even a simple section of the ventral nerve cord, without the removal of either end of the body, is sufficient to release regeneration in a polychaete (Okada, cit. after Berrill, 1952).

Much the same holds true for planarians: regeneration blastemas are formed in conjunction with cut nerve cords. The cerebral ganglion of a planarian excised with a piece of surrounding tissue and transplanted to a different body level causes the formation of a complete new head at the site of transplantation (Santos, 1931).

The experiments described so far prove beyond doubt that the influence of the nervous system is necessary for regeneration. They do not show, however, in what way the nervous system acts — whether it acts in the same way as when transmitting stimuli that release movement or secretion or in some other way. An indication in this respect has been obtained in an experiment confronting a limb with nerve fibers of various origins (Weiss, 1950). A piece of nervous tissue taken from the brain or the spinal cord may be cultivated in the loose parenchyme filling the dorsal fin of urodele amphibians. After an initial partial degeneration the tissue starts growing, and nerve fibers are produced by the surviving nerve cells. If a limb-bud is simultaneously transplanted into the dorsal fin, connections may be established between the piece of nervous tissue and the limb; the outgrowing nerve fibers supply the skin and the muscles of the limb. The fibers in question have been found to be neither the normal motor nor the sensory fibers but are rather equivalent to the "association neurons" which connect different parts of the central nervous system. If the piece of nervous tissue supplying the nerves was derived from the spinal cord or the medulla, the limb muscles could perform contractions, either spontaneously or in answer to an irritation of the limb. The contractions were, however, entirely uncoordinated, in the nature of epileptic seizures rather than normal movements. No contractions occurred, however, if the nervous tissue was taken from the forebrain, diencephalon or midbrain. The transplanted limbs could then be amputated, and they regenerated no matter what part of brain or spinal cord supplied the nerves to the limbs. Nerves which cannot release muscle contractions are thus adequate for supporting regeneration. The conclusion is thus reached that probably any kind of nerve supply can be the source of influence necessary for regeneration, and that the nature of the influence is different from the ordinary transmission of stimuli by nerves.

It may be further suggested that it is hardly possible for the nerve fiber to be in contact with all the cells of a regeneration blastema while these are in motion taking up their positions under the wound surface. In these conditions the normal mechanism of transmission of impulses could hardly operate, and it is thus more likely that the nerve endings act through the release of some substance. What such a substance may be remains a problem for future research.

19—8 RELATION OF THE REGENERATING PARTS TO THE REMAINDER OF THE ORGAN AND TO THE ORGANISM AS A WHOLE

Considering the factors on which regeneration is dependent one can subdivide them in two groups:

1. The factors which are responsible for the regeneration taking place.
2. The factors which determine that the right sort of organ regenerates.

So far, we have been dealing mainly with the first group of factors. It has been shown, however, that sometimes a regenerating organ does not fit into the organization of the whole animal, as when a new limb regenerates without the original limb having been removed (section 19–6). Still, as a general rule, what regenerates corresponds to what has been lost. This can only mean that the position of the wound in some way determines the nature of the regenerating part. If the cut is through a limb, a limb will regenerate (if any regeneration occurs at all); if the cut is through a tail, a tail will regenerate. If the limb is cut at the lower arm level, parts of the lower arm, wrist and digits will develop; if the cut is at the upper arm level, the upper arm will regenerate as well. A part of the shoulder girdle may also be removed, and the whole of the arm together with the shoulder girdle will be renewed. If, however, the whole of the shoulder girdle together with the muscles of the shoulder is completely removed, the arm cannot regenerate any more. This shows that a remnant of the original organ must remain, so as to enable the organ to regenerate. The arm and the shoulder girdle with its muscles form one unit in respect of regeneration. Such a unit has been termed a "regeneration territory" (Guyénot and Ponse, 1930) or "regeneration field" (Weiss, 1926a). A similar regeneration territory is responsible for the regeneration of the tail in adult newts; so long as a small piece of the tail remains, regeneration is possible. If, however, the tail is amputated at the level of the last sacral vertebra, the whole "tail territory" is removed, and no regeneration takes place. The wound heals without any regeneration blastema being formed.

It is not inevitable that the regeneration should be completely repressed if the whole of a regeneration territory is destroyed. Regeneration may occur, but in some different way. In the shrimp *Palinurus*, the eye may regenerate after being removed. The cut, however, must be made through the eye stalk, just proximal to the eye and distal to the nerve ganglion lying at the base of the eye (inside the stalk). If the cut is made at the base of the stalk, so that the ganglion is removed together with the eye, the eye will not regenerate. A regeneration blastema is formed, however, but instead of the lost eye, it develops into an antennalike organ (Fig. 432). This phenomenon—a differ-

Figure 432. Heteromorphic regeneration of an antenna in place of an amputated eye in *Palinurus. an*, Antenna, regenerated; *b*, brain; *e.g.*, eye ganglion. (After Herbst, from Hartmann: Allg. Biol., 1947.)

ent organ developing from the one that has been removed—has been called **heteromorphosis**. The most plausible explanation of heteromorphosis in this case is that the ganglion and the eye constitute together one regeneration territory. If a part of the territory (the ganglion) remains intact, the complete system may be restored. If the whole territory is lost, it cannot be renewed at the expense of other parts of the body.

A different result, yet illustrating the same principle, has been observed in the regeneration from anterior cut surfaces in the earthworm. As shown previously (section 19–2), a new "head" is regenerated at the anterior end of the earthworm if it is cut off. This is possible, however, only if the cut is not too far from the anterior end of the animal. If the cut is beyond the middle of the worm, the posterior part cannot regenerate a new "head" any more. Regeneration takes place, but what is regenerated is a second tail. As this tail is at the anterior end of the sectioned worm, it is a case of heteromorphosis (Morgan, 1901). Again we see that a new anterior end of the animal can only be restored if not too much of the anterior body part has been removed. With more than half of the animal removed, the regeneration territory or regeneration field of the head is completely gone, and what regenerates can only be a tail end. There is an interesting peculiarity in this case which should be noted. By making deep lateral incisions in the body of the earthworm, it has been observed that the ability to regenerate a head diminishes gradually in an anteroposterior direction. The heads which are formed at the site of the wound become smaller and smaller, as the wound is made further away from the anterior end, and beyond the middle of the animal's body no head is regenerated although a tail may be formed.

The same is the case in the regeneration of planarians. If the body is cut transversely at different levels, the tail piece will regenerate a head only if the cut is not too far posterior. Conversely, a very short piece cut from the anterior end of the body of a planarian does not regenerate a tail, at its posterior surface, but a second head. At the anterior end there is thus no competence for tail development present, or else the tendency to develop a head is so strong that the morphogenetic processes cannot proceed in any other way.

If the cut surface determines the nature of the organ or part of the body to be produced in regeneration, it may be questioned whether there are any special cells or tissues at the cut surface which are responsible for the course of regeneration. The problem may be approached experimentally by removing parts of the organ at the level of amputation one by one and observing the result. A classical experiment of this kind was performed by Weiss (1925). After making a slit through the skin and the muscle of the arm in the newt, Weiss removed the humerus. After such an operation, the humerus is not restored. The wound healed, and then the limb was amputated through the upper arm. Owing to the first operation, there was no bone or cartilage at the level of amputation. Nevertheless the regeneration proceeded in the normal way. A regeneration bud was formed and this developed all the parts of the limb distal to the level of amputation. The skeleton of the regenerated part was complete, including the distal part of the humerus. The proximal part of the humerus was lacking, as before (Fig. 433). The first conclusion that can be drawn from this experiment is that the tissues of the regenerated limb are not derived from corresponding tissues at the level of amputation; rather the cells of the regeneration blastema are to be considered as undifferentiated, in so far as the various parts of the limb are concerned, and capable of fitting into any part of the limb.

This has also been confirmed in a very different way. The distal part of a newt's limb may be split lengthwise by a longitudinal cut and then each half amputated and allowed to regenerate. Two regeneration buds are then formed, one at the end of each portion of the limb. Each develops subsequently into a complete distal part, with a complete carpus or tarsus as the case may be, and not into half of one. Thus the cells derived from one half of a transverse section of the limb are capable of producing a complete organ (Weiss, 1926b). It is interesting to compare this result with the splitting of the early limb-bud of an embryo (see section 14–3). With regard to the animal as a whole the development of two limbs, where only one was amputated, is excessive; it is a case of super-regeneration.

Returning to the experiment with regeneration of a complete distal part of a limb in the absence of skeletal parts at the amputation level, we may note a second conclusion: the skeleton at the amputation level does not appear to be necessary for determining the nature of the regenerating organ. In another experiment, the skin (corium) was shown similarly not to be necessary as a carrier of forces determining the specific nature of the regenerate.

level of amputation

normal

humerus removed

regenerated

Figure 433. Regeneration of a forelimb in a newt from which the humerus has been previously removed (diagrammatic). (After Weiss, 1925.)

A strip of skin around the circumference of a newt's limb was removed and replaced by a section of the trachea turned inside out, so as to bring the tracheal epithelium into the position occupied normally by the epithelium of the limb and to put the connective tissue layer of the trachea in the place of the corium of the limb. After amputation through the "collar" made of tracheal wall, the regeneration proceeded normally, and the regenerated limb possessed a corium indistinguishable from that in normal limbs (Weiss, 1927a).

With the exclusion of the skeleton and the corium as carriers of the factors determining the course of regeneration, our attention turns naturally to the muscles and connective tissue of the limb. Excluding these tissues from the level of amputation cannot easily be done, but the action of muscles has been tested in a different way. Muscles from one regeneration territory (e.g., the tail) were transplanted in place of muscles of a different regeneration territory (e.g., the limb) and *vice versa*. If the organ was then amputated, the regeneration was no longer normal; the transplanted muscles exerted a specific influence on the nature of the regenerating organ. Thus if the arm muscles were removed as completely as possible and pieces of tail muscle were stuffed into the space between the arm skeleton and the skin, and then the limb was amputated, the distal part of the regenerating organ was no longer an arm but a structure resembling a tail (Liosner and Woronzowa, 1936).

If the cells of the regeneration blastema are capable of producing any part (any tissue) of the regenerating organ, the question further arises whether different kinds of organs may be produced from a regeneration blastema, other than the organ from the stump of which the blastema had been derived. Two opposing views have been held on this subject by different investigators.

According to one view, the cells of a regeneration blastema are completely undifferentiated and capable of developing into any part of the animal's body, except perhaps that mesodermal cells do not give rise to skin epithelium, though the transformation of epithelial cells into connective tissue cells has been considered as possible by a number of zoologists. In support of this view it is said that a very young blastema, corresponding in stage of development to those depicted in Figure 423,*a* (page 588), may be transplanted to the amputation stump of a different organ and then may develop in correspondence to its new position. Transplantations have been carried out to exchange the regeneration blastema of the fore- and the hind-limbs in the newt. An early forelimb blastema transplanted to the stump of an amputated hindlimb is said to be capable of developing into a hindlimb, and *vice versa*. Furthermore, the regeneration blastema of the tail has been transplanted to the shoulder region, and it was reported that it developed into a forelimb (Weiss, 1927b). As regeneration does not proceed in the absence of nerve supply, a limb nerve had to be diverted to the site of transplantation to make the transplanted blastema grow and differentiate. The latter procedure, however, introduces a serious source of error in the experiment; we have seen that the deviation of a nerve into the area around the basis of a limb alone, without the transplantation of a regeneration blastema, may induce the development of a supernumerary limb (experiments by Locatelli, section 19–7).

It may well have happened that the grafted regeneration blastema of the tail was gradually destroyed and replaced by local cells, which were activated for limb formation by the diverted nerve. The results of transplantation of regeneration buds between the fore- and hindlimbs have also been proved to be inconclusive; the mobilization of regeneration cells in the early stages to which the above experiments refer is not yet completed, and therefore the grafted cells could be replaced by local cells, with the result that the nature of the regenerated organ conforms to the position in which it develops. Careful experiments have proved that no change can be produced in the specific type of development of a regeneration blastema, no matter in what way it is transplanted, at least in the case of amphibian limb regeneration.

In planarians, on the other hand, the tail regeneration blastema has been grafted onto the anterior amputation surface, with the result that it developed into a new head (Gebhardt, 1926). This result has not yet been challenged, and it may be possible that the regeneration cells in lower animals are more plastic, retaining broader possibilities for differentiation. This is perhaps to be expected, as the regeneration territories in these animals are not strictly delimited; the competence to produce a tail or a head fades away gradually starting from the anterior or posterior end of the animals.

It is thus fairly safe to conclude that the capacities of regeneration cells have very definite limits, and that these limits are more narrow in the highly organized animals than in the lower forms of life. There is no question of the regeneration cells acquiring the same abilities for development as the egg or the early cleavage cells. A further difference between the early embryonic cells and the regeneration cells is that the first may develop in complete isolation; the second can develop only in conjunction with the remainder of the organism, which provides the regeneration blastema with nourishment, supplies it with nerves, and exerts a certain degree of influence on the processes of differentiation of the regeneration blastema.

19—9   RECONSTITUTION FROM ISOLATED CELLS

Related to regeneration is the reaggregation of isolated cells into a new whole animal. This remarkable phenomenon has been discovered in sponges (H. V. Wilson, 1907). A sponge may be rubbed through bolting silk, so that the entire organization of the sponge is broken up, and the tissues of the animal are reduced to a pulp consisting of isolated cells and cell debris. If the pulp is allowed to stand, the isolated cells begin crawling about and aggregating themselves into larger masses. These masses then become organized into new sponges. Among the isolated cells one can distinguish the archeocytes, the collar cells and the dermal cells of the adult sponge. When the cells reaggregate, each type of cells sorts itself out and takes up in the aggregate a position which belongs to it because of its specific properties: the dermal cells cover the whole aggregate from without; the collar cells join together and rebuild the collar cell chambers in the inside. The archeocytes take up their normal position; they also play an active part in the formation of the complex, owing to their greater ability for ameboid movement; their rate of movement is 0.6 to 3.5 μ per minute. Moving about, the archeocytes help the other cells to aggregate. About 2000 cells are necessary to produce a new individual (Galtsoff, 1925). The whole process, up to the opening of new oscula, takes about three weeks.

The phenomenon has been called **reconstitution**. Although reconstitution starts from individual cells, it has nothing in common with embryonic development, as the individual cells into which the sponge is broken up each retain their specific histologic character, and the whole process rests mainly on a rearrangement of the cells in space rather than on a progressive differentiation, although minor readjustments may possibly occur. The whole process can thus best be compared to regeneration by morphallaxis (see section 19–2).

Reconstitution by reaggregation of isolated cells as observed in adult sponges bears an obvious relationship to the reaggregation of embryonic cells which has been described in sections 9–1 and 16–5 and shows that the mechanisms of differential cellular affinity are present and active throughout the life of a metazoon, even if we do not always observe them. It would probably not be too far-fetched to say that these mechanisms, after having participated in producing a multicellular organism, serve to maintain it and preserve its integrity.

Asexual Reproduction

Asexual reproduction is the development of a new individual without the participation of any stages of the sexual cycle, that is, without maturation and copulation of sex cells with concomitant reduction of the number of chromosomes in meiosis. As applied to multicellular animals, asexual reproduction means development of new individuals at the expense of **somatic** cells — cells of the **soma**, or body, as opposed to generative or sex cells (**gametes**).

In this chapter we shall not be concerned with the evolution and adaptive significance of asexual reproduction; neither shall we deal with the factors regulating the alternation of sexual and asexual reproductive cycles. What will interest us is how a part of an already differentiated organism may again embark on an active process of morphogenesis. The part of the parental organism giving rise to a new individual in asexual reproduction may be called a **blastema**, and it always consists of a group of cells, whereas in sexual reproduction the new individual develops from one cell — the fertilized or parthenogenetically activated ovum. The development that starts from a blastema may be termed **blastogenesis** as opposed to **embryogenesis**, or development from the ovum. The individuals resulting from asexual reproduction are often referred to as **blastozooids**; individuals developing from an egg are then termed **oozooids**.

The blastozooids may have the same general organization as oozooids or they may even be indistinguishable from the latter. How this is achieved, in spite of the profoundly different initial stages, is the second major problem in relation to asexual reproduction.

20–1 OCCURRENCE AND FORMS OF ASEXUAL REPRODUCTION

Asexual reproduction takes on a variety of forms, largely because of the amount of tissue set aside for the production of a new individual and, correlated with this, the degree of organization of this tissue. Taking the size of the fragment and the degree of its organization as a guiding principle, we may subdivide the infinite multiplicity of modifications occurring in different Metazoa into three main types:

1. Fission—the new individual is formed from a relatively large portion of the body of the maternal organism, and differentiated organs and tissues or their parts are passed on to the offspring.
2. Budding—the new individual develops from a small outgrowth on the surface of the parent. No organs of the parent are passed on as such to the offspring, but the bud is supported by the parental organism at least during the initial stages of its development.
3. Gemmule formation—the new individual develops from groups of cells which become completely cut off from the maternal individual and disseminated, so that the development is, from the start, quite independent of the maternal body.

Fission.   The simplest form of fission is the separation of an adult individual into two parts of approximately equal size, similar to the binary fission in protozoans. In Metazoa it occurs in the most typical form in coelenterates and worms. In some corals (Anthozoa) fission occurs in the rather

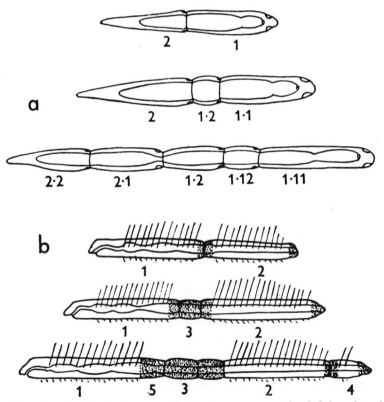

Figure 434.   Reproduction by transverse fission in worms: *a*, in the rhabdocoele turbellarian *Stenostomum* (after Child); *b*, in the oligochaete *Nais* (after Stolte). The numbers show the succession in the formation of the individual blastozooids. (From Berrill, 1952.)

rare form of longitudinal fission, with the division plane in the long axis of the body. Fission also occurs in some brittle stars, as for instance in *Ophiactis savignyi*, in which parental individuals break across the disc, and each half then proceeds to regenerate the missing half of the disc and three arms. In the worms (see Berrill, 1952), the planes of division are transverse to the body axis, so that the worm is divided into anterior and posterior halves. This type of reproduction is found in rhabdocoele turbellarians and in annelids, both polychaetes and oligochaetes. Both halves inherit from the parent the skin, a section of the alimentary canal, sections of the nerve cord, and, in annelids, a number of mesodermal segments, with muscles and nephridia, and correspondingly, sections of parenchymatous mesoderm in rhabdocoeles. The posterior individual is at first devoid of a head and therefore lacks initially the supraesophageal ganglion, sense organs (eyes), tentacles and mouth parts, where these occur. The head is produced either subsequent to division or, more often, in preparation for the division, so that the posterior individual is fully developed when the two blastozooids separate.

In rhabdocoeles and some oligochaetes, new fissions may be started by one or both filial individuals even before they are separated from one another (Fig. 434). The result is a chain of blastozooids, some of them in different stages of reconstitution (degree of head development). The division may also be very unequal, so that of the two or several zooids one may be clearly distinguishable as the parent and the other, or others, as offspring.

Cases in which subsequent transverse divisions occur prior to the earlier divisions being completed lead to a special form of transverse fission, known as **strobilation**, in which numerous transverse divisions occur more or less simultaneously or in close succession, giving rise to a number of filial blastozooids. This is the classical method of propagation by which, in Scyphozoa, the asexual polypoid generation gives rise to the sexual medusoid generation. Similar multiple transverse division occurs in some polychaetes and also in ascidians (see Berrill, 1951). In the latter, the part undergoing transverse division is the abdominal section of the body, which is devoid of the branchial chamber but contains the intestinal loop.

Both in worms and in ascidians, the initial separation of the zooids is performed through the activity of the ectodermal epidermis. The epidermis forms a circular constriction which cuts inward, severs the internal organs and eventually cuts the body of the animal in two (Fig. 435; Berrill, 1951, 1952).

Figure 435. The initial stages of transverse division in annelids. *a, Pristina; b, Chaetogaster.* The epidermal thickenings are clearly indicated. (From Berrill, 1952.)

Budding.   The most typical examples of budding are found in coelenterates and tunicates. Superficially, the early bud appears as a small swelling or nodule on the lateral surface of the body of the parental animal. The nodule grows, takes shape and develops a mouth and a whorl of perioral tentacles, in the case of the coelenterates, or in the tunicates develops a branchial chamber and other associated structures including the atrial cavity and the oral and atrial siphons. The bud may become completely separated from the maternal body or remain permanently in connection with the latter, thus leading to the formation of a colony. In the fresh-water hydra, which normally exists in the form of single polyps, the daughter individuals may remain connected to the maternal body and occasionally even start forming secondary buds, but eventually this temporary colony splits into single individuals.

Not always are the buds directly formed on the body of the parental zooids. Often the buds develop on special outgrowths of the maternal animals; the outgrowths are then called **stolons**. These are typically present in many tunicates, but the branches of a hydrozoan colony on which the polyps develop have the same significance.

Gemmule Formation.   This form of asexual reproduction is found in fresh-water sponges and in bryozoans, and in both cases bodies are produced— called **gemmules** in sponges and **statoblasts** in bryozoans—that can survive after the maternal individual (or rather maternal colony) dies off during an unfavorable season (winter in temperate countries, periods of drought in warmer climates). The gemmules and statoblasts are formed in the interior of the parental body from a number of undifferentiated cells, which become enclosed in a shell with special spicules in sponges (Fig. 436) or in a chitinous envelope in bryozoans. On destruction of the parental body, the gemmules or statoblasts are set free, and after conditions have become favorable, the cells contained inside burst out and develop a new individual. For the

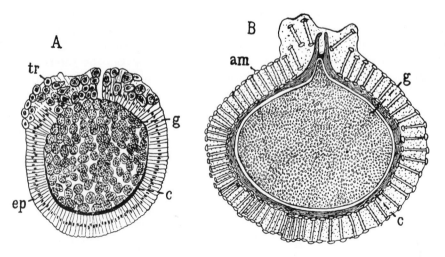

Figure 436.   Gemmule of the sponge *Ephydatia: A*, in the process of formation; *B*, in the mature stage. *am*, Amphidiscs; *c*, cuticular membrane; *ep*, epithelium; *g*, archeocytes; *tr*, trophocytes. (After Evans, from Bounoure, 1940.)

gemmules of sponges, such favorable conditions are created by the temperature rising above 16° C. (Brien, 1932).

20 – 2 SOURCES OF CELLULAR MATERIAL IN ASEXUAL REPRODUCTION

The major problem with which we are faced in asexual reproduction is: what resources does a differentiated organism have in order to start building new parts in a new burst of morphogenetic activity?

The least difficulty in interpreting the development of new parts is encountered in asexual reproduction by **fission**. It will be evident from what has been said before that reproduction by fission is closely related to regeneration, or, to put it another way, regeneration is an essential part of asexual reproduction by fission. In both cases, a comparatively large part of the body is isolated and reconstructed into a new complete whole by the regeneration of the missing parts. There is every reason to believe that the actual mechanism of development of the missing parts is the same in the two cases. We have seen that the organs which are produced anew during regeneration in annelids and in turbellarians owe their origin in large measure to undifferentiated "reserve" cells: neoblasts in annelids, parenchyme cells in turbellarians (see pp. 599-600). The same cells are available for the development of missing parts in daughter zooids. Neoblasts are actually reported to concentrate in the fission zone of oligochaetes. As in regeneration, the epidermis gives rise to the nervous system and sense organs in the new head of the posterior zooid.

Where transverse fission occurs as a form of asexual reproduction in ascidians such as *Eudistoma* (Berrill, 1951), the daughter zooids consist of a section of the parent's body, including epidermis, mesenchyme and a section of the intestinal tube, but do not include the branchial chamber and associated structures such as the atrial cavity, the nerve ganglia and the siphons. The missing parts are replaced by regeneration.

In the process of regeneration, a most important role is played by the **epicardium** — a mesodermal tube lying ventral to the intestine (Fig. 437). The mesodermal lining of the epicardium has the properties of an undifferentiated reserve tissue, at the expense of which most of the internal organs in the anterior part of the new zooid develop. Remarkably enough, the branchial chamber does not regenerate at the expense of the remaining part of the endodermal alimentary canal but is also produced by the epicardium and secondarily becomes fused onto the endodermal esophagus.

In **budding**, only very little of the organization of the parent is passed on to the daughter zooid. In a scyphozoan polyp, the first sign of impending budding is the formation of a pocketlike evagination of the endodermal epithelium which pushes through the mesoglea and reaches the ectodermal layer. The ectodermal layer now becomes activated, and both ectoderm and endoderm form a conical protrusion on the surface of the body. This protrusion gradually increases and elongates and becomes a cylindrical body with an internal cavity which is in open communication with the gastric cavity of the parent (Gilchrist, 1937). At a later stage, a mouth is formed at the tip of the bud, and a whorl of tentacles develops around it; the bud has become a new polyp.

Figure 437. Reproduction by transverse fission in the tunicate *Eudistoma*. *a*, Individual in the process of fission. *b, c*, Blastozooid regenerating the anterior end. *d*, Newly metamorphosed oozooid. *at*, Atrial siphon; *br*, oral siphon; *c*, constrictions; *en*, endostyle; *ep*, epicardium; *es*, esophagus; *ht*, heart, *r*, rectum; *sg*, gill clefts; *t*, remnant of tail. (From Berrill, 1947.)

    The budding in hydrozoan polyps is essentially similar. From this one would tend to draw the conclusion that if not the pattern of organization then at least the two main layers of the body, the ectoderm and the endoderm of the daughter zooid, are directly taken over from the parental organism. The majority of students of coelenterate development and reproduction believe, however, that the process is not nearly so simple (see Hadzi, 1909; Schulze, 1918; Weiler-Stolt, 1960). We have seen that regeneration in the hydra is due in part to the activity of so-called interstitial cells, small undifferentiated cells located between the larger functioning cells both of the ectoderm and endoderm (compare p. 597). These cells serve for the replacement of differentiated cells, especially of the cnidoblast cells, and in cases of injury the interstitial cells assemble in the regeneration blastema. The same interstitial cells are supposed to be the main source for the formation of the bud in asexual reproduction. The interstitial cells either accumulate locally and form the first thickening which is to become the bud, or possibly they infiltrate the bud in the process of its formation and continue flowing into the bud and increasing its size even after it has been formed. Eventually the whole or almost the whole of the daughter zooid is built from interstitial cells, the differentiated ectodermal and endodermal cells taking very little, if any, part (Fig. 438; Weiler-Stolt, 1960).

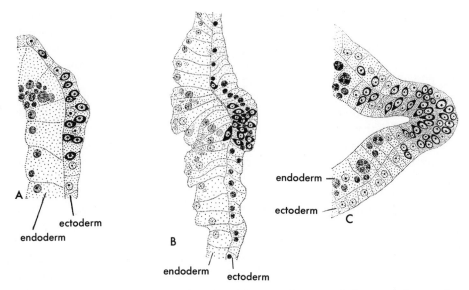

Figure 438.   Three stages of development of a bud in the polyp *Cladonema radiatum*, showing the aggregation of interstitial cells (black) in the bud. The endoderm is initially free of
interstitial cells (*A*) but becomes invaded by these cells later (in *B* and *C*). (From Weiler-Stolt,
1960.)

In Hydromedusae *(Lizzia claparedi, Rathkea octopunctata*—see Bounoure, 1940), it was observed that endoderm does not contribute to the formation of the bud at all. The bud is at first represented by a nodule of cells in the
ectodermal layer. Some of the cells lying in the interior of the nodule become
arranged in the form of a vesicle, and it is from this vesicle that the endoderm
of the daughter medusa becomes developed (Fig. 439). This observation can
be better understood if it is accepted that in the hydrozoans a new zooid is
derived neither from the endoderm nor from the ectoderm of the parent but
from the undifferentiated interstitial cells, an interpretation which has been
proved by direct observation (Weiler-Stolt, 1960).

The budding in tunicates presents an almost infinite variety of forms, but
in the great majority of these animals—in particular, in the ascidians—there
is a very distinct common pattern which presents some remarkable features.

Figure 439.   Development of a bud in the medusa *Rathkea. ec,* Ectoderm; *en,* endoderm.
(After Chun, from Bounoure, 1940.)

The bud is essentially an outgrowth of the ectodermal epidermis, supported by another tissue which forms a hollow vesicle inside the outgrowth. In some cases, parts of the gonads are included as a third element. The epidermis of tunicates is a very specialized tissue which produces the mantle, the cellulose layer covering the surface of the skin in these animals. In budding, the epidermis produces only more epidermis and provides the external covering for the blastozooid. The internal organs are developed from the previously mentioned vesicle formed inside the bud. Now it is most remarkable that the inner vesicle may be derived from a number of different tissues, namely: (1) an outgrowth of the atrial cavity (*Botryllus*); (2) an outgrowth from the pharyngeal wall at the posterior end of the endostyle (*Salpa, Pyrosoma*); (3) an outgrowth of the epicardium, which was already mentioned before (*Distaplia*); or (4) a group of blood cells (*Botryllus;* Oka and Watanabe, 1957). All these types of development are found in cases in which the bud is developed on the body of the parent or on a short stolon connected to the body.

In some ascidians (*Clavellina, Perophora*), the buds develop on long rhizoidlike stolons. These consist only of epidermis and a longitudinal mesodermal septum, splitting the cavity of the stolon into two canals which allow for the backward and forward circulation of blood. Buds developing on such a stolon consist of the epidermal covering epithelium and the inner vesicle, which in this case is produced from the cells of the mesodermal septum (Fig. 440; see Berrill, 1951).

Regardless of the origin of the internal vesicle, it produces a variety of organs and tissues: the alimentary canal with the branchial chamber, the atrial cavities, the heart, the nervous system (except in *Salpa*), and sometimes also the gonads. It is thus evident that several parts in the fully differentiated body of an ascidian retain very wide potentialities for development. These potentialities embrace practically the whole organization of the ascidian except the epidermis, and even of this limitation we cannot be sure, as the epidermis is always provided and so there would appear to be no incentive for the inner vesicle to produce the epidermis as well. It may well

Figure 440. Budding from the stolon in the tunicate *Perophora. e,* Endostyle; *h,* heart; *s,* stolonial septum. (From Berrill, 1935.)

be that the potentiality for forming epidermis is not lacking, and then the cells of the inner vesicle would be truly **totipotent**—capable of producing every differentiation found in the animal species in question.

The existence of really totipotent cells is indisputable in the case of **gemmule formation** in the fresh-water sponges. The first rudiment of a gemmule in the interior of the sponge appears in the form of an accumulation of archeocytes—undifferentiated ameboid cells which are dispersed in between the differentiated elements of the body of a sponge. Around the central core, consisting of archeocytes, other migrating cells are lodged and become arranged in the form of a columnar epithelium. The role of the epithelium is to produce the shell on the surface of the gemmule. This is strengthened by the action of special skeleton building cells—**scleroblasts**—which deposit in the shell peculiar spicules, the amphidiscs (see Fig. 436). Both the columnar epithelial cells and the scleroblasts are later withdrawn or they degenerate. A small opening, the micropyle, remains temporarily open in the shell. It has been claimed that feeder cells, **trophocytes**, enter the interior of the developing gemmule and pass on food reserves to the archeocytes and in their turn disappear. The archeocytes, on the other hand, accumulate in their cytoplasm food reserves consisting of glycoproteins in the form of discoidal platelets (see Fig. 443). When the development of the gemmule is completed, the archeocytes are the only living cells left in it, and all the tissues and cell types in the new sponge which develop eventually from the gemmule, including its sex cells, are derived from the archeocytes.

Summing up our review of the sources of materials for asexual reproduction, we see that the renewal of morphogenetic processes depends on the persistence, in the body of the adult animals, of cells which do not become as highly differentiated as the rest and are capable of developing into a variety of cell types. The role of these undifferentiated or "reserve" cells is the greater, the smaller the part of the parental body that is used in asexual propagation. In extreme cases, the undifferentiated cells are totipotent and are in this respect equivalent to the egg cell, a similarity which may be further enhanced by the presence of deutoplasmic (food reserve) inclusions, as in the case of the gemmules of sponges.

Although asexual reproduction is a special form of morphogenesis which has been acquired, probably independently, only in some groups of the animal kingdom, it is evident from the above that it falls back on a very general property of all developing organisms: the potential equivalence of the daughter cells resulting from the cleavage of the fertilized egg. We have seen (section 7–5) that the cleavage cells retain the full complement of hereditary factors (genome) independently of the prospective significance of the individual cells, and that the nuclei are unrestricted in their potencies even after determination of the various areas of the embryo has set in (p. 145). The cytoplasm of cleavage cells may show differences in early stages, and later the elaboration of special cytoplasmic mechanisms (histological differentiation) may go so far that the specific types of cells lose the ability to change the direction of their development. The loss of plasticity, however, is not inevitable; neither does it proceed at an equal tempo in all parts and in all cells of a differentiated organism. Cells which do not achieve a high degree of differentiation retain their plasticity and, being in possession of the complete genome, can be made use of in asexual reproduction (see Bounoure, 1940).

20–3 COMPARISON OF BLASTOGENESIS AND EMBRYOGENESIS

In the general survey of ontogenetic development (section 1–2), we have found it useful to consider what tasks have to be performed by the embryo before the final condition (the development of the new adult individual) is achieved. If from this same viewpoint we compare embryogenesis (development of the egg) with blastogenesis (development from a blastema in asexual reproduction), we see at once that the task is very much simpler in the latter case.

The process of producing a new individual is simplest in reproduction by fission, when the blastozooid is derived from half the parental organism and in this way is provided with a large proportion of the organs and parts which are necessary for making the new individual self-sufficient. What has to be done is the regeneration of missing parts. The whole mechanism of regeneration, as considered in Chapter 19, is brought into play, including the factors determining the regenerating parts (pp. 611-615). The remnant of the old individual determines the nature, position and orientation of the newly differentiated organs. The polarity and bilaterality of the parent organism prevail in the blastozooids.

The task of development is more complicated in the case of budding, since all organs and differentiated parts of the blastozooid have to be produced anew. Nevertheless the initial system, the bud, always has a higher degree of complexity than a fertilized egg or even than a blastula as it occurs in embryogenesis. A typical bud, as we have explained above, always consists of two layers of epithelial cells. The young zooid is thus already in possession of the concentric stratification of body layers, a condition which in embryogenesis is achieved only after gastrulation. It is very noteworthy, however, that the layers formed in the blastozooid do not necessarily correspond to the germinal layers developing in embryogenesis.

In the case of budding in coelenterates, there is a closer correspondence between the outer and inner layer of the bud and the ectoderm and endoderm of the gastrula. The fate of the two layers is the same, but we have seen that the inner layer may be derived not from the endodermal epithelium of the parent, but from a thickening in the ectodermal epithelium (in all probability it is actually produced by the reserve interstitial cells).

When we turn to the buds of tunicates, we find that the inner vesicle corresponds to the endoderm neither in its origin nor its fate. It has been shown (p. 623) that, although in some tunicates the inner vesicle may be derived from the endoderm of the parent (in the form of an outgrowth from the pharyngeal epithelium), it can be also derived from mesoderm (epicardium, mesodermal septum of the stolon, blood cells) or even ectoderm (lining of the atrial cavity). What is even more important, the inner vesicle gives rise to parts derived in embryogenesis from any of the three germinal layers. In spite of the diversity of origin of the inner vesicle, its later differentiation shows a considerable degree of uniformity in different tunicates. After the bud has grown to a certain degree—a minimal size, varying of course in different species, is essential (Berrill, 1941), it becomes constricted at least partially from the parent zooid. Then folds start subdividing the inner vesicle into sections. (The following description refers to the development of the blastozooid in *Botryllus*.)

First of all, two folds cut in from what will be the distal part of the new zooid, subdividing the inner vesicle into a median part, which will become the branchial chamber, and two lateral parts, which give rise to the atrial cavity (Fig. 441). (In embryogenesis, the atrial cavity develops as a pair of invaginations of the ectoderm which partially fuse and later have a common opening to the exterior.) In addition to these three main subdivisions, further smaller pocketlike evaginations of the vesicle appear. One evagination, near the anterior end of the central cavity, gives rise to the nerve center. (In embryogenesis, the nerve ganglion is a remnant of the neural tube formed by infolding of the ectodermal neural plate, as in *Amphioxus* and in vertebrates.) Two pockets at the posterior end give rise to the intestinal loop (including the esophagus and the stomach) and to the pericardium, respectively. (In embryogenesis the intestine is, of course, of endodermal origin and the pericardium develops from mesodermal mesenchyme.) The initial state of the system in blastogenesis being not the same as that in embryogenesis, the course of development is different. The morphogenetic processes in budding appear to be simpler and more straightforward than in embryogenesis; the actively developing part, which is the inner vesicle (the epidermis of the bud is a differentiated tissue all the time, specialized in secreting the cellulose mantle), proceeds directly to the formation of organ rudiments, omitting the stage of germ layer development.

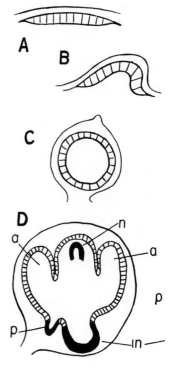

Figure 441. Development of the bud in *Botryllus. a*, Rudiment of atrial cavity; *in*, rudiment of intestine; *n*, rudiment of ganglion; *p*, rudiment of pericardium. (From Berrill, 1951.)

In one further respect the morphogenetic processes in budding are simpler than in embryogenesis: the new individual inherits its polarity direct from the parent zooid. The point of attachment of the bud to the maternal body or the stolon always becomes the proximal end of the blastozooid.

In the development of gemmules, the task of producing a new individual becomes most complicated and approaches that of the development of the egg. The special difficulties encountered are:

1. The germination of the gemmule occurs after the death and decomposition of the parent animal; consequently, the polarity of the new individual has to be worked out by itself, and the parent body is no longer there to influence the polarity of the offspring.

2. The complete homogeneity of the contents of the gemmule (in the case of the gemmules of sponges) deprives the new individual of any remnant of morphological organization. The structure of the new sponge has to be established by the interaction of practically independent cells.

As has been shown (p. 625), the interior of the gemmule consists of only one type of cell—the archeocytes, which are rather large cells containing platelets of glycoprotein. Even before the germination of the gemmule, some of the archeocytes become activated; they start dividing and in so doing give rise to smaller and smaller cells, very much like the blastomeres which diminish in size as cleavage progresses. The glycoprotein platelets gradually disappear; the nuclei become richer in chromatin, as is usual in actively growing and metabolizing cells. These small and active cells have been referred to as **histioblasts**—cells producing tissues (Brien, 1932). When the gemmule germinates, the contents of the gemmule crawl out through the micropyle and form an irregular mass, surrounding the empty shell of the gemmule (Fig. 442, *a*). Both the histioblasts and the remaining glycoprotein-containing archeocytes leave the shell. Outside the shell, the divisions of archeocytes and their conversion into histioblasts continue (Fig. 443). The histioblasts now become arranged into an irregular meshwork (Fig. 442, *b*), cavities appear, and some of the histioblasts surrounding these cavities differ-

Figure 442. Germination of gemmules. *left,* Contents of the gemmule of *Spongilla,* leaving the shell. *right,* Transformation of the contents of the gemmule of *Ephydatia* into a new sponge. (From Brien, 1932.)

entiate into choanocytes. Other histioblasts become epidermal cells, sclero-blasts, pore cells or mesenchyme cells arranged in a typical way, so that the mass of cells soon becomes a small sponge, with a system of internal canals with ciliated chambers, ostia, etc.

Figure 443. Transformation of archeocytes into histioblasts during development of a new sponge from a gemmule. Archeocytes still with deutoplasmic inclusions; one is in mitosis. (From Brien, 1932.)

It may be significant that the sponges are capable of reconstituting their structure after complete disaggregation, as has been described in section 19–9. The development of the gemmule proceeds along very much the same lines; the development is direct in the extreme, the individual cells differentiating and taking up their positions in the whole.

A review of different forms of asexual reproduction reveals a principle of general significance. It shows that the complexity of morphogenetic processes is largely determined by the degree of difference that exists between the initial stage of development and the final condition. The initial stage in embryogenesis is a single cell; therefore a period of cleavage is necessary, which brings the system into a multicellular condition. In asexual reproduction, the initial system is already multicellular and cleavage falls away. (Something resembling cleavage occurs, as has been indicated, in the gemmules of sponges, where the archeocytes accumulate food reserves, similarly to oocytes in the ovary.) In asexual reproduction, the initial system may have the cells arranged in more than one layer, and this makes gastrulation dispensable. What remains of the main periods of development outlined in section 1–2 are: organogenesis, differentiation and growth.

A second very suggestive fact which emerges from a study of asexual reproduction is that, given normal environment, the organization of the animal's body is entirely determined, in the last instance, by the hereditary constitution of the species-specific cells. The structure of the egg cell with its polarity and heterogeneous arrangement of cytoplasmic substances is a mechanism which provides for the orderly course of differentiation of the cells in a developing embryo. This mechanism is, however, dispensable; the same end product can be attained starting from a different initial constellation, provided that the cells have the same hereditary constitution. In principle, the orderly organization of an animal's body should be attainable by the interaction of an assortment of different types of cells produced on the basis of species-specific hereditary potentialities (compare the reaggregation of cell suspensions, section 16–5); in practice, this is possible only in relatively very simple biological systems.

References[*]

ABELOOS, M., 1956. Les métamorphoses. Armand Collin, Paris.

ABELSON, J., 1963. Transfer of genetic information. Science 139, 774–776.

ABRAMS, R., 1951. Synthesis of nucleic acid purines in the sea urchin embryo. Exp. Cell Res. 2, 235–242.

ADELMANN, H. B., 1932. The development of the prechordal plate and mesoderm of Amblystoma punctatum. J. Morph. 54, 1–67.

———, 1936. The problem of cyclopia. I. II. Quart. Rev. Biol. 11, 161–182, 284–304.

———, 1937. Experimental studies on the development of the eye. IV. The effect of the partial and complete excision of the prechordal substrate on the development of the eyes of Amblystoma punctatum. J. exp. Zool. 75, 199–237.

ADLER, L., 1914. Metamorphosestudien an Batrachierlarven. Roux Arch. 39, 21–45.

AFZELIUS, B. A., 1956. The ultrastructure of the cortical granules and their products in the sea urchin egg as studied with the electron microscope. Exp. Cell Res. 10, 257–285.

———, 1959. Electron microscopy of the sperm tail. Results obtained with a new fixative. J. Biophys. Biochem. Cytol. 5, 269–278.

ALBAUM, H. G., and NESTLER, H. A., 1937. Xenoplastic ear induction between Rana pipiens and Amblystoma punctatum. J. exp. Zool. 75, 1–9.

ALDERMAN, A. L., 1935. The determination of the eye in the anuran Hyla regilla. J. exp. Zool. 70, 205–232.

———, 1938. A factor influencing the bilaterality of the eye rudiment in Hyla regilla. Anat. Rec. 72, 297–302.

ALFERT, M., and SWIFT, H., 1953. Nuclear DNA constancy: a critical evaluation of some exceptions reported by Lison and Pasteels. Exp. Cell. Res. 5, 455–460.

ALLEN, B. M., 1918. The results of thyroid removal in larvae of Rana pipiens. J. exp. Zool. 24, 499–519.

———, 1929. The influence of the thyroid and hypophysis upon growth and development of amphibian larvae. Quart. Rev. Biol. 4, 325–352.

———, 1938. The endocrine control of amphibian metamorphosis. Biol. Rev. 13, 1–19.

ALLFREY, V. G., and MIRSKY, A. E., 1961. How cells make molecules. Sci. Amer. 205(3), 74–82.

———, LITTAU, V. C., and MIRSKY, A. E., 1963. On the role of histones in regulating ribonucleic acid synthesis in the cell nucleus. Proc. Nat. Acad. Sci. (Wash.) 49, 414–421.

---

[*]For brevity the title of the journal "Wilhelm Roux' Archiv für Entwicklungsmechanik der Organismen," previously "Archiv für Entwicklungsmechanik der Organismen," is given as "Roux Arch." Other abbreviations are according to W. A. Smith, F. L. Kent, and G. B. Stratton. 1952, World List of Scientific Periodicals, Butterworth, London.

ANCEL, P., and VINTEMBERGER, P., 1948. Recherches sur le déterminisme de la symétrie bilaterale dans l'oeuf des amphibiens. Bull. biol. Suppl. *31*, 1–182.

ANDERSON, E., and BEAMS, H. W., 1960. Cytological observations on the fine structure of the guinea pig ovary with special reference to the oogonium, primary oocyte and associated follicle cells. J. Ultrastruct. Research, *3*, 432–446.

ANDRÉ, J., and ROUILLER, C., 1957. The ultrastructure of the vitelline body in the oocyte of the spider *Tegenaria parietina*. J. Biophys. Biochem. Cytol. 3, 977–984.

ANDRES, G., 1953. Experiments on the fate of dissociated embryonic cells (chick) disseminated by the vascular route. Part II. Teratomas. J. exp. Zool. *122*, 507–540.

ANDREW, A., 1963. A study of the developmental relationship between enterochromaffin cells and the neural crest. J. Embr. Exp. Morph. *11*, 307–324.

ANTON, H. J., 1961. Zur Frage der Aktivierung der Gewebe im Extremitätenstumpf bei Urodelen vor der Blastembildung. Roux Arch. *153*, 363–369.

AREY, L. B., 1947. Developmental anatomy. 5th ed. Saunders, Philadelphia.

———, 1954. Developmental anatomy. 6th ed. Saunders, Philadelphia.

AUSTIN, C. R., 1961. The mammalian egg. Blackwell Scientific Publications, Oxford.

BACON, R. L., 1945. Self-differentiation and induction in the heart of *Amblystoma*. J. exp. Zool. *98*, 87–121.

BAER, K. E. VON, 1828. Ueber Entwicklungsgeschichte der Tiere, Beobachtung und Reflexion. Königsberg.

BALFOUR, F. M., 1880. A treatise on comparative embryology. Macmillan Co., London.

BALINSKY, B. I., 1925. Transplantation des Ohrbläschens bei *Triton*. Roux Arch. *105*, 718–731.

———, 1931. Zur Dynamik der Extremitätenknospenbildung. Roux Arch. *123*, 565–648.

———, 1933. Das Extremitätenseitenfeld, seine Ausdehnung und Beschaffenheit. Roux Arch. *130*, 704–747.

———, 1939. Experiments on total extirpation of the whole entoderm in *Triton* embryos. C.R. Acad. Sci. URSS *23*, 196–198.

———, 1947. Kinematik des entodermalen Materials bei der Gestaltung der wichtigsten Teile des Darmkanals bei den Amphibien. Roux Arch. *143*, 126–166.

———, 1948. Korrelationen in der Entwicklung der Mund- und Kiemenregion und des Darmkanals bei Amphibien. Roux Arch. *143*, 365–395.

———, 1950. On the developmental processes in mammary glands and other epidermal structures. Trans. roy. Soc. Edinb. *62*, 1–31.

———, 1951. On the eye cup–lens correlation in some South African amphibians. Experientia 7, 180.

———, 1956. Discussion of Dr. Zwilling's paper. Cold Spr. Harb. Symp. quant. Biol., *21*, 354.

———, 1958. On the factors controlling the size of the brain and eyes in anuran embryos. J. exp. Zool. *139*, 403–442.

———, 1961a. The role of cortical granules in the formation of the fertilization membrane and the surface membrane of fertilized sea urchin eggs. Symp. on Germ Cells and Development, Inst. Internat. d' Embryologie and Fondazione A. Baselli, Pavia, 205–219.

———, 1961b. Ultrastructural mechanisms of gastrulation and neurulation. Symp. on Germ Cells and Development, Inst. Internat. d'Embryologie and Fondazione A. Baselli, Pavia, 550–563.

——— and DEVIS, R. J., 1963. Origin and differentiation of cytoplasmic structures in the oocytes of *Xenopus laevis*. Acta Embryol. et Morphol. Exper. *6*, 55–108.

——— and WALTHER, H., 1961. The immigration of presumptive mesoblast from the primitive streak in the chick as studied with the electron microscope. Acta Embryol. et Morphol. Exper. *4*, 261–283.

BALTZER, F., 1940. Ueber erbliche letale Entwicklung und Austauschbarkeit artverschiedener Kerne bei Bastarden. Naturwissenschaften *28*, 177–187, 196–206.

———, 1941. Ueber die Pigmentierung merogonisch-haploider Bastarde zwischen der schwarzen und weissen Axolotlrasse. Verh. schweiz. naturf. Ges. 121 Jahresvers, Basel, 169–179.

BANDIER, J., 1937. Histologische Untersuchungen über die Regeneration von Landplanarien. Roux Arch. *135*, 316–348.

BANKI, O., 1929. Die Entstehung der äusseren Zeichen der bilateralen Symmetrie am Axolotlei nach Versuchen mit örtlicher Vitalfärbung. Verh. X. int. Zool. Kongr. Budapest.

BARR, G. C., and BUTLER, J. A. V., 1963. Histones and gene function. Nature (Lond.), *199*, 1170–1172.

BARTH, L. G., 1940. The process of regeneration in hydroids. Biol. Rev. *15*, 405–420.

—— and BARTH, L. J., 1954. The energetics of development. Columbia University Press, New York.

BATAILLON, E., 1910. L'embryogenèse complète provoquée chez les Amphibiens par picûre de l'oeuf vierge, larves parthénogénétiques de *Rana fusca*. C. R. Acad. Sci. Paris. *150*, 996.

BATTEN, E. H., 1958. The origin of the acoustic ganglion in the sheep. J. Embr. exp. Morph. *6*, 597–615.

BAUTZMANN, H., 1926. Experimentelle Untersuchungen zur Abgrenzung des Organisationszentrums bei *Triton taeniatus*, mit einem Anhang: Ueber Induktion durch Blàstulamaterial. Roux Arch. *108*, 283–321.

——, HOLTFRETER, J., SPEMANN, H., and MANGOLD, O., 1932. Versuche zur Analyse der Induktionsmittel in der Embryonalentwicklung. Naturwissenschaften 971–974.

BEATTY, R. A., 1957. Parthenogenesis and polyploidy in mammalian development. University Press, Cambridge.

BECKER, H. J., 1962. Die Puffs der Speicheldrüsenchromosomen von *Drosophila melanogaster*. II Mitteilung. Die Auslösung der Puffbildung, ihre Spezifität und ihre Beziehung zur Funktion der Ringdrüse. Chromosoma (Berl.) *13*, 341–384.

BEER, G. R. DE, 1947. The differentiation of neural crest cells into visceral cartilages and odontoblasts in *Amblystoma*, and a re-examination of the germ layer theory. Proc. roy. Soc. B *134*, 377–398.

BEERMANN, W., and CLEVER, U., 1964. Chromosome puffs. Sci. Amer. *210*(4), 50–58.

BELLAIRS, R., 1953. Studies on the development of the foregut in the chick blastoderm. 2. The morphogenetic movements. J. Embr. exp. Morph. *1*, 369–385.

——, 1961. The structure of the yolk of the hen's egg as studied by electron microscopy. I. The yolk of the unincubated egg. J. Biophys. Biochem. Cytol. *11*, 207–225.

——, 1963. Personal communication.

——, 1964. Biological aspects of the yolk in the hen's egg. In Abercrombie, M., and Brachet, J. (Eds.): Advances in morphogenesis, *4*. Academic Press, New York, 217–272.

——, HARKNESS, M., and HARKNESS, R. D., 1963. The vitelline membrane of the hen's egg: a chemical and electron microscopic study. J. Ultrastruct. Research *8*, 339–359.

BERRILL, N. J., 1935. Studies on tunicate development. III. Differential retardation and acceleration. Phil. Trans. B *225*, 255–379.

——, 1941. Size and morphogenesis in the bud of *Botryllus*. Biol. Bull. Woods Hole *80*, 185–193.

——, 1947. The structure, development and budding of the ascidian *Eudistoma*. J. Morph. *81*, 269–281.

——, 1951. Regeneration and budding in tunicates. Biol. Rev. *26*, 456–475.

——, 1952. Regeneration and budding in worms. Biol. Rev. *27*, 401–438.

BERTALANFFY, L. VON, 1948. Das organische Wachstum und seine Gesetzmässigkeiten. Experientia *4*, 255.

——, 1949. Problems of organic growth. Nature (Lond.) *163*, 156–158.

BIER, K., 1963. Autoradiographische Untersuchungen über die Leistungen des Follikelepithels und der Nährzellen bei der Dotterbildung und Eiweisssynthese im Fliegenovar. Roux Arch. *154*, 552–575.

BIJTEL, J. H., 1931. Ueber die Entwicklung des Schwanzes bei Amphibien. Roux Arch. *125*, 448–486.

——, 1936. Die Mesodermbildungspotenzen der hinteren Medullarplattenbezirke bei *Amblystoma mexicanum* in bezug auf die Schwanzbildung. Roux Arch. *134*, 262–282.

BIRBECK, M. S. C., and MERCER, E. H., 1957. Electron microscopic, x-ray and birefringence studies on the proteins of the hair follicle. In SJÖSTRAND, F. S., and RHODIN, J.: Electron microscopy. Almqvist and Wiksell. Stockholm, 158–160.

BLACKLER, A. W., 1958. Contribution to the study of germ-cells in the anura J. Embr. exp. Morph. *6*, 491–503.

——, 1962. Transfer of primordial germ-cells between two subspecies of *Xenopus laevis*. J. Embr. exp. Morph. *10*, 641–651.

—— and FISCHBERG, M., 1961. Transfer of primordial germ-cells in *Xenopus laevis*. J. Embr. exp. Morph. *9*, 634–641.

BLANCHETTE, E. J., 1961. A study of the fine structure of rabbit primary oocyte. J. Ultrastruct. Research *5*, 349–363.

BLOCH, D. P., 1962. On the derivation of histone specificity. Proc. Nat. Acad. Sci. (Wash.) *48*, 324–326.

BOELL, E. J., 1945. Functional differentiation in embryonic development. II. Respiration and cytochrome oxidase activity in *Amblystoma punctatum*. J. exp. Zool. *100*, 331–352.

——, 1948. Biochemical differentiation during amphibian development. Ann. N.Y. Acad. Sci. *49*, 773–800.

——, 1955. Energy exchange and enzyme development during embryogenesis. In WILLIER, B. H., WEISS, P. A., and HAMBURGER, V. (Eds.): Analysis of development. Saunders, Philadelphia, 520–555.

BONNER, J., HUANG, R. C., and GILDEN, R. V., 1963. Chromosomally directed protein synthesis. Proc. Nat. Acad. Sci. (Wash.) *50*, 893–900.

BONNET, C., 1745. Traité d'Insectologie, Paris. Quoted after J. Needham, 1959.

BORGHESE, E., 1950. The development *in vitro* of the submandibular and sublingual glands of *Mus musculus*. J. Anat. Lond. *84*, 287–302.

BOUNHIOL, J., 1937. La métamorphose des insectes serait inhibée dans leur jeune age par les corpora allata? C.R. Soc. Biol. Paris *126*, 1189–1191.

BOUNOURE, L., 1934. Recherches sur la lignée germinale chez la grenouille rousse aux premier stades du développement. Ann. Sci. natur. zool. 10 ser. *17*, 67–248.

——, 1939. L'origine des cellules reproductrices et le problème de la lignée germinale. Gauthier-Villars, Paris.

——, 1940. Continuité germinale et reproduction agame. Gauthier-Villars, Paris.

BOYCOTT, A. E., DIVER, C., GARSTANG, S. L., and TURNER, F. M., 1930. The inheritance of sinistrality in *Limnaea peregra* (Mollusca, Pulmonata). Phil. Trans. B, *219*, 51–131.

BRACHET, A., 1935. Traité d'embryologie des vertébrés. 2nd ed., revised by A. DALCQ, and P. GÊRARD. Masson, Paris.

BRACHET, J., 1941. La localisation des acides pentosenucléiques dans les tissus animaux et les oeufs d'Amphibiens en voie de développement. Arch. Biol. Paris *53*, 207–257.

——, 1947. The metabolism of nucleic acids during embryonic development. Cold Spr. Harb. Symp. quant. Biol. *12*, 18–27.

——, 1950a. Les caractéristiques biochémique de la compétence et de l'induction. Rev. Suisse Zool. *57*, Fascicule suppl. 1, 57–75.

——, 1950b. Chemical embryology Interscience Publishers, New York.

—— and QUERTIER, J., 1963. Cytochemical detection of cytoplasmic deoxyribonucleic acid /DNA/ in amphibian ovocytes. Experimental Cell Research *32*, 410–413.

BRAMBELL, W. F. R., HEMMINGS, W. A., and HENDERSON, M., 1951. Antibodies and embryos. Athlone Press, London.

BRAUER, A., 1902. Beiträge zur Kenntniss der Entwicklung und Anatomie der Gymnophionen. III. Die Entwicklung der Excretionsorgane. Zool. Jb. Abt. Anat. u. Ont. *16*, 1–176.

BRENNER, S., JACOB, F., and MESELSON, M., 1961. An unstable intermediate carrying information from genes to ribosomes for protein synthesis. Nature (Lond.) *190*, 576–581.

BRETSCHNEIDER, L. H., and RAVEN, C. P., 1951. Structural and topochemical changes in the egg cells of *Limnaea stagnalis* L. during oogenesis. Arch. néerl. Zool. *10*, 1–31.

BRIEN, P., 1932. Contribution a l'étude de la régénération naturelle chez les Spongillidae. Arch. Zool. exp. gén. *74*, 461–506.

BRIGGS, R., and KING, T. J., 1952. Transplantation of living nuclei from blastula cells into enucleated frogs' eggs. Proc. Nat. Acad. Sci. (Wash.) *38*, 455–463.

—— and ——, 1953. Factors affecting the transplantability of nuclei of frog embryonic cells. J. exp. Zool. *122*, 485–506.

—— and ——, 1957. Changes in the nuclei of differentiating endoderm cells as revealed by nuclear transplantation. J. Morph. *100*, 269–312.

BROMLEY, N. W., and ORECHOWITSCH, W. N., 1934. Ueber die Proteolyse in den regenerierenden Geweben. II. Die Aktivität der Gewebeprotease in verschiedenen Gebieten des Regenerats. Biochem. Z. 272, 324–331.

BROWN, D. D., and GURDON, J. B., 1964. Absence of ribosomal RNA synthesis in the anucleolate mutant of *Xenopus laevia*. Proc. Nat. Acad. Sci. (Wash.) 51, 139–146.

BRUNST, V. V., 1950. Influence of x-rays on limb regeneration in urodele amphibians. Quart. Rev. Biol. 25, 1–29.

—— and CHÉRÉMÉTIEVA, E. A., 1936. Sur la perte locale du pouvoir régénerateur chez le triton et l'axolotl causée par l'irradiation avec les rayons x. Arch. Zool. exp. gén. 78, 57–67.

—— and SCHEREMETJEWA, E. A., 1933. Untersuchung des Einflusses von Röntgenstrahlen auf die Regeneration der Extremitäten beim Triton. Roux Arch. 128, 181.

BRUYN, P. P. H. DE, 1945. The motion of migrating cells in tissue cultures of lymph nodes. Anat. Rec. 93, 295–315.

BUEKER, E. D., 1947. Limb ablation experiments on the embryonic chick and its effect as observed on the mature nervous system. Anat. Rec. 97, 157–174.

BURGOS, M. H., and FAWCETT, D. W., 1955. Studies on the fine structure of the mammalian testis. I. Differentiation of the spermatids in the cat (*Felis domestica*). J. Biophys. Biochem. Cytol. 1, 287–300.

—— and ——, 1956. An electron microscope study of spermatid differentiation in the toad, *Bufo arenarum* Hensel. J. Biophys. Biochem. Cytol. 2, 223–240.

BURKE, V., SULLIVAN, N. P., PETERSEN, H., and WEED, R., 1944. Ontogenetic change in antigenic specificity of the organs of the chick. J. infect. Dis. 74, 225–233.

BURNETT, A. L., 1962. The maintenance of form in Hydra. Regeneration. 20th Symp. of the Soc. for the Study of Develop. and Growth. D. Rudnick, (Ed.) Ronald Press Co., New York. 27–52.

BURNS, R. K., 1961. Role of hormones in the differentiation of sex. In Young, W. C.: Sex and internal secretions. Williams and Wilkins Co., Baltimore, 76–160.

BURR, H. S., 1916. The effect of removal of the nasal pits in *Amblystoma* embryos. J. exp. Zool. 20, 27–57.

——, 1930. Hyperplasia in the brain of *Amblystoma*. J. exp. Zool. 55, 171–191.

BUTENANDT, A., and KARLSON, P., 1954. Ueber die Isolierung eines Metamorphose-Hormons der Insecten in kristallisierter Form. Z. Naturf. 9b, 389–391.

BUTLER, E. G., 1933. The effects of x-radiation on the regeneration of the fore limb of *Amblystoma* larvae. J. exp. Zool. 65, 271–315.

——, 1935. Studies on limb regeneration in x-rayed *Amblystoma* larvae. Anat. Rec. 62, 295–307.

BYTINSKI-SALZ, H., 1936. Lo sviluppo della coda negli anfibi. II. Alterazioni della correlazioni fra i territori costituenti l'abbozzo codale e comportamento dell' ectoderma della pinna caudale. R. C. Accad. Lincei. 24, 82–88.

——, 1937. Trapianti di "organizzatore" nelle uova di Lampreda. Arch. ital. Anat. Embriol. 39, 177–228.

CAMPENHOUT, E. VAN, 1935. Experimental researches on the origin of the acoustic ganglion in amphibian embryos. J. exp. Zool. 72, 175–193.

CARASSO, N. and FAVARD, P., 1960. Vitellogenèse de la planorbe. Ultrastructure des plaquettes vitellines. 4th Internat. Conference on Electron Microscopy. Berlin, Vol. II. Berlin, Göttingen, Heidelberg, 431–435.

CARTER, T. C., 1954. The genetics of luxate mice. IV. Embryology. J. Genet. 52, 1–35.

CASTLE, W. E., and GREGORY, P. W., 1929. The embryological basis of size inheritance in the rabbit. J. Morph. 48, 81.

CHALKLEY, D. T., 1954. A quantitative histological analysis of forelimb regeneration in *Triturus viridescens*. J. Morph. 94, 21–70.

CHANG, M. C., 1954. Development of parthenogenetic rabbit blastocysts induced by low temperature storage of unfertilized ova. J. exp. Zool. 125, 127–149.

CHILD, C. M., 1936. Differential reduction of vital dyes in the early development of echinoderms. Roux Arch. 135, 426–456.

——, 1941. Patterns and problems of development. University of Chicago Press, Chicago.

——, 1948. Exogastrulation by sodium azide and other inhibiting conditions in *Strongylocentrotus purpuratus*. J. exp. Zool. 107, 1–38.

CLAYTON, R. M., 1951. Antigens in the developing newt embryo. Nature (Lond.) *168*, 120–121.

CLERMONT, Y., and LEBLOND, C. P., 1955. Spermiogenesis of man, monkey, ram and other mammals as shown by the "periodic acid–Schiff" technique. Amer. J. Anat. *96*, 229–253.

CLEVER, U., 1961. Genaktivitaten in den Riesenchromosomen von *Chironomus tentans* und ihre Beziehung zur Entwicklung. I. Genaktivierung durch Ecdyson. Chromosoma (Berl.) *12*, 607–675.

―― and KARLSON, P., 1960. Induktion von Puff-Veränderungen in den Speicheldrüsenchromosomen von *Chironomus tentans* durch Ecdyson. Exp. Cell Res. *20*, 623–626.

COLWIN, A. L., and COLWIN, L. H., 1957. Morphology of fertilization: Acrosome filament formation and sperm entry. In TYLER, A., BORSTEL, R. C. VON, and METZ, C. B.: The beginnings of embryonic development. American Association for the Advancement of Science. Washington.

―― and ――, 1961. Fine structure of the spermatozoon of *Hydroides hexagonus* (Annelida) with special reference to the acrosomal region. J. Biophys. Biochem. Cytol. *10*, 211–230.

―― and ――, 1963. Role of the gamete membranes in fertilization in *Saccoglossus kowalevskii* (Enteropneusta). I. The acrosomal region and its changes in early stages of fertilization. J. Cell Biol. *19*, 477–500.

COLWIN, L. H., and COLWIN, A. L., 1961. Changes in the spermatozoon during fertilization in *Hydroides hexagonus* (Annelida). I. Passage of the acromosal region through the vitelline membrane. J. Biophys. Biochem. Cytol. *10*, 231–254.

―― and ――, 1963. Role of the gamete membranes in fertilization in *Saccoglossus kowalevskii* (Enteropneusta). II. Zygote formation by gamete membrane fusion. J. Cell Biol. *19*, 501–518.

CONKLIN, E. G., 1905. The orientation and cell-lineage of the ascidian egg. J. Acad. nat. Sci. Philad. Ser. 2, *13*.

――, 1931. The development of centrifuged eggs of ascidians. J. exp. Zool. *60*, 1–119.

――, 1932. The embryology of *Amphioxus*. J. Morph. *54*, 69–118.

COOPER, R. S., 1948. Antigens in development. J. exp. Zool. *107*, 397–433.

COPENHAVER, W. M., 1926. Experiments on the development of the heart of *Amblystoma punctatum*. J. exp. Zool. *43*, 321–371.

――, 1930. Results of heteroplastic transplantation of anterior and posterior parts of the heart rudiment in *Amblystoma* embryos. J. exp. Zool. *55*, 293–318.

――, 1933. Transplantation of heart and limb rudiments between *Amblystoma* and *Triton* embryos. J. exp. Zool. *65*, 131–157.

CRICK, F. H. C., 1962. The genetic code. Sci. Amer. *207* (4), 66–74.

CURTIS, A. S. G., 1960. Cortical grafting in *Xenopus laevis*. J. Embr. exp. Morph. *8*, 163–173.

――, 1962. Cell contact and adhesion. Biol. Rev. *37*, 82–129.

――, 1963. The cell cortex. Endeavour *22* (No. 87), 134–137.

CUSIMANO, T., FAGONE, A., and REVERBERI, G., 1962. On the origin of the larval mouth in the anurans. Acta Embryol. Morphol. Exper. *5*, 82–103.

DALCQ, A. M., 1954. Nouvelles données structurales et cytochimiques sur l'oeuf des mammifères. Rev. gén. Sci. pur. appl. *61*, 19–41.

――, 1960. Réflexions sur la morphologie du cou. Soc. oto-rhino-laryngologica latina, 30 conventus, Brussels, 15–22.

―― and PASTEELS, J., 1937. Une conception nouvelle des bases physiologique de la morphogénèse. Arch. Biol. Liége, *48*, 121–147.

DAN, J. C., and WADA, S. K., 1955. Studies on the acrosome. IV. The acrosome reaction in some bivalve spermatozoa. Biol. Bull. Woods Hole *109*, 40–55.

DANFORTH, C. H., 1930. Developmental anomalies in a special strain of mice. Amer. J. Anat. *45*, 275–288.

DANIELLI, J. F., 1953. Cytochemistry—a critical approach. Chapman and Hall, London.

DANTSCHAKOFF, V., 1941. Der Aufbau des Geschlechts beim höheren Wirbeltier. Gustav Fischer, Jena.

DAVENPORT, C. B., 1895. Studies in morphogenesis. IV. A preliminary catalogue of the processes concerned in ontogeny. Bull. Mus. comp. Zool. Harv. *27*, 173–199.

DAVIDSON, J. N., 1947. Some factors influencing the nucleic acid content of cells and tissues. Cold Spr. Harb. Symp. quant. Biol. *12*, 50–59.

———— and LESLIE, I., 1950. A new approach in the biochemistry of growth and development. Nature (Lond.) *165*, 49–53.

DAVIS, C. L., 1923. Description of a human embryo having twenty paired somites. Contr. Embryol. Carneg. Instn. *15*, 3–51.

DELAGE, Y., 1884. Evolution de la Sacculine. Arch. Z. expér. *2*, 417–736.

DETWILER, S. R., 1918. Experiments on the development of the shoulder girdle and the anterior limb of *Amblystoma punctatum*. J. exp. Zool. *25*, 499–538.

————, 1920. Experiments on the transplantation of limbs in *Amblystoma*. The formation of nerve plexuses and the function of the limbs. J. exp. Zool. *31*, 117–169.

————, 1926a. The effect of reduction of skin and muscle on the development of spinal ganglia. J. exp. Zool. *45*, 399–414.

————, 1926b. Experimental studies on morphogenesis in the nervous system. Quart. Rev. Biol. *1*, 61–86.

————, 1930. Observations upon the growth, function and nerve supply of limbs when grafted to the head of salamander embryos. J. exp. Zool. *55*, 319–379.

————, 1934. An experimental study of spinal nerve segmentation in *Amblystoma* with reference to the pluri-segmental contribution to the brachial plexus. J. exp. Zool. *67*, 395–441.

————, 1936. Neuroembryology: An experimental study. Macmillan Co., New York.

————, 1949. The swimming capacity of *Amblystoma* larvae following reversal of the embryonic hindbrain. J. exp. Zool. *111*, 79–94.

———— and VAN DYKE, R. H., 1934. Further observations upon abnormal growth responses of spinal nerves in *Amblystoma* embryos. J. exp. Zool. *69*, 137–164.

DI BERARDINO, M. A., KING, T. J., and McKINNEL, R. G., 1963. Chromosome studies of a frog renal adenocarcinoma line carried by serial intraocular transplantation. J. nat. Cancer. Inst. *31*, 769–789.

DOLJANSKI, L., and ROULET, F., 1934. Zur Frage der Entstehung der bindegewebigen Strukturen. Roux Arch. *131*, 512–531.

DOLLANDER, A., 1953. Observations relatives à certaines propriétés du cortex de l'oeuf d'amphibien. Arch. Anat. micr. Morph. exp. *42*, 185–193.

DORRIS, F., 1935. The development of structure and function in the digestive tract of *Amblystoma punctatum*. J. exp. Zool. *70*, 491–527.

DRAGOMIROW, N., 1929. Ueber die Faktoren der embryonalen Entwicklung der Linse bei Amphibien. Roux Arch. *116*, 633–668.

————, 1933. Ueber Koordination der Teilprocesse in der embryonalen Morphogenese des Augenbechers. Roux Arch. *129*, 522–560.

————, 1936. Ueber Induktion sekundärer Retina im transplantierten Augenbecher bei *Triton* und *Pelobates*. Roux Arch. *134*, 716–737.

DREW, A. H., 1923. Growth and differentiation in tissue cultures. Brit. J. Exp. Path. *4*, 46–52.

DRIESCH, H., 1891. Entwicklungsmechanische Studien. I-II. Z. wiss. Zool. *53*, 160–182.

DUBOIS, F., and WOLFF, E., 1947. Sur une méthode d'irradiation localisée permettant de mettre en évidence la migration des cellules de régéneration chez les Planaires. C. R. Soc. Biol. Paris *141*, 903–906.

DÜRKEN, B., 1913. Ueber einseitige Augenexstirpation bei jungen Froschlarven. Z. wiss. Zool. *105*, 192–242.

DU SHANE, G. P., 1935. An experimental study of the origin of pigment cells in amphibia. J. exp. Zool. *72*, 1–31.

EAKIN, R. M., 1961. Photoreceptors in the amphibian frontal organ. Proc. Nat. Acad. Sci. (Wash.) *47*, 1084–1088.

————, 1963. Ultrastructural differentiation of the oral sucker in the treefrog *Hyla regilla*. Develop. Biol. *7*, 169–179.

EDSTRÖM, J. E., and BEERMANN, W., 1962. The base composition of nucleic acids in chromosomes, puffs, nucleoli and cytoplasm of *Chironomus* salivary gland cells. J. Cell Biol. *14*, 371–379.

EKMAN, G., 1925. Experimentelle Beiträge zur Herzentwicklung der Amphibien. Roux Arch. *106*, 320–352.

ENDO, Y., 1952. The role of the cortical granules in the formation of the fertilization membrane in the eggs from Japanese sea urchins. Exp. Cell Res. *3*, 406–418.

ENDRES, H., 1895. Ueber Anstich- und Schnürversuche an Eiern von *Triton taeniatus*. Jber. Schles. Ges. vaterländ. Kultur. *73*.

EPHRUSSI, B., 1942. Chemistry of the "eye color hormones" of *Drosophila*. Quart. Rev. Biol. *17*, 327-338.

EVANS, H. M., SIMPSON, M. E., MEYER, R. K., and REICHERT, 1933. The growth and gonad-stimulating hormones of the anterior hypophysis. Mem. Univ. Calif. *11*, 1-446.

FALES, D. E., 1935. Experiments on the development of the pronephros of *Amblystoma punctatum*. J. exp. Zool. *72*, 147-173.

FAURÉ-FREMIET, E., 1925. La cinétique du developpement. Presses Universit. de France, Paris.

FAWCETT, D. W., and PORTER, K. R., 1954. A study of the fine structure of ciliated epithelia. J. Morph. *94*, 221-281.

FICQ, A., 1954. Analyse de l'induction neurale chez les Amphibiens au moyen d'organisateurs marqués: J. Embr. exp. Morph. *2*, 194-203.

FILATOFF, D., 1916. The removal and transplantation of the auditory vesicle of the embryo of *Bufo* (the correlations at the formation of the cartilaginous skeleton). Russk. zool. Zh. *1*, 48-54.

FISCHEL, A., 1919. Ueber den Einfluss des Auges auf die Entwicklung und Erhaltung der Hornhaut. Klin. Mbl. Augenheilk. *62*, 1-5.

FISCHER, F. G., WEHMEIER, E., LEHMANN, H., JÜHLING, L., and HULTZSCH, K., 1935. Zur Kenntnis der Induktionsmittel in der Embryonal-Entwicklung. Ber. dtsch. chem. Ges. *68*, 1196-1199.

FLICKINGER, R. A., 1961. Formation, biochemical composition and utilization of amphibian egg yolk. Symp. on Germ Cells and Development, Inst. Internat. d'Embryologie and Fondazione A. Baselli, Pavia, 29-48.

——— and ROUNDS, D. E., 1956. The maternal synthesis of egg yolk proteins as demonstrated by isotopic and serological means. Biochim. et biophys. Acta *22*, 38-72.

FLYNN, T. T., and HILL, J. P., 1939. The development of the Monotremata. IV. Growth of the ovarian ovum, maturation, fertilization, and early cleavage. Trans. zool. Soc. Lond. *24*, 445-582.

FRANCHI, L. L., 1960. Electron microscopy of oocyte-follicle cell relationships in the rat ovary. J. Biophys. Biochem. Cytol. *7*, 397-399.

FRANK, G. M., 1925. Ueber Gesetzmässigkeiten in der Mitosenverteilung in den Gehirnblasen im Zusammenhang mit Formbildungsprozessen. Arch. mikr. Anat. u. Entw. mech. *104*, 262-272.

FRASER, E. A., 1950. The development of the vertebrate excretory system. Biol. Rev. *25*, 159-187.

FRASER, R. C., 1954. Studies on the hypoblast of the young chick embryo. J. exp. Zool. *126*, 349-399.

FRIEDEN, E., 1963. The chemistry of amphibian metamorphosis. Sci. Amer. *209* (5), 110-118.

GABRIEL, M. L., and FOGEL, S., 1955. Great experiments in biology. Prentice-Hall, Englewood Cliffs, N. J.

GAILLARD, P. J., 1942. Hormones regulating growth and differentiation in embryonic explants. Hermann and Co., Paris.

GALL, J. G., 1963. Chromosomes and cytodifferentiation. In LOCKE, M. (Ed.): Cytodifferentiation and macromolecular synthesis. Academic Press, New York, 119-143.

GALTSOFF, P. S., 1925. Regeneration after dissociation (an experimental study on sponges). I. Behavior of dissociated cells of *Microciona prolifera* under normal and altered conditions. J. exp. Zool. *42*, 183-255.

——— and PHILPOTT, D. E., 1960. Ultrastructure of the spermatozoon of the oyster *Crassostrea virginica*. J. Ultrastruct. Research *3*, 241-253.

GEBHARDT, H., 1926. Untersuchungen über die Determination bei Planarienregeneraten. Roux Arch. *107*, 684-726.

GERALD, P. S., 1961. The abnormal haemoglobins. In PENROSE, L. A. (Ed.): Recent advances in human genetics. J. & A. Churchill, Ltd., London.

GILCHRIST, F. G., 1937. Budding and locomotion in the Scyphostomas of *Aurelia*. Biol. Bull. Woods Hole *72*, 99-124.

GINSBURG, A., 1953. The origin of bilateral symmetry in the eggs of acipenserid fishes. C.R. Acad. Sci. URSS *90*, 477-480.

——— and DETTLAFF, T., 1944. Experiments on transplantation and removal of organ rudiments in embryos of *Acipenser stellatus* in early developmental stages. C.R. Acad. Sci. URSS *44*, 209-212.

GLATTHAAR, E., and TÖNDURY, G., 1950. Untersuchungen an abortierten Früchten nach Rubeolaerkrankung der Mutter in der Frühschwangerschaft. Gynaecologia *129*, 315–320.

GLUECKSOHN-SCHOENHEIMER, S., 1943. The morphological manifestation of a dominant mutation in mice affecting tail and urogenital system. Genetics *28*, 341–348.

——, 1945. The embryonic development of mutants of the Sd-strain in mice. Genetics *30*, 29–38.

——, 1949. The effects of a lethal mutation responsible for duplications and twinning in mouse embryos. J. exp. Zool. *110*, 47–76.

GOERTTLER, K., 1928. Die Bedeutung der ventrolateralen Mesodermbezirke für die Herzanlage der Amphibienkeime. Anat. Anz. Erg. Heft *66*, 132–139.

GOETZ, R. H., 1938. On the early development of the Tenrecoidea (*Hemicentetes semispinosus*). Biomorphosis *1*, 67–79.

GOODRICH, E. S., 1930. Studies on the structure and development of vertebrates. Macmillan, London.

GORBMAN, A., and BERN, H. A., 1962. A textbook of comparative endocrinology. Wiley and Sons, New York.

GORBUNOVA, G. P., 1939. On the inducing properties of the medulla oblongata in amphibian embryos. C. R. Acad. Sci. URSS *23*, 298–301.

GRANT, P., 1953. Phosphate metabolism during oogenesis in *Rana temporaria*. J. exp. Zool. *124*, 513–543.

——, 1958a. The synthesis of deoxyribonucleic acid during early embryonic development of Rana pipiens. J. Cellular Comparative Physiology 52, 227–247.

——, 1958b. The incorporation of P^{32} and glycine $-2-C^{14}$ into nucleic acids during early embryonic development of Rana pipiens. J. Cellular Comparative Physiology 52, 249–268.

GREGORY, P. W., and CASTLE, W. E., 1931. Further studies on the embryological basis of size inheritance in the rabbit. J. exp. Zool. *59*, 199–211.

GROBSTEIN, C., 1953a. Analysis in vitro of the early organization of the rudiment of the mouse sub-mandibular gland. J. Morph. *93*, 19–44.

——, 1953b. Epithelio-mesenchymal specificity in the morphogenesis of mouse sub-mandibular rudiments *in vitro*. J. exp. Zool. *124*, 383–413.

——, 1953c. Morphogenetic interaction between embryonic mouse tissues separated by a membrane filter. Nature (Lond.) *172*, 869.

——, 1955. Inductive interaction in the development of the mouse metanephros. J. exp. Zool. *130*, 319–339.

——, 1957. Some transmission characteristics of the tubule-inducing influence on mouse metanephrogenic mesenchyme. Exp. Cell Res. *13*, 575–587.

——, and DALTON, A. J., 1957. Kidney tubule induction in mouse metanephrogenic mesenchyme without cytoplasmic contact. J. exp. Zool. *135*, 57–73.

GROSSER, O., 1945. Grundriss der Entwicklungsgeschichte des Menschen. Springer, Berlin.

GRUENWALD, P., 1952. Development of the excretory system. Ann. N.Y. Acad. Sci. *55*, 142–146.

GRUNEBERG, H., 1936. Gray-lethal, a new mutation in the house mouse. J. Hered. *27*, 105–109.

——, 1938. An analysis of the "pleiotropic" effects of a new lethal mutation in the rat (*Mus norvegicus*). Proc. roy. Soc. B *125*, 123–144.

——, 1952. The genetics of the mouse. Martinus Nijhoff, Hague.

GUARESCHI, C., 1935. Studi sulla determinazione dell' orechio interno degli anfibi anuri. Arch. ital. Anat. Embriol. *35*, 97–129.

GUDERNATSCH, F., 1912. Feeding experiments on tadpoles. Roux Arch. *35*, 457–483.

GUDERNATSCH, J. F., 1913. Concerning the mechanism and direction of the embryonic foldings. Anat. Rec. *7*, 411–431.

GUSTAFSON, T., 1950. Survey of the morphological action of the lithium ion and the chemical basis of its action. Rev. Suisse Zool. *57*, Suppl. 1, 77–92.

—— and HASSELBERG, I., 1951. Studies on enzymes in the developing sea urchin egg. Exp. Cell Res. *2*, 642–672.

—— and HJELTE, M., 1951. The amino-acid metabolism of the developing sea urchin egg. Exp. Cell Res. *2*, 474–490.

—— and KINNANDER, H., 1956. Microaquaria for time lapse cinematographic studies of morphogenesis in swimming larvae and observations on sea urchin gastrulation. Exp. Cell Res. *11*, 36–51.

—— and WOLPERT, L., 1961. The forces that shape the embryo. Discovery *22*, 470–477.

GUYÉNOT, E., and PONSE, K., 1930. Territoires de régénération et transplantations. Bull. biol. *64*, 251–287.

HADEK, R., 1963a. Submicroscopic study on the cortical granules in the rabbit ovum. J. Ultrastruct. Research *8*, 170–175.
———, 1963b. Submicroscopic study on the sperm-induced cortical reaction in the rabbit ovum. J. Ultrastruct. Research *9*, 99–109.
HADORN, E., 1932. Ueber Organentwicklung und histologische Differenzierung in transplantierten merogonischen Bastardgeweben (*Triton palmatus* (♀) × *Triton cristatus* ♂). Roux Arch. *125*, 495–565.
HADZI, J., 1909. Die Entstehung der Knospe bei *Hydra*. Arb. zool. Inst. Univ. Wien, *18*.
HAECKEL, E., 1868. Natürliche Schöpfungsgeschichte. Berlin.
HALL, T. S., 1951. A source book in animal biology. McGraw-Hill, New York.
HAMBURGER, V., 1929. Experimentelle Beiträge zur Entwicklungsphysiologie der Nervenbahnen in der Froschextremität. Roux Arch. *119*, 47–99.
———, 1934. The effect of wing bud extirpation on the development of the central nervous system in chick embryos. J. exp. Zool. *68*, 449–494.
———, 1947. A manual of experimental embryology. (2nd imp.) University Press, Chicago.
———, 1956. Developmental correlations in neurogenesis. In RUDNICK, D. (Ed.): Cellular mechanisms in differentiation and growth. Princeton University Press, 191–212.
———, 1961. Experimental analysis of the dual origin of the trigeminal ganglion in the chick embryo. J. exp. Zool. *148* (2), 91–124.
———, 1962. Specificity in neurogenesis. J. Cell. Comp. Physiol., *60*, No. 2, Suppl. 1, 81–92.
——— and HAMILTON, H. L., 1951. A series of normal stages in the development of the chick embryo. J. Morph. *88*, 49–92.
——— and LEVI-MONTALCINI, R., 1949. Proliferation, differentiation and degeneration in the spinal ganglia of the chick embryo under normal and experimental conditions. J. exp. Zool. *111*, 457–501.
HAMILTON, W. J., BOYD, J. D., and MOSSMAN, H. W., 1947. Human embryology. Heffer and Sons, Cambridge.
HAMMOND, W. S., and YNTEMA, C. L., 1947. Depletions in the thoracolumbar sympathetic system following removal of neural crest in the chick. J. comp. Neurol. *86*, 237–265.
——— and ———, 1958. Origin of ciliary ganglia in the chick. J. comp. Neurol. *110*, 367–390.
HARDING, C. V., HARDING, D., and PERELMAN, P., 1954. Antigens in sea urchin embryos. Exp. Cell Res. *6*, 202–210.
HARDY, M. H., 1952. The histochemistry of hair follicles in the mouse. J. Anat. Lond. *90*, 285–337. ·
———, 1953. Vaginal cornification of the mouse produced by oestrogens *in vitro*. Nature (Lond.) *172*, 1196.
HARRIS, H., and LACOUR, L. F., 1963. Site of synthesis of cytoplasmic ribonucleic acid. Nature (Lond.) *200*, 227–229.
HARRISON, R. G., 1903. Experimentelle Untersuchungen über die Entwicklung der Sinnesorgane der Seitenlinie bei den Amphibien. Arch. mikr. Anat. *63*, 35–149.
———, 1908. Embryonic transplantation and development of the nervous system. Anat. Rec. *2*, 385.
———, 1918. Experiments on the development of the forelimb of *Amblystoma*, a self-differentiating equipotential system. J. exp. Zool. *25*, 413–461.
———, 1921a. Experiments on the development of the gills in the amphibian embryos. Biol. Bull. Woods Hole *41*, 156–168.
———, 1921b. On relations of symmetry in transplanted limbs. J. exp. Zool. *32*, 1–136.
———, 1925a. The development of the balancer in *Amblystoma*, studied by the method of transplantation and in relation to the connective tissue problem. J. exp. Zool. *41*, 349–427.
———, 1925b. The effect of reversing the medio-lateral or transverse axis of the forelimb bud in the salamander embryo (*Amblystoma punctatum*). Roux Arch. *106*, 469–502.
———, 1929. Correlation in the development and growth of the eye studied by means of heteroplastic transplantation. Roux Arch. *120*, 1–55.

HARRISON, R. G., 1935. Factors concerned in the development of the ear in *Amblystoma punctatum*. Anat. Rec. *64*, 38–39.

HARVEY, E. B., 1936. Parthenogenetic merogony or cleavage without nuclei in *Arbacia punctulata*. Biol. Bull. Woods Hole *17*, 101–121.

——, 1946. Structure and development of the clear quarter of the *Arbacia punctulata* egg. J. exp. Zool. *102*, 253–275.

——, 1956. The American *Arbacia* and other sea urchins. Princeton University Press, Princeton.

HAUENSCHILD, C., 1964. Postembryonale Entwicklungssteuerung durch ein Gehirn-Hormon bei *Platynereis dumerilii*. Zool. Anz. *27*, Suppl., 111–120.

HAY, E. D., 1962. Cytological studies of dedifferentiation and differentiation in regenerating amphibian limbs. In RUDNICK, D. (Ed.): Regeneration. Symp. of the Soc. for the Study of Develop. and Growth. Ronald Press Co., New York, 177–210.

—— and FISCHMAN, D. A., 1961. Origin of the blastema in regenerating limbs of the newt *Triturus viridescens*. An autoradiographic study using tritiated thymidine to follow cell proliferation and migration. Develop. Biol. *3*, 26–59.

HAYASHI, Y., 1955. Inductive effect of some fractions of tissue extracts after removal of pentose nucleic acid, tested on the isolated ectoderm of *Triturus* gastrula. Embryologia *2*, 145–162.

——, 1956. Morphogenetic effects of pentose nucleoprotein from the liver upon the isolated ectoderm. Embryologia *3*, 57–67.

——, 1958. The effects of pepsin and trypsin on the inductive ability of pentose nucleoprotein from guinea pig liver. Embryologia *4*, 33–53.

HAYNES, J., and BURNETT, A. L., 1963. Dedifferentiation and redifferentiation of cells in *Hydra viridis*. Science *142*, 1481–1483.

HELFF, O. M., 1928. Studies on amphibian metamorphosis. III. Physiol. Zool. *1*, 463–495.

HERBST, C., 1893. Experimentelle Untersuchungen über den Einfluss der veränderten chemischen Zusammensetzung des umgebenden Mediums auf die Entwicklung der Tiere. II. Mitt. zool. Sta. Neapel. *11*, 136–220.

HERRICK, C. J., 1934. An introduction to neurology. Saunders, Philadelphia.

HERRMANN, H., and NICHOLAS, J. S., 1948. Quantitative changes in muscle protein fractions during development. J. exp. Zool. *107*, 165–176.

—— and ——, 1949. Nucleic acid content of whole homogenates and of fractions of developing rat muscle. J. exp. Zool. *112*, 341–360.

HERTIG, A. T., and ROCK, J., 1941. Two human ova of the pre-villous stage, having an ovulation age of about eleven and twelve days respectively. Contr. Embryol. Carneg. Instn. *29*, 127–156.

—— and ——, 1945. Two human ova in the pre-villous stage, having a developmental age of about seven and nine days respectively. Contr. Embryol. Carneg. Instn. *31*, 67–84.

HERTWIG, O., 1906. Handbuch der vergleichenden und experimentellen Entwicklungslehre der Wirbeltiere. G. Fischer, Jena.

HERTWIG, R., 1896. Ueber die Entwicklung des unbefruchteten Seeigeleies. Festschr. f. Gegenbaur, Leipzig.

HEUSER, C. H., 1923. The branchial vessels and their derivatives in the pig. Contr. Embryol. Carneg. Instn. *15*, 123–139.

—— and CORNER, G. W., 1957. Developmental horizons in human embryos. Description of age group X, 4 to 12 somites. Contr. Embryol. Carneg. Instn. *36*, 31–39.

—— and STREETER, G. L., 1941. Development of the macaque embryo. Contr. Embryol. Carneg. Instn. *29*, 17–56.

HILL, J. P., 1918. Some observations on the early development of *Didelphis aurita*. Quart. J. micr. Sci. *63*, 91–140.

HIRAMOTO, Y., 1957. The thickness of the cortex and the refractive index of the protoplasm in sea urchin eggs. Embryologia *3*, 361–374.

HOAGLAND, M. B., 1959. Nucleic acids and proteins. Sci. Amer. *201*(6), 55–61.

HOLTFRETER, J., 1934a. Der Einfluss thermischer, mechanischer und chemischer Eingriffe auf die Induzierfähigkeit von *Triton*-Keimteilen. Roux Arch. *132*, 225–306.

——, 1934b. Ueber die Verbreitung induzierender Substanzen und ihre Leistungen im *Triton*-Keim. Roux Arch. *132*, 307–383.

——, 1938a. Differenzierungspotenzen isolierter Teile der Urodelengastrula. Roux Arch. *138*, 522–656.

HOLTFRETER, J., 1938b. Differenzierungspotenzen isolierter Teile der Anuren-gastrula. Roux Arch. *138*, 657–738.

——, 1939a. Gewebeaffinität, ein Mittel der embryonalen Formbildung. Arch. exp. Zellforsch. *23*, 169–209.

——, 1939b. Studien zur Ermittlung der Gestaltungsfaktoren in der Organetwick-lung der Amphibien. I and II. Roux Arch. *139*, 110–190, 227–273.

——, 1943a. Properties and functions of the surface coat in amphibian embryos. J. exp. Zool. *93*, 251–323.

——, 1943b. A study of the mechanics of gastrulation. I. J. exp. Zool. *94*, 261–318.

——, 1943c. Experimental studies on the development of the pronephros. Rev. canad. Biol. *3*, 220–250.

——, 1946. Experiments on the formed inclusions of the amphibian egg. I. The effect of pH and electrolytes on yolk and lipochondria. J. exp. Zool. *101*, 355–405.

——, 1947a. Observations on the migration, aggregation and phagocytosis of em-bryonic cells. J. Morph. *80*, 25–56.

——, 1947b. Changes of structure and the kinetics of differentiating embryonic cells. J. Morph. *80*, 57–62.

——, 1947c. Neural induction in explants which have passed through a sublethal cytolysis. J. exp. Zool. *106*, 197–222.

HOLTZER, H., 1961. Aspects of chondrogenesis and myogenesis. In RUDNICK, D. (Ed.): Synthesis of molecular and cellular structure. Symp. of the Soc. for the Study of Develop. and Growth. Ronald Press Co., New York.

—— and DETWILER, S. R., 1953. An experimental analysis of the development of the spinal column. III. Induction of skeletogenous cells. J. exp. Zool. *123*, 335–368.

HORST, C. J. VAN DER, 1942. Early stages in the embryonic development of *Elephan-tulus*. S. Afr. J. Med. Sci. 7, Biol. Suppl., 55–65.

HÖRSTADIUS, S., 1928. Ueber die Determination des Keimes der Echinodermen. Acta zool. Stockh. *9*, 1–192.

——, 1935. Ueber die Determination im Verlaufe der Eiachse bei Seeigeln. Pubbl. Staz. zool. Napoli. *14*, 251–479.

——, 1944. Ueber die Folgen von Chordaexstirpation an spaeten Gastrulae und Neurulae von *Amblystoma punctatum*. Acta zool. Stockh. *25*, 75–87.

——, 1950. The neural crest. Oxford University Press, London.

——, 1952. Induction and inhibition of reduction gradients by the micromeres in the sea urchin egg. J. exp. Zool. *120*, 421–436.

——, 1953a. Influence of implanted micromeres on reduction gradients and mito-chondrial distribution in developing sea urchin eggs. J. Embr. exp. Morph. *1*, 257–259.

——, 1953b. Vegetalization of the sea-urchin egg by dinitrophenol and animaliza-tion by trypsin and ficin. J. Embr. exp. Morph. *1*, 327–348.

——, 1955. Reduction gradients in animalized and vegetalized sea urchin eggs. J. exp. Zool. *129*, 249–256.

—— and SELLMAN, S., 1946. Experimentelle Untersuchungen über die Deter-mination des knorpeligen Kopfskelettes bei Urodelen. Nova Acta So. Sci. Upsal. *13*.

—— and WOLSKY, A., 1936. Studien über die Determination der Bilateralsym-metrie des jungen Seeigelkeimes. Roux Arch. *135*, 69–113.

HUANG, R. C., and BONNER, J., 1962. Histone, a suppressor of chromosome RNA synthesis. Proc. Nat. Acad. Sci. (Wash.) *48*, 1216–1222.

HUMPHREYS, W. J., 1962. Electron microscope studies on eggs of *Mytilus edulis*. J. Ultrastruct. Research 7, 467–487.

HUNT, T. E., 1937. The origin of entodermal cells from the primitive streak of the chick embryo. Anat. Rec. *68*, 449–460.

HURWITZ, J., and FURTH, J. J., 1962. Messenger RNA. Sci. Amer. *206*(2), 41–49.

HUXLEY, J. S., 1932. Problems of relative growth. Methuen and Co., London.

—— and DE BEER, G. R., 1934. The elements of experimental embryology. University Press, Cambridge.

HYMAN, L. H., 1951. The invertebrates, Vol. 3. McGraw-Hill, New York.

JACOB, F., and MONOD, J., 1961. On the regulation of gene activity. Cold Spr. Harb. Symp. quant. Biol. *26*, 193–211.

JACOBSON, A. G., 1955. The roles of the optic vesicle and other head tissues in lens induction. Proc. Nat. Acad. Sci. (Wash.) *41*, 522–525.

JACOBSON, A. G., 1960. Influences of ectoderm and endoderm on heart differentiation in the newt. Develop. Biol. 2, 138–154.

JOHANNSEN, O. A., and BUTT, F. H., 1941. Embryology of insects and myriapods. McGraw-Hill, New York.

JONES, H. O., and BREWER, J. I., 1941. A human embryo in the primitive-streak stage. Contr. Embryol. Carneg. Instn. 29, 157–165.

JONES-SEATON, A., 1950. Étude de l'organisation cytoplasmique de l'oeuf des rongeurs, principalement quant à la basophilie ribonucléique. Arch. Biol. Paris. 61, 291–444.

JOST, A., 1953. Problems of fetal endocrinology: the gonadal and hypophyseal hormones. Recent Prog. Hormone Res. 8, 379–418.

KAMER, J. C. VAN DE, 1949. Over de ontwikkeling de determinatie en de betekenis van de epiphyse en de paraphyse van de amphibiën. Dissertation. Van der Weil, Arnhem.

KANAJEW, J., 1926. Ueber die histologischen Vorgänge bei der Regeneration von *Pelmatohydra oligactis* Pall. Zool. Anz. 65, 217–226.

KARASAKI, S., 1957. On the mechanism of the dorsalization in the ectoderm of *Triturus* gastrulae caused by precytolytic treatments. 1. Embryologia 3, 317–334.

———, 1963a. Studies on amphibian yolk. I. The ultrastructure of the yolk platelet. J. Cell Biol. 18, 135–151.

———, 1963b. Studies on amphibian yolk. 5. Electron microscopic observations on the utilization of yolk platelets during embryogenesis. J. Ultrastruct. Research 9, 225–247.

KARLSON, P., and HOFFMEISTER, H., 1963. Zur Chemie des Ecdysons. Just. Liebig's Ann. Chem. 662, 1–20.

KAYE, J. S., 1962. Acrosome formation in the house cricket. J. Cell Biol. 12, 411–432.

KEMP, N. E., 1953. Synthesis of yolk in oocytes of *Rana pipiens* after induced ovulation. J. Morph. 92, 487–511.

———, 1956. Electron microscopy of growing oocytes of *Rana pipiens*. J. Biophys. Biochem. Cytol. 2, 281–292.

KERR, J. G., 1919. Textbook of embryology. Vol. II. Vertebrata with the exception of mammalia. Macmillan, London.

KESSEL, R. G., 1963. Electron microscope studies on the origin of annulate lamellae in oocytes of *Necturus*. J. Cell Biol. 19, 391–414.

KING, R. C., 1960. Oogenesis in adult *Drosophila melanogaster*. IX. Studies on the cytochemistry and ultrastructure of developing oocytes. Growth 24, 265–323.

——— and DEVINE, R. L., 1958. Oogenesis in adult *Drosophila melanogaster*. VII. The submicroscopic morphology of the ovary. Growth 22, 299–326.

——— and KOCH, E. A., 1963. Studies on the ovarian follicle cells of *Drosophila*. Quart. J. micr. Sci. 104, 297–320.

——— and MILLS, R. P., 1962. Oogenesis in adult *Drosophila*. XI. Studies of some organelles of the nutrient stream in egg chambers of *D. melanogaster* and *D. willistoni*. Growth 26, 235–253.

KING, T. J., and BRIGGS, R., 1954. Transplantation of living nuclei of late gastrulae into enucleated eggs of *Rana pipiens*. J. Embr. exp. Morph. 2, 73–80.

——— and ———, 1956. Serial transplantation of embryonic nuclei. Cold Spr. Harb. Symp. quant. Biol. 21, 271–290.

KINNANDER, H., and GUSTAFSON, T., 1960. Further studies on the cellular basis of gastrulation in the sea urchin larva. Exp. Cell Res. 19, 278–290.

KITCHIN, I. C., 1949. The effect of notochordectomy in *Amblystoma mexicanum*. J. exp. Zool. 112, 393–416.

KOGAN, R. E., 1939. Inducing action of the medulla oblongata on the trunk epithelium in amphibia. C.R. Acad. Sci. URSS 23, 307–310.

KORSCHELT, E., 1936. Vergleichende Entwicklungsgeschichte der Tiere. G. Fischer, Jena.

KOWALEVSKY, A., 1866. Entwicklungsgeschichte der einfachen Ascidien. Mem. Acad. Sci. St. Petersb. 10.

KROEGER, H., 1963. Chemical nature of the system controlling gene activities in insect cells. Nature (Lond.) 200, 1234–1235.

———, 1964. Zellphysiologische Mechanismen bei der regulation von genaktivitäten in den Riesenchromosomen von *Chironomus thummi*. Chromosoma (Berl.) 15, 36–70.

KUHL, W., 1941. Untersuchungen über die Cytodynamik der Furchung und Frühentwicklung des Eies der weissen Maus. Abh. senckenb. naturf. Ges. 456, 1–17.

KÜHN, A., 1936. Versuche über die Wirkungsweise der Erbanlagen. Naturwissenschaften *24*, 1–10.

———, 1939. Zur Entwicklungsphysiologie der Schmetterlingsmetamorphose. Verh. 7 internat. Kongr. Ent. Berlin 780–796.

———, 1941. Ueber die Gen-Wirkkette der Pigmentbildung bei Insecten. Nachr. Akad. Wiss. Göttingen *6*, 231–261.

———, 1955. Vorlesungen über Entwicklungsphysiologie. Springer, Berlin.

———, and PIEPHO, H., 1936. Ueber hormonale Wirkungen bei der Verpuppung der Schmetterlinge. Nachr. Ges. Wiss. Göttingen *2*, 141–154.

KUYPER, C. M. A., SMETS, L. A., and PIECK, A. C. M., 1962. The life cycle of a strain of liver cells cultivated in vitro. Exp. Cell Res. *26*, 217–219.

LALLIER, R., 1956. Les ions de métaux lourds et le problème de la détermination embryonnaire chez les Echinodermes. J. Embr. exp. Morph. *4*, 265–278.

———, 1957. Recherches sur l'animalisation de l'oeuf de l'oursin *Paracentrotus lividus* par les dérivés polysulfoniques. Pubbl. Staz. zool. Napoli *30/2*, 185–209.

LANDACRE, F. L., 1910. The origin of the cranial ganglia in *Ameiurus*. J. Comp. Neurology and Psychology *20*, 309–411.

LANZAVECCHIA, G., 1960. The formation of the yolk in frog oocytes. The proceedings of the European Regional Conference on Electron Microscopy, Delft, *2*, 746.

LEHMANN, F. E., 1937. Mesodermisierung des präsumptiven Chordamaterials durch Einwirkung von Lithiumchlorid auf die Gastrula von *Triton alpestris*. Roux Arch. *136*, 112–146.

———, 1945. Einführung in die physiologische Embryologie. Birkhäuser, Basel.

LENICQUE, P., HÖRSTADIUS, S., and GUSTAFSON, T., 1953. Change of distribution of mitochondria in animal halves of sea urchin eggs by the action of micromeres. Exp. Cell Res. *5*, 400–403.

LEVI-MONTALCINI, R., and AMPRINO, R., 1947. Recherches experimentales sur l'origine du ganglion ciliaire dans l'embryon de poulet. Arch. Biol. *58*, 265–288.

LEVITT, M. M., 1932. On the post-embryonic growth of larvae of some Lepidoptera. Trav. Inst. Biol. Kiev. *5*, 451–468.

LEWIS, W. H., 1904. Experimental studies on the development of the eye in Amphibia. I. On the origin of the lens in *Rana palustris*. Amer. J. Anat. *3*, 505–536.

———, 1907. On the origin and differentiation of the otic vesicle in amphibian embryos. Anat. Rec. *1*, 141–145.

——— and HARTMANN, C. G., 1933. Early cleavage stages of the egg of the monkey (*Macacus rhesus*). Contr. Embryol. Carneg. Instn. *24*, 189–202.

LIEDKE, K. B., 1951. Lens competence in *Amblystoma punctatum*. J. exp. Zool. *117*, 573–591.

———, 1955. Studies on lens induction in *Amblystoma punctatum*. J. exp. Zool. *117*, 353–379.

LILLIE, F. R., 1911. Studies on fertilization in *Nereis*. I. The cortical changes in the egg. II. Partial fertilization. J. Morph. *22*, 361–394.

———, 1919a. Problems of fertilization. University of Chicago Press, Chicago.

———, 1919b. The development of the chick. 2nd ed. Henry Holt, New York.

LINDAHL, P. E., 1933. Ueber "animalisierte" und "vegetativisierte" Seeigellarven. Roux Arch. *128*, 661–664.

———, 1936. Zur Kenntnis der physiologischen Grundlagen der Determination im Seeigelkeim, Acta Zool. (Stockh.) *17*, 179–395.

LIOSNER, L. D., and WORONZOWA, M. A., 1936. Regeneration des Organs mit transplantierten ortsfremden Muskeln. 2. Mitteilung. Zool. Anz. *115*, 55–58.

LITTLE, C. C., and BAGG, H. J., 1924. The occurrence of four inheritable morphological variations in mice and their possible relation to treatment with x-rays. J. exp. Zool. *41*, 45–92.

LOCATELLI, P., 1924. Sulla formazione di arti sopranumerari. Boll. Soc. med-chir. Pavia *36*.

LOEB, J., 1913. Artificial parthenogenesis and fertilization. University of Chicago Press, Chicago.

LOGACHEV, E. D., 1956. On the mutual relations between the nucleus and the cytoplasm in growing egg-cells of Platyhelminthes. C.R. Acad. Sci. URSS *111*. 507–509.

LOPASHOV, G. V., 1950. Experimental investigations of the sources of cellular material and condition of formation of the pectoral fins in teleost fishes. C.R. Acad. Sci. URSS *70*, 137–140.

Lopashov, G. V., 1956. Mechanisms of formation and origin of the choroid coat in the amphibian eye. C. R. Acad. Sci. URSS *109*, 653–656.

Løvtrup, S., and Werdinius, B., 1957. Metabolic phases during amphibian embryogenesis. J. exp. Zool. *135*, 203–220.

Luther, W., 1935. Entwicklungsphysiologische Untersuchungen am Forellenkeim: die Rolle des Organizationszentrums bei der Entstehung der Embryonalanlage. Biol. Zbl. 55, 114–137.

Lynch, W. F., 1961. Extrinsic factors influencing metamorphosis in bryozoan and ascidian larvae. Am. Zoologist *1*, 59–66.

Machemer, H., 1929. Differenzierungsfähigkeit der Urnierenanlage von *Triton alpestris*. Roux Arch. *118*, 200–251.

———, 1932. Experimentelle Untersuchung über die Induktionsleistungen der oberen Urmundlippe in älteren Urodelenkeimen. Roux Arch. *126*, 391–456.

Maggio, R., and Catalano, C., 1963. Activation of amino acids during sea urchin development. Arch. Biochem. Biophysics *103*, 164–167.

Manchot, E., 1929. Abgrenzung des Augenmaterials und anderer Teilbezirke der Medullarplatte; die Teilbewegungen wärend der Auffaltung (Farbmarkierungsversuche an Keimen von Urodelen). Roux Arch. *116*, 689–708.

Mangold, O., 1923. Transplantationsversuche zur Frage der Spezifität und der Bildung der Keimblätter bei *Triton*. Arch. micr. Anat. u. Entw. mech. *100*, 198–301.

———, 1928. Das Determinationsproblem. I. Das Nervensystem und die Sinnesorgane der Seitenlinie unter spezieller Berücksichtigung der Amphibien. Ergebn. Biol. *3*, 152–227.

———, 1929. Das Determinationsproblem. II. Die paarigen Extremitäten der Wirbeltiere in der Entwicklung. Ergebn. Biol. *5*, 290–404.

———, 1931a. Versuche zur Analyse der Entwicklung des Haftfadens bei Urodelen: ein beispiel für die Induktion artfremder Organe. Naturwissenschaften *19*, 905–911.

———, 1931b. Das Determinationsproblem. III. Das Wirbeltierauge in der Entwicklung und Regeneration. Ergebn. Biol. *7*, 193–403.

———, 1936. Experimente zur Analyse der Zusammenarbeit der Keimblätter. Naturwissenschaften *24*, 753–760.

———, 1949. Totale Keimblattchimären bei *Triton*. Naturwissenshaften *36*, 112–120.

——— and Spemann, H., 1927. Ueber Induktion von Medullarplatte durch Medullarplatte im jüngeren Keim, ein Beispiel homeogenetischer oder assimilatorischer Induktion. Roux Arch. *111*, 341–422.

Markert, C. L., 1961. Isozymes in kidney development. In Metcoff, J. (Ed.): Hereditary, developmental and immunological aspects of kidney diseases. Northwestern Univ. Press, Evanston.

———, 1963. Lactate dehydrogenase isozymes: dissociation and recombination of subunits. Science *140*, 1329–1330.

Martini, E., 1912. Studien über die Konstanz histologischer Elemente. 3. *Hydatina senta*. Z. wiss. Zool. *102*, 425–645.

Marx, L., 1935. Bedingungen für die Metamorphose des Axolotls. Ergebn. Biol. *11*, 244–334.

McConnell, C. H., 1936. Mitosis in *Hydra*. Mitosis in the indifferent interstitial cells of *Hydra*. Roux Arch. *135*, 202–210.

McKeehan, M. S., 1951. Cytological aspects of embryonic lens induction in the chick. J. exp. Zool. *117*, 31–64.

———, 1956. The relative ribonucleic acid content of lens and retina during lens induction in the chick. Amer. J. Anat. *99*, 131–156.

———, 1958. Induction of portions of the chick lens without contact with the optic cup. Anat. Rec. *132*, 297–306.

McMaster, R. D., 1955. Desoxyribose nucleic acid in cleavage and larval stages of the sea urchin. J. exp. Zool. *130*, 1–27.

Mercer, E. H., and Wolpert, L., 1962. An electron microscope study of the cortex of the sea urchin (*Psammechinus miliaris*) egg. Exp. Cell Res. 27, 1–13.

Merriam, R. W., 1959. The origin and fate of annulate lamellae in maturing sand dollar eggs. J. Biophys. Biochem. Cytol. 5, 117–122.

Mestscherskaia. K. A., 1935 (cited after Needham, J., 1942.)

Metz, C. B., 1957. Specific egg and sperm substances and activation of the egg. In

TYLER, A., BORSTEL, R. C. VON, and METZ, C. B.: The beginnings of embryonic development. Amer. Ass. Adv. Sci. Washington.

MILAIRE, J., 1956. Contribution à l'étude morphologique et cytochimique des bourgeons de membres chez le rat. Arch. Biol. 67, 297–391.

MILLARD, N., 1945. The development of the arterial system of *Xenopus laevis*, including experiments on the destruction of the larval aortic arches. Trans. roy. Soc. S. Afr. 30, 217–234.

MINOT, C. S., 1891. Senescence and rejuvenation. J. Physiol. 12, 97–153.

———, 1908. The problem of age, growth and death. London.

MINTZ, B., 1960. Embryological phases of mammalian gametogenesis. J. cell. comp. Physiol. 56, Suppl. 1, 31–47.

MIRSKY, A. E., and RIS, H., 1949. Variable and constant components of chromosomes. Nature (Lond.) 163, 666–667.

MITCHISON, J. M., 1956. The thickness of the cortex of the sea urchin egg and the problem of the vitelline membrane. Quart. J. micr. Sci. 97, 109–121.

MOK, C. C., MARTIN, W. J., and COMMON, R. H., 1961. A comparison of phosvitins prepared from hen's serum and from hen's egg yolk. Canad. J. Biochem. Physiol. 39, 109–117.

MONROY, A., 1939. Sulla localizzazione delle celluli genitali primordiali in fasi precoci di sviluppo. Richerche sperimentali in Anfibi Anuri. Arch. ital. Anat. Embriol. 41, 368–389.

——— and TYLER, A., 1963. Formation of active ribosomal aggregates (polysomes) upon fertilization and development of sea urchin eggs. Arch. Biochem. and Biophys. 103, 431–435.

——— and VITTORELLI, M. L., 1962. Utilization of C¹⁴-glucose for amino acids and protein synthesis by the sea urchin embryo. J. cell. comp. Physiol. 60, 285–287.

MOOG, F., 1946. The physiological significance of the phosphomono-esterases. Biol. Rev. 21, 41–59.

MOORE, A. B. C., 1950. The development of reciprocal androgenetic frog hybrids. Biol. Bull. Woods Hole 99, 88–111.

MOORE, A. R., 1933. Is cleavage rate a function of the cytoplasm or of the nucleus? J. exp. Biol. 10, 230–236.

MOORE, J. A., 1946. Studies in the development of frog hybrids. I. Embryonic development in the cross *Rana pipens* ♀ × *Rana sylvatica* ♂ . J. exp. Zool. 101, 173-213.

———, 1962. Nuclear transplantation and problems of specificity in developing embryos. J. Cellular Comparative Physiology 60 (Supplement 1), 19–34.

MORGAN, T. H., 1901. Regeneration. Macmillan Co., New York.

———, 1919. The physical basis of heredity. J. B. Lippincott Co., Philadelphia.

———, 1927. Experimental embryology. Columbia University Press, New York.

———, 1933. The formation of the antipolar lobe in *Ilyanassa*. J. exp. Zool. 64, 433–467.

MOSCONA, A., 1952. Cell suspensions from organ rudiments of chick embryos. Exp. Cell Res. 3, 535.

———, 1956. Development of heterotypic combinations of dissociated embryonic chick cells. Proc. Soc. Exp. Biol. Med. 92, 410–416.

MOSES, M. J., 1961. Spermiogenesis in the crayfish (*Procambarus clarkii*). 1. Structural characterization of the mature sperm. J. Biophys. Biochem. Cytol. 9, 222–228.

MOSSMAN, H. W., 1937. Comparative morphogenesis of the foetal membranes and accessory uterine structures. Contr. Embryol. Carneg. Instn. 26, 133–246.

MUCHMORE, W. B., 1951. Differentiation of the trunk mesoderm in *Amblystoma maculatum*. J. exp. Zool. 118, 137–185.

MÜLLER, F., 1864. Für Darwin. Leipzig.

MUNRO, A. F., 1939. Nitrogen excretion and arginase activity during amphibian development. Biochem. J. 33, 1957–1965.

NAGANO, T., 1962. Observations on the fine structure of the developing spermatid in the domestic chicken. J. Cell Biol. 14, 193–205.

NAKAMURA, O., and TAHARA, Y., 1953. Formation of the stomach in Anura. Mem. Osaka Univ. Lib. Arts & Ed. 2, 1–8.

NASSONOV, N. V., 1930. Die Regeneration der Axolotl Extremitäten nach Ligaturanlegung. Roux Arch. 121, 639–657.

———, 1936. Influence of various factors on morphogenesis following homotopical subcutaneous insertions of cartilage in the axolotl. C.R. Acad. Sci. URSS 4, 97–100.

NAWAR, G., 1956. Experimental analysis of the origin of the autonomic ganglia in the chick embryo. Amer. J. Anat. *99*, 473–506.

NEEDHAM, A. E., 1941. Some experimental biological uses of the element beryllium (glucinum). Proc. Zool. Soc. A. *111*, 59–85.

———, 1952. Regeneration and wound-healing. Methuen, London.

NEEDHAM, J., 1931. Chemical embryology. University Press, Cambridge.

———, 1942. Biochemistry and morphogenesis. University Press, Cambridge.

———, 1959. A history of embryology, 2nd ed. University Press, Cambridge.

NELSEN, O. E., 1953. Comparative embryology of the vertebrates. Blakiston, New York.

NICHOLAS, J. S., 1950. Development of contractility. Proc. Amer. phil. Soc. *94*, 175–183.

——— and RUDNICK, D., 1933. The development of embryonic rat tissues upon the chick chorio-allantois. J. exp. Zool. *66*, 193–261.

NIEUWKOOP, P. D., 1946. Experimental investigations on the origin and determination of the germ cells, and on the development of the lateral plates and germ ridges in urodeles. Arch. néerl. Zool. 8, 1–205.

——— and FABER, J., 1956. Normal table of *Xenopus laevis* (Daudin). North Holland Publishing Co., Amsterdam.

——— ET AL. 1952. Activation and organization of the central nervous system in amphibians. J. exp. Zool. *120*, 1–108.

NIRENBERG, M. W., 1963. The genetic code: II. Sci. Amer. *208*(3), 80–94.

NIU, M. C., 1947. The axial organization of the neural crest, studied with particular reference to the pigmentary component. J. exp. Zool. *105*, 79–114.

———, 1956. New approaches to the problem of embryonic induction. In RUDNICK, D. (Ed.): Cellular mechanisms in differentiation and growth. University Press, Princeton, 155–171.

——— and TWITTY, V. C., 1953. The differentiation of gastrula ectoderm in medium conditioned by axial mesoderm. Proc. Nat. Acad. Sci. (Wash.) *39*, 985–989.

NORDENSKIÖLD, E., 1929. The history of biology. Kegan Paul, Trench and Trubner, London.

O'CONNOR, R. J., 1939. Experiments on the development of the amphibian mesonephros. J. Anat. Lond. *74*, 34–44.

ODOR, D. L., 1960. Electron microscopic studies on ovarian oocytes and unfertilized tubal ova in the rat. J. Biophys. Biochem. Cytol. 7, 567–577.

OGI, K. I., 1957. Influence of sodium iodide and sodium thiocyanate upon the development of frog's embryos. Embryologia *3*, 221–236.

OKA, H., 1943. Metamorphosis of *Polycitor mutabilis* (Ascidiae compositae). Annot. zool. jap. *22*, 54–58.

———, 1958. Eksperimentaj studoj pri metamorfozo de ascidioj. Sciencaj Studoj Kopenhago, 217–220.

——— and WATANABE, H., 1957. Vascular budding. A new type of budding in *Botryllus*. Biol. Bull. Woods Hole *112*, 225–240.

OKADA, E. W., 1955. Isolationsversuche zur Analyse der Knorpelbildung aus Neuralleistenzellen bei Urodelenkeim. Mem. Coll. Sci., Univ. Kyoto *22*, 23–28.

——— and WADDINGTON, C. H., 1959. The submicroscopic structure of the *Drosophila* egg. J. Embr. exp. Morph. 7, 583–597.

OKADA, T. S., 1955a. Experimental studies on the differentiation of the endodermal organs in amphibia. III. The relation between the differentiation of pharynx and head-mesenchyme. Mem. Coll. Sci., Univ. Kyoto *22*, 17–22.

———, 1955b. Experimental studies on the differentiation of the endodermal organs in amphibia. IV. The differentiation of the intestine from the foregut. Annot. zool. jap. *28*, 210–214.

OKUNEFF, N., 1928. Ueber einige physiko-chemische Erscheinungen während der Regeneration. I. Messung der Wasserstoffionenkonzentration in regenerierenden Extremitäten des Axolotl. Biochem. Z. *195*, 421–427.

———, 1933. Ueber einige physiko-chemische Erscheinungen während der Regeneration. V. Ueber den Milchsäuregehalt regenerierender Axolotlextremitäten. Biochem. Z. *257*, 242–244.

OLSEN, M. W., 1960a. Nine-year summary of parthenogenesis in turkeys. Proc. Soc. exp. Biol., N.Y., 279–281.

———, 1960b. Performance record of a parthenogenetic turkey male. Science *132*, 1661.

OPPENHEIMER, J. M., 1936. Transplantation experiments on developing teleosts (*Fundulus* and *Perca*). J. exp. Zool. 72, 409–437.

———, 1947. Organization of the teleost blastoderm. Quart Rev. Biol. *22*, 105–118.

ORECHOWITSCH, W. N., and BROMLEY, N. W., 1934. Die histolysierenden Eigenschaften des Regenerationsblastems. Biol. Zbl. *54*, 524–535.

———, ——— and KOSMINA, N. A., 1935. Ueber die Proteolyse in den regenerierenden Geweben. III. Die Veränderung der Aktivität der Gewebeprotease während des Regenerationsprozesses der Organe von Amphibien. Biochem. Z. *277*, 186.

PASTEELS, J. J., 1937. Études sur la gastrulation des vertébrés méroblastiques. II. Reptiles. Arch. Biol. Paris *48*, 105–184.

———, 1940. Un aperçu comparatif de la gastrulation chez les chordés. Biol. Rev. *15*, 59–106.

———, 1945. On the formation of the primary entoderm of the duck (*Anas domestica*) and on the significance of the bilaminar embryo in birds. Anat. Rec. *93*, 5–21.

———, 1957. La formation de l'endophylle et de l'endoblaste vitelline chez les reptiles, chéloniens et lacertiliens. Acta anat. *30*, 601–612.

———, 1961. La réaction corticale de fécondation ou d'activation. Bull. Soc. zool. Fr. *86*, 600–629.

——— and DE HARVEN, E., 1962. Étude au microscope électronique du cortex de l'oeuf de *Barnea candida* (mollusque bivalve), et son évolution au moment de la fécondation, de la maturation, et de la segmentation. Arch. Biol. Paris *73*, 465–490.

PATTEN, B. M., 1944. The embryology of the pig, 2nd ed. Blakiston, Philadelphia.

———, 1957. Early embrology of the chick, 4th ed. McGraw-Hill, New York.

———, 1958. Foundations of embryology. McGraw-Hill, New York.

PATTERSON, J. T., 1910. Studies on the early development of the hen's egg. I. History of the early cleavage and the accessory cleavage. J. Morph. *21*, 101–134.

PAULING, L., ITANO, H. A., SINGER, S. J., and WELLS, I. C., 1949. Sickle cell anemia, a molecular disease. Science *110*, 543–548.

PELTRERA, A., 1940. La capacita regolative dell' uovo di *Aplysia limacina* L. studiate con la centrifugazione e con le reazioni vitali. Pubbl. Staz. zool. Napoli *18*, 20.

PENNERS, A., 1924. Experimentelle Untersuchungen zum Determinationsproblem am Keim von *Tubifex rivulorum* Lam. I. Die Duplicitas cruciata und organbildende Keimbezirke. Arch. mikr. Anat. u. Entw. mech. *102*, 53–100.

———, 1925. Experimentelle Untersuchungen zum Determinationsproblem am Keim von *Tubifex rivulorum* Lam. II. Die Entwicklung teilweise abgetöteter Keime. Z. wiss. Zool. *127*, 1–140.

PERLMAN, P., and GUSTAFSON, T., 1948. Antigens in the egg and early development stages of the sea urchin. Experientia *4*, 481–483.

PERUTZ, M. F., 1961. Proteins and nucleic acids. Structure and function. Elsevier Publ. Co., Amsterdam, London, New York.

PIATT, J., 1948. Form and causality in neurogenesis. Biol. Rev. *23*, 1–45.

———, 1951. Transplantation experiments between pigmentless and pigmented eggs of *Ambystoma punctatum*. J. exp. Zool. *118*, 101–135.

PIEPHO, H., and MEYER, H., 1951. Reactionen der Schmetterlingshaut auf Häutungshormone. Biol. Zbl. *70*, 252–260.

PINCUS, G., 1936. The eggs of mammals. Macmillan, New York.

———, 1939. The comparative behavior of mammalian eggs *in vivo* and *in vitro*. IV. The development of fertilized and artificially activated rabbit eggs. J. exp. Zool. *82*, 85–129.

——— and SHAPIRO, H., 1940. The comparative behavior of mammalian eggs *in vivo* and *in vitro*. VII. Further studies on the activation of rabbit eggs. Proc. Amer. Phil. Soc. *83*, 631–647.

PITT-RIVERS, R., and TATA, J. R., 1959. The thyroid hormones. Pergamon Press, London, New York, Paris.

POLEZHAYEV, L. W., 1946. The loss and restoration of regenerative capacity in the limbs of tailless amphibia. Biol. Rev. *21*, 141–147.

POLLISTER, A. W., and MOORE, J. A., 1937. Tables for the normal development of *Rana sylvatica*. Anat. Rec. *68*, 486–496.

PRENTISS, C. W., and AREY, L. B., 1917. A laboratory manual and text-book of embryology, 2nd ed. Saunders, Philadelphia.

PRESCOTT, D. M., 1957. Relations between cell growth and cell division. In RUD-

NICK, D. (Ed.): Rhythmic and synthetic processes in growth. University Press. Princeton, 59–74.

—— and BENDER, M. A., 1962. Synthesis of RNA and protein during mitosis in mammalian tissue culture cells. Exp. Cell Res. 26, 260–268.

—— and ——, 1963. Autoradiographic study of chromatid distribution of labeled DNA in two types of mammalian cells in vitro. Exp. Cell Res. 29, 430–442.

—— and KIMBALL, R. F., 1961. Relation between RNA, DNA and protein synthesis in the replicating nucleus of Euplotes. Proc. Nat. Acad. Sci. (Wash.) 47, 686–693.

PRESS, N., 1959. An electron microscopic study of a mechanism for the delivery of follicular cytoplasm to an avian egg. Exp. Cell Res. 18, 194–196.

PROTASS, J. J., SPEYER, J. F., and LENGYEL, P., 1964. Amino acid code in Alcaligenes faecalis. Science 143, 1174–1176.

PULLINGER, B. D., 1949. Squamous differentiation in mouse mammae: spontaneous and induced. Brit. J. Cancer 3, 494–501.

RANZI, S., 1957. Early determination of development under normal and experimental conditions. In TYLER, A., BORSTEL, R. C. VON, and METZ, C. B.: The beginnings of embryonic development. Amer. Ass. Adv. Sci. Washington, 291–318.

—— and TAMINI, E., 1939. Die Wirkung von NaSCN auf die Entwicklung von Froschembryonen. Naturwissenschaften 27, 566–567.

RAVEN, C. P., 1931. Zur Entwicklung der Ganglienleiste. I. Die Kinematik der Ganglienleistenentwicklung bei den Urodelen. Roux Arch. 125, 210–292.

——, 1936. Zur Entwicklung der Ganglienleiste. V. Ueber die Differenzierung des Rumpfganglienleistenmaterials. Roux Arch. 134, 122–146.

——, 1958. Morphogenesis: the analysis of molluscan development. Pergamon Press, London, New York, Paris.

——, 1961. Oogenesis: the storage of developmental information. Pergamon Press, London, New York, Paris.

RAWLES, M. E., 1947. Origin of pigment cells from the neural crest in the mouse embryo. Physiol. Zool. 20, 248–265.

——, 1948. Origin of melanophores and their role in development of the color patterns in vertebrates. Physiol. Rev. 28, 383–408.

REBHUN, L. I., 1961. Some electron microscope observations on membranous basophilic elements of invertebrate eggs. J. Ultrastruct. Research 5, 208–225.

——, 1962. Electron microscope studies on the vitelline membrane of the surf clam Spisula solidissima. J. Ultrastruct. Research 6, 107–122.

RECOURT, A., 1961. Elektronenmicroscopisch onderzoek naar de oogenese bij Limnaea stagnalis L. Thesis, Utrecht.

REVERBERI, G., and MANCUSO, V., 1961. The constituents of the egg of Mytilus as seen at the electron microscope. Acta Embryol. et Morph. Exper. 4, 102–121.

——, ORTOLANI, G., and FARINELLA-FERRUZZA, N., 1960. The causal formation of the brain in the ascidian larva. Acta. Embryol. et Morph. Exper. 3, 296–336.

RICH, A., 1963. Polyribosomes. Sci. Amer. 209(6), 44–53.

ROBERTSON, T. B., 1908. On the normal rate of growth of an individual and its biochemical significance. Roux Arch. 25, 571–614.

ROCHE, V. DE, 1937. Differenzierungen von Geweben und ganzen Organen in Transplantaten der bastardmerogonischen Kombination Triton alpestris (♀) × Triton palmatus ♂. Roux Arch. 135, 620–663.

ROMANOFF, A. L., 1960. The avian embryo, structural and functional development. Macmillan Co., New York.

—— and ROMANOFF, A. J., 1949. The avian egg. J. Wiley and Sons, New York.

ROSE, S. M., 1942. A method of inducing limb regeneration in adult Anura. Proc. Soc. exp. Biol. N.Y. 49, 408–410.

ROTH, J. S., 1964. Biological information in a single strand of deoxyribonucleic acid. Nature (Lond.) 202, 182–183.

ROTH, P. C. J., 1955. Les métamorphoses des batraciens. Dunod, Paris.

ROTHSCHILD, L., 1951. Sea urchin spermatozoa. Biol. Rev. 26, 1–27.

——, 1956. Fertilization. Methuen, London.

ROTMANN, E., 1935. Der Anteil von Induktor und reagierenden Gewebe an der Entwicklung des Haftfadens. Roux Arch. 133, 193–224.

ROUNDS, D. E., and FLICKINGER, R. A., 1958. Distribution of ribonucleoprotein during neural induction in the frog embryo. J. exp. Zool. 137, 479–500.

ROUX, W., 1885. Ueber die Bestimmung der Hauptrichtungen des Froschembryo im Ei und über die erste Theilung des Froscheies. Breslauer ärtztl. Zeitschr. 1–54.

———, 1888. Beiträge zur Entwicklungsmechanick des Embryo. 5. Ueber die künstliche Hervorbringung halber Embryonen durch Zerstörung einer der beiden ersten Furchungskugeln, sowie über die Nachentwicklung (Postgeneration) der fehlenden Körperhälfte. Virchows Arch. *64*, 113–154, 246–291.

———, 1905. Die Entwicklungsmechanick, ein neuer Zweig der biologischen Wissenschaft, Leipzig.

RUDNICK, D., 1948. Prospective areas and differentiation potencies in the chick blastoderm. Ann. N.Y. Acad. Sci. *49*, 761–772.

———, 1952. Development of the digestive tube and its derivatives. Ann. N.Y. Acad. Sci. *55*, 109–116.

———, and RAWLES, M. E., 1937. Differentiation of the gut in chorio-allantoic grafts from chick blastoderms. Physiol. Zool. *10*, 381–395.

RUGH, R., 1948. Experimental embryology. Burgess, Minneapolis.

RUNNSTRÖM, J., 1928. Plasmabau und Determination bei dem Ei von *Paracentrotus lividus* Lk. Roux Arch. *113*, 556–581.

———, 1952. The cell surface in relation to fertilization. Symp. Soc. exp. Biol. *6*, 39–88.

———, HAGSTRÖM, B. E., and PERLMAN, P., 1959. Fertilization. In BRACHET, J., and MIRSKY, A. E.: The cell, Vol. 1. Academic Press, London and New York, 327–397.

RUTH, R. F., ALLEN, C. P., and WOLFE, H. R., 1964. The effect of thymus on lymphoid tissue. In GOOD, R. A., and GABRIELSEN, A. E. (Eds.): The thymus in immunobiology. Harper and Row, New York.

RUUD, G., 1929. Heteronom-orthotopische Transplantationen von Extremitätenanlagen bei Axolotlembryonen. Roux Arch. *118*, 308–351.

RYVKINA, D. E., 1945. Respiratory quotient in regenerating tissues. C.R. Acad. Sci. URSS *49*, 457–459.

SADOV, I. A., 1956. Micropyle formation in oocytes of Acipenseridae. C.R. Acad. Sci. URSS *111*, 1400–1402.

SANTOS, F., 1931. Studies on transplantation in Planaria. Physiol. Zool. *4*, 111–164.

SAUNDERS, J. W., 1948. The proximo-distal sequence of origin of the parts of the chick wing and the role of the ectoderm. J. exp. Zool. *108*, 363–403.

———, GASSELING, M. T., and SAUNDERS, L. C., 1962. Cellular death in morphogenesis of the avian wing. Develop. Biol. *5*, 147–178.

SAXÉN, L., 1961. Transfilter neural induction of amphibian ectoderm. Develop. Biol. *3*, 140–152.

——— and TOIVONEN, S., 1962. Primary embryonic induction. Logos Press, London.

SCHEREMETJEWA, E. A., and BRUNST, V. V., 1938. Preservation of the regeneration capacity in the middle part of the limb of newt and its simultaneous loss in the distal and proximal parts of the same limb. Bull. Biol. Méd. exp. URSS *6*, 723–724.

SCHMALHAUSEN, I. I., 1927. Beiträge zur quantitativen Analyse der Formbildung. I. Ueber Gesetzmässigkeiten des embryonalen Wachstums. Roux Arch. *109*, 455–512.

———, 1930a. Ueber Wachstumsformeln und Wachstumstheorien. Biol. Zbl. *50*, 292–307.

———, 1930b. Das Wachstumsgesetz als Gesetz der progressiven Differenzierung. Roux Arch. *123*, 153–178.

———, 1949. Factors of evolution. Blakiston, Philadelphia.

——— and BORDZILOWSKAJA, N., 1930. Das Wachstum niederer Organismen. I. Das individuelle Wachstum der Bakterien und Hefe. Roux Arch. *121*, 726.

——— and SYNGAJEWSKAJA, E., 1925. Studien über Wachstum und Differenzierung. I. Die individuelle Wachstumskurve von *Paramaecium caudatum* Roux Arch. *105*, 711–717.

SCHMALHAUSEN, O. I., 1939. The role of the olfactory sac in the development of the cartilaginous capsule of the olfactory organ in urodeles. C.R. Acad. Sci. URSS *23*, 395–397.

———, 1950. A comparative experimental investigation of the early stages of development of the olfactory rudiments in amphibians. C.R. Acad. Sci. URSS *74*, 863–865.

SCHMIDT, G. A., 1933. Schnürungs- und Durchschneidungsversuche am Amphibienkeim. Roux Arch. *129*, 1–44.

SCHNEIDERMAN, H. A., and GILBERT, L. I., 1964. Control of growth and development in insects. Science *143*, 325–333.

SCHOTTÉ, O. E., 1923. Influence de la section tardive des nerfs sur les pattes de Tritons en régénération. C.R. Soc. Phys. Hist. nat. Genève *40*, 86–88.

———, 1926. Système nerveux et régénération chez le *Triton*. Rev. Suisse Zool. *33*, 1–211.

———, 1930. Der Determinationszustand der Anurengastrula im Transplantationsexperiment. Roux Arch. *122*, 663–664.

——— and BUTLER, E. G., 1941. Morphological effects of denervation and amputation of limbs in urodele larvae. J. exp. Zool. 87, 279–322.

——— and HARLAND, M., 1943. Effects of denervation and amputation of hindlimbs in Anuran tadpoles. J. exp. Zool. *93*, 453–493.

SCHULZE, P., 1918. Die Bedeutung der interstitiellen Zellen, etc. Sitz. Ber. Ges. Nat. Freunde, Berlin.

SCHWIDEFSKY, G., 1934. Entwicklung und determination der Extremitätanregenerate bei den Molchen. Roux Arch. *132*, 57–114.

SCHWIND, J., 1933. Tissue specificity at the time of metamorphosis in frog larvae. J. exp. Zool. *66*, 1–14.

SEIDEL, F., 1932. Die Potenzen der Furchungskerne im Libellenei und ihre Rolle bei der Aktivierund des Bildungszentrums. Roux Arch. *126*, 213–276.

———, 1960. Die Entwicklungsfähigkeiten isolierter Furchungszellen aus dem Ei des Kaninchens *Oryctolagus cuniculus*. Roux Arch. *152*, 43–130.

SEVERINGHAUS, A. E., 1930. Gill development in *Amblystoma punctatum*. J. exp. Zool. *56*, 1–30.

SEWERTZOFF, A. N., 1931. Morphologische Gesetzmässigkeiten der Evolution. G. Fischer, Jena.

SHAVER, J. R., 1953. Studies on the initiation of cleavage in the frog egg. J. exp. Zool. *122*, 169–192.

SHUMWAY, W., 1940. Stages in the normal development of *Rana pipiens*. I. External form. Anat. Rec. *78*, 139–148.

SINGER, C., 1931. A short history of biology. Clarendon Press, Oxford.

SINGER, M., 1950. Induction of regeneration of the limb of the adult frog by augmentation of the nerve supply. Anat. Rec. *108*, 518–519.

SIRLIN, J. L., and BRAHMA, S. K., 1959. Studies on embryonic induction using radioactive tracers. II. The mobilization of protein components during induction of the lens. Develop. Biol. *1*, 234–246.

———, ———, and WADDINGTON, C. H., 1956. Studies on embryonic induction using radioactive tracers. J. Emb. exp. Morph. *4*, 248–253.

SLAYTER, H. S., WARNER, J. R., RICH, A., and HALL, C. E., 1963. The visualization of polyribosomal structure. J. Mol. Biol. *7*, 652–657.

SMITH, P. E., and MACDOWELL, E. C., 1930. An hereditary anterior-pituitary deficiency in the mouse. Anat. Rec. *46*, 249–257.

SNELL, J. D. (Editor), 1941. Biology of the laboratory mouse. Dover, New York.

SOTELO, J. R., and PORTER, K. R., 1959. An electron microscope study of the rat ovum. J. Biophys. Biochem. Cytol. *5*, 327–342.

——— and TRUJILLO-CENÓZ, O., 1957. Electron microscope study of the vitelline body of some spider oocytes. J. Biophys. Biochem. Cytol. *3*, 301–310.

SPEMANN, H., 1901. Ueber Korrelationen in der Entwicklung des Auges. Verh. anat. Ges. Jena Verslg. Bonn *15*, 61–79.

———, 1901/1903. Entwicklungsphysiologische Studien am Tritonei. I, II, III. Roux Arch. *12*, 224–264; *15*, 448–534; *16*, 551–631.

———, 1912a. Zur Entwicklung des Wirbeltierauges. Zool. Jahrb. Jena, Abt. allg. Zool. *32*, 1–98.

———, 1912b. Ueber die Entwicklung umgedrehter Hirnteile bei Amphibienembryonen. Zool. Jahrb. Jena Suppl. *15*, 1–48.

———, 1919. Experimentelle Forschungen zum Determinations- und Individualitätsproblem. Naturwissenschaften *32*, 1–33.

———, 1921. Die Erzeugung tierischer Chimären durch heteroplastische embryonale Transplantation zwischen *Triton cristatus* und *taeniatus*. Roux Arch. *48*, 533–570.

———, 1928. Die Entwicklung seitlicher und dorso-ventraler Keimhälften bei verzögerter Kernversorgung. Z. wiss. Zool. *132*, 105–134.

———, 1931. Ueber den Anteil von Implantat und Wirtskeim an der Orientierung und Beschaffenheit der induzierten Embryonalanlage. Roux Arch. *123*, 389-517.

SPEMANN, H., 1936. Experimentelle Beiträge zu einer Theorie der Entwicklung. Springer, Berlin.

———, 1938. Embryonic development and induction. Yale University Press, New Haven.

——— and MANGOLD, H., 1924. Ueber Induktion von Embryonalanlagen durch Implantation artfremder Organisatoren. Arch. mikr. Anat. u. Entw. mech. *100*, 599–638.

——— and SCHOTTÉ, O., 1932. Ueber xenoplastische Transplantation als Mittel zur Analyse der embryonalen Induktion. Naturwissenschaften *20*, 463–467.

SPIEGELMAN, S., 1948. Differentiation as the controlled production of unique enzymatic patterns. Symp. Soc. exp. Biol. *2*, 286–325.

SPRATT, N. T., JR., 1946. Formation of the primitive streak in the explanted chick blastoderm marked with carbon particles. J. exp. Zool. *103*, 259–304.

———, 1947. Regression and shortening of the primitive streak in the explanted chick blastoderm. J. exp. Zool. *104*, 69–100.

———, 1948. Development of the early chick blastoderm on synthetic media. J. exp. Zool. *107*, 39–64.

STEBBINS, R. C., and EAKIN, R. M., 1958. The role of the "third eye" in reptilian behavior. American Museum Novitates No. 1870, 1–40.

STEDMAN, E., and STEDMAN, E., 1950. Cell specificity of histones. Nature (Lond.) *166*, 780–781.

STEINBERG, M. S., 1963. Reconstitution of tissues by dissociated cells. Science *141*, 401–408.

STÉPHAN, F., 1949. Les suppléances obtenues expérimentalement dans le système des arcs aortiques de l'embryon d'oiseau. C.R. Ass. Anat. *36*, 647.

STEVENS, L. C., 1954. The origin and development of chromatophores of *Xenopus laevis* and other anurans. J. exp. Zool. *125*, 221–246.

STÖHR, P., JR., 1924. Experimentelle Studien an embryonalen Amphibienherzen. I. Ueber Explantation embryonaler Amphibienherzen. Arch. Mikr. Anat. u. Entw. mech. *102*, 426–451.

STONE, L. S., 1922. Experiments on the development of the cranial ganglia and the lateral line sense organs in *Amblystoma punctatum*. J. exp. Zool. *35*, 421–496.

———, 1926. Further experiments on the extirpation and transplantation of mesectoderm in *Amblystoma punctatum*. J. exp. Zool. *44*, 95–131.

STREETER, G. L., 1906. On the development of the membranous labyrinth and the acoustic and facial nerves in the human embryos. Amer. J. Anat. *6*, 139–165.

———, 1942, 1945, 1948, 1949, 1951.   Developmental horizons in human embryos. Contr. Embryol. Carneg. Instn. *30*, 211–245; *31*, 29–64; *32*, 133–203; *33*, 149–167; *34*, 165–196.

STRÖER, W. F. H., 1933. Experimentelle Untersuchungen über die Mundentwicklung bei den Urodelen. Roux Arch. *130*, 131–186.

SWETT, F. H., 1926. On the production of double limbs in amphibians. J. exp. Zool. *44*, 419–473.

———, 1927. Differentiation of the amphibian limb. J. exp. Zool. *47*, 385–432.

———, 1937. Determination of limb-axes. Quart. Rev. Biol. *12*, 322–339.

SWIFT, C. H., 1914. Origin and early history of the primordial germ-cells in the chick. Amer. J. Anat. *15*, 483–516.

———, 1916. Origin of the sex-cords and definitive spermatogonia in the male chick. Amer. J. Anat. *20*, 375–410.

SWIFT, H. H., 1950. The desoxyribose nucleic acid content of animal nuclei. Physiol. Zool. *23*, 169–198.

SYNGAJEWSKAJA, E., 1935. The individual growth of Protozoa: *Blepharisma lateritia* and *Actinophrys* sp. Trav. de l'Inst. Zool. Biol. Acad. Sci. Ukr. *8*, 151–157.

SYNGAJEWSKAJA, K., 1936. Die Wachstumsgeschwindigkeit bei der Regeneration der Extremitäten bei *Siredon pisciformis*. Zool. Jahrb. Abt. allg. Zool. *56*, 487–500.

———, 1937. Die reaktiven Eigenschaften des axialen Mesoderms. Trav. de l'Inst. Zool. Biol. Acad. Sci. Ukr. *17*, 41–59.

SZE, L. C., 1953. Changes in the amount of desoxyribonucleic acid in the development of *Rana pipiens*. J. exp. Zool. *122*, 577–601.

TAHARA, Y., 1962. Formation of the independent lens in Japanese amphibians. Embryologia 7, 127–149.

——— and NAKAMURA, O., 1961. Topography of the presumptive rudiments in the endoderm of the anuran neurula. J. Embr. exp. Morph. *9*, 138–158.

TAKAYA, H., 1955. Thermal influence upon the inducing specficity of the organizer. Proc. imp. Acad. Japan *31*, 366–371.

—— and WATANABE, T., 1961. Differential proliferation of the ependyma in the developing neural tube of amphibian embryo. Embryologia *6*, 169–176.

TAYLOR, J. H., 1960a. Asynchronous duplication of chromosomes in cultured cells of Chinese hamster. J. Biophys. Biochem. Cytol. *7*, 455–464.

——, 1960b. Nucleic acid synthesis in relation to the cell division cycle. Ann. N.Y. Acad. Sci. *90*, 409–421.

——, WOODS, P. S., and HUGHES, W. L., 1957. The organization and duplication of chromosomes as revealed by autoradiographic studies using tritium-labeled thymidine. Proc. Nat. Acad. Sci. (Wash.) *43*, 122–128.

TELFER, W. H., 1954. Immunological studies of insect metamorphosis. II. The role of a sex limited blood protein in egg formation of the cecropia silkworm. J. General Physiol. *37*, 539–558.

TELKKA, A., FAWCETT, D. W., and CHRISTENSEN, A. K., 1961. Further observations on the structure of the mammalian sperm tail. Anat. Rec. *141*, 231–245.

TEN CATE, G., 1953. The intrinsic development of amphibian embryos. Dissertation. North Holland Publishing Co., Amsterdam.

—— and DOORENMAALEN, W. J. VAN, 1950. Analysis of the development of the eye-lens in chicken and frog embryos by means of the precipitin reaction. Proc. Konink. Nederl. Akad. van Wetensch. Amsterdam *53*, 894–909.

TENNENT, D. H., 1914. The early influence of the spermatozoon upon the characters of Echinoid larvae. Pap. Tortugas Lab. *182*.

TERENTIEV, I. B., 1941. On the role played by the neural crest in the development of the dorsal fin in Urodela. C.R. Acad. Sci. URSS *31*, 91–94.

TERNI, T., 1934. Studio sperimentale della capacita pinnoformativa dei cercini midollari. Arch. ital. Anat. Embriol. *33*, 667–692.

THORELL, B., 1947. The relation of nucleic acids to the formation and differentiation of cellular proteins. Cold Spr. Harb. Symp. quant. Biol. *12*, 247–255.

TIEDEMANN, H., 1961. Ueber die chemische Natur der organdeterminierenden Stoffe beim Organizator-Effekt Spemanns. Verh. d. Deutschen Zool. Ges., 251–258.

——, 1962. Biochemische Untersuchungen ueber die Induktionsstoffe und die Determination der ersten Organanlagen bei Amphibien. 13 Colloquium d. Ges. f. physiolog. Chemie, Mosbach, 177–204.

——, BECKER, U., and TIEDEMANN, H., 1961. Ueber die primären Schritte bei der embryonalen Induktion. Embryologia *6*, 204–218.

—— and TIEDEMANN, H., 1954. Einbau von $^{14}CO_2$ in gefurchte und ungefurchte Eihälften und in verschiedene Entwicklungsstadien von *Triton* Die Naturwissenschaften *41*, 535.

TING, H. P., 1951. Diploid, androgenetic and gynogenetic haploid development in anuran hybridization. J. exp. Zool. *116*, 21–57.

TOIVONEN, S., 1940. Ueber die Leistungspezifität der abnormen Induktoren im Implantatversuch bei *Triton*. Ann. Acad. Sci. Fenn. A. *55*, 1–150.

——, 1945. Zur Frage der Induktion selbständiger Linsen durch abnorme Induktoren im Implantationsversuch bei *Triton*. Ann. Soc. zool-bot. Fenn. Vanamo. *11*, 1–28.

——, 1949. Zur Frage der Leistungspezifität abnormer Induktoren. Experientia *5*, 323.

——, 1950. Stoffliche Induktoren. Rev. Suisse Zool. *57*, suppl. 1, 41–56.

——, 1953. Bone-marrow of the guinea-pig as a mesodermal inductor in implantation experiments with embryos of *Triturus*. J. Embr. exp. Morph. *1*, 97–104.

——, 1958. The dependence of the cellular transformation of the competent ectoderm on temporal relationships in the induction process. J. Embr. exp. Morph. *6*, 479–485.

—— and SAXÉN, L., 1955. Ueber die Induktion des Neuralrohrs bei Trituruskeimen als simultane Leistung des Leber- und Knochenmarkgewebes vom Meerschweinchen. Ann. Acad. Sci. Fenn. A. *30*, 1–29.

TOKIN, B., and GORBUNOWA, G., 1934. Untersuchungen über die Ontogenie der Zellen. Biol. Zh. *3*, 294–306.

TOWNES, P. L., and HOLTFRETER, J., 1955. Directed movements and selective adhesion of embryonic amphibian cells. J. exp. Zool. *128*, 53–120.

TRUJILLO-CENÓZ, O., and SOTELO, J. R., 1959. Relationships of the ovular surface with follicle cells and origin of the zona pellucida in rabbit oocytes. J. Biophys. Biochem. Cytol. *5*, 347–350.

TUNG, T. C., WU, S. C., and TUNG, Y. Y. F., 1962a. The presumptive areas of the egg of *Amphioxus*. Scientia Sinica *11*, 629–644.

——, ——, and ——, 1962b. Experimental studies on the neural induction in *Amphioxus*. Scientia Sinica *11*, 805–820.

TWITTY, V. C., 1949. Developmental analysis of amphibian pigmentation. Symp. Soc. Study Develop. Growth. *9*, 133–161.

—— and NIU, M. C., 1948. Causal analysis of chromatophore migration. J. exp. Zool. *108*, 405–437.

TYLER, A., 1948. Fertilization and immunity. Physiol. Rev. *28*, 180–219.

——, BORSTEL, R. C. VON, and METZ, C. B. (Editors), 1957. The beginnings of embryonic development. Amer. Ass. Adv. Sc., Washington.

UMANSKI, E., 1935. Ueber die gegenseitige Vertretbarkeit präsumptiver Anlagen der Rückenmark- und Gehirnteile bei den Amphibien. Zool. Anz. *110*, 25–30.

VAHS, W., 1962. Quantitative cytochemische Untersuchungen über die Veränderungen des Ribonucleoproteid-Status im heterogenen Induktor und im Reaktionssystem des *Triturus* Embryos während der Induktions- und frühen Differenzierungsphase. Roux Arch. *153*, 504–550.

VAINIO, T., SAXÉN, S., TOIVONEN, S., and RAPOLA, J., 1962. The transmission problem in primary embryonic induction. Exp. Cell Res. *27*, 527–538.

VENDRELY, R., and VENDRELY, C., 1949. La teneur du noyau cellulaire en acide désoxyribonucléique à travers les organes, les individus et les espèces animales. Experientia *5*, 327–329.

VINCENTIIS, M. DE, 1954. Ulteriori indagini sull' organogenesi del cristallino. Riv. Biol. *36*.

VOGEL, H. J., BRYSON, V., and LAMPEN, J. O., 1962. Informational macromolecules. Science *138*, 912–918.

VOGT, W., 1925. Gestaltungsanalyse am Amphibienkeim mit örtlicher Vitalfärbung. Vorwort über Wege und Ziele. I. Methodik und Wirkungsweise der ortlichen Vitalfärbung mit Agar als Farbträger. Roux Arch. *106*, 542–610.

——, 1929. Gestaltungsanalyse am Amphibienkeim mit örtlicher Vitalfärbung. II. Gastrulation und Mesodermbildung bei Urodelen und Anuren. Roux Arch. *120*, 385–706.

WADDINGTON, C. H., 1933. Induction by the endoderm in birds. Roux Arch. *128*, 502–521.

——, 1934. Experiments on embryonic induction. III. A note on inductions by chick primitive streak transplanted to the rabbit embryo. J. exp. Biol. *11*, 224–226.

——, 1936. Organizers in mammalian development. Nature (Lond.) *138*, 125.

——, 1938. The morphogenetic function of a vestigial organ in the chick. J. exp. Biol. *15*, 371–376.

——, 1939. Order of magnitude of morphogenetic forces. Nature (Lond.) *144*, 637.

——, 1952. The epigenetics of birds. University Press, Cambridge.

—— and MULHERKAR, L., 1957. The diffusion of substances during embryonic induction in the chick. Proc. Zool. Soc., Calcutta, Mookerjee Memor. Vol., 141–147.

——, NEEDHAM, J., and BRACHET, J., 1936. Studies on the nature of the amphibian organization centre. III. The activation of the evocator. Proc. roy. Soc., B *120*, 173–198.

——, ——, NOWINSKY, W. W., NEEDHAM, D. M., and LEMBERG, R., 1934. Active principle of the amphibian organization centre. Nature (Lond.) *134*, 103.

—— and SCHMIDT, G. A., 1933. Induction by heteroplastic grafts of the primitive streak in birds. Roux Arch. *128*, 522–563.

WALLACE, R. A., 1963. Studies on amphibian yolk. IV. An analysis of the main-body component of yolk platelets. Biochim. Biophys. Acta *74*, 505–518.

——, 1964. Studies on amphibian yolk. VI. A protein kinase from the ovary of *Rana pipiens*. Biochem. Biophys. Acta *86*, 286–294.

WARBURG, O., 1908. Beobachtungen über die Oxydationsprozesse im Seeigelei. Z. physiol. Chem. *57*, 1–16.

WARD, R. T., 1962. The origin of protein and fatty yolk in *Rana pipiens*. II. Electron microscopical and chemical observations of young and mature oocytes. J. Cell Biol. *14*, 309–341.

WARNER, J. R., RICH, A., and HALL, C. E., 1962. Electron microscope studies of ribosomal clusters synthesizing hemoglobin. Science *138*, 1399–1403.

WARTENBERG, H., 1962. Elektronenmikroskopische und histochemische Studien über die Oogenese der Amphibieneizelle. Zeit. Zellforsch. *58*, 427–482.

—— and SCHMIDT, W., 1961. Elektronenmikroskopische Untersuchungen der strukturellen Veränderungen im Rindenbereich des Amphibieneies im Ovar und nach der Befruchtung. Zeit. Zellforsch. *54*, 118–146.

—— and STEGNER, H. E., 1960. Ueber die Elektronenmikroskopische Feinstruktur des menschlichen Ovarialeies. Zeit. Zellforsch. *52*, 450–474.

WATERMAN, A. J., 1936. Developmental capacities of transplanted hepatic, pancreatic and lung tissues of the rabbit embryo. Amer. J. Anat. *58*, 2–57.

WATSON, J. D., 1963. Involvement of RNA in the synthesis of protein. Science *140*, 17–26.

—— and CRICK, F. H. C., 1953. Molecular structure of nucleic acids. A structure for deoxyribose nucleic acid. Nature (Lond.) *171*, 737–738.

WEBER, R., and BOELL, E. J., 1955. Ueber die Cytochromoxydaseaktivität der Mitochondrien von frühen Entwicklungsstadien des Krallenfrosches (*Xenopus laevis* Daud.) Rev. Suisse Zool. *62*, 260–268.

WEHMEIER, E., 1934. Versuche zur Analyse der Induktionsmittel bei der Medullarplatteninduktion von Urodelen. Roux Arch. *132*, 384–423.

WEILER-STOLT, B., 1960. Ueber die Bedeutung der interstitiellen Zellen für die Entwicklung und Fortpflanzung mariner Hydroiden. Roux Arch. *152*, 398–454.

WEISS, P., 1925. Unabhängigkeit der Extremitätenregeneration vom Skelett (bei *Triton cristatus*). Roux Arch. *104*, 359–394.

——, 1926a. Morphodynamik. Bornträger, Berlin.

——, 1926b. Ganzregenerate aus halbem Extremitätenquerschnitt. Roux Arch. *107*, 1–53.

——, 1927a. Die Herkunft der Haut im Extremitätenregenerat. Roux Arch. *109*, 584–610.

——, 1927b. Potenzprüfung am Regenerationsblastem. I. Extremitätenbildung aus Schwanzblastem im Extremitätenfeld bei *Triton*. Roux Arch. *111*, 317.

——, 1928. Experimentelle Untersuchungen zur Metamorphose der Ascidien; Beschleunigung des Metamorphoseeintrittes durch Thyreoideabehandlung der Larve. Biol. Zbl. *48*, 69–79.

——, 1929. Erzwingung elementarer Strukturverschiedenheiten am in vitro wachsenden Gewebe (Die Wirkung mechanischer Spannung auf Richtung und Intensität des Gewebewachstums und ihre Analyse). Roux Arch. *116*, 438–554.

——, 1934. *In vitro* experiments on the factors determining the course of the outgrowing nerve fiber. J. exp. Zool. *68*, 393–448.

——, 1939. Principles of development, Henry Holt, New York.

——, 1947. The problem of specificity in growth and development. Yale J. Biol. Med. *19*, 235–278.

——, 1950. The deplantation of fragments of nervous system in amphibians. I. Central reorganization and the formation of nerves. J. exp. Zool. *113*, 397–461.

——, 1955. Nervous system. In WILLIER, B. H., WEISS, P. A., and HAMBURGER, V.: Analysis of development. Saunders, Philadelphia, 346–401.

—— and ANDRES, G., 1952. Experiments on the fate of embryonic cells (chick) disseminated by the vascular route. J. exp. Zool. *121*, 449–488.

—— and JAMES, R., 1955. Skin metaplasia in vitro induced by brief exposure to vitamin A. Exp. Cell Res. Suppl. *3*, 381–394.

WEISSMANN, A., 1904. Vorträge über Descendenztheorie. Jena. 2 vols.

WENRICH, D. H., 1916. The spermatogenesis of *Phrynotettix magnus* with special reference to synapsis and the individuality of the chromosomes. Bull. Mus. comp. Zool. Harv. *60*, No. 3, 57–133.

WETZEL, R., 1929. Untersuchungen am Hühnchen. Die Entwicklung des Keims während der ersten beiden Bruttage. Roux Arch. *119*, 118–321.

WHITE, E. L., 1948. An experimental study of the relationship between the size of the eye and the size of the optic tectum in the brain of the developing teleost *Fundulus heteroclitus*. J. exp. Zool. *108*, 439–469.

WIEMAN, H. L., 1949. An introduction to vertebrate embryology. McGraw-Hill, New York.

WIGGLESWORTH, V. B., 1939. The principles of insect physiology. Methuen, London.

——, 1954. The physiology of insect metamorphosis. University Press, Cambridge.

WILENS, S., 1955. The migration of heart mesoderm and associated areas in *Amblystoma punctatum*. J. exp. Zool. *129*, 579–606.

WILKINS, L., 1960. The thyroid gland. Sci. Amer. *202* (3), 119–129.

WILKINS, M. H. F., 1956. Physical studies of the molecular structure of deoxyribose nucleic acid and nucleoprotein. Cold Spr. Harb. Symp. quant. Biol. *22*, 75–90.

——, 1963. Molecular configuration of nucleic acids. Science *140*, 941–950.

WILLIAMS, C. M., 1946. Physiology of insect diapause: the role of the brain in the production and termination of pupal dormancy in the giant silkworm *Platysamia cecropia*. Biol. Bull. Woods Hole *90*, 234–243.

——, 1947. Physiology of insect diapause. II. Interaction between the pupal brain and prothoracic glands in the metamorphosis of the giant silkworm *Platysamia cecropia*. Biol. Bull. Woods Hole *93*, 89–98.

——, MOORHEAD, L. V., and PULIS, J., 1959. Juvenile hormone in thymus, human placenta and other mammalian organs. Nature (Lond.) *183*, 405.

WILLIER, B. H., 1952. Cells, feathers and colors. Bios *23*, 109–125.

——, 1955. Ontogeny of endocrine correlation. In WILLIER, B. H., WEISS, P. A., and HAMBURGER, V. (Eds.): Analysis of development. Saunders, Philadelphia, 574–619.

—— and RAWLES, M. E., 1931. Developmental relations of heart and liver in chorio-allantoic grafts of whole chick blastoderms. Anat. Rec. *48*, 277–301.

——, WEISS, P. A., and HAMBURGER, V., 1955. Analysis of development. Saunders, Philadelphia.

WILSON, E. B., 1904. Experimental studies on germinal localization. I. The germ regions in the egg of *Dentalium*. II. Experiments on the cleavage-mosaic in *Patella* and *Dentalium*. J. exp. Zool. *1*, 1–72.

——, 1925. The cell in development and heredity, 3d ed. Macmillan, New York.

WILSON, H. V., 1907. On some phenomena of coalescence and regeneration in sponges. J. exp. Zool. *5*, 245–258.

WISCHNITZER, S., 1960. Observations on the annulate lamellae of immature amphibian oocytes. J. Biophys. Biochem. Cytol. *8*, 558–563.

WITSCHI, E., 1929. Studies on sex differentiation and sex determination in amphibians. I. Development and sexual differentiation of the gonads of *Rana sylvatica*. J. exp. Zool. *52*, 235–263.

——, 1948. Migration of the germ cells of human embryos from the yolk sac to the primitive gonadal folds. Contr. Embryol. Carneg. Instn. *32*, 67–80.

——, 1956. Development of vertebrates. Saunders, Philadelphia.

WITTEK, M., 1952. La vitellogénèse chez les Amphibiens. Arch. Biol. Paris. *63*, 133–198.

WOERDEMAN, M. W., 1933. Ueber den Glykogenstoffwechsel des Organisationszentrums in der Amphibiengastrulation. Proc. Koninkl. Akad. Wetensch. Amsterdam, *36*, 189–193.

WOLFF, C. F., 1759. Theoria generationis (cited after NEEDHAM, J., 1931).

WOLPERT, L., and MERCER, E. H., 1961. An electron microscope study of fertilization of the sea urchin egg *Psammechinus miliaris*. Exp. Cell Res. *22*, 45–55.

WRIGHT, S., and WAGNER, K., 1934. Types of subnormal development of the head from inbred strains of guinea pigs and their bearing on the classification of vertebrate monsters. Amer. J. Anat. *54*, 383–447.

YAMADA, T., 1937. Der Determinationszustand des Rumpfmesoderms im Molchkeim nach der Gastrulation. Roux Arch. *137*, 151–270.

——, 1938. Induktion der sekundären Embryonalanlage im Neunaugenkeim. Okajimas Folia anat. jap. *17*, 369–388.

——, 1950. Dorsalization of the ventral marginal zone of the *Triturus* gastrula. I. Ammonia-treatment of the medio-ventral marginal zone. Biol. Bull. Woods Hole *98*, 98–121.

——, 1958. Induction of specific differentiation by samples of proteins and nucleoproteins in the isolated ectoderm of *Triturus* gastrulae. Experientia *14*, 81–87.

——, 1962. The inductive phenomenon as a tool for understanding the basic mechanism of differentiation. J. cell. comp. Physiol. *60*, Suppl. 1, 49–64.

—— and TAKATA, K., 1961. A technique for testing macromolecular samples in solution for morphogenetic effects on the isolated ectoderm of the amphibian gastrula. Develop. Biol. *3*, 411–423.

YAMAMOTO, T., 1954. Physiological studies on fertilization and activation of fish eggs. V. The role of calcium in activation of *Oryzias latipes*. Exp. Cell Res. *6*, 56–68.

YASUZUMI, G., 1956. Spermatogenesis in animals as revealed by electron microscopy. I. Formation and submicroscopic structure of the middle-piece of the albino rat. J. Biophys. Biochem. Cytol. *2*, 445–450.

——, TANAKA, H., and TEZUKA, O., 1960. Spermatogenesis in animals as revealed by electron microscopy.VIII. Relation between the nutritive cells and the developing spermatids in a pond snail *Cipangopaludina malleata* Reeve. J. Biophys. Biochem. Cytol. *7*, 499–504.

YNTEMA, C. L., 1950. An analysis of induction of the ear from foreign ectoderm in the salamander embryo. J. exp. Zool. *113*, 211–244.

—— and HAMMOND, W. S., 1947. The development of the autonomic nervous system. Biol. Reviews (Cambridge) *22*, 344–359.

ZALOKAR, M., 1960. Sites of protein and ribonucleic acid synthesis in the cell. Exp. Cell Res. *19*, 559–576.

ZHINKIN, L., 1934. Ueber die Wirkung der Röntgenstrahlen auf die Regeneration bei *Lumbriculus variegatus* Gr. Trav. Lab. Zool. exp. Morph. Anim. *3*, 71–97.

ZWILLING, E., 1940. An experimental analysis of the development of the anuran olfactory organ. J. exp. Zool. *84*, 291–323.

——, 1955. Ectoderm-mesoderm relationship in the development of the chick embryo limb bud. J. exp. Zool. *128*, 423–441.

——, 1956. Interaction between limb bud ectoderm and mesoderm in the chick embryo. IV. Experiments with a wingless mutant. J. exp. Zool. *132*, 241–253.

——, 1963. Formation of endoderm from ectoderm in *Cordylophora*. Biol. Bull. Woods Hole *124*, 368–378.

Index